Some Physical Constants

Quantity	Symbol	Value[a]
Atomic mass unit	u	$1.660\ 538\ 86\ (28) \times 10^{-27}$ kg $931.494\ 043\ (80)$ MeV/c^2
Avogadro's number	N_A	$6.022\ 141\ 5\ (10) \times 10^{23}$ particles/mol
Bohr magneton	$\mu_B = \dfrac{e\hbar}{2m_e}$	$9.274\ 009\ 49\ (80) \times 10^{-24}$ J/T
Bohr radius	$a_0 = \dfrac{\hbar^2}{m_e e^2 k_e}$	$5.291\ 772\ 108\ (18) \times 10^{-11}$ m
Boltzmann's constant	$k_B = \dfrac{R}{N_A}$	$1.380\ 650\ 5\ (24) \times 10^{-23}$ J/K
Compton wavelength	$\lambda_C = \dfrac{h}{m_e c}$	$2.426\ 310\ 238\ (16) \times 10^{-12}$ m
Coulomb constant	$k_e = \dfrac{1}{4\pi\epsilon_0}$	$8.987\ 551\ 788 \ldots \times 10^9$ N·m²/C² (exact)
Deuteron mass	m_d	$3.343\ 583\ 35\ (57) \times 10^{-27}$ kg $2.013\ 553\ 212\ 70\ (35)$ u
Electron mass	m_e	$9.109\ 382\ 6\ (16) \times 10^{-31}$ kg $5.485\ 799\ 094\ 5\ (24) \times 10^{-4}$ u $0.510\ 998\ 918\ (44)$ MeV/c^2
Electron volt	eV	$1.602\ 176\ 53\ (14) \times 10^{-19}$ J
Elementary charge	e	$1.602\ 176\ 53\ (14) \times 10^{-19}$ C
Gas constant	R	$8.314\ 472\ (15)$ J/mol·K
Gravitational constant	G	$6.674\ 2\ (10) \times 10^{-11}$ N·m²/kg²
Josephson frequency–voltage ratio	$\dfrac{2e}{h}$	$4.835\ 978\ 79\ (41) \times 10^{14}$ Hz/V
Magnetic flux quantum	$\Phi_0 = \dfrac{h}{2e}$	$2.067\ 833\ 72\ (18) \times 10^{-15}$ T·m²
Neutron mass	m_n	$1.674\ 927\ 28\ (29) \times 10^{-27}$ kg $1.008\ 664\ 915\ 60\ (55)$ u $939.565\ 360\ (81)$ MeV/c^2
Nuclear magneton	$\mu_n = \dfrac{e\hbar}{2m_p}$	$5.050\ 783\ 43\ (43) \times 10^{-27}$ J/T
Permeability of free space	μ_0	$4\pi \times 10^{-7}$ T·m/A (exact)
Permittivity of free space	$\epsilon_0 = \dfrac{1}{\mu_0 c^2}$	$8.854\ 187\ 817 \ldots \times 10^{-12}$ C²/N·m² (exact)
Planck's constant	h $\hbar = \dfrac{h}{2\pi}$	$6.626\ 069\ 3\ (11) \times 10^{-34}$ J·s $1.054\ 571\ 68\ (18) \times 10^{-34}$ J·s
Proton mass	m_p	$1.672\ 621\ 71\ (29) \times 10^{-27}$ kg $1.007\ 276\ 466\ 88\ (13)$ u $938.272\ 029\ (80)$ MeV/c^2
Rydberg constant	R_H	$1.097\ 373\ 156\ 852\ 5\ (73) \times 10^7$ m^{-1}
Speed of light in vacuum	c	$2.997\ 924\ 58 \times 10^8$ m/s (exact)

Note: These constants are the values recommended in 2002 by CODATA, based on a least-squares adjustment of data from different measurements. For a more complete list, see P. J. Mohr and B. N. Taylor, "CODATA Recommended Values of the Fundamental Physical Constants: 2002." *Rev. Mod. Phys.* **77**:1, 2005.

[a] The numbers in parentheses for the values represent the uncertainties of the last two digits.

Solar System Data

Body	Mass (kg)	Mean Radius (m)	Period (s)	Distance from the Sun (m)
Mercury	3.18×10^{23}	2.43×10^{6}	7.60×10^{6}	5.79×10^{10}
Venus	4.88×10^{24}	6.06×10^{6}	1.94×10^{7}	1.08×10^{11}
Earth	5.98×10^{24}	6.37×10^{6}	3.156×10^{7}	1.496×10^{11}
Mars	6.42×10^{23}	3.37×10^{6}	5.94×10^{7}	2.28×10^{11}
Jupiter	1.90×10^{27}	6.99×10^{7}	3.74×10^{8}	7.78×10^{11}
Saturn	5.68×10^{26}	5.85×10^{7}	9.35×10^{8}	1.43×10^{12}
Uranus	8.68×10^{25}	2.33×10^{7}	2.64×10^{9}	2.87×10^{12}
Neptune	1.03×10^{26}	2.21×10^{7}	5.22×10^{9}	4.50×10^{12}
Pluto[a]	$\approx 1.4 \times 10^{22}$	$\approx 1.5 \times 10^{6}$	7.82×10^{9}	5.91×10^{12}
Moon	7.36×10^{22}	1.74×10^{6}	—	—
Sun	1.991×10^{30}	6.96×10^{8}	—	—

[a] In August 2006, the International Astronomical Union adopted a definition of a planet that separates Pluto from the other eight planets. Pluto is now defined as a "dwarf planet" (like the asteroid Ceres).

Physical Data Often Used

Average Earth–Moon distance	3.84×10^{8} m
Average Earth–Sun distance	1.496×10^{11} m
Average radius of the Earth	6.37×10^{6} m
Density of air (20°C and 1 atm)	1.20 kg/m^3
Density of water (20°C and 1 atm)	1.00×10^{3} kg/m^3
Free-fall acceleration	9.80 m/s^2
Mass of the Earth	5.98×10^{24} kg
Mass of the Moon	7.36×10^{22} kg
Mass of the Sun	1.99×10^{30} kg
Standard atmospheric pressure	1.013×10^{5} Pa

Note: These values are the ones used in the text.

Some Prefixes for Powers of Ten

Power	Prefix	Abbreviation	Power	Prefix	Abbreviation
10^{-24}	yocto	y	10^{1}	deka	da
10^{-21}	zepto	z	10^{2}	hecto	h
10^{-18}	atto	a	10^{3}	kilo	k
10^{-15}	femto	f	10^{6}	mega	M
10^{-12}	pico	p	10^{9}	giga	G
10^{-9}	nano	n	10^{12}	tera	T
10^{-6}	micro	μ	10^{15}	peta	P
10^{-3}	milli	m	10^{18}	exa	E
10^{-2}	centi	c	10^{21}	zetta	Z
10^{-1}	deci	d	10^{24}	yotta	Y

PHYSICS
for Scientists and Engineers

PHYSICS

for Scientists and Engineers

4 Chapters 35–39

Seventh Edition

Raymond A. Serway
Emeritus, James Madison University

John W. Jewett, Jr.
California State Polytechnic University, Pomona

Australia • Brazil • Canada • Mexico • Singapore • Spain • United Kingdom • United States

THOMSON
BROOKS/COLE

Physics for Scientists and Engineers, Chapters 35–39, Seventh Edition
Raymond A. Serway and John W. Jewett, Jr.

Physics Acquisition Editor: Chris Hall
Publisher: David Harris
Vice President, Editor-in-Chief, Sciences: Michelle Julet
Development Editor: Ed Dodd
Assistant Editor: Brandi Kirksey
Editorial Assistant: Shawn Vasquez
Technology Project Manager: Sam Subity
Marketing Manager: Mark Santee
Marketing Assistant: Melissa Wong
Managing Marketing Communications Manager: Bryan Vann
Project Manager, Editorial Production: Teri Hyde
Creative Director: Rob Hugel
Art Director: Lee Friedman
Print Buyers: Barbara Britton, Karen Hunt
Permissions Editors: Joohee Lee, Bob Kauser
Production Service: Lachina Publishing Services
Text Designer: Patrick Devine Design
Photo Researcher: Jane Sanders Miller
Copy Editor: Kathleen Lafferty
Illustrator: Rolin Graphics, Progressive Information Technologies, Lachina Publishing Services
Cover Designer: Patrick Devine Design
Cover Image: Front: © 2005 Tony Dunn; Back: © 2005 Kurt Hoffmann, Abra Marketing
Cover Printer: R.R. Donnelley/Willard
Compositor: Lachina Publishing Services
Printer: R.R. Donnelley/Willard

Printed in the United States of America
1 2 3 4 5 6 7 11 10 09 08 07

Library of Congress Control Number: 2006936870

ISBN-13: 978-0-495-11237-2
ISBN-10: 0-495-11237-2

Thomson Higher Education
10 Davis Drive
Belmont, CA 94002-3098
USA

For more information about our products, contact us at:

Thomson Learning Academic Resource Center
(+1) 1-800-423-0563

For permission to use material from this text or product, submit a request online at
http://www.thomsonrights.com.

Any additional questions about permissions can be submitted by e-mail to **thomsonrights@thomson.com.**

John W. Jewett, Jr.

Courtesy of NASA

© Thomson Learning/Charles D. Winters

Courtesy of Henry Leap and Jim Lehman

Contents

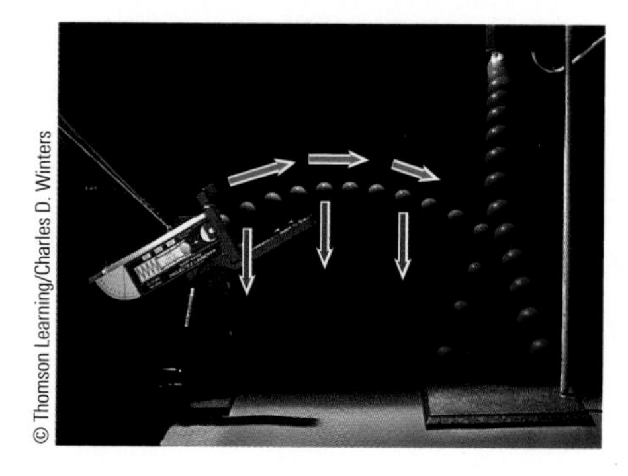

NASA

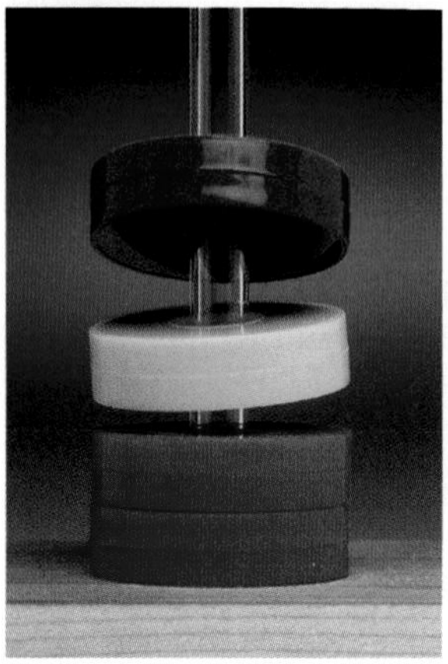
© Thomson Learning/Charles D. Winters

© Thomson Learning/Charles D. Winters

We dedicate this book to our wives
Elizabeth and Lisa and all our children
and grandchildren for their loving
understanding when we spent time on
writing instead of being with them.

Raymond A. Serway received his doctorate at Illinois Institute of Technology and is Professor Emeritus at James Madison University. In 1990, he received the Madison Scholar Award at James Madison University, where he taught for 17 years. Dr. Serway began his teaching career at Clarkson University, where he conducted research and taught from 1967 to 1980. He was the recipient of the Distinguished Teaching Award at Clarkson University in 1977 and of the Alumni Achievement Award from Utica College in 1985. As Guest Scientist at the IBM Research Laboratory in Zurich, Switzerland, he worked with K. Alex Müller, 1987 Nobel Prize recipient. Dr. Serway also was a visiting scientist at Argonne National Laboratory, where he collaborated with his mentor and friend, Sam Marshall. In addition to earlier editions of this textbook, Dr. Serway is the coauthor of *Principles of Physics,* fourth edition; *College Physics,* seventh edition; *Essentials of College Physics;* and *Modern Physics,* third edition. He also is the coauthor of the high school textbook *Physics,* published by Holt, Rinehart, & Winston. In addition, Dr. Serway has published more than 40 research papers in the field of condensed matter physics and has given more than 70 presentations at professional meetings. Dr. Serway and his wife, Elizabeth, enjoy traveling, golf, singing in a church choir, and spending quality time with their four children and eight grandchildren.

John W. Jewett, Jr., earned his doctorate at Ohio State University, specializing in optical and magnetic properties of condensed matter. Dr. Jewett began his academic career at Richard Stockton College of New Jersey, where he taught from 1974 to 1984. He is currently Professor of Physics at California State Polytechnic University, Pomona. Throughout his teaching career, Dr. Jewett has been active in promoting science education. In addition to receiving four National Science Foundation grants, he helped found and direct the Southern California Area Modern Physics Institute. He also directed Science IMPACT (Institute for Modern Pedagogy and Creative Teaching), which works with teachers and schools to develop effective science curricula. Dr. Jewett's honors include the Stockton Merit Award at Richard Stockton College in 1980, the Outstanding Professor Award at California State Polytechnic University for 1991–1992, and the Excellence in Undergraduate Physics Teaching Award from the American Association of Physics Teachers in 1998. He has given more than 80 presentations at professional meetings, including presentations at international conferences in China and Japan. In addition to his work on this textbook, he is coauthor of *Principles of Physics,* fourth edition, with Dr. Serway and author of *The World of Physics . . . Mysteries, Magic, and Myth.* Dr. Jewett enjoys playing keyboard with his all-physicist band, traveling, and collecting antiques that can be used as demonstration apparatus in physics lectures. Most importantly, he relishes spending time with his wife, Lisa, and their children and grandchildren.

In writing this seventh edition of *Physics for Scientists and Engineers*, we continue our ongoing efforts to improve the clarity of presentation and include new pedagogical features that help support the learning and teaching processes. Drawing on positive feedback from users of the sixth edition and reviewers' suggestions, we have refined the text to better meet the needs of students and teachers.

This textbook is intended for a course in introductory physics for students majoring in science or engineering. The entire contents of the book in its extended version could be covered in a three-semester course, but it is possible to use the material in shorter sequences with the omission of selected chapters and sections. The mathematical background of the student taking this course should ideally include one semester of calculus. If that is not possible, the student should be enrolled in a concurrent course in introductory calculus.

Objectives

This introductory physics textbook has two main objectives: to provide the student with a clear and logical presentation of the basic concepts and principles of physics and to strengthen an understanding of the concepts and principles through a broad range of interesting applications to the real world. To meet these objectives, we have placed emphasis on sound physical arguments and problem-solving methodology. At the same time, we have attempted to motivate the student through practical examples that demonstrate the role of physics in other disciplines, including engineering, chemistry, and medicine.

Changes in the Seventh Edition

A large number of changes and improvements have been made in preparing the seventh edition of this text. Some of the new features are based on our experiences and on current trends in science education. Other changes have been incorporated in response to comments and suggestions offered by users of the sixth edition and by reviewers of the manuscript. The features listed here represent the major changes in the seventh edition.

QUESTIONS AND PROBLEMS A substantial revision to the end-of-chapter questions and problems was made in an effort to improve their variety, interest, and pedagogical value, while maintaining their clarity and quality. Approximately 23% of the questions and problems are new or substantially changed. Several of the questions for each chapter are in objective format. Several problems in each chapter explicitly ask for qualitative reasoning in some parts as well as for quantitative answers in other parts:

> **19.** ● Assume a parcel of air in a straight tube moves with a constant acceleration of $-4.00\ \text{m/s}^2$ and has a velocity of 13.0 m/s at 10:05:00 a.m. on a certain date. (a) What is its velocity at 10:05:01 a.m.? (b) At 10:05:02 a.m.? (c) At 10:05:02.5 a.m.? (d) At 10:05:04 a.m.? (e) At 10:04:59 a.m.? (f) Describe the shape of a graph of velocity versus time for this parcel of air. (g) Argue for or against the statement, "Knowing the single value of an object's constant acceleration is like knowing a whole list of values for its velocity."

WORKED EXAMPLES All in-text worked examples have been recast and are now presented in a two-column format to better reinforce physical concepts. The left column shows textual information that describes the steps for solving the problem. The right column shows the mathematical manipulations and results of taking these steps. This layout facilitates matching the concept with its mathematical execution and helps students organize their work. These reconstituted examples closely follow a General Problem-Solving Strategy introduced in Chapter 2 to reinforce effective problem-solving habits. A sample of a worked example can be found on the next page.

Each solution has been reconstituted to more closely follow the General Problem-Solving Strategy as outlined in Chapter 2, to reinforce good problem-solving habits.

EXAMPLE 3.2 **A Vacation Trip**

A car travels 20.0 km due north and then 35.0 km in a direction 60.0° west of north as shown in Figure 3.11a. Find the magnitude and direction of the car's resultant displacement.

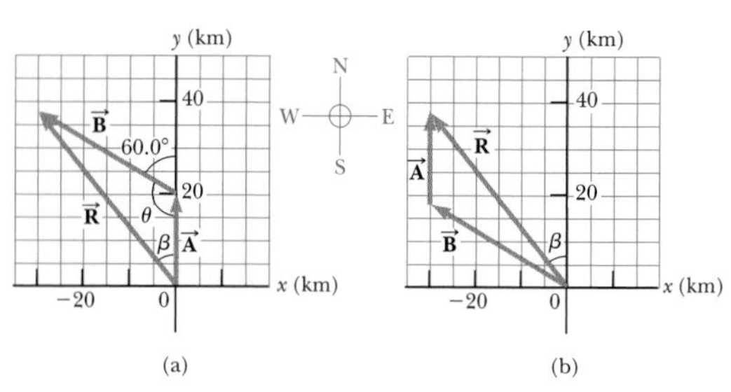

Figure 3.11 (Example 3.2) (a) Graphical method for finding the resultant displacement vector $\vec{R} = \vec{A} + \vec{B}$. (b) Adding the vectors in reverse order $(\vec{B} + \vec{A})$ gives the same result for $\vec{R}$.

SOLUTION

Conceptualize The vectors $\vec{A}$ and $\vec{B}$ drawn in Figure 3.11a help us conceptualize the problem.

Categorize We can categorize this example as a simple analysis problem in vector addition. The displacement $\vec{R}$ is the resultant when the two individual displacements $\vec{A}$ and $\vec{B}$ are added. We can further categorize it as a problem about the analysis of triangles, so we appeal to our expertise in geometry and trigonometry.

Each step of the solution is detailed in a two-column format. The left column provides an explanation for each mathematical step in the right column, to better reinforce the physical concepts.

Analyze In this example, we show two ways to analyze the problem of finding the resultant of two vectors. The first way is to solve the problem geometrically, using graph paper and a protractor to measure the magnitude of $\vec{R}$ and its direction in Figure 3.11a. (In fact, even when you know you are going to be carrying out a calculation, you should sketch the vectors to check your results.) With an ordinary ruler and protractor, a large diagram typically gives answers to two-digit but not to three-digit precision.

The second way to solve the problem is to analyze it algebraically. The magnitude of $\vec{R}$ can be obtained from the law of cosines as applied to the triangle (see Appendix B.4).

Use $R^2 = A^2 + B^2 - 2AB\cos\theta$ from the law of cosines to find R:

$$R = \sqrt{A^2 + B^2 - 2AB\cos\theta}$$

Substitute numerical values, noting that $\theta = 180° - 60° = 120°$:

$$R = \sqrt{(20.0\text{ km})^2 + (35.0\text{ km})^2 - 2(20.0\text{ km})(35.0\text{ km})\cos 120°}$$
$$= 48.2\text{ km}$$

Use the law of sines (Appendix B.4) to find the direction of $\vec{R}$ measured from the northerly direction:

$$\frac{\sin\beta}{B} = \frac{\sin\theta}{R}$$

$$\sin\beta = \frac{B}{R}\sin\theta = \frac{35.0\text{ km}}{48.2\text{ km}}\sin 120° = 0.629$$

$$\beta = 38.9°$$

The resultant displacement of the car is 48.2 km in a direction 38.9° west of north.

Finalize Does the angle β that we calculated agree with an estimate made by looking at Figure 3.11a or with an actual angle measured from the diagram using the graphical method? Is it reasonable that the magnitude of $\vec{R}$ is larger than that of both $\vec{A}$ and $\vec{B}$? Are the units of $\vec{R}$ correct?

Although the graphical method of adding vectors works well, it suffers from two disadvantages. First, some people find using the laws of cosines and sines to be awkward. Second, a triangle only results if you are adding two vectors. If you are adding three or more vectors, the resulting geometric shape is usually not a triangle. In Section 3.4, we explore a new method of adding vectors that will address both of these disadvantages.

What If? Suppose the trip were taken with the two vectors in reverse order: 35.0 km at 60.0° west of north first and then 20.0 km due north. How would the magnitude and the direction of the resultant vector change?

Answer They would not change. The commutative law for vector addition tells us that the order of vectors in an addition is irrelevant. Graphically, Figure 3.11b shows that the vectors added in the reverse order give us the same resultant vector.

What If? statements appear in about 1/3 of the worked examples and offer a variation on the situation posed in the text of the example. For instance, this feature might explore the effects of changing the conditions of the situation, determine what happens when a quantity is taken to a particular limiting value, or question whether additional information can be determined about the problem situation. This feature encourages students to think about the results of the example and assists in conceptual understanding of the principles.

All worked examples are also available to be assigned as interactive examples in the Enhanced WebAssign homework management system (visit **www.pse7.com** for more details).

ONLINE HOMEWORK It is now easier to assign online homework with Serway and Jewett and Enhanced WebAssign. All worked examples, end-of-chapter problems, active figures, quick quizzes, and most questions are available in WebAssign. Most problems include hints and feedback to provide instantaneous reinforcement or direction for that problem. In addition to the text content, we have also added math remediation tools to help students get up to speed in algebra, trigonometry, and calculus.

SUMMARIES Each chapter contains a summary that reviews the important concepts and equations discussed in that chapter. A marginal note next to each chapter summary directs students to additional quizzes, animations, and interactive exercises for that chapter on the book's companion Web site. The format of the end-of-chapter summary has been completely revised for this edition. The summary is divided into three sections: Definitions, Concepts and Principles, and Analysis Models for Problem-Solving. In each section, flashcard-type boxes focus on each separate definition, concept, principle, or analysis model.

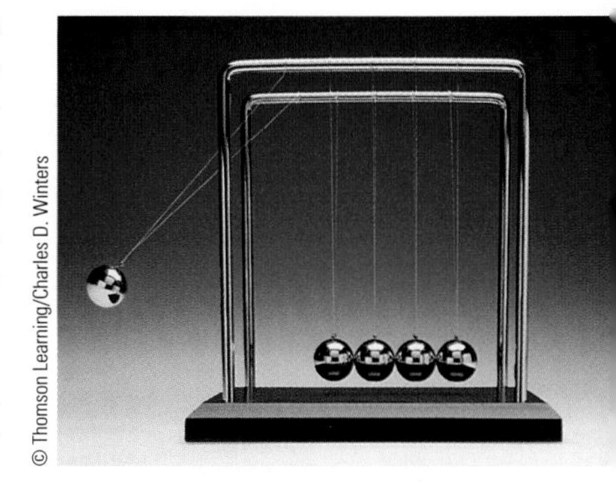
© Thomson Learning/Charles D. Winters

MATH APPENDIX The math appendix, a valuable tool for students, has been updated to show the math tools in a physics context. This resource is ideal for students who need a quick review on topics such as algebra, trigonometry, and calculus.

CONTENT CHANGES The content and organization of the textbook are essentially the same as in the sixth edition. Many sections in various chapters have been streamlined, deleted, or combined with other sections to allow for a more balanced presentation. Vectors are now denoted in boldface with an arrow over them (for example, $\vec{\mathbf{v}}$), making them easier to recognize. Chapters 7 and 8 have been completely reorganized to prepare students for a unified approach to energy that is used throughout the text. A new section in Chapter 9 teaches students how to analyze deformable systems with the conservation of energy equation and the impulse-momentum theorem. Chapter 34 is longer than in the sixth edition because of the movement into that chapter of the material on displacement current from Chapter 30 and Maxwell's equations from Chapter 31. A more detailed list of content changes can be found on the instructor's companion Web site.

Content

The material in this book covers fundamental topics in classical physics and provides an introduction to modern physics. The book is divided into six parts. Part 1 (Chapters 1 to 14) deals with the fundamentals of Newtonian mechanics and the physics of fluids; Part 2 (Chapters 15 to 18) covers oscillations, mechanical waves, and sound; Part 3 (Chapters 19 to 22) addresses heat and thermodynamics; Part 4 (Chapters 23 to 34) treats electricity and magnetism; Part 5 (Chapters 35 to 38) covers light and optics; and Part 6 (Chapters 39 to 46) deals with relativity and modern physics.

Text Features

Most instructors believe that the textbook selected for a course should be the student's primary guide for understanding and learning the subject matter. Furthermore, the textbook should be easily accessible and should be styled and written to facilitate instruction and learning. With these points in mind, we have included many pedagogical features, listed below, that are intended to enhance its usefulness to both students and instructors.

Problem Solving and Conceptual Understanding

GENERAL PROBLEM-SOLVING STRATEGY A general strategy outlined at the end of Chapter 2 provides students with a structured process for solving problems. In all remaining chapters, the strategy is employed explicitly in every example so that students learn how it is applied. Students are encouraged to follow this strategy when working end-of-chapter problems.

MODELING Although students are faced with hundreds of problems during their physics courses, instructors realize that a relatively small number of physical situations form the basis of these problems. When faced with a new problem, a physicist forms a *model* of the problem that can be solved in a simple way by identifying the common physical situation that occurs in the problem. For example, many problems involve particles under constant acceleration, isolated systems, or waves under refraction. Because the physicist has studied these situations extensively and understands the associated behavior, he or she can apply this knowledge as a model for solving a new problem. In certain chapters, this edition identifies Analysis Models, which are physical situations (such as the particle under constant acceleration, the isolated system, or the wave under refraction) that occur so often that they can be used as a model for solving an unfamiliar problem. These models are discussed in the chapter text, and the student is reminded of them in the end-of-chapter summary under the heading "Analysis Models for Problem-Solving."

PROBLEMS An extensive set of problems is included at the end of each chapter; in all, the text contains approximately three thousand problems. Answers to odd-numbered problems are provided at the end of the book. For the convenience of both the student and the instructor, about two-thirds of the problems are keyed to specific sections of the chapter. The remaining problems, labeled "Additional Problems," are not keyed to specific sections. The problem numbers for straightforward problems are printed in black, intermediate-level problems are in blue, and challenging problems are in magenta.

- **"Not-just-a-number" problems** Each chapter includes several marked problems that require students to think qualitatively in some parts and quantitatively in others. Instructors can assign such problems to guide students to display deeper understanding, practice good problem-solving techniques, and prepare for exams.
- **Problems for developing symbolic reasoning** Each chapter contains problems that ask for solutions in symbolic form as well as many problems asking for numerical answers. To help students develop skill in symbolic reasoning, each chapter contains a pair of otherwise identical problems, one asking for a numerical solution and one asking for a symbolic derivation. In this edition, each chapter also contains a problem giving a numerical value for every datum but one so that the answer displays how the unknown depends on the datum represented symbolically. The answer to such a problem has the form of a function of one variable. Reasoning about the behavior of this function puts emphasis on the *Finalize* step of the General Problem-Solving Strategy. All problems developing symbolic reasoning are identified by a tan background screen:

> 53. ● A light spring has an unstressed length of 15.5 cm. It is described by Hooke's law with spring constant 4.30 N/m. One end of the horizontal spring is held on a fixed vertical axle, and the other end is attached to a puck of mass m that can move without friction over a horizontal surface. The puck is set into motion in a circle with a period of 1.30 s. (a) Find the extension of the spring x as it depends on m. Evaluate x for (b) $m = 0.070\,0$ kg, (c) $m = 0.140$ kg, (d) $m = 0.180$ kg, and (e) $m = 0.190$ kg. (f) Describe the pattern of variation of x as it depends on m.

- **Review problems** Many chapters include review problems requiring the student to combine concepts covered in the chapter with those discussed in previous chapters. These problems reflect the cohesive nature of the principles in the text and verify that physics is not a scattered set of ideas. When facing a real-world issue such as global warming or nuclear weapons, it may be necessary to call on ideas in physics from several parts of a textbook such as this one.
- **"Fermi problems"** As in previous editions, at least one problem in each chapter asks the student to reason in order-of-magnitude terms.

- **Design problems** Several chapters contain problems that ask the student to determine design parameters for a practical device so that it can function as required.
- **"*Jeopardy!*" problems** Some chapters give students practice in changing between different representations by stating equations and asking for a description of a situation to which they apply as well as for a numerical answer.
- **Calculus-based problems** Every chapter contains at least one problem applying ideas and methods from differential calculus and one problem using integral calculus.

The instructor's Web site, **www.thomsonedu.com/physics/serway,** provides lists of problems using calculus, problems encouraging or requiring computer use, problems with "**What If?**" parts, problems referred to in the chapter text, problems based on experimental data, order-of-magnitude problems, problems about biological applications, design problems, *Jeopardy!* problems, review problems, problems reflecting historical reasoning about confusing ideas, problems developing symbolic reasoning skill, problems with qualitative parts, ranking questions, and other objective questions.

QUESTIONS The questions section at the end of each chapter has been significantly revised. Multiple-choice, ranking, and true–false questions have been added. The instructor may select items to assign as homework or use in the classroom, possibly with "peer instruction" methods and possibly with "clicker" systems. More than eight hundred questions are included in this edition. Answers to selected questions are included in the *Student Solutions Manual/Study Guide,* and answers to all questions are found in the *Instructor's Solutions Manual.*

19. O (i) Rank the gravitational accelerations you would measure for (a) a 2-kg object 5 cm above the floor, (b) a 2-kg object 120 cm above the floor, (c) a 3-kg object 120 cm above the floor, and (d) a 3-kg object 80 cm above the floor. List the one with the largest-magnitude acceleration first. If two are equal, show their equality in your list. **(ii)** Rank the gravitational forces on the same four objects, largest magnitude first. **(iii)** Rank the gravitational potential energies (of the object–Earth system) for the same four objects, largest first, taking $y = 0$ at the floor.

23. O An ice cube has been given a push and slides without friction on a level table. Which is correct? (a) It is in stable equilibrium. (b) It is in unstable equilibrium. (c) It is in neutral equilibrium (d) It is not in equilibrium.

WORKED EXAMPLES Two types of worked examples are presented to aid student comprehension. All worked examples in the text may be assigned for homework in WebAssign.

The first example type presents a problem and numerical answer. As discussed earlier, solutions to these examples have been altered in this edition to feature a two-column layout to explain the physical concepts and the mathematical steps side by side. Every example follows the explicit steps of the General Problem-Solving Strategy outlined in Chapter 2.

The second type of example is conceptual in nature. To accommodate increased emphasis on understanding physical concepts, the many conceptual examples are labeled as such, set off in boxes, and designed to focus students on the physical situation in the problem.

WHAT IF? Approximately one-third of the worked examples in the text contain a **What If?** feature. At the completion of the example solution, a **What If?** question offers a variation on the situation posed in the text of the example. For instance, this feature might explore the effects of changing the conditions of the situation, determine what happens when a quantity is taken to a particular limiting value, or question whether additional information can be determined about the situation. This feature encourages students to think about the results of the example, and it also assists in conceptual understanding of the principles. **What If?** questions also prepare students to encounter novel problems that may be included on exams. Some of the end-of-chapter problems also include this feature.

QUICK QUIZZES Quick Quizzes provide students an opportunity to test their understanding of the physical concepts presented. The questions require students to make decisions on the basis of sound reasoning, and some of the questions have been written to help students overcome common misconceptions. Quick Quizzes have been cast in an objective format, including multiple-choice, true–false, and ranking. Answers to all Quick Quiz questions are found at the end of each chapter. Additional Quick Quizzes that can be used in classroom teaching are available on the instructor's companion Web site. Many instructors choose to use such questions in a "peer instruction" teaching style or with the use of personal response system "clickers," but they can be used in standard quiz format as well. Quick Quizzes are set off from the text by horizontal lines:

Quick Quiz 7.5 A dart is loaded into a spring-loaded toy dart gun by pushing the spring in by a distance x. For the next loading, the spring is compressed a distance $2x$. How much faster does the second dart leave the gun compared with the first? (a) four times as fast (b) two times as fast (c) the same (d) half as fast (e) one-fourth as fast

---

PITFALL PREVENTION 16.2
Two Kinds of Speed/Velocity

Do not confuse v, the speed of the wave as it propagates along the string, with v_y, the transverse velocity of a point on the string. The speed v is constant for a uniform medium, whereas v_y varies sinusoidally.

PITFALL PREVENTIONS More than two hundred Pitfall Preventions (such as the one to the left) are provided to help students avoid common mistakes and misunderstandings. These features, which are placed in the margins of the text, address both common student misconceptions and situations in which students often follow unproductive paths.

Helpful Features

STYLE To facilitate rapid comprehension, we have written the book in a clear, logical, and engaging style. We have chosen a writing style that is somewhat informal and relaxed so that students will find the text appealing and enjoyable to read. New terms are carefully defined, and we have avoided the use of jargon.

IMPORTANT STATEMENTS AND EQUATIONS Most important statements and definitions are set in **boldface** or are highlighted with a background screen for added emphasis and ease of review. Similarly, important equations are highlighted with a background screen to facilitate location.

MARGINAL NOTES Comments and notes appearing in the margin with a ▶ icon can be used to locate important statements, equations, and concepts in the text.

PEDAGOGICAL USE OF COLOR Readers should consult the **pedagogical color chart** (inside the front cover) for a listing of the color-coded symbols used in the text diagrams. This system is followed consistently throughout the text.

MATHEMATICAL LEVEL We have introduced calculus gradually, keeping in mind that students often take introductory courses in calculus and physics concurrently. Most steps are shown when basic equations are developed, and reference is often made to mathematical appendices near the end of the textbook. Vector products are introduced later in the text, where they are needed in physical applications. The dot product is introduced in Chapter 7, which addresses energy of a system; the cross product is introduced in Chapter 11, which deals with angular momentum.

SIGNIFICANT FIGURES Significant figures in both worked examples and end-of-chapter problems have been handled with care. Most numerical examples are worked to either two or three significant figures, depending on the precision of the data provided. End-of-chapter problems regularly state data and answers to three-digit precision.

UNITS The international system of units (SI) is used throughout the text. The U.S. customary system of units is used only to a limited extent in the chapters on mechanics and thermodynamics.

APPENDICES AND ENDPAPERS Several appendices are provided near the end of the textbook. Most of the appendix material represents a review of mathematical concepts and techniques used in the text, including scientific notation, algebra, geometry, trigonometry, differential calculus, and integral calculus. Reference to these appendices is made throughout the text. Most mathematical review sections in the appendices include worked examples and exercises with answers. In addition to the mathematical reviews, the appendices contain tables of physical data, conversion factors, and the SI units of physical quantities as well as a periodic table of the elements. Other useful information—fundamental constants and physical data, planetary data, a list of standard prefixes, mathematical symbols, the Greek alphabet, and standard abbreviations of units of measure—appears on the endpapers.

Course Solutions That Fit Your Teaching Goals and Your Students' Learning Needs

Recent advances in educational technology have made homework management systems and audience response systems powerful and affordable tools to enhance the way you teach your course. Whether you offer a more traditional text-based course, are interested in using or are currently using an online homework management system such as WebAssign, or are ready to turn your lecture into an interactive learning environment with JoinIn on TurningPoint, you can be confident that the text's proven content provides the foundation for each and every component of our technology and ancillary package.

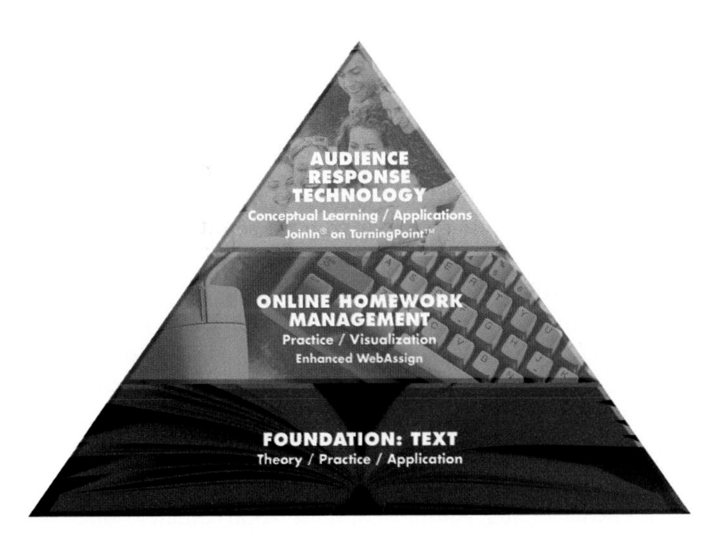

Homework Management Systems

Enhanced WebAssign Whether you're an experienced veteran or a beginner, Enhanced WebAssign is the perfect solution to fit your homework management needs. Designed by physicists for physicists, this system is a reliable and user-friendly teaching companion. Enhanced WebAssign is available for *Physics for Scientists and Engineers*, giving you the freedom to assign

- every end-of-chapter Problem and Question, enhanced with hints and feedback
- every worked example, enhanced with hints and feedback, to help strengthen students' problem-solving skills
- every Quick Quiz, giving your students ample opportunity to test their conceptual understanding.

- animated Active Figures, enhanced with hints and feedback, to help students develop their visualization skills
- a math review to help students brush up on key quantitative concepts

Please visit **www.thomsonedu.com/physics/serway** to view a live demonstration of Enhanced WebAssign.

The text also supports the following Homework Management Systems:

LON-CAPA: A Computer-Assisted Personalized Approach
http://www.lon-capa.org/

The University of Texas Homework Service
contact **moore@physics.utexas.edu**

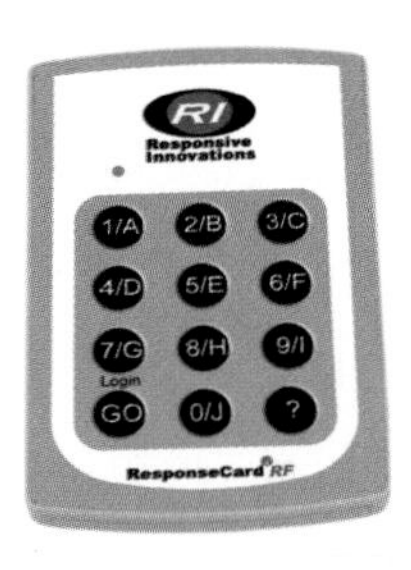

Personal Response Systems

JoinIn on TurningPoint Pose book-specific questions and display students' answers seamlessly within the Microsoft® PowerPoint slides of your own lecture in conjunction with the "clicker" hardware of your choice. JoinIn on TurningPoint works with most infrared or radio frequency keypad systems, including Responsecard, EduCue, H-ITT, and even laptops. Contact your local sales representative to learn more about our personal response software and hardware.

Personal Response System Content Regardless of the response system you are using, we provide the tested content to support it. Our ready-to-go content includes all the questions from the Quick Quizzes, test questions, and a selection of end-of-chapter questions to provide helpful conceptual checkpoints to drop into your lecture. Our series of Active Figure animations have also been enhanced with multiple-choice questions to help test students' observational skills.

We also feature the Assessing to Learn in the Classroom content from the University of Massachusetts at Amherst. This collection of 250 advanced conceptual questions has been tested in the classroom for more than ten years and takes peer learning to a new level.

Visit **www.thomsonedu.com/physics/serway** to download samples of our personal response system content.

Lecture Presentation Resources

The following resources provide support for your presentations in lecture.

MULTIMEDIA MANAGER INSTRUCTOR'S RESOURCE CD An easy-to-use multimedia lecture tool, the Multimedia Manager Instructor's Resource CD allows you to quickly assemble art, animations, digital video, and database files with notes to create fluid lectures. The two-volume set (Volume 1: Chapters 1–22; Volume 2: Chapters 23–46) includes prebuilt PowerPoint lectures, a database of animations, video clips, and digital art from the text as well as editable electronic files of the *Instructor's Solutions Manual* and *Test Bank*.

TRANSPARENCY ACETATES Each volume contains approximately one hundred transparency acetates featuring art from the text. Volume 1 contains Chapters 1 through 22, and Volume 2 contains Chapters 23 through 46.

Assessment and Course Preparation Resources

A number of resources listed below will assist with your assessment and preparation processes.

INSTRUCTOR'S SOLUTIONS MANUAL by Ralph McGrew. This two-volume manual contains complete worked solutions to all end-of-chapter problems in the textbook as well as answers to the even-numbered problems and all the questions. The solutions to problems new to the seventh edition are marked for easy identification. Volume 1 contains

Chapters 1 through 22, and Volume 2 contains Chapters 23 through 46. Electronic files of the Instructor's Solutions are available on the Multimedia Manager CD as well.

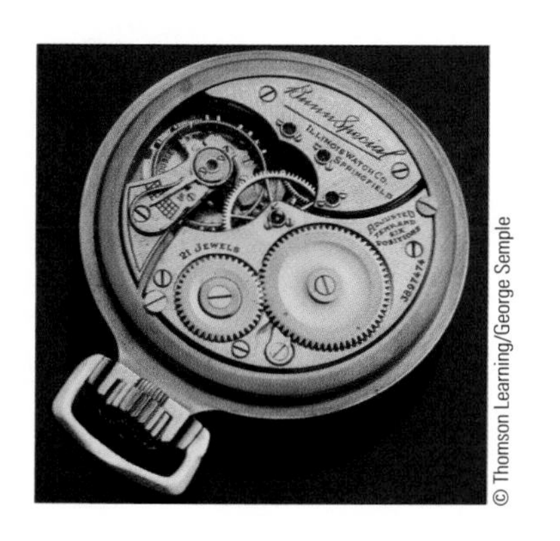
© Thomson Learning/George Semple

PRINTED TEST BANK by Edward Adelson. This two-volume test bank contains approximately 2 200 multiple-choice questions. These questions are also available in electronic format with complete answers and solutions in the ExamView test software and as editable Word® files on the Multimedia Manager CD. Volume 1 contains Chapters 1 through 22, and Volume 2 contains Chapters 23 through 46.

EXAMVIEW This easy-to-use test generator CD features all of the questions from the printed test bank in an editable format.

WEBCT AND BLACKBOARD CONTENT For users of either course management system, we provide our test bank questions in the proper format for easy upload into your online course. In addition, you can integrate the ThomsonNOW for Physics student tutorial content into your WebCT or Blackboard course, providing your students a single sign-on to all their Web-based learning resources. Contact your local sales representative to learn more about our WebCT and Blackboard resources.

INSTRUCTOR'S COMPANION WEB SITE Consult the instructor's site by pointing your browser to **www.thomsonedu.com/physics/serway** for additional Quick Quiz questions, a detailed list of content changes since the sixth edition, a problem correlation guide, images from the text, and sample PowerPoint lectures. Instructors adopting the seventh edition of *Physics for Scientists and Engineers* may download these materials after securing the appropriate password from their local Thomson•Brooks/Cole sales representative.

Student Resources

STUDENT SOLUTIONS MANUAL/STUDY GUIDE by John R. Gordon, Ralph McGrew, Raymond Serway, and John W. Jewett, Jr. This two-volume manual features detailed solutions to 20% of the end-of-chapter problems from the text. The manual also features a list of important equations, concepts, and notes from key sections of the text in addition to answers to selected end-of-chapter questions. Volume 1 contains Chapters 1 through 22, and Volume 2 contains Chapters 23 through 46.

THOMSONNOW PERSONAL STUDY This assessment-based student tutorial system provides students with a personalized learning plan based on their performance on a series of diagnostic pre-tests. Rich interactive content, including Active Figures, Coached Problems, and Interactive Examples, helps students prepare for tests and exams.

Teaching Options

The topics in this textbook are presented in the following sequence: classical mechanics, oscillations and mechanical waves, and heat and thermodynamics followed by electricity and magnetism, electromagnetic waves, optics, relativity, and modern physics. This presentation represents a traditional sequence, with the subject of mechanical waves being presented before electricity and magnetism. Some instructors may prefer to discuss both mechanical and electromagnetic waves together after completing electricity and magnetism. In this case, Chapters 16 through 18 could be covered along with Chapter 34. The chapter on relativity is placed near the end of the text because this topic often is treated as an introduction to the era of "modern physics." If time permits, instructors may choose to cover Chapter 39 after completing Chapter 13 as a conclusion to the material on Newtonian mechanics.

For those instructors teaching a two-semester sequence, some sections and chapters could be deleted without any loss of continuity. The following sections can be considered optional for this purpose:

2.8	Kinematic Equations Derived from Calculus
4.6	Relative Velocity and Relative Acceleration
6.3	Motion in Accelerated Frames
6.4	Motion in the Presence of Resistive Forces
7.9	Energy Diagrams and Equilibrium of a System
9.8	Rocket Propulsion
11.5	The Motion of Gyroscopes and Tops
14.7	Other Applications of Fluid Dynamics
15.6	Damped Oscillations
15.7	Forced Oscillations
17.5	Digital Sound Recording
17.6	Motion Picture Sound
18.6	Standing Waves in Rods and Membranes
18.8	Nonsinusoidal Wave Patterns
22.8	Entropy on a Microscopic Scale
25.7	The Millikan Oil-Drop Experiment
25.8	Applications of Electrostatics
26.7	An Atomic Description of Dielectrics
27.5	Superconductors
28.5	Electrical Meters
28.6	Household Wiring and Electrical Safety
29.3	Applications Involving Charged Particles Moving in a Magnetic Field
29.6	The Hall Effect
30.6	Magnetism in Matter
30.7	The Magnetic Field of the Earth
31.6	Eddy Currents
33.9	Rectifiers and Filters
34.6	Production of Electromagnetic Waves by an Antenna
36.5	Lens Aberrations
36.6	The Camera
36.7	The Eye
36.8	The Simple Magnifier
36.9	The Compound Microscope
36.10	The Telescope
38.5	Diffraction of X-Rays by Crystals
39.10	The General Theory of Relativity

Acknowledgments

This seventh edition of *Physics for Scientists and Engineers* was prepared with the guidance and assistance of many professors who reviewed selections of the manuscript, the prerevision text, or both. We wish to acknowledge the following scholars and express our sincere appreciation for their suggestions, criticisms, and encouragement:

David P. Balogh, *Fresno City College*
Leonard X. Finegold, *Drexel University*
Raymond Hall, *California State University, Fresno*
Bob Jacobsen, *University of California, Berkeley*
Robin Jordan, *Florida Atlantic University*
Rafael Lopez-Mobilia, *University of Texas at San Antonio*
Diana Lininger Markham, *City College of San Francisco*
Steven Morris, *Los Angeles Harbor City College*
Taha Mzoughi, *Kennesaw State University*
Nobel Sanjay Rebello, *Kansas State University*
John Rosendahl, *University of California, Irvine*
Mikolaj Sawicki, *John A. Logan College*

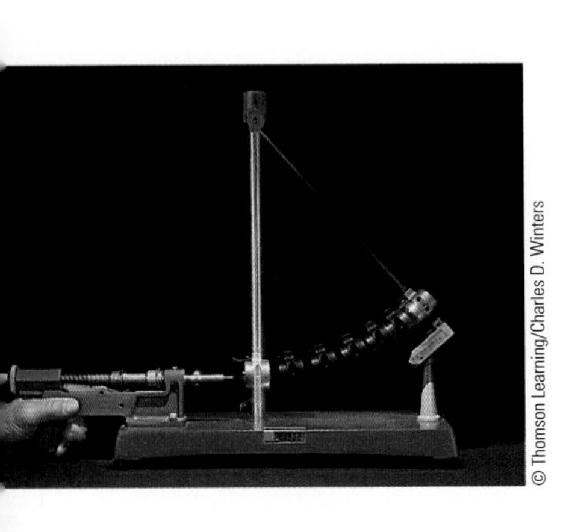

Glenn B. Stracher, *East Georgia College*
Som Tyagi, *Drexel University*
Robert Weidman, *Michigan Technological University*
Edward A. Whittaker, *Stevens Institute of Technology*

This title was carefully checked for accuracy by Zinoviy Akkerman, *City College of New York;* Grant Hart, *Brigham Young University;* Michael Kotlarchyk, *Rochester Institute of Technology;* Andres LaRosa, *Portland State University;* Bruce Mason, *University of Oklahoma at Norman;* Peter Moeck, *Portland State University;* Brian A. Raue, *Florida International University;* James E. Rutledge, *University of California at Irvine;* Bjoern Seipel, *Portland State University;* Z. M. Stadnick, *University of Ottawa;* and Harry W. K. Tom, *University of California at Riverside.* We thank them for their diligent efforts under schedule pressure.

We are grateful to Ralph McGrew for organizing the end-of-chapter problems, writing many new problems, and suggesting improvements in the content of the textbook. Problems and questions new to this edition were written by Duane Deardorff, Thomas Grace, Francisco Izaguirre, John Jewett, Robert Forsythe, Randall Jones, Ralph McGrew, Kurt Vandervoort, and Jerzy Wrobel. Help was very kindly given by Dwight Neuenschwander, Michael Kinney, Amy Smith, Will Mackin, and the Sewer Department of Grand Forks, North Dakota. Daniel Kim, Jennifer Hoffman, Ed Oberhofer, Richard Webb, Wesley Smith, Kevin Kilty, Zinoviy Akkerman, Michael Rudmin, Paul Cox, Robert LaMontagne, Ken Menningen, and Chris Church made corrections to problems taken from previous editions. We are grateful to authors John R. Gordon and Ralph McGrew for preparing the *Student Solutions Manual/Study Guide.* Author Ralph McGrew has prepared an excellent *Instructor's Solutions Manual.* Edward Adelson has carefully edited and improved the test bank. Kurt Vandervoort prepared extra Quick Quiz questions for the instructor's companion Web site.

Special thanks and recognition go to the professional staff at the Brooks/Cole Publishing Company—in particular, Ed Dodd, Brandi Kirksey (who managed the ancillary program and so much more), Shawn Vasquez, Sam Subity, Teri Hyde, Michelle Julet, David Harris, and Chris Hall—for their fine work during the development and production of this textbook. Mark Santee is our seasoned marketing manager, and Bryan Vann coordinates our marketing communications. We recognize the skilled production service and excellent artwork provided by the staff at Lachina Publishing Services, and the dedicated photo research efforts of Jane Sanders Miller.

Finally, we are deeply indebted to our wives, children, and grandchildren for their love, support, and long-term sacrifices.

Raymond A. Serway
St. Petersburg, Florida

John W. Jewett, Jr.
Pomona, California

It is appropriate to offer some words of advice that should be of benefit to you, the student. Before doing so, we assume you have read the Preface, which describes the various features of the text and support materials that will help you through the course.

How to Study

Instructors are often asked, "How should I study physics and prepare for examinations?" There is no simple answer to this question, but we can offer some suggestions based on our own experiences in learning and teaching over the years.

First and foremost, maintain a positive attitude toward the subject matter, keeping in mind that physics is the most fundamental of all natural sciences. Other science courses that follow will use the same physical principles, so it is important that you understand and are able to apply the various concepts and theories discussed in the text.

Concepts and Principles

It is essential that you understand the basic concepts and principles before attempting to solve assigned problems. You can best accomplish this goal by carefully reading the textbook before you attend your lecture on the covered material. When reading the text, you should jot down those points that are not clear to you. Also be sure to make a diligent attempt at answering the questions in the Quick Quizzes as you come to them in your reading. We have worked hard to prepare questions that help you judge for yourself how well you understand the material. Study the **What If?** features that appear in many of the worked examples carefully. They will help you extend your understanding beyond the simple act of arriving at a numerical result. The Pitfall Preventions will also help guide you away from common misunderstandings about physics. During class, take careful notes and ask questions about those ideas that are unclear to you. Keep in mind that few people are able to absorb the full meaning of scientific material after only one reading; several readings of the text and your notes may be necessary. Your lectures and laboratory work supplement the textbook and should clarify some of the more difficult material. You should minimize your memorization of material. Successful memorization of passages from the text, equations, and derivations does not necessarily indicate that you understand the material. Your understanding of the material will be enhanced through a combination of efficient study habits, discussions with other students and with instructors, and your ability to solve the problems presented in the textbook. Ask questions whenever you believe that clarification of a concept is necessary.

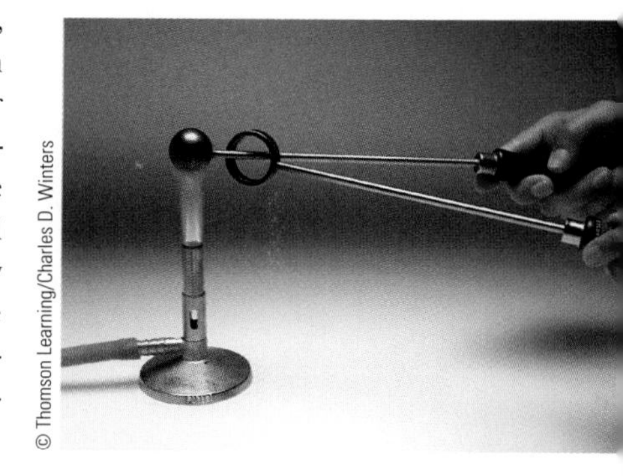

Study Schedule

It is important that you set up a regular study schedule, preferably a daily one. Make sure that you read the syllabus for the course and adhere to the schedule set by your instructor. The lectures will make much more sense if you read the corresponding text material *before* attending them. As a general rule, you should devote about two hours of study time for each hour you are in class. If you are having trouble with the course, seek the advice of the instructor or other students who have taken the course. You may find it necessary to seek further instruction from experienced students. Very often, instructors offer review sessions in addition to regular class periods. Avoid the practice of delaying study until a day or two before an exam. More often than not, this approach has disastrous results. Rather than undertake an all-night study session before a test, briefly review the basic concepts and equations, and then get a good night's rest. If you believe that you need additional help in understanding the concepts, in preparing for exams, or in problem solving, we suggest that you acquire a copy of the *Student Solutions Manual/Study Guide* that accompanies this textbook; this manual should be available at your college bookstore or through the publisher.

Use the Features

You should make full use of the various features of the text discussed in the Preface. For example, marginal notes are useful for locating and describing important equations and concepts, and **boldface** indicates important statements and definitions. Many useful tables are contained in the appendices, but most are incorporated in the text where they are most often referenced. Appendix B is a convenient review of mathematical tools used in the text.

Answers to odd-numbered problems are given at the end of the textbook, answers to Quick Quizzes are located at the end of each chapter, and solutions to selected end-of-chapter questions and problems are provided in the *Student Solutions Manual/Study Guide*. The table of contents provides an overview of the entire text, and the index enables you to locate specific material quickly. Footnotes are sometimes used to supplement the text or to cite other references on the subject discussed.

After reading a chapter, you should be able to define any new quantities introduced in that chapter and discuss the principles and assumptions that were used to arrive at certain key relations. The chapter summaries and the review sections of the *Student Solutions Manual/Study Guide* should help you in this regard. In some cases, you may find it necessary to refer to the textbook's index to locate certain topics. You should be able to associate with each physical quantity the correct symbol used to represent that quantity and the unit in which the quantity is specified. Furthermore, you should be able to express each important equation in concise and accurate prose.

Problem Solving

R. P. Feynman, Nobel laureate in physics, once said, "You do not know anything until you have practiced." In keeping with this statement, we strongly advise you to develop the skills necessary to solve a wide range of problems. Your ability to solve problems will be one of the main tests of your knowledge of physics; therefore, you should try to solve as many problems as possible. It is essential that you understand basic concepts and principles before attempting to solve problems. It is good practice to try to find alternate solutions to the same problem. For example, you can solve problems in mechanics using Newton's laws, but very often an alternative method that draws on energy considerations is more direct. You should not deceive yourself into thinking that you understand a problem merely because you have seen it solved in class. You must be able to solve the problem and similar problems on your own.

The approach to solving problems should be carefully planned. A systematic plan is especially important when a problem involves several concepts. First, read the problem several times until you are confident you understand what is being asked. Look for any key words that will help you interpret the problem and perhaps allow you to make certain assumptions. Your ability to interpret a question properly is an integral part of problem solving. Second, you should acquire the habit of writing down the information given in a problem and those quantities that need to be found; for example, you might construct a table listing both the quantities given and the quantities to be found. This procedure is sometimes used in the worked examples of the textbook. Finally, after you have decided on the method you believe is appropriate for a given problem, proceed with your solution. The General Problem-Solving Strategy will guide you through complex problems. If you follow the steps of this procedure *(Conceptualize, Categorize, Analyze, Finalize)*, you will find it easier to come up with a solution and gain more from your efforts. This Strategy, located at the end of Chapter 2, is used in all worked examples in the remaining chapters so that you can learn how to apply it. Specific problem-solving strategies for certain types of situations are included in the text and appear with a blue heading. These specific strategies follow the outline of the General Problem-Solving Strategy.

Often, students fail to recognize the limitations of certain equations or physical laws in a particular situation. It is very important that you understand and remember the assumptions that underlie a particular theory or formalism. For example, certain equations in kinematics apply only to a particle moving with constant acceleration. These equations are not valid for describing motion whose acceleration is not constant such as the motion of an object connected to a spring or the motion of an object through a fluid. Study the Analysis Models for Problem-Solving in the chapter summaries carefully so that you know how each model can be applied to a specific situation.

Experiments

Physics is a science based on experimental observations. Therefore, we recommend that you try to supplement the text by performing various types of "hands-on" experiments either at home or in the laboratory. These experiments can be used to test ideas and models discussed in class or in the textbook. For example, the common Slinky toy is excellent for studying traveling waves, a ball swinging on the end of a long string can be used to investigate pendulum motion, various masses attached to the end of a vertical spring or rubber band can be used to determine their elastic nature, an old pair of Polaroid sunglasses and some discarded lenses and a magnifying glass are the components of various experiments in optics, and an approximate measure of the free-fall acceleration can be determined simply by measuring with a stopwatch the time it takes for a ball to drop from a known height. The list of such experiments is endless. When physical models are not available, be imaginative and try to develop models of your own.

New Media

We strongly encourage you to use the **ThomsonNOW** Web-based learning system that accompanies this textbook. It is far easier to understand physics if you see it in action, and these new materials will enable you to become a part of that action. **ThomsonNOW** media described in the Preface and accessed at **www.thomsonedu.com/physics/serway** feature a three-step learning process consisting of a pre-test, a personalized learning plan, and a post-test.

It is our sincere hope that you will find physics an exciting and enjoyable experience and that you will benefit from this experience, regardless of your chosen profession. Welcome to the exciting world of physics!

The scientist does not study nature because it is useful; he studies it because he delights in it, and he delights in it because it is beautiful. If nature were not beautiful, it would not be worth knowing, and if nature were not worth knowing, life would not be worth living.

—Henri Poincaré

PART 5

Light and Optics

Light is basic to almost all life on the Earth. For example, plants convert the energy transferred by sunlight to chemical energy through photosynthesis. In addition, light is the principal means by which we are able to transmit and receive information to and from objects around us and throughout the Universe. Light is a form of electromagnetic radiation and represents energy transfer from the source to the observer.

Many phenomena in our everyday life depend on the properties of light. When you watch a color television or view photos on a computer monitor, you are seeing millions of colors formed from combinations of only three colors that are physically on the screen: red, blue, and green. The blue color of the daytime sky is a result of the optical phenomenon of *scattering* of light by air molecules, as are the red and orange colors of sunrises and sunsets. You see your image in your bathroom mirror in the morning or the images of other cars in your car's rearview mirror when you are driving. These images result from *reflection* of light. If you wear glasses or contact lenses, you are depending on *refraction* of light for clear vision. The colors of a rainbow result from *dispersion* of light as it passes through raindrops hovering in the sky after a rainstorm. If you have ever seen the colored circles of the glory surrounding the shadow of your airplane on clouds as you fly above them, you are seeing an effect that results from *interference* of light. The phenomena mentioned here have been studied by scientists and are well understood.

In the introduction to Chapter 35, we discuss the dual nature of light. In some cases, it is best to model light as a stream of particles; in others, a wave model works better. Chapters 35 through 38 concentrate on those aspects of light that are best understood through the wave model of light. In Part 6, we will investigate the particle nature of light.

The Grand Tetons in western Wyoming are reflected in a smooth lake at sunset. The optical principles we study in this part of the book will explain the nature of the reflected image of the mountains and why the sky appears red. (David Muench/CORBIS)

This photograph of a rainbow shows a distinct secondary rainbow with the colors reversed. The appearance of the rainbow depends on three optical phenomena discussed in this chapter: reflection, refraction, and dispersion. (Mark D. Phillips/Photo Researchers, Inc.)

35 The Nature of Light and the Laws of Geometric Optics

Courtesy of Rijksmuseum voor de Geschiedenis der Natuurwetenschappen and Niels Bohr Library

CHRISTIAN HUYGENS
Dutch Physicist and Astronomer (1629–1695)
Huygens is best known for his contributions to the fields of optics and dynamics. To Huygens, light was a type of vibratory motion, spreading out and producing the sensation of light when impinging on the eye. On the basis of this theory, he deduced the laws of reflection and refraction and explained the phenomenon of double refraction.

This first chapter on optics begins by introducing two historical models for light and discussing early methods for measuring the speed of light. Next we study the fundamental phenomena of geometric optics: reflection of light from a surface and refraction as the light crosses the boundary between two media. We will also study the dispersion of light as it refracts into materials, resulting in visual displays such as the rainbow. Finally, we investigate the phenomenon of total internal reflection, which is the basis for the operation of optical fibers and the burgeoning technology of fiber optics.

35.1 The Nature of Light

Before the beginning of the nineteenth century, light was considered to be a stream of particles that either was emitted by the object being viewed or emanated from the eyes of the viewer. Newton, the chief architect of the particle model of light, held that particles were emitted from a light source and that these particles stimulated the sense of sight upon entering the eye. Using this idea, he was able to explain reflection and refraction.

Most scientists accepted Newton's particle model. During Newton's lifetime, however, another model was proposed, one that argued that light might be some sort of wave motion. In 1678, Dutch physicist and astronomer Christian Huygens showed that a wave model of light could also explain reflection and refraction.

In 1801, Thomas Young (1773–1829) provided the first clear experimental demonstration of the wave nature of light. Young showed that under appropriate conditions light rays interfere with one another. Such behavior could not be explained at that time by a particle model because there was no conceivable way in which two or more particles could come together and cancel one another. Additional developments during the nineteenth century led to the general acceptance of the wave model of light, the most important resulting from the work of Maxwell, who in 1873 asserted that light was a form of high-frequency electromagnetic wave. As discussed in Chapter 34, Hertz provided experimental confirmation of Maxwell's theory in 1887 by producing and detecting electromagnetic waves.

Although the wave model and the classical theory of electricity and magnetism were able to explain most known properties of light, they could not explain some subsequent experiments. The most striking phenomenon is the photoelectric effect, also discovered by Hertz: when light strikes a metal surface, electrons are sometimes ejected from the surface. As one example of the difficulties that arose, experiments showed that the kinetic energy of an ejected electron is independent of the light intensity. This finding contradicted the wave model, which held that a more intense beam of light should add more energy to the electron. Einstein proposed an explanation of the photoelectric effect in 1905 using a model based on the concept of quantization developed by Max Planck (1858–1947) in 1900. The quantization model assumes the energy of a light wave is present in particles called *photons;* hence, the energy is said to be quantized. According to Einstein's theory, the energy of a photon is proportional to the frequency of the electromagnetic wave:

$$E = hf \qquad (35.1)$$

◀ Energy of a photon

where the constant of proportionality $h = 6.63 \times 10^{-34}$ J · s is called *Planck's constant.* We study this theory in Chapter 40.

In view of these developments, light must be regarded as having a dual nature. **Light exhibits the characteristics of a wave in some situations and the characteristics of a particle in other situations.** Light is light, to be sure. The question "Is light a wave or a particle?" is inappropriate, however. Sometimes light acts like a wave, and other times it acts like a particle. In the next few chapters, we investigate the wave nature of light.

35.2 Measurements of the Speed of Light

Light travels at such a high speed (to three digits, $c = 3.00 \times 10^8$ m/s) that early attempts to measure its speed were unsuccessful. Galileo attempted to measure the speed of light by positioning two observers in towers separated by approximately 10 km. Each observer carried a shuttered lantern. One observer would open his lantern first, and then the other would open his lantern at the moment he saw the light from the first lantern. Galileo reasoned that by knowing the transit time of the light beams from one lantern to the other and the distance between the two lanterns, he could obtain the speed. His results were inconclusive. Today, we realize (as Galileo concluded) that it is impossible to measure the speed of light in this manner because the transit time for the light is so much less than the reaction time of the observers.

Roemer's Method

In 1675, Danish astronomer Ole Roemer (1644–1710) made the first successful estimate of the speed of light. Roemer's technique involved astronomical observations of Io, one of the moons of Jupiter. Io has a period of revolution around Jupiter of approximately 42.5 h. The period of revolution of Jupiter around the Sun is about 12 yr; therefore, as the Earth moves through 90° around the Sun, Jupiter revolves through only $(\frac{1}{12})90° = 7.5°$ (Fig. 35.1).

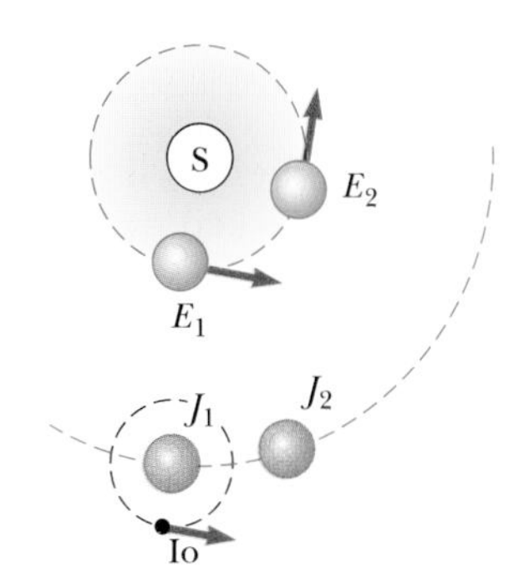

Figure 35.1 Roemer's method for measuring the speed of light. In the time interval during which the Earth travels 90° around the Sun (three months), Jupiter travels only about 7.5° (drawing not to scale).

An observer using the orbital motion of Io as a clock would expect the orbit to have a constant period. After collecting data for more than a year, however, Roemer observed a systematic variation in Io's period. He found that the periods were longer than average when the Earth was receding from Jupiter and shorter than average when the Earth was approaching Jupiter. Roemer attributed this variation in period to the distance between the Earth and Jupiter changing from one observation to the next.

Using Roemer's data, Huygens estimated the lower limit for the speed of light to be approximately 2.3×10^8 m/s. This experiment is important historically because it demonstrated that light does have a finite speed and gave an estimate of this speed.

Fizeau's Method

The first successful method for measuring the speed of light by means of purely terrestrial techniques was developed in 1849 by French physicist Armand H. L. Fizeau (1819–1896). Figure 35.2 represents a simplified diagram of Fizeau's apparatus. The basic procedure is to measure the total time interval during which light travels from some point to a distant mirror and back. If d is the distance between the light source (considered to be at the location of the wheel) and the mirror and if the time interval for one round trip is Δt, the speed of light is $c = 2d/\Delta t$.

To measure the transit time, Fizeau used a rotating toothed wheel, which converts a continuous beam of light into a series of light pulses. The rotation of such a wheel controls what an observer at the light source sees. For example, if the pulse traveling toward the mirror and passing the opening at point A in Figure 35.2 should return to the wheel at the instant tooth B had rotated into position to cover the return path, the pulse would not reach the observer. At a greater rate of rotation, the opening at point C could move into position to allow the reflected pulse to reach the observer. Knowing the distance d, the number of teeth in the wheel, and the angular speed of the wheel, Fizeau arrived at a value of 3.1×10^8 m/s. Similar measurements made by subsequent investigators yielded more precise values for c, which led to the currently accepted value of $2.997\,9 \times 10^8$ m/s.

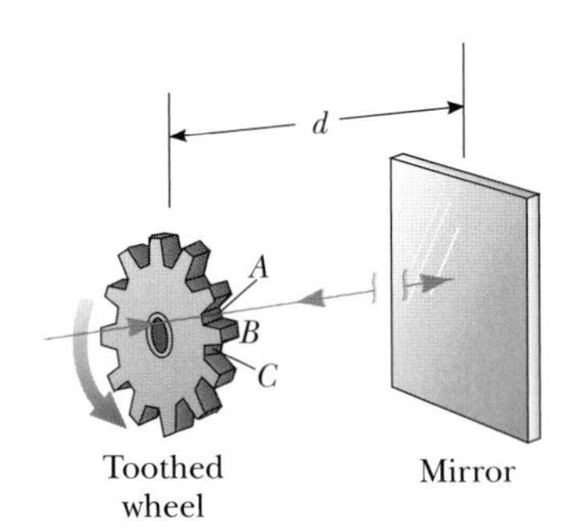

Figure 35.2 Fizeau's method for measuring the speed of light using a rotating toothed wheel. The light source is considered to be at the location of the wheel; therefore, the distance d is known.

EXAMPLE 35.1 Measuring the Speed of Light with Fizeau's Wheel

Assume Fizeau's wheel has 360 teeth and rotates at 27.5 rev/s when a pulse of light passing through opening A in Figure 35.2 is blocked by tooth B on its return. If the distance to the mirror is 7 500 m, what is the speed of light?

SOLUTION

Conceptualize Imagine a pulse of light passing through opening A in Figure 35.2 and reflecting from the mirror. By the time the pulse arrives back at the wheel, tooth B has rotated into the position previously occupied by opening A.

Categorize We model the wheel as a rigid object under constant angular speed and the pulse of light as a particle under constant speed.

Analyze The wheel has 360 teeth, so it must have 360 openings. Therefore, because the light passes through opening A but is blocked by the tooth immediately adjacent to A, the wheel must rotate through an angular displacement of $\frac{1}{720}$ rev in the time interval during which the light pulse makes its round trip.

Use the rigid object under constant angular speed model to find the time interval for the pulse's round trip:

$$\Delta t = \frac{\Delta \theta}{\omega} = \frac{\frac{1}{720} \text{ rev}}{27.5 \text{ rev/s}} = 5.05 \times 10^{-5} \text{ s}$$

From the particle under constant speed model, find the speed of the pulse of light:

$$c = \frac{2d}{\Delta t} = \frac{2(7\,500 \text{ m})}{5.05 \times 10^{-5} \text{ s}} = 2.97 \times 10^8 \text{ m/s}$$

Finalize This result is very close to the actual value of the speed of light.

35.3 The Ray Approximation in Geometric Optics

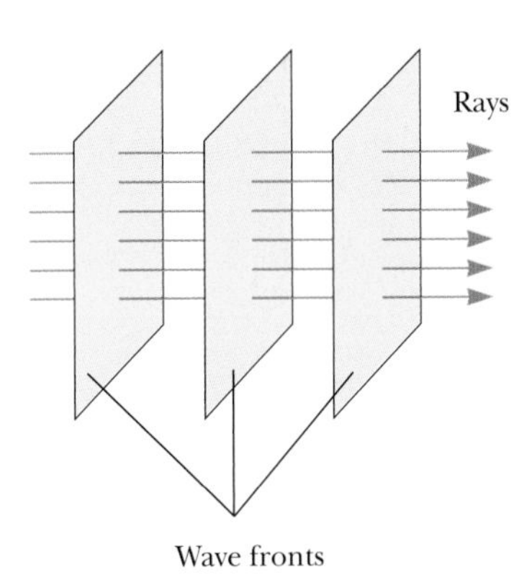

Figure 35.3 A plane wave propagating to the right. Notice that the rays, which always point in the direction of the wave propagation, are straight lines perpendicular to the wave fronts.

The field of **geometric optics** involves the study of the propagation of light. Geometric optics assumes light travels in a fixed direction in a straight line as it passes through a uniform medium and changes its direction when it meets the surface of a different medium or if the optical properties of the medium are nonuniform in either space or time. In our study of geometric optics here and in Chapter 36, we use what is called the **ray approximation.** To understand this approximation, first notice that the rays of a given wave are straight lines perpendicular to the wave fronts as illustrated in Figure 35.3 for a plane wave. In the ray approximation, a wave moving through a medium travels in a straight line in the direction of its rays.

If the wave meets a barrier in which there is a circular opening whose diameter is much larger than the wavelength as in Active Figure 35.4a, the wave emerging from the opening continues to move in a straight line (apart from some small edge effects); hence, the ray approximation is valid. If the diameter of the opening is on the order of the wavelength as in Active Figure 35.4b, the waves spread out from the opening in all directions. This effect, called *diffraction,* will be studied in Chapter 37. Finally, if the opening is much smaller than the wavelength, the opening can be approximated as a point source of waves as shown in Active Fig. 35.4c.

Similar effects are seen when waves encounter an opaque object of dimension d. In that case, when $\lambda \ll d$, the object casts a sharp shadow.

The ray approximation and the assumption that $\lambda \ll d$ are used in this chapter and in Chapter 36, both of which deal with geometric optics. This approximation is very good for the study of mirrors, lenses, prisms, and associated optical instruments such as telescopes, cameras, and eyeglasses.

35.4 The Wave Under Reflection

We introduced the concept of reflection of waves in a discussion of waves on strings in Section 16.4. As with waves on strings, when a light ray traveling in one medium encounters a boundary with another medium, part of the incident light is reflected. For waves on a one-dimensional string, the reflected wave must necessarily be restricted to a direction along the string. For light waves traveling in three-dimensional space, no such restriction applies and the reflected light waves can be

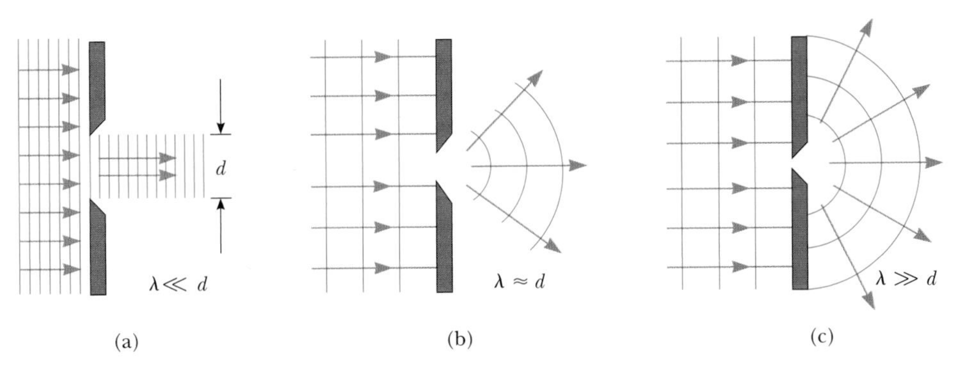

ACTIVE FIGURE 35.4

A plane wave of wavelength λ is incident on a barrier in which there is an opening of diameter d. (a) When $\lambda \ll d$, the rays continue in a straight-line path and the ray approximation remains valid. (b) When $\lambda \approx d$, the rays spread out after passing through the opening. (c) When $\lambda \gg d$, the opening behaves as a point source emitting spherical waves.

Sign in at www.thomsonedu.com and go to ThomsonNOW to adjust the size of the opening and observe the effect on the waves passing through.

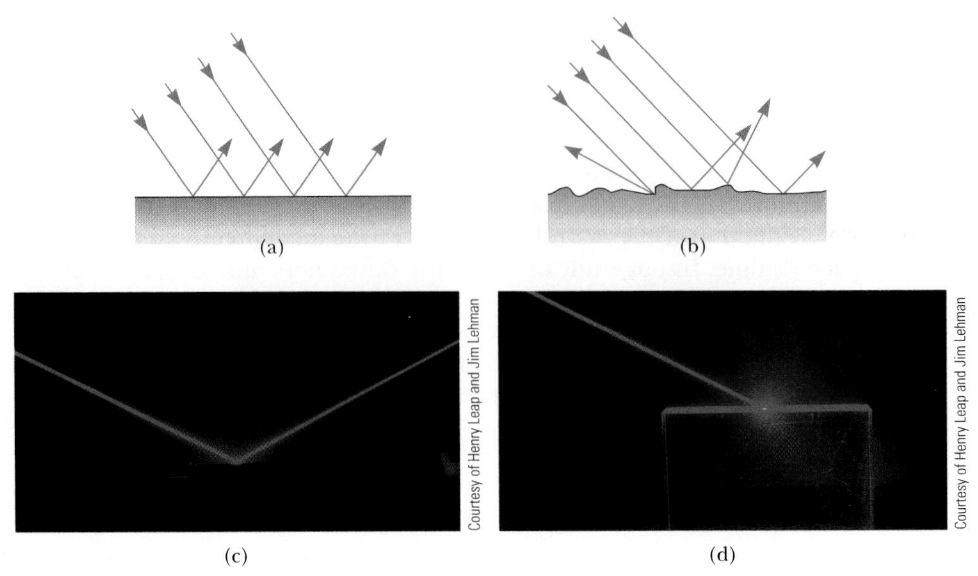

Figure 35.5 Schematic representation of (a) specular reflection, where the reflected rays are all parallel to each other, and (b) diffuse reflection, where the reflected rays travel in random directions. (c) and (d) Photographs of specular and diffuse reflection using laser light.

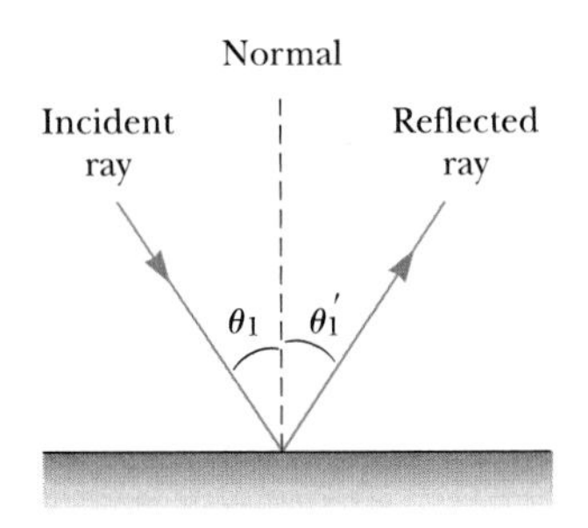

ACTIVE FIGURE 35.6

According to the wave under reflection model, $\theta_1' = \theta_1$. The incident ray, the reflected ray, and the normal all lie in the same plane.

Sign in at www.thomsonedu.com and go to ThomsonNOW to vary the incident angle and see the effect on the reflected ray.

in directions different from the direction of the incident waves. Figure 35.5a shows several rays of a beam of light incident on a smooth, mirror-like, reflecting surface. The reflected rays are parallel to one another as indicated in the figure. The direction of a reflected ray is in the plane perpendicular to the reflecting surface that contains the incident ray. Reflection of light from such a smooth surface is called **specular reflection.** If the reflecting surface is rough as in Figure 35.5b, the surface reflects the rays not as a parallel set but in various directions. Reflection from any rough surface is known as **diffuse reflection.** A surface behaves as a smooth surface as long as the surface variations are much smaller than the wavelength of the incident light.

The difference between these two kinds of reflection explains why it is more difficult to see while driving on a rainy night than on a dry, sunny day. If the road is wet, the smooth surface of the water specularly reflects most of your headlight beams away from your car (and perhaps into the eyes of oncoming drivers). When the road is dry, its rough surface diffusely reflects part of your headlight beam back toward you, allowing you to see the road more clearly. In this book, we restrict our study to specular reflection and use the term *reflection* to mean specular reflection.

Consider a light ray traveling in air and incident at an angle on a flat, smooth surface as shown in Active Figure 35.6. The incident and reflected rays make angles θ_1 and θ_1', respectively, where the angles are measured between the normal and the rays. (The normal is a line drawn perpendicular to the surface at the point where the incident ray strikes the surface.) Experiments and theory show that **the angle of reflection equals the angle of incidence:**

Law of reflection ▶

$$\theta_1' = \theta_1 \tag{35.2}$$

This relationship is called the **law of reflection.** Because reflection of waves from an interface between two media is a common phenomenon, we identify an analysis model for this situation: the **wave under reflection.** Equation 35.2 is the mathematical representation of this model.

PITFALL PREVENTION 35.1
Subscript Notation

The subscript 1 refers to parameters for the light in the initial medium. When light travels from one medium to another, we use the subscript 2 for the parameters associated with the light in the new medium. In this discussion, the light stays in the same medium, so we only have to use the subscript 1.

Quick Quiz 35.1 In the movies, you sometimes see an actor looking in a mirror and you can see his face in the mirror. During the filming of such a scene, what does the actor see in the mirror? (a) his face (b) your face (c) the director's face (d) the movie camera (e) impossible to determine

EXAMPLE 35.2 The Double-Reflected Light Ray

Two mirrors make an angle of 120° with each other as illustrated in Figure 35.7a. A ray is incident on mirror M_1 at an angle of 65° to the normal. Find the direction of the ray after it is reflected from mirror M_2.

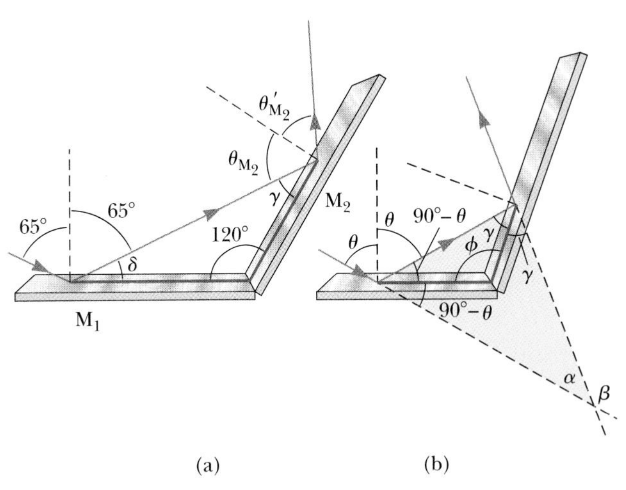

Figure 35.7 (Example 35.2) (a) Mirrors M_1 and M_2 make an angle of 120° with each other. (b) The geometry for an arbitrary mirror angle.

SOLUTION

Conceptualize Figure 35.7a helps conceptualize this situation. The incoming ray reflects from the first mirror, and the reflected ray is directed toward the second mirror. Therefore, there is a second reflection from the second mirror.

Categorize Because the interactions with both mirrors are simple reflections, we apply the wave under reflection model and some geometry.

Analyze From the law of reflection, the first reflected ray makes an angle of 65° with the normal.

Find the angle the first reflected ray makes with the horizontal:

$$\delta = 90° - 65° = 25°$$

From the triangle made by the first reflected ray and the two mirrors, find the angle the reflected ray makes with M_2:

$$\gamma = 180° - 25° - 120° = 35°$$

Find the angle the first reflected ray makes with the normal to M_2:

$$\theta_{M_2} = 90° - 35° = 55°$$

From the law of reflection, find the angle the second reflected ray makes with the normal to M_2:

$$\theta'_{M_2} = \theta_{M_2} = 55°$$

Finalize Let's explore variations in the angle between the mirrors as follows.

What If? If the incoming and outgoing rays in Figure 35.7a are extended behind the mirror, they cross at an angle of 60° and the overall change in direction of the light ray is 120°. This angle is the same as that between the mirrors. What if the angle between the mirrors is changed? Is the overall change in the direction of the light ray always equal to the angle between the mirrors?

Answer Making a general statement based on one data point or one observation is always a dangerous practice! Let's investigate the change in direction for a general situation. Figure 35.7b shows the mirrors at an arbitrary angle ϕ and the incoming light ray striking the mirror at an arbitrary angle θ with respect to the normal to the mirror surface. In accordance with the law of reflection and the sum of the interior angles of a triangle, the angle γ is given by $180° - (90° - \theta) - \phi = 90° + \theta - \phi$.

Consider the triangle highlighted in blue in Figure 35.7b and determine α:

$$\alpha + 2\gamma + 2(90° - \theta) = 180° \quad \rightarrow \quad \alpha = 2(\theta - \gamma)$$

Notice from Figure 35.7b that the change in direction of the light ray is angle β. Use the geometry in the figure to solve for β:

$$\beta = 180° - \alpha = 180° - 2(\theta - \gamma)$$
$$= 180° - 2[\theta - (90° + \theta - \phi)] = 360° - 2\phi$$

Notice that β is not equal to ϕ. For $\phi = 120°$, we obtain $\beta = 120°$, which happens to be the same as the mirror angle; that is true only for this special angle between the mirrors, however. For example, if $\phi = 90°$, we obtain $\beta = 180°$. In that case, the light is reflected straight back to its origin.

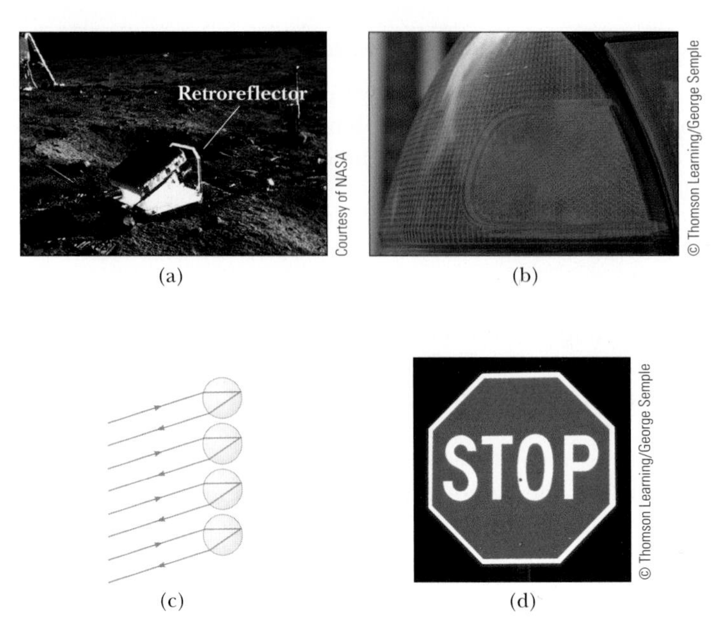

(a) (b) (c) (d)

Figure 35.8 Applications of retroreflection. (a) This panel on the Moon reflects a laser beam directly back to its source on the Earth. (b) An automobile taillight has small retroreflectors to ensure that headlight beams are reflected back toward the car that sent them. (c) A light ray hitting a transparent sphere at the proper position is retroreflected. (d) This stop sign appears to glow in headlight beams because its surface is covered with a layer of many tiny retroreflecting spheres. What would you see if the sign had a mirror-like surface?

If the angle between two mirrors is 90°, the reflected beam returns to the source parallel to its original path as discussed in the **What If?** section of the preceding example. This phenomenon, called *retroreflection,* has many practical applications. If a third mirror is placed perpendicular to the first two so that the three form the corner of a cube, retroreflection works in three dimensions. In 1969, a panel of many small reflectors was placed on the Moon by the *Apollo 11* astronauts (Fig. 35.8a). A laser beam from the Earth is reflected directly back on itself, and its transit time is measured. This information is used to determine the distance to the Moon with an uncertainty of 15 cm. (Imagine how difficult it would be to align a regular flat mirror so that the reflected laser beam would hit a particular location on the Earth!) A more everyday application is found in automobile taillights. Part of the plastic making up the taillight is formed into many tiny cube corners (Fig. 35.8b) so that headlight beams from cars approaching from the rear are reflected back to the drivers. Instead of cube corners, small spherical bumps are sometimes used (Fig. 35.8c). Tiny clear spheres are used in a coating material found on many road signs. Due to retroreflection from these spheres, the stop sign in Figure 35.8d appears much brighter than it would if it were simply a flat, shiny surface. Retroreflectors are also used for reflective panels on running shoes and running clothing to allow joggers to be seen at night.

Another practical application of the law of reflection is the digital projection of movies, television shows, and computer presentations. A digital projector uses an optical semiconductor chip called a *digital micromirror device.* This device contains an array of tiny mirrors (Fig. 35.9a) that can be individually tilted by means of signals to an address electrode underneath the edge of the mirror. Each mirror corresponds to a pixel in the projected image. When the pixel corresponding to a given mirror is to be bright, the mirror is in the "on" position and is oriented so as to reflect light from a source illuminating the array to the screen (Fig. 35.9b). When the pixel for this mirror is to be dark, the mirror is "off" and is tilted so that the light is reflected away from the screen. The brightness of the pixel is determined by the total time interval during which the mirror is in the "on" position during the display of one image.

Digital movie projectors use three micromirror devices, one for each of the primary colors red, blue, and green, so that movies can be displayed with up to 35

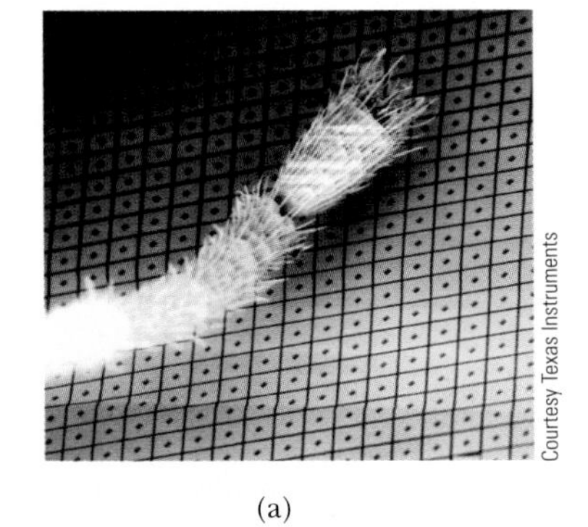

(a)

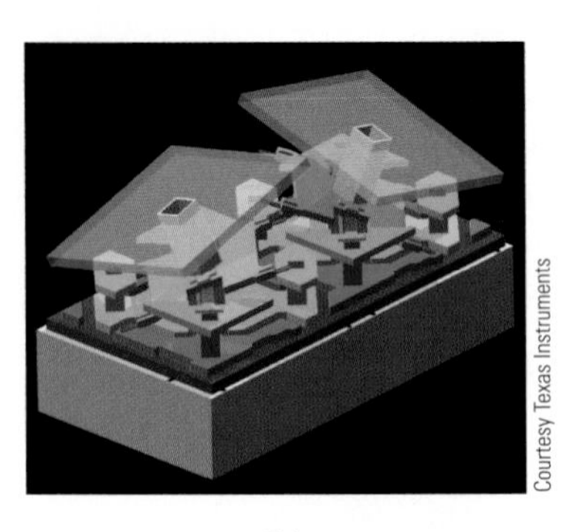

(b)

Figure 35.9 (a) An array of mirrors on the surface of a digital micromirror device. Each mirror has an area of approximately 16 μm^2. To provide a sense of scale, the leg of an ant appears in the photograph. (b) A close-up view of two single micromirrors. The mirror on the left is "on," and the one on the right is "off."

trillion colors. Because information is stored as binary data, a digital movie does not degrade with time as does film. Furthermore, because the movie is entirely in the form of computer software, it can be delivered to theaters by means of satellites, optical discs, or optical fiber networks.

Several movies have been projected digitally to audiences, and polls show that 85% of viewers describe the image quality as "excellent." The first all-digital movie, from cinematography to postproduction to projection, was *Star Wars Episode II: Attack of the Clones* in 2002.

35.5 The Wave Under Refraction

In addition to the phenomenon of reflection discussed for waves on strings in Section 16.4, we also found that some of the energy of the incident wave transmits into the new medium. Similarly, when a ray of light traveling through a transparent medium encounters a boundary leading into another transparent medium as shown in Active Figure 35.10, part of the energy is reflected and part enters the second medium. As with reflection, the direction of the transmitted wave exhibits an interesting behavior because of the three-dimensional nature of the light waves. The ray that enters the second medium is bent at the boundary and is said to be **refracted.** The incident ray, the reflected ray, and the refracted ray all lie in the same plane. The **angle of refraction,** θ_2 in Active Figure 35.10a, depends on the properties of the two media and on the angle of incidence θ_1 through the relationship

$$\frac{\sin\theta_2}{\sin\theta_1} = \frac{v_2}{v_1} \qquad \textbf{(35.3)}$$

where v_1 is the speed of light in the first medium and v_2 is the speed of light in the second medium.

The path of a light ray through a refracting surface is reversible. For example, the ray shown in Active Figure 35.10a travels from point A to point B. If the ray originated at B, it would travel along line BA to reach point A and the reflected ray would point downward and to the left in the glass.

Quick Quiz 35.2 If beam ① is the incoming beam in Active Figure 35.10b, which of the other four red lines are reflected beams and which are refracted beams?

From Equation 35.3, we can infer that when light moves from a material in which its speed is high to a material in which its speed is lower as shown in Active

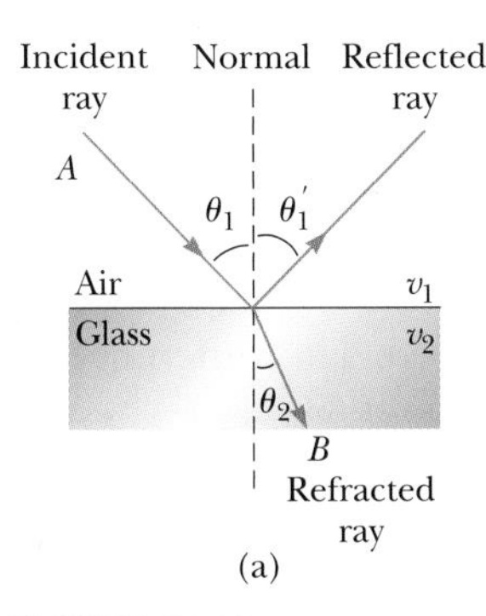

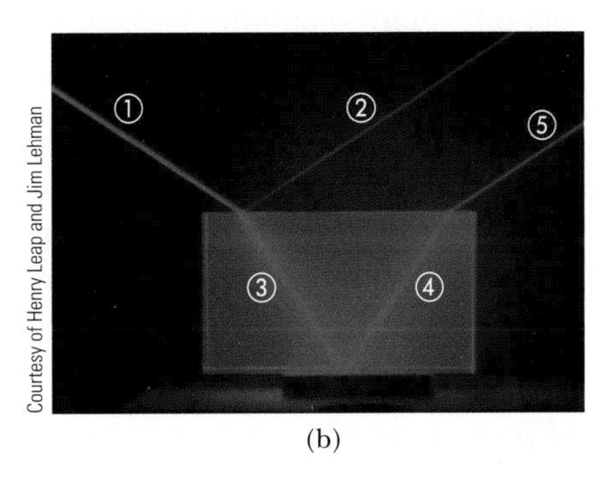

ACTIVE FIGURE 35.10

(a) A ray obliquely incident on an air–glass interface behaves according to the wave under refraction model. The refracted ray is bent toward the normal because $v_2 < v_1$. All rays and the normal lie in the same plane. (b) Light incident on the Lucite block refracts both when it enters the block and when it leaves the block.

Sign in at www.thomsonedu.com and go to ThomsonNOW to vary the incident angle and see the effect on the reflected and refracted rays.

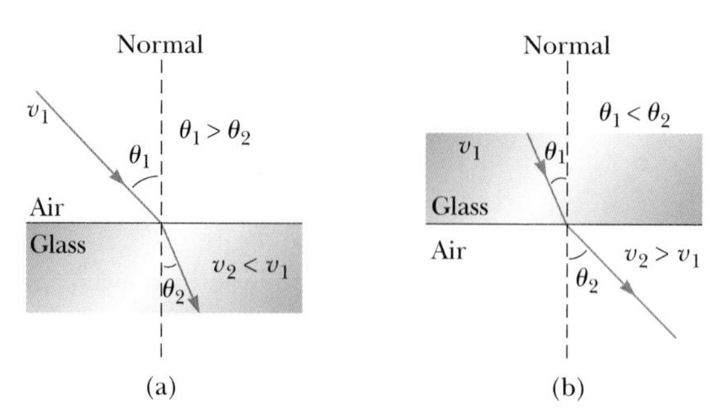

ACTIVE FIGURE 35.11

(a) When the light beam moves from air into glass, the light slows down upon entering the glass and its path is bent toward the normal. (b) When the beam moves from glass into air, the light speeds up upon entering the air and its path is bent away from the normal.

Sign in at www.thomsonedu.com and go to ThomsonNOW to observe light passing through three layers of material. You can vary the incident angle and see the effect on the refracted rays for a variety of values of the index of refraction (defined in Equation 35.4) of the three materials.

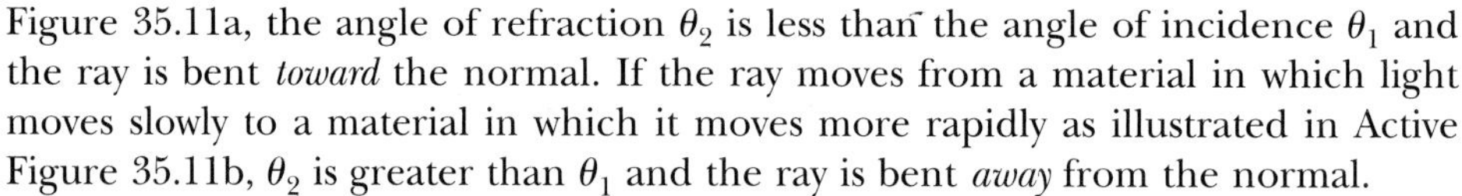

Figure 35.11a, the angle of refraction θ_2 is less than the angle of incidence θ_1 and the ray is bent *toward* the normal. If the ray moves from a material in which light moves slowly to a material in which it moves more rapidly as illustrated in Active Figure 35.11b, θ_2 is greater than θ_1 and the ray is bent *away* from the normal.

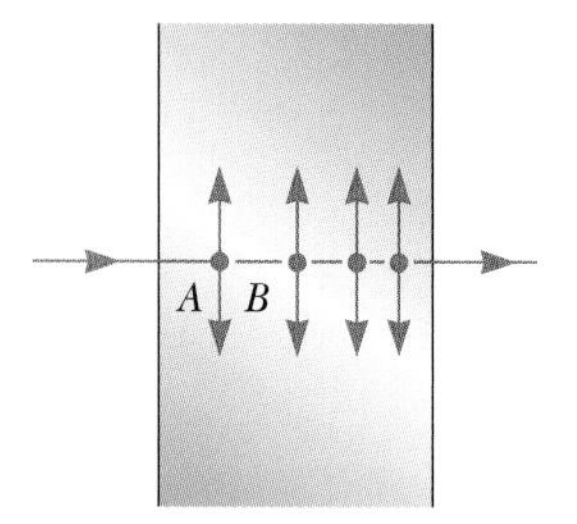

Figure 35.12 Light passing from one atom to another in a medium. The dots are electrons, and the vertical arrows represent their oscillations.

The behavior of light as it passes from air into another substance and then re-emerges into air is often a source of confusion to students. When light travels in air, its speed is 3.00×10^8 m/s, but this speed is reduced to approximately 2×10^8 m/s when the light enters a block of glass. When the light re-emerges into air, its speed instantaneously increases to its original value of 3.00×10^8 m/s. This effect is far different from what happens, for example, when a bullet is fired through a block of wood. In that case, the speed of the bullet decreases as it moves through the wood because some of its original energy is used to tear apart the wood fibers. When the bullet enters the air once again, it emerges at a speed lower than it had when it entered the wood.

To see why light behaves as it does, consider Figure 35.12, which represents a beam of light entering a piece of glass from the left. Once inside the glass, the light may encounter an electron bound to an atom, indicated as point *A*. Let's assume light is absorbed by the atom, which causes the electron to oscillate (a detail represented by the double-headed vertical arrows). The oscillating electron then acts as an antenna and radiates the beam of light toward an atom at *B*, where the light is again absorbed. The details of these absorptions and radiations are best explained in terms of quantum mechanics (Chapter 42). For now, it is sufficient to think of light passing from one atom to another through the glass. Although light travels from one atom to another at 3.00×10^8 m/s, the absorption and radiation that take place cause the *average* light speed through the material to fall to about 2×10^8 m/s. Once the light emerges into the air, absorption and radiation cease and the light travels at a constant speed of 3.00×10^8 m/s.

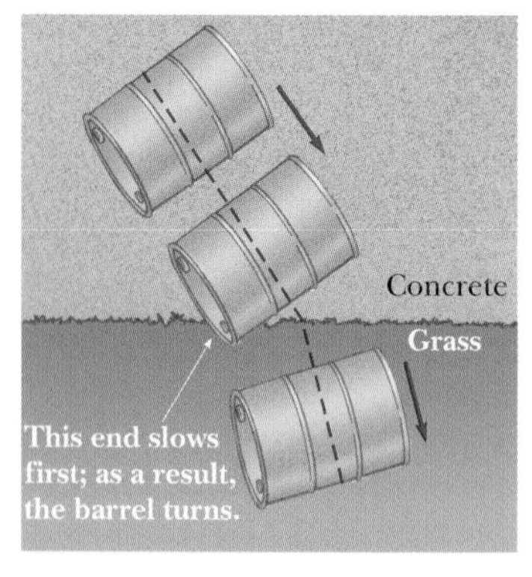

Figure 35.13 Overhead view of a barrel rolling from concrete onto grass.

A mechanical analog of refraction is shown in Figure 35.13. When the left end of the rolling barrel reaches the grass, it slows down, whereas the right end remains on the concrete and moves at its original speed. This difference in speeds causes the barrel to pivot, which changes the direction of travel.

Index of Refraction

In general, the speed of light in any material is *less* than its speed in vacuum. In fact, *light travels at its maximum speed c in vacuum.* It is convenient to define the **index of refraction** n of a medium to be the ratio

Index of refraction ▶

$$n \equiv \frac{\text{speed of light in vacuum}}{\text{speed of light in a medium}} \equiv \frac{c}{v} \tag{35.4}$$

TABLE 35.1

Indices of Refraction

Substance	Index of Refraction	Substance	Index of Refraction
Solids at 20°C		*Liquids at 20°C*	
Cubic zirconia	2.20	Benzene	1.501
Diamond (C)	2.419	Carbon disulfide	1.628
Fluorite (CaF_2)	1.434	Carbon tetrachloride	1.461
Fused quartz (SiO_2)	1.458	Ethyl alcohol	1.361
Gallium phosphide	3.50	Glycerin	1.473
Glass, crown	1.52	Water	1.333
Glass, flint	1.66		
Ice (H_2O)	1.309	*Gases at 0°C, 1 atm*	
Polystyrene	1.49	Air	1.000 293
Sodium chloride (NaCl)	1.544	Carbon dioxide	1.000 45

Note: All values are for light having a wavelength of 589 nm in vacuum.

PITFALL PREVENTION 35.2

***n* Is Not an Integer Here**

The symbol n has been used several times as an integer, such as in Chapter 18 to indicate the standing wave mode on a string or in an air column. The index of refraction n is *not* an integer.

This definition shows that the index of refraction is a dimensionless number greater than unity because v is always less than c. Furthermore, n is equal to unity for vacuum. The indices of refraction for various substances are listed in Table 35.1.

As light travels from one medium to another, its frequency does not change but its wavelength does. To see why that is true, consider Figure 35.14. Waves pass an observer at point A in medium 1 with a certain frequency and are incident on the boundary between medium 1 and medium 2. The frequency with which the waves pass an observer at point B in medium 2 must equal the frequency at which they pass point A. If that were not the case, energy would be piling up or disappearing at the boundary. Because there is no mechanism for that to occur, the frequency must be a constant as a light ray passes from one medium into another. Therefore, because the relationship $v = \lambda f$ (Eq. 16.12) must be valid in both media and because $f_1 = f_2 = f$, we see that

$$v_1 = \lambda_1 f \quad \text{and} \quad v_2 = \lambda_2 f \tag{35.5}$$

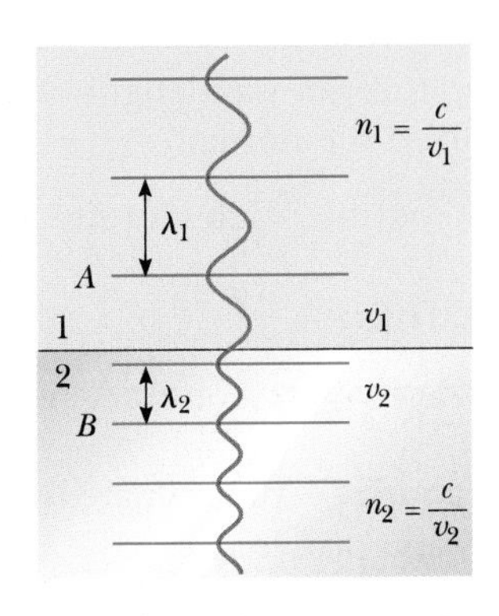

Figure 35.14 As a wave moves from medium 1 to medium 2, its wavelength changes but its frequency remains constant.

Because $v_1 \neq v_2$, it follows that $\lambda_1 \neq \lambda_2$ as shown in Figure 35.14.

We can obtain a relationship between index of refraction and wavelength by dividing the first Equation 35.5 by the second and then using Equation 35.4:

$$\frac{\lambda_1}{\lambda_2} = \frac{v_1}{v_2} = \frac{c/n_1}{c/n_2} = \frac{n_2}{n_1} \tag{35.6}$$

This expression gives

$$\lambda_1 n_1 = \lambda_2 n_2$$

If medium 1 is vacuum or, for all practical purposes, air, then $n_1 = 1$. Hence, it follows from Equation 35.6 that the index of refraction of any medium can be expressed as the ratio

$$n = \frac{\lambda}{\lambda_n} \tag{35.7}$$

where λ is the wavelength of light in vacuum and λ_n is the wavelength of light in the medium whose index of refraction is n. From Equation 35.7, we see that because $n > 1$, $\lambda_n < \lambda$.

PITFALL PREVENTION 35.3

An Inverse Relationship

The index of refraction is *inversely* proportional to the wave speed. As the wave speed v decreases, the index of refraction n increases. Therefore, the higher the index of refraction of a material, the more it *slows down* light from its speed in vacuum. The more the light slows down, the more θ_2 differs from θ_1 in Equation 35.8.

We are now in a position to express Equation 35.3 in an alternative form. Replacing the v_2/v_1 term in Equation 35.3 with n_1/n_2 from Equation 35.6 gives

$$n_1 \sin\theta_1 = n_2 \sin\theta_2 \tag{35.8}$$

◀ Snell's law of refraction

The experimental discovery of this relationship is usually credited to Willebrord Snell (1591–1626) and it is therefore known as **Snell's law of refraction.** We shall examine this equation further in Section 35.6. Refraction of waves at an interface between two media is a common phenomenon, so we identify an analysis model for this situation: the **wave under refraction.** Equation 35.8 is the mathematical representation of this model for electromagnetic radiation. Other waves, such as seismic waves and sound waves, also exhibit refraction according to this model, and the mathematical representation for these waves is Equation 35.3.

Quick Quiz 35.3 Light passes from a material with index of refraction 1.3 into one with index of refraction 1.2. Compared to the incident ray, what happens to the refracted ray? (a) It bends toward the normal. (b) It is undeflected. (c) It bends away from the normal.

EXAMPLE 35.3 Angle of Refraction for Glass

A light ray of wavelength 589 nm traveling through air is incident on a smooth, flat slab of crown glass at an angle of 30.0° to the normal.

(A) Find the angle of refraction.

SOLUTION

Conceptualize Study Active Figure 35.11a, which illustrates the refraction process occurring in this problem.

Categorize We evaluate results by using equations developed in this section, so we categorize this example as a substitution problem.

Rearrange Snell's law of refraction to find $\sin\theta_2$:

$$\sin\theta_2 = \frac{n_1}{n_2}\sin\theta_1$$

Substitute the incident angle and, from Table 35.1, $n_1 = 1.00$ for air and $n_2 = 1.52$ for crown glass:

$$\sin\theta_2 = \left(\frac{1.00}{1.52}\right)\sin 30.0° = 0.329$$

Solve for θ_2:

$$\theta_2 = \sin^{-1}(0.329)$$
$$= 19.2°$$

(B) Find the speed of this light once it enters the glass.

SOLUTION

Solve Equation 35.4 for the speed of light in the glass:

$$v = \frac{c}{n}$$

Substitute numerical values:

$$v = \frac{3.00 \times 10^8 \text{ m/s}}{1.52} = 1.97 \times 10^8 \text{ m/s}$$

(C) What is the wavelength of this light in the glass?

SOLUTION

Use Equation 35.7 to find the wavelength in the glass:

$$\lambda_n = \frac{\lambda}{n} = \frac{589 \text{ nm}}{1.52} = 388 \text{ nm}$$

EXAMPLE 35.4 Light Passing Through a Slab

A light beam passes from medium 1 to medium 2, with the latter medium being a thick slab of material whose index of refraction is n_2 (Fig. 35.15). Show that the beam emerging into medium 1 from the other side is parallel to the incident beam.

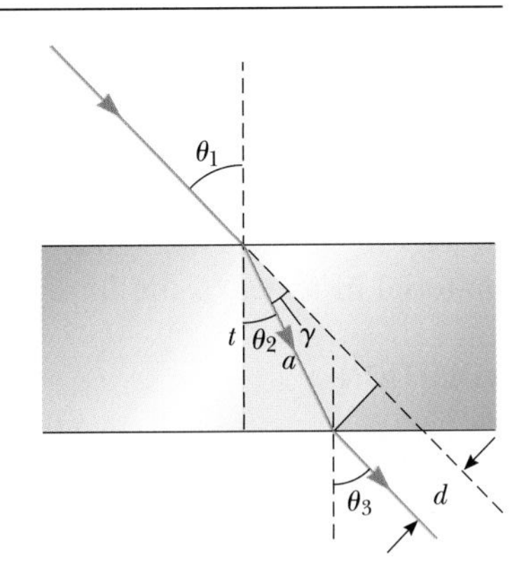

Figure 35.15 (Example 35.4) When light passes through a flat slab of material, the emerging beam is parallel to the incident beam; therefore, $\theta_1 = \theta_3$. The dashed line drawn parallel to the ray coming out the bottom of the slab represents the path the light would take were the slab not there.

SOLUTION

Conceptualize Follow the path of the light beam as it enters and exits the slab of material in Figure 35.15. The ray bends toward the normal upon entering and away from the normal upon leaving.

Categorize We evaluate results by using equations developed in this section, so we categorize this example as a substitution problem.

Apply Snell's law of refraction to the upper surface:

$$(1) \quad \sin\theta_2 = \frac{n_1}{n_2}\sin\theta_1$$

Apply Snell's law to the lower surface:

$$(2) \quad \sin\theta_3 = \frac{n_2}{n_1}\sin\theta_2$$

Substitute Equation (1) into Equation (2):

$$\sin\theta_3 = \frac{n_2}{n_1}\left(\frac{n_1}{n_2}\sin\theta_1\right) = \sin\theta_1$$

Therefore, $\theta_3 = \theta_1$ and the slab does not alter the direction of the beam. It does, however, offset the beam parallel to itself by the distance d shown in Figure 35.15.

What If? What if the thickness t of the slab is doubled? Does the offset distance d also double?

Answer Consider the region of the light path within the slab in Figure 35.15. The distance a is the hypotenuse of two right triangles.

Find an expression for a from the gold triangle:

$$a = \frac{t}{\cos\theta_2}$$

Find an expression for d from the blue triangle:

$$d = a\sin\gamma = a\sin(\theta_1 - \theta_2)$$

Combine these equations:

$$d = \frac{t}{\cos\theta_2}\sin(\theta_1 - \theta_2)$$

For a given incident angle θ_1, the refracted angle θ_2 is determined solely by the index of refraction, so the offset distance d is proportional to t. If the thickness doubles, so does the offset distance.

In Example 35.4, the light passes through a slab of material with parallel sides. What happens when light strikes a prism with nonparallel sides as shown in Figure 35.16? In this case, the outgoing ray does not propagate in the same direction as the incoming ray. A ray of single-wavelength light incident on the prism from the left emerges at angle δ from its original direction of travel. This angle δ is called the **angle of deviation.** The **apex angle** Φ of the prism, shown in the figure, is defined as the angle between the surface at which the light enters the prism and the second surface that the light encounters.

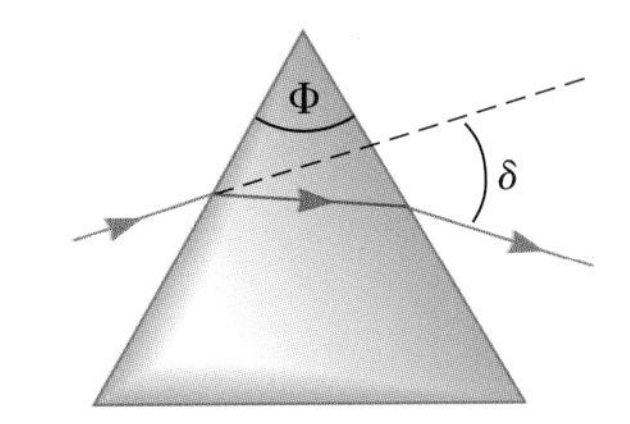

Figure 35.16 A prism refracts a single-wavelength light ray through an angle of deviation δ.

EXAMPLE 35.5 Measuring *n* Using a Prism

Although we do not prove it here, the minimum angle of deviation δ_{min} for a prism occurs when the angle of incidence θ_1 is such that the refracted ray inside the prism makes the same angle with the normal to the two prism faces[1] as shown in Figure 35.17. Obtain an expression for the index of refraction of the prism material in terms of the minimum angle of deviation and the apex angle Φ.

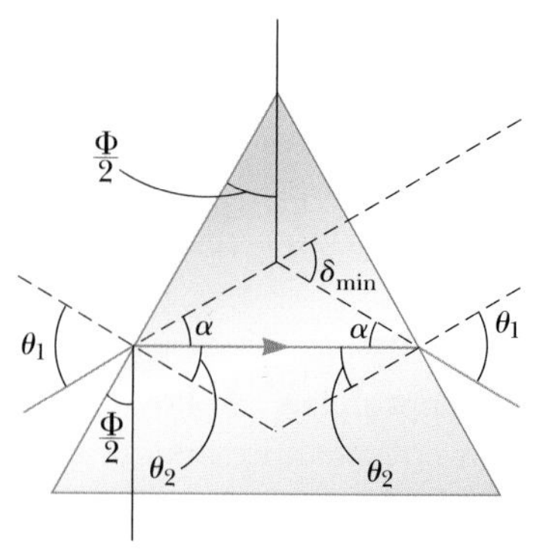

Figure 35.17 (Example 35.5) A light ray passing through a prism at the minimum angle of deviation δ_{min}.

SOLUTION

Conceptualize Study Figure 35.17 carefully and be sure you understand why the light ray comes out of the prism traveling in a different direction.

Categorize In this example, light enters a material through one surface and leaves the material at another surface. Let's apply the wave under refraction model at each surface.

Analyze Consider the geometry in Figure 35.17. The reproduction of the angle $\Phi/2$ at the location of the incoming light ray shows that $\theta_2 = \Phi/2$. The theorem that an exterior angle of any triangle equals the sum of the two opposite interior angles shows that $\delta_{min} = 2\alpha$. The geometry also shows that $\theta_1 = \theta_2 + \alpha$.

Combine these three geometric results:

$$\theta_1 = \theta_2 + \alpha = \frac{\Phi}{2} + \frac{\delta_{min}}{2} = \frac{\Phi + \delta_{min}}{2}$$

Apply the wave under refraction model at the left surface and solve for n:

$$(1.00) \sin \theta_1 = n \sin \theta_2 \quad \rightarrow \quad n = \frac{\sin \theta_1}{\sin \theta_2}$$

Substitute for the incident and refracted angles:

$$n = \frac{\sin\left(\dfrac{\Phi + \delta_{min}}{2}\right)}{\sin (\Phi/2)} \qquad (35.9)$$

Finalize Knowing the apex angle Φ of the prism and measuring δ_{min}, you can calculate the index of refraction of the prism material. Furthermore, a hollow prism can be used to determine the values of n for various liquids filling the prism.

35.6 Huygens's Principle

PITFALL PREVENTION 35.4
Of What Use Is Huygens's Principle?

At this point, the importance of Huygens's principle may not be evident. Predicting the position of a future wave front may not seem to be very critical. We will use Huygens's principle in later chapters to explain additional wave phenomena for light, however.

In this section, we develop the laws of reflection and refraction by using a geometric method proposed by Huygens in 1678. **Huygens's principle** is a geometric construction for using knowledge of an earlier wave front to determine the position of a new wave front at some instant. In Huygens's construction, **all points on a given wave front are taken as point sources for the production of spherical secondary waves, called wavelets, that propagate outward through a medium with speeds characteristic of waves in that medium. After some time interval has passed, the new position of the wave front is the surface tangent to the wavelets.**

First, consider a plane wave moving through free space as shown in Figure 35.18a. At $t = 0$, the wave front is indicated by the plane labeled AA'. In Huygens's construction, each point on this wave front is considered a point source. For clarity, only three points on AA' are shown. With these points as sources for the wavelets, we draw circles, each of radius $c\,\Delta t$, where c is the speed of light in vacuum and Δt is some time interval during which the wave propagates. The surface drawn tangent to these wavelets is the plane BB', which is the wave front at a later

[1] The details of this proof are available in texts on optics.

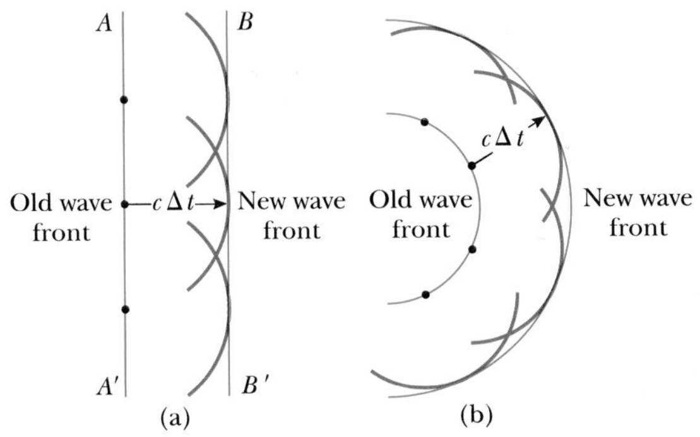

Figure 35.18 Huygens's construction for (a) a plane wave propagating to the right and (b) a spherical wave propagating to the right.

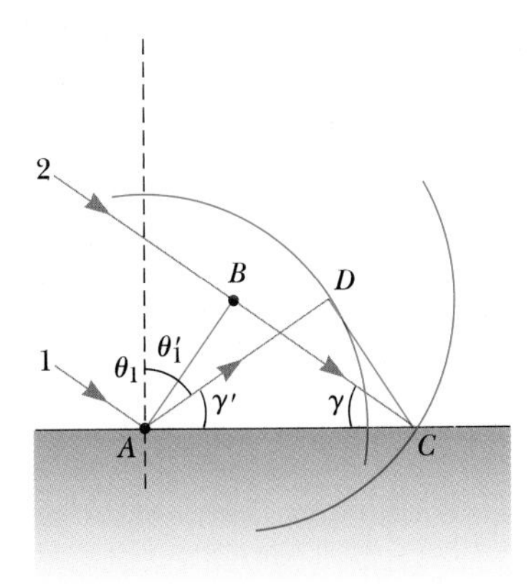

Figure 35.19 Huygens's construction for proving the law of reflection. The instant ray 1 strikes the surface, it sends out a Huygens wavelet from A and ray 2 sends out a Huygens wavelet from B. We choose a radius of the wavelet to be $c\,\Delta t$, where Δt is the time interval for ray 2 to travel from B to C. Triangle ADC is congruent to triangle ABC.

time, and is parallel to AA'. In a similar manner, Figure 35.18b shows Huygens's construction for a spherical wave.

Huygens's Principle Applied to Reflection and Refraction

The laws of reflection and refraction were stated earlier in this chapter without proof. We now derive these laws, using Huygens's principle.

For the law of reflection, refer to Figure 35.19. The line AB represents a plane wave front of the incident light just as ray 1 strikes the surface. At this instant, the wave at A sends out a Huygens wavelet (the red circular arc centered on A). The reflected light propagates toward D. At the same time, the wave at B emits a Huygens wavelet (the red circular arc centered on B) with the light propagating toward C. Figure 35.19 shows these wavelets after a time interval Δt, after which ray 2 strikes the surface. Because both rays 1 and 2 move with the same speed, we must have $AD = BC = c\,\Delta t$.

The remainder of our analysis depends on geometry. Notice that the two triangles ABC and ADC are congruent because they have the same hypotenuse AC and because $AD = BC$. Figure 35.19 shows that

$$\cos\gamma = \frac{BC}{AC} \quad \text{and} \quad \cos\gamma' = \frac{AD}{AC}$$

where $\gamma = 90° - \theta_1$ and $\gamma' = 90° - \theta_1'$. Because $AD = BC$,

$$\cos\gamma = \cos\gamma'$$

Therefore,

$$\gamma = \gamma'$$

$$90° - \theta_1 = 90° - \theta_1'$$

and

$$\theta_1 = \theta_1'$$

which is the law of reflection.

Now let's use Huygens's principle and Figure 35.20 to derive Snell's law of refraction. We focus our attention on the instant ray 1 strikes the surface and the subsequent time interval until ray 2 strikes the surface. During this time interval, the wave at A sends out a Huygens wavelet (the red arc centered on A) and the light refracts toward D. In the same time interval, the wave at B sends out a Huygens wavelet (the red arc centered on B) and the light continues to propagate toward C. Because these two wavelets travel through different media, the radii of the wavelets are different. The radius of the wavelet from A is $AD = v_2\,\Delta t$, where v_2 is the wave speed in the second medium. The radius of the wavelet from B is $BC = v_1\,\Delta t$, where v_1 is the wave speed in the original medium.

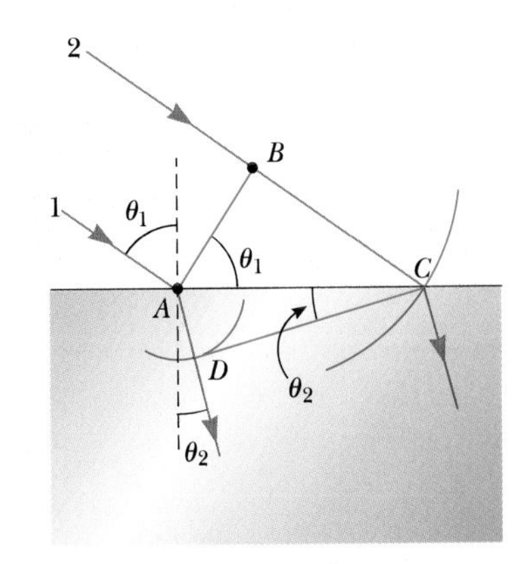

Figure 35.20 Huygens's construction for proving Snell's law of refraction. The instant ray 1 strikes the surface, it sends out a Huygens wavelet from A and ray 2 sends out a Huygens wavelet from B. The two wavelets have different radii because they travel in different media.

From triangles ABC and ADC, we find that

$$\sin\theta_1 = \frac{BC}{AC} = \frac{v_1\,\Delta t}{AC} \quad \text{and} \quad \sin\theta_2 = \frac{AD}{AC} = \frac{v_2\,\Delta t}{AC}$$

Dividing the first equation by the second gives

$$\frac{\sin\theta_1}{\sin\theta_2} = \frac{v_1}{v_2}$$

From Equation 35.4, however, we know that $v_1 = c/n_1$ and $v_2 = c/n_2$. Therefore,

$$\frac{\sin\theta_1}{\sin\theta_2} = \frac{c/n_1}{c/n_2} = \frac{n_2}{n_1}$$

and

$$n_1 \sin\theta_1 = n_2 \sin\theta_2$$

which is Snell's law of refraction.

35.7 Dispersion

An important property of the index of refraction n is that, for a given material, the index varies with the wavelength of the light passing through the material as Figure 35.21 shows. This behavior is called **dispersion.** Because n is a function of wavelength, Snell's law of refraction indicates that light of different wavelengths is refracted at different angles when incident on a material.

Figure 35.21 shows that the index of refraction generally decreases with increasing wavelength. For example, violet light refracts more than red light does when passing into a material.

Now suppose a beam of *white light* (a combination of all visible wavelengths) is incident on a prism as illustrated in Figure 35.22. Clearly, the angle of deviation δ depends on wavelength. The rays that emerge spread out in a series of colors known as the **visible spectrum.** These colors, in order of decreasing wavelength, are red, orange, yellow, green, blue, and violet. Newton showed that each color has a particular angle of deviation and that the colors can be recombined to form the original white light.

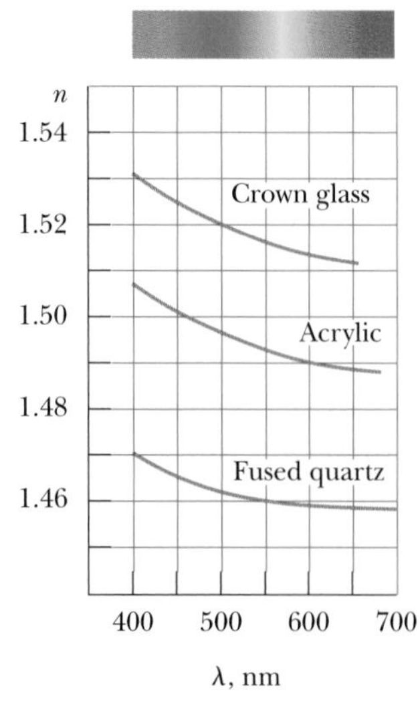

Figure 35.21 Variation of index of refraction with vacuum wavelength for three materials.

David Parker/Science Photo Library/Photo Researchers, Inc.

Figure 35.22 White light enters a glass prism at the upper left. A reflected beam of light comes out of the prism below the incoming beam. The beam moving toward the lower right shows distinct colors. Different colors are refracted at different angles because the index of refraction of the glass depends on wavelength. Violet light deviates the most; red light deviates the least.

The dispersion of light into a spectrum is demonstrated most vividly in nature by the formation of a rainbow, which is often seen by an observer positioned between the Sun and a rain shower. To understand how a rainbow is formed, consider Active Figure 35.23. A ray of sunlight (which is white light) passing overhead strikes a drop of water in the atmosphere and is refracted and reflected as follows. It is first refracted at the front surface of the drop, with the violet light deviating the most and the red light the least. At the back surface of the drop, the light is reflected and returns to the front surface, where it again undergoes refraction as it moves from water into air. The rays leave the drop such that the angle between the incident white light and the most intense returning violet ray is 40° and the angle between the incident white light and the most intense returning red ray is 42°. This small angular difference between the returning rays causes us to see a colored bow.

Now suppose an observer is viewing a rainbow as shown in Figure 35.24. If a raindrop high in the sky is being observed, the most intense red light returning from the drop reaches the observer because it is deviated the most; the most intense violet light, however, passes over the observer because it is deviated the least. Hence, the observer sees red light coming from this drop. Similarly, a drop lower in the sky directs the most intense violet light toward the observer and appears violet to the observer. (The most intense red light from this drop passes below the observer's eye and is not seen.) The most intense light from other colors of the spectrum reaches the observer from raindrops lying between these two extreme positions.

The opening photograph for this chapter shows a *double rainbow.* The secondary rainbow is fainter than the primary rainbow, and the colors are reversed. The secondary rainbow arises from light that makes two reflections from the interior surface before exiting the raindrop. In the laboratory, rainbows have been observed in which the light makes more than 30 reflections before exiting the water drop. Because each reflection involves some loss of light due to refraction out of the water drop, the intensity of these higher-order rainbows is small compared with that of the primary rainbow.

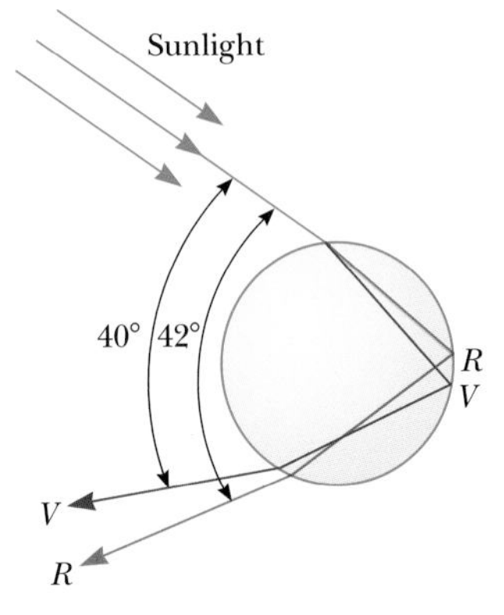

ACTIVE FIGURE 35.23

Path of sunlight through a spherical raindrop. Light following this path contributes to the visible rainbow.

Sign in at www.thomsonedu.com and go to ThomsonNOW to vary the point at which the sunlight enters the raindrop and verify that the angles shown are the maximum angles.

PITFALL PREVENTION 35.5

A Rainbow of Many Light Rays

Pictorial representations such as Active Figure 35.23 are subject to misinterpretation. The figure shows one ray of light entering the raindrop and undergoing reflection and refraction, exiting the raindrop in a range of 40° to 42° from the entering ray. This illustration might be interpreted incorrectly as meaning that *all* light entering the raindrop exits in this small range of angles. In reality, light exits the raindrop over a much larger range of angles, from 0° to 42°. A careful analysis of the reflection and refraction from the spherical raindrop shows that the range of 40° to 42° is where the *highest-intensity light* exits the raindrop.

Quick Quiz 35.4 In film photography, lenses in a camera use refraction to form an image on a film. Ideally, you want all the colors in the light from the object being photographed to be refracted by the same amount. Of the materials shown in Figure 35.21, which would you choose for a single-element camera lens? (a) crown glass (b) acrylic (c) fused quartz (d) impossible to determine

35.8 Total Internal Reflection

An interesting effect called **total internal reflection** can occur when light is directed from a medium having a given index of refraction toward one having a lower index of refraction. Consider Active Figure 35.25a (page 994), in which a light ray travels in medium 1 and meets the boundary between medium 1 and medium 2, where n_1 is greater than n_2. In the figure, labels 1 through 5 indicate various possible directions of the ray consistent with the wave under refraction model. The refracted rays are bent away from the normal because n_1 is greater than n_2. At some particular angle of incidence θ_c, called the **critical angle,** the refracted light ray moves parallel to the boundary so that $\theta_2 = 90°$ (Active Fig. 35.25b). For angles of incidence greater than θ_c, the ray is entirely reflected at the boundary as shown by ray 5 in Active Figure 35.25a.

We can use Snell's law of refraction to find the critical angle. When $\theta_1 = \theta_c$, $\theta_2 = 90°$ and Equation 35.8 gives

$$n_1 \sin \theta_c = n_2 \sin 90° = n_2$$

$$\sin \theta_c = \frac{n_2}{n_1} \quad (\text{for } n_1 > n_2) \tag{35.10}$$

◄ Critical angle for total internal reflection

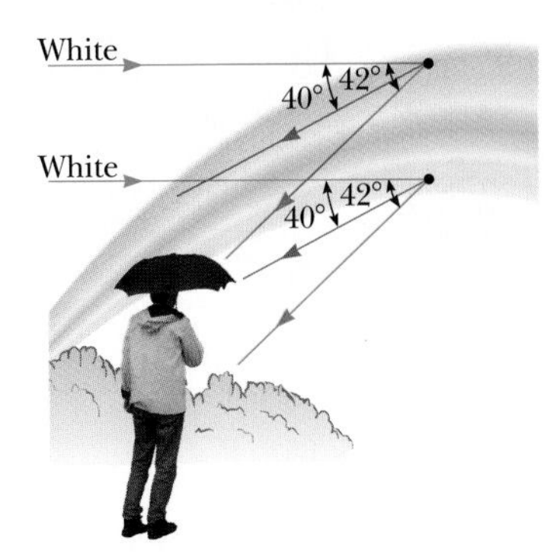

Figure 35.24 The formation of a rainbow seen by an observer standing with the Sun behind his back.

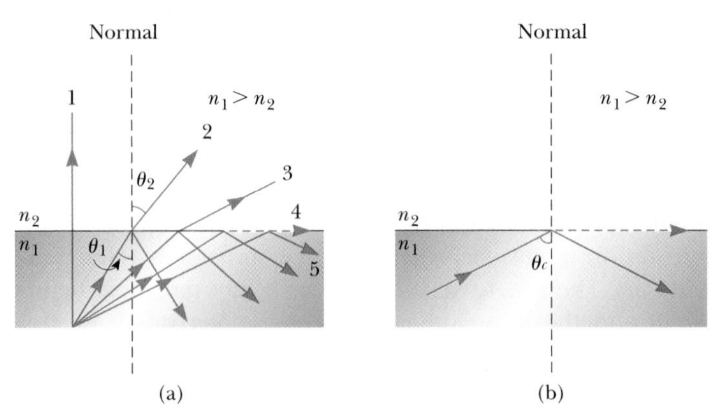

ACTIVE FIGURE 35.25

(a) Rays travel from a medium of index of refraction n_1 into a medium of index of refraction n_2, where $n_2 < n_1$. As the angle of incidence θ_1 increases, the angle of refraction θ_2 increases until θ_2 is 90° (ray 4). The dashed line indicates that no energy actually propagates in this direction. For even larger angles of incidence, total internal reflection occurs (ray 5). (b) The angle of incidence producing an angle of refraction equal to 90° is the critical angle θ_c. At this angle of incidence, all the energy of the incident light is reflected.

Sign in at www.thomsonedu.com and go to ThomsonNOW to vary the incident angle and see the effect on the refracted ray and the distribution of incident energy between the reflected and refracted rays.

This equation can be used only when n_1 is greater than n_2. That is, **total internal reflection occurs only when light is directed from a medium of a given index of refraction toward a medium of lower index of refraction.** If n_1 were less than n_2, Equation 35.10 would give $\sin\theta_c > 1$, which is a meaningless result because the sine of an angle can never be greater than unity.

The critical angle for total internal reflection is small when n_1 is considerably greater than n_2. For example, the critical angle for a diamond in air is 24°. Any ray inside the diamond that approaches the surface at an angle greater than 24° is completely reflected back into the crystal. This property, combined with proper faceting, causes diamonds to sparkle. The angles of the facets are cut so that light is "caught" inside the crystal through multiple internal reflections. These multiple reflections give the light a long path through the medium, and substantial dispersion of colors occurs. By the time the light exits through the top surface of the crystal, the rays associated with different colors have been fairly widely separated from one another.

Cubic zirconia also has a high index of refraction and can be made to sparkle very much like a diamond. If a suspect jewel is immersed in corn syrup, the difference in n for the cubic zirconia and that for the corn syrup is small and the critical angle is therefore great. Hence, more rays escape sooner; as a result, the sparkle completely disappears. A real diamond does not lose all its sparkle when placed in corn syrup.

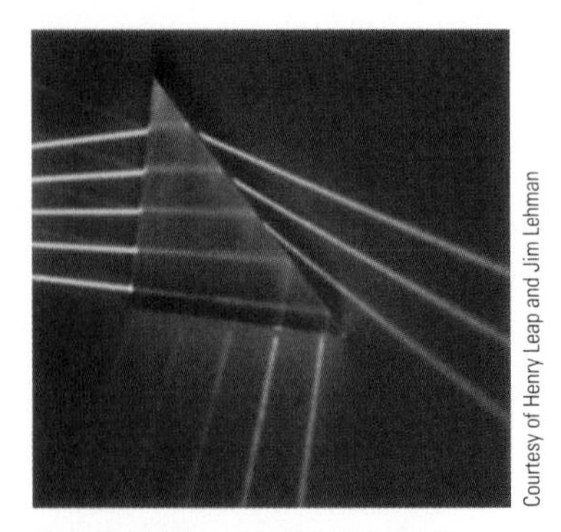

Courtesy of Henry Leap and Jim Lehman

Figure 35.26 (Quick Quiz 35.5) Five nonparallel light rays enter a glass prism from the left.

Quick Quiz 35.5 In Figure 35.26, five light rays enter a glass prism from the left. **(i)** How many of these rays undergo total internal reflection at the slanted surface of the prism? (a) 1 (b) 2 (c) 3 (d) 4 (e) 5 **(ii)** Suppose the prism in Figure 35.26 can be rotated in the plane of the paper. For *all five* rays to experience total internal reflection from the slanted surface, should the prism be rotated (a) clockwise or (b) counterclockwise?

EXAMPLE 35.6 A View from the Fish's Eye

Find the critical angle for an air–water boundary. (The index of refraction of water is 1.33.)

SOLUTION

Conceptualize Study Active Figure 35.25 to understand the concept of total internal reflection and the significance of the critical angle.

Categorize We use concepts developed in this section, so we categorize this example as a substitution problem.

Apply Equation 35.10 to the air–water interface:

$$\sin\theta_c = \frac{n_2}{n_1} = \frac{1.00}{1.33} = 0.752$$

$$\theta_c = 48.8°$$

What If? What if a fish in a still pond looks upward toward the water's surface at different angles relative to the surface as in Figure 35.27? What does it see?

Answer Because the path of a light ray is reversible, light traveling from medium 2 into medium 1 in Active Figure 35.25a follows the paths shown, but in the *opposite* direction. A fish looking upward toward the water surface as in Figure 35.27 can see out of the water if it looks toward the surface at an angle less than the critical angle. Therefore, when the fish's line of vision makes an angle of $\theta = 40°$ with the normal to the surface, for example, light from above the water reaches the fish's eye. At $\theta = 48.8°$, the critical angle for water, the light has to skim along the water's surface before being refracted to the fish's eye; at this angle, the fish can, in principle, see the entire shore of the pond. At angles greater than the critical angle, the light reaching the fish comes by means of total internal reflection at the surface. Therefore, at $\theta = 60°$, the fish sees a reflection of the bottom of the pond.

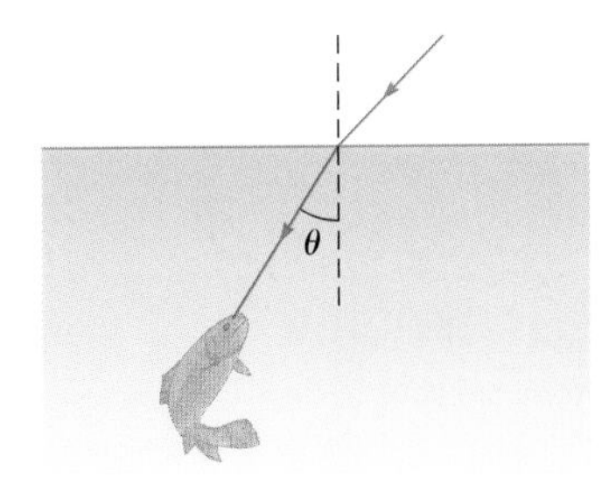

Figure 35.27 (Example 35.6) **What If?** A fish looks upward toward the water surface.

Optical Fibers

Another interesting application of total internal reflection is the use of glass or transparent plastic rods to "pipe" light from one place to another. As indicated in Figure 35.28, light is confined to traveling within a rod, even around curves, as the result of successive total internal reflections. Such a light pipe is flexible if thin fibers are used rather than thick rods. A flexible light pipe is called an **optical fiber.** If a bundle of parallel fibers is used to construct an optical transmission line, images can be transferred from one point to another. This technique is used in a sizable industry known as *fiber optics.*

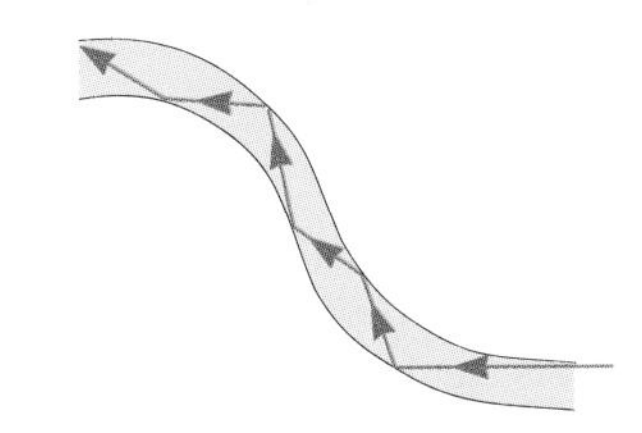

Figure 35.28 Light travels in a curved transparent rod by multiple internal reflections.

A practical optical fiber consists of a transparent core surrounded by a *cladding,* a material that has a lower index of refraction than the core. The combination may be surrounded by a plastic *jacket* to prevent mechanical damage. Figure 35.29 shows a cutaway view of this construction. Because the index of refraction of the cladding is less than that of the core, light traveling in the core experiences total internal reflection if it arrives at the interface between the core and the cladding at an angle

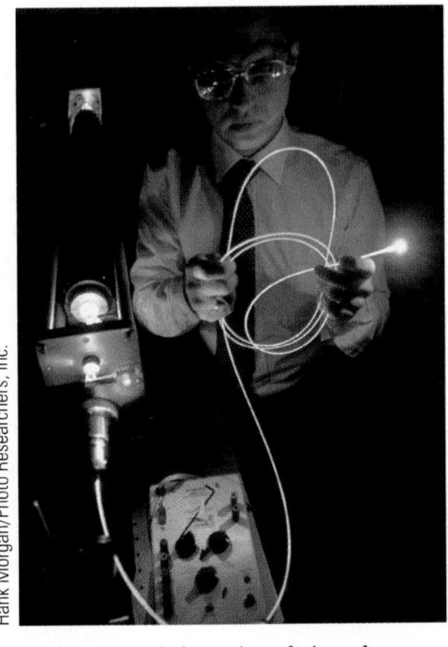

(Left) Strands of glass optical fibers are used to carry voice, video, and data signals in telecommunication networks. *(Right)* A bundle of optical fibers is illuminated by a laser.

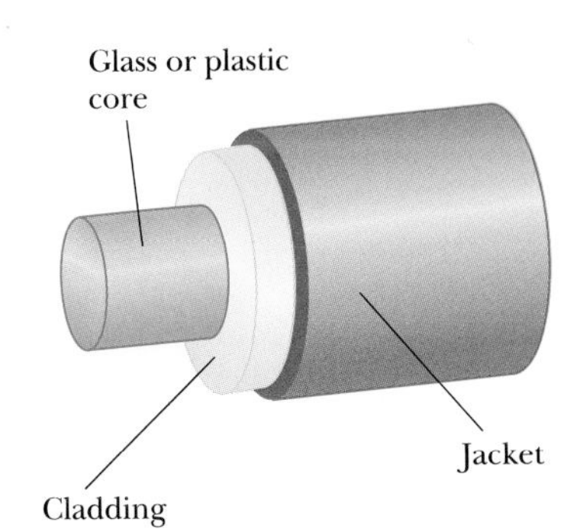

Figure 35.29 The construction of an optical fiber. Light travels in the core, which is surrounded by a cladding and a protective jacket.

of incidence that exceeds the critical angle. In this case, light "bounces" along the core of the optical fiber, losing very little of its intensity as it travels.

Any loss in intensity in an optical fiber is essentially due to reflections from the two ends and absorption by the fiber material. Optical fiber devices are particularly useful for viewing an object at an inaccessible location. For example, physicians often use such devices to examine internal organs of the body or to perform surgery without making large incisions. Optical fiber cables are replacing copper wiring and coaxial cables for telecommunications because the fibers can carry a much greater volume of telephone calls or other forms of communication than electrical wires can.

Summary

DEFINITION

The **index of refraction** n of a medium is defined by the ratio

$$n \equiv \frac{c}{v} \qquad \textbf{(35.4)}$$

where c is the speed of light in a vacuum and v is the speed of light in the medium.

CONCEPTS AND PRINCIPLES

In geometric optics, we use the **ray approximation,** in which a wave travels through a uniform medium in straight lines in the direction of the rays.

Total internal reflection occurs when light travels from a medium of high index of refraction to one of lower index of refraction. The **critical angle** θ_c for which total internal reflection occurs at an interface is given by

$$\sin\theta_c = \frac{n_2}{n_1} \quad (\text{for } n_1 > n_2) \qquad \textbf{(35.10)}$$

ANALYSIS MODELS FOR PROBLEM SOLVING

Wave Under Reflection. The **law of reflection** states that for a light ray (or other type of wave) incident on a smooth surface, the angle of reflection θ_1' equals the angle of incidence θ_1:

$$\theta_1' = \theta_1 \qquad \textbf{(35.2)}$$

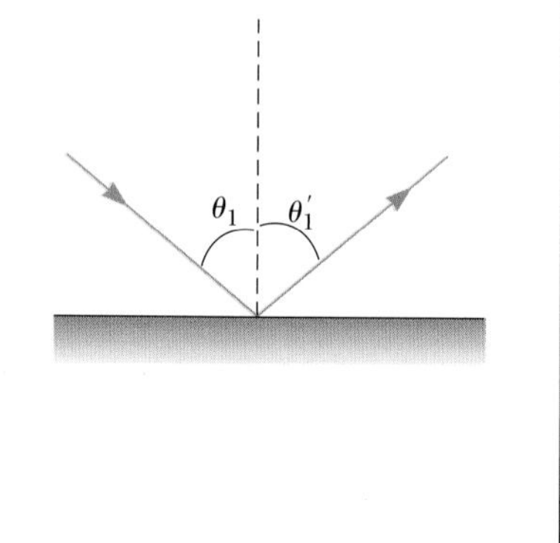

Wave Under Refraction. A wave crossing a boundary as it travels from medium 1 to medium 2 is **refracted,** or bent. The angle of refraction θ_2 is related to the incident angle θ_1 by the relationship

$$\frac{\sin\theta_2}{\sin\theta_1} = \frac{v_2}{v_1} \qquad \textbf{(35.3)}$$

where v_1 and v_2 are the speeds of the wave in medium 1 and medium 2, respectively. The incident ray, the reflected ray, the refracted ray, and the normal to the surface all lie in the same plane.

For light waves, **Snell's law of refraction** states that

$$n_1 \sin\theta_1 = n_2 \sin\theta_2 \qquad \textbf{(35.8)}$$

where n_1 and n_2 are the indices of refraction in the two media.

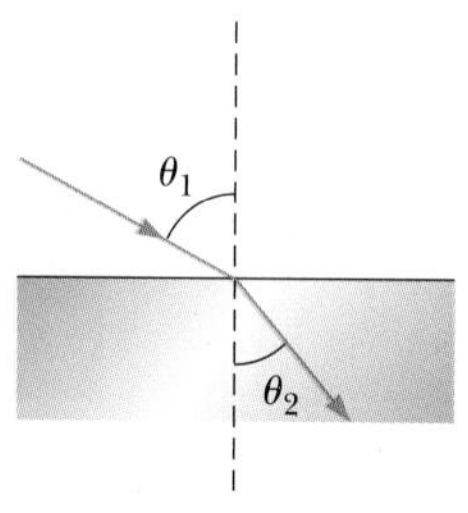

Questions

☐ denotes answer available in *Student Solutions Manual/Study Guide;* **O** denotes objective question

1. Why do astronomers looking at distant galaxies talk about looking backward in time?

2. O What is the order of magnitude of the time interval required for light to travel 10 km as in Galileo's attempt to measure the speed of light? (a) several seconds (b) several milliseconds (c) several microseconds (d) several nanoseconds

3. O In each of the following situations, a wave passes through an opening in an absorbing wall. Rank the situations in order from the one in which the wave is best described by the ray approximation to the one in which the wave coming through the opening spreads out most nearly equally in all directions in the hemisphere beyond the wall. (a) The sound of a low whistle at 1 kHz passes through a doorway 1 m wide. (b) Red light passes through the pupil of your eye. (c) Blue light passes through the pupil of your eye. (d) The wave broadcast by an AM radio station passes through a doorway 1 m wide. (e) An x-ray passes through the space between bones in your elbow joint.

4. The display windows of some department stores are slanted slightly inward at the bottom. This tilt is to decrease the glare from streetlights and the Sun, which would make it difficult for shoppers to see the display inside. Sketch a light ray reflecting from such a window to show how this design works.

5. You take a child for walks around the neighborhood. She loves to listen to echoes from houses when she shouts or when you clap loudly. A house with a large, flat front wall can produce an echo if you stand straight in front of it and reasonably far away. Draw a bird's-eye view of the situation to explain the production of the echo. Shade the area where you can stand to hear the echo. **What If?** The child helps you discover that a house with an L-shaped floor plan can produce echoes if you are standing in a wider range of locations. You can be standing at any reasonably distant location from which you can see the inside corner. Explain the echo in this case and draw another diagram for comparison. **What If?** What if the two wings of the house are not perpendicular? Will you and the child, standing close together, hear echoes? **What If?** What if a rectangular house and its garage have perpendicular walls that would form an inside corner but have a breezeway between them so that the walls do not meet? Will this structure produce strong echoes for people in a wide range of locations? Explain your answers with diagrams.

6. The F-117A stealth fighter (Figure Q35.6) is specifically designed to be a *non*retroreflector of radar. What aspects of its design help accomplish this purpose? *Suggestion:* Answer the previous question as preparation for this one. Notice that the bottom of the plane is flat and that all the flat exterior panels meet at odd angles.

Courtesy of U.S. Air Force, Langley Air Force Base

Figure Q35.6

7. O A light wave moves between medium 1 and medium 2. Which of the following are correct statements relating its speed, frequency, and wavelength in the two media, the indices of refraction of the media, and the angles of incidence and refraction? Choose all correct statements. (a) $v_1/\sin\theta_1 = v_2/\sin\theta_2$ (b) $\csc\theta_1/n_1 = \csc\theta_2/n_2$ (c) $\lambda_1/\sin\theta_1 = \lambda_2/\sin\theta_2$ (d) $f_1/\sin\theta_1 = f_2/\sin\theta_2$ (e) $n_1/\cos\theta_1 = n_2/\cos\theta_2$

8. Sound waves have much in common with light waves, including the properties of reflection and refraction. Give examples of these phenomena for sound waves.

9. O Consider light traveling from one medium into another with a different index of refraction. (a) Does its wavelength change? (b) Does its frequency change? (c) Does its speed change? (d) Does its direction always change?

10. A laser beam passing through a nonhomogeneous sugar solution follows a curved path. Explain.

11. **O** (a) Can light undergo total internal reflection at a smooth interface between air and water? If so, in which medium must it be traveling originally? (b) Can sound undergo total internal reflection at a smooth interface between air and water? If so, in which medium must it be traveling originally?

12. Explain why a diamond sparkles more than a glass crystal of the same shape and size.

13. Total internal reflection is applied in the periscope of a submarine to let the user "see around corners." In this device, two prisms are arranged as shown in Figure Q35.13 so that an incident beam of light follows the path shown. Parallel tilted, silvered mirrors could be used, but glass prisms with no silvered surfaces give higher light throughput. Propose a reason for the higher efficiency.

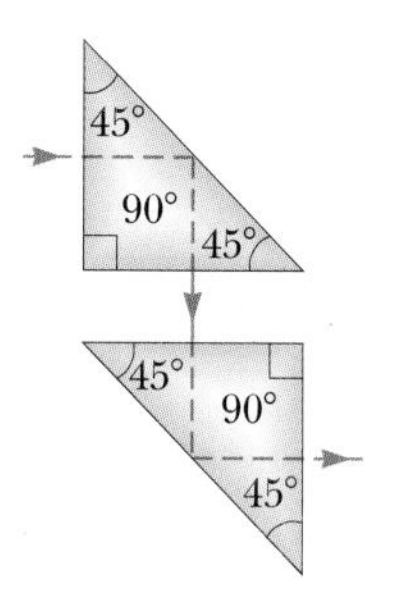

Figure Q35.13

14. **O** Suppose you find experimentally that two colors of light, A and B, originally traveling in the same direction in air, are sent through a glass prism, and A changes direction more than B. Which travels more slowly in the prism, A or B? Alternatively, is there insufficient information to determine which moves more slowly?

15. Retroreflection by transparent spheres, mentioned in Section 35.4, can be observed with dewdrops. To do so, look at the shadow of your head where it falls on dewy grass. Compare your observations to the reactions of two other people: Renaissance artist Benvenuto Cellini described the phenomenon and his reaction in his *Autobiography,* at the end of Part One, and American philosopher Henry David Thoreau did the same in *Walden,* "Baker Farm," second paragraph. The optical display around the shadow of your head is called *heiligenschein,* which is German for *holy light.* Try to find a person you know who has seen the heiligenschein. What did that person think about it?

16. How is it possible that a complete circle of a rainbow can sometimes be seen from an airplane? With a stepladder, a lawn sprinkler, and a sunny day, how can you show the complete circle to children?

17. At one restaurant, a worker uses colored chalk to write the daily specials on a blackboard illuminated with a spotlight. At another restaurant, a worker writes with colored grease pencils onto a flat, smooth sheet of transparent acrylic plastic with index of refraction 1.55. The panel hangs in front of a piece of black felt. Small, bright electric lights are installed all along the edges of the sheet, inside an opaque channel. Figure Q35.17 shows a cutaway view of the sign. Explain why viewers at both restaurants see the letters shining against a black background. Explain why the sign at the second restaurant may use less energy from the electric company than the illuminated blackboard at the first restaurant. What would be a good choice for the index of refraction of the material in the grease pencils?

Figure Q35.17

18. **O** The core of an optical fiber transmits light with minimal loss if it is surrounded by what? (a) water (b) diamond (c) air (d) glass (e) fused quartz.

19. Under what conditions is a mirage formed? On a hot day, what are we seeing when we observe "water on the road"?

Problems

WebAssign The Problems from this chapter may be assigned online in WebAssign.

ThomsonNOW Sign in at **www.thomsonedu.com** and go to ThomsonNOW to assess your understanding of this chapter's topics with additional quizzing and conceptual questions.

1, 2, 3 denotes straightforward, intermediate, challenging; □ denotes full solution available in *Student Solutions Manual/Study Guide;* ▲ denotes coached solution with hints available at **www.thomsonedu.com;** denotes developing symbolic reasoning; ● denotes asking for qualitative reasoning; denotes computer useful in solving problem

Section 35.1 The Nature of Light

Section 35.2 Measurements of the Speed of Light

1. ● The *Apollo 11* astronauts set up a panel of efficient corner-cube retroreflectors on the Moon's surface (Fig. 35.8a). The speed of light can be found by measuring the time interval required for a laser beam to travel from the Earth, reflect from the panel, and return to the Earth. Assume this interval is measured to be 2.51 s at a station where the Moon is at the zenith. What is the measured speed of light? Take the center-to-center distance from the Earth to the Moon to be 3.84×10^8 m. Explain whether it is necessary to consider the sizes of the Earth and the Moon in your calculation.

2. As a result of his observations, Roemer concluded that eclipses of Io by Jupiter were delayed by 22 min during a six-month period as the Earth moved from the point in its orbit where it is closest to Jupiter to the diametrically opposite point where it is farthest from Jupiter. Using 1.50×10^8 km as the average radius of the Earth's orbit around the Sun, calculate the speed of light from these data.

3. In an experiment to measure the speed of light using the apparatus of Fizeau (see Fig. 35.2), the distance between light source and mirror was 11.45 km and the wheel had 720 notches. The experimentally determined value of c was 2.998×10^8 m/s. Calculate the minimum angular speed of the wheel for this experiment.

Section 35.3 The Ray Approximation in Geometric Optics

Section 35.4 The Wave Under Reflection

Section 35.5 The Wave Under Refraction

Note: You may look up indices of refraction in Table 35.1.

4. A dance hall is built without pillars and with a horizontal ceiling 7.20 m above the floor. A mirror is fastened flat against one section of the ceiling. Following an earthquake, the mirror is in place and unbroken. An engineer makes a quick check of whether the ceiling is sagging by directing a vertical beam of laser light up at the mirror and observing its reflection on the floor. (a) Show that if the mirror has rotated to make an angle ϕ with the horizontal, the normal to the mirror makes an angle ϕ with the vertical. (b) Show that the reflected laser light makes an angle 2ϕ with the vertical. (c) Assume the reflected laser light makes a spot on the floor 1.40 cm away from the point vertically below the laser. Find the angle ϕ.

5. The two mirrors illustrated in Figure P35.5 meet at a right angle. The beam of light in the vertical plane P strikes mirror 1 as shown. (a) Determine the distance the reflected light beam travels before striking mirror 2. (b) In what direction does the light beam travel after being reflected from mirror 2?

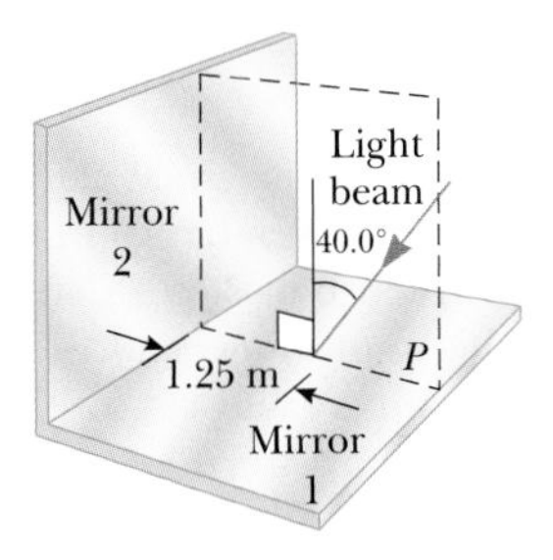

Figure P35.5

6. Two flat, rectangular mirrors, both perpendicular to a horizontal sheet of paper, are set edge to edge with their reflecting surfaces perpendicular to each other. (a) A light ray in the plane of the paper strikes one of the mirrors at an arbitrary angle of incidence θ_1. Prove that the final direction of the ray, after reflection from both mirrors, is opposite its initial direction. In a clothing store, such a pair of mirrors shows you an image of yourself as others see you, with no apparent right–left reversal. (b) **What If?** Now assume the paper is replaced with a third flat mirror, touching edges with the other two and perpendicular to both. The set of three mirrors is called a *corner-cube reflector.* A ray of light is incident from any direction within the octant of space bounded by the reflecting surfaces. Argue that the ray will reflect once from each mirror and that its final direction will be opposite to its original direction. The *Apollo 11* astronauts placed a panel of corner-cube retroreflectors on the Moon. Analysis of timing data taken with it reveals that the radius of the Moon's orbit is increasing at the rate of 3.8 cm/yr as it loses kinetic energy because of tidal friction.

7. The distance of a lightbulb from a large plane mirror is twice the distance of a person from the plane mirror. Light from the lightbulb reaches the person by two paths. It travels to the mirror at an angle of incidence θ and reflects from the mirror to the person. It also travels directly to the person without reflecting off the mirror. The total distance traveled by the light in the first case is twice the distance traveled by the light in the second case. Find the value of the angle θ.

8. Two light pulses are emitted simultaneously from a source. Both pulses travel to a detector, but mirrors shunt one pulse along a path that carries it through 6.20 m of ice along the way. Determine the difference in the pulses' times of arrival at the detector.

9. A narrow beam of sodium yellow light, with wavelength 589 nm in vacuum, is incident from air onto a smooth water surface at an angle of incidence of 35.0°. Determine the angle of refraction and the wavelength of the light in water.

10. ● A plane sound wave in air at 20°C, with wavelength 589 mm, is incident on a smooth surface of water at 25°C at an angle of incidence of 3.50°. Determine the angle of refraction for the sound wave and the wavelength of the sound in water. Compare and contrast the behavior of the sound in this problem with the behavior of the light in Problem 9.

11. An underwater scuba diver sees the Sun at an apparent angle of 45.0° above the horizontal. What is the actual elevation angle of the Sun above the horizontal?

12. The wavelength of red helium–neon laser light in air is 632.8 nm. (a) What is its frequency? (b) What is its wavelength in glass that has an index of refraction of 1.50? (c) What is its speed in the glass?

13. A ray of light is incident on a flat surface of a block of crown glass that is surrounded by water. The angle of refraction is 19.6°. Find the angle of reflection.

14. A laser beam with vacuum wavelength 632.8 nm is incident from air onto a block of Lucite as shown in Active Figure 35.10b. The line of sight of the photograph is perpendicular to the plane in which the light moves. Find (a) the speed, (b) the frequency, and (c) the wavelength of the light in the Lucite. *Suggestion:* Use a protractor.

15. Find the speed of light in (a) flint glass, (b) water, and (c) cubic zirconia.

16. A narrow beam of ultrasonic waves reflects off the liver tumor illustrated in Figure P35.16. The speed of the wave is 10.0% less in the liver than in the surrounding medium. Determine the depth of the tumor.

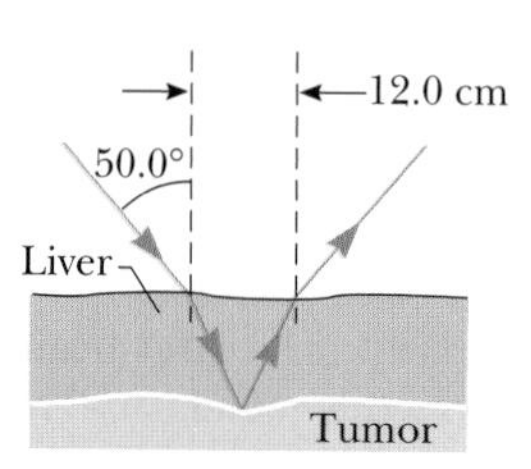

Figure P35.16

17. ▲ A ray of light strikes a flat block of glass ($n = 1.50$) of thickness 2.00 cm at an angle of 30.0° with the normal. Trace the light beam through the glass and find the angles of incidence and refraction at each surface.

18. An opaque cylindrical tank with an open top has a diameter of 3.00 m and is completely filled with water. When the afternoon Sun reaches an angle of 28.0° above the horizon, sunlight ceases to illuminate any part of the bottom of the tank. How deep is the tank?

19. When the light illustrated in Figure P35.19 passes through the glass block, it is shifted laterally by the distance d. Taking $n = 1.50$, find the value of d.

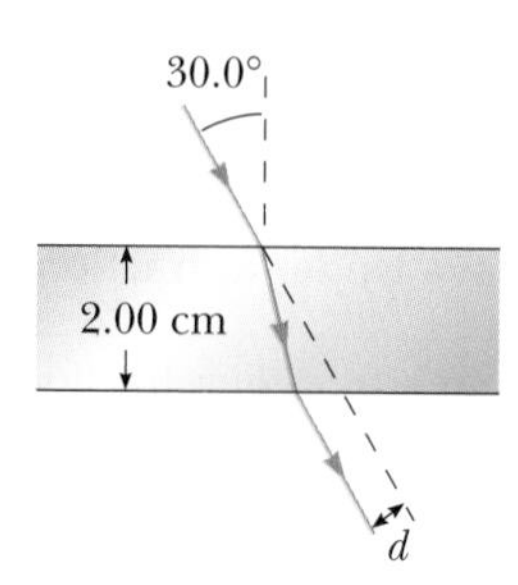

Figure P35.19

20. Find the time interval required for the light to pass through the glass block described in Problem 19.

21. The light beam shown in Figure P35.21 makes an angle of 20.0° with the normal line NN' in the linseed oil. Determine the angles θ and θ'. (The index of refraction of linseed oil is 1.48.)

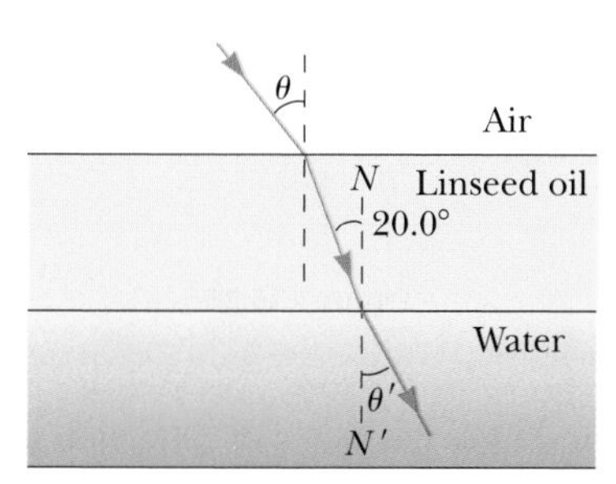

Figure P35.21

22. Three sheets of plastic have unknown indices of refraction. Sheet 1 is placed on top of sheet 2, and a laser beam is directed onto the sheets from above so that it strikes the interface at an angle of 26.5° with the normal. The refracted beam in sheet 2 makes an angle of 31.7° with the normal. The experiment is repeated with sheet 3 on top of sheet 2, and, with the same angle of incidence, the refracted beam makes an angle of 36.7° with the normal. If the experiment is repeated again with sheet 1 on top of sheet 3, what is the expected angle of refraction in sheet 3? Assume the same angle of incidence.

23. ● Light passes from air into flint glass. (a) Is it possible for the component of its velocity perpendicular to the interface to remain constant? Explain your answer. (b) **What If?** Can the component of velocity parallel to the interface remain constant during refraction? Explain your answer.

24. When you look through a window, by what time interval is the light you see delayed by having to go through glass instead of air? Make an order-of-magnitude estimate on the basis of data you specify. By how many wavelengths is it delayed?

25. A prism that has an apex angle of 50.0° is made of cubic zirconia, with $n = 2.20$. What is its angle of minimum deviation?

26. Light of wavelength 700 nm is incident on the face of a fused quartz prism at an angle of 75.0° (with respect to the normal to the surface). The apex angle of the prism is 60.0°. Use the value of n from Figure 35.21 and calculate the angle (a) of refraction at the first surface, (b) of incidence at the second surface, (c) of refraction at the second surface, and (d) between the incident and emerging rays.

27. A triangular glass prism with apex angle $\Phi = 60.0°$ has an index of refraction $n = 1.50$ (Fig. P35.27). What is the smallest angle of incidence θ_1 for which a light ray can emerge from the other side?

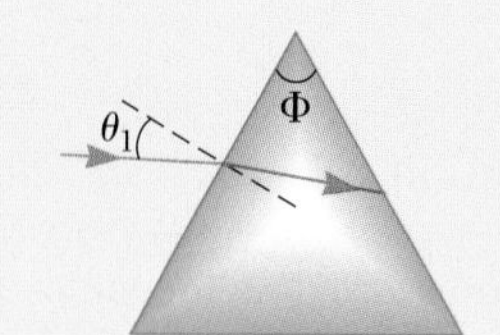

Figure P35.27 Problems 27 and 28.

28. A triangular glass prism with apex angle Φ has index of refraction n. (See Fig. P35.27.) What is the smallest angle of incidence θ_1 for which a light ray can emerge from the other side?

29. A triangular glass prism with apex angle 60.0° has an index of refraction of 1.50. (a) Show that if its angle of incidence on the first surface is $\theta_1 = 48.6°$, light will pass symmetrically through the prism as shown in Figure 35.17. (b) Find the angle of deviation δ_{min} for $\theta_1 = 48.6°$. (c) **What If?** Find the angle of deviation if the angle of incidence on the first surface is 45.6°. (d) Find the angle of deviation if $\theta_1 = 51.6°$.

Section 35.6 Huygens's Principle

30. The speed of a water wave is described by $v = \sqrt{gd}$, where d is the water depth, assumed to be small compared to the wavelength. Because their speed changes, water waves refract when moving into a region of different depth. Sketch a map of an ocean beach on the eastern side of a landmass. Show contour lines of constant depth under water, assuming reasonably uniform slope. (a) Suppose waves approach the coast from a storm far away to the north–northeast. Demonstrate that the waves move nearly perpendicular to the shoreline when they reach the beach. (b) Sketch a map of a coastline with alternating bays and headlands as suggested in Figure P35.30. Again

Ray Atkeson/Image Archive

Figure P35.30

make a reasonable guess about the shape of contour lines of constant depth. Suppose waves approach the coast, carrying energy with uniform density along originally straight wave fronts. Show that the energy reaching the coast is concentrated at the headlands and has lower intensity in the bays.

Section 35.7 Dispersion

31. ▲ The index of refraction for violet light in silica flint glass is 1.66 and that for red light is 1.62. What is the angular spread of visible light passing through a prism of apex angle 60.0° if the angle of incidence is 50.0°? See Figure P35.31.

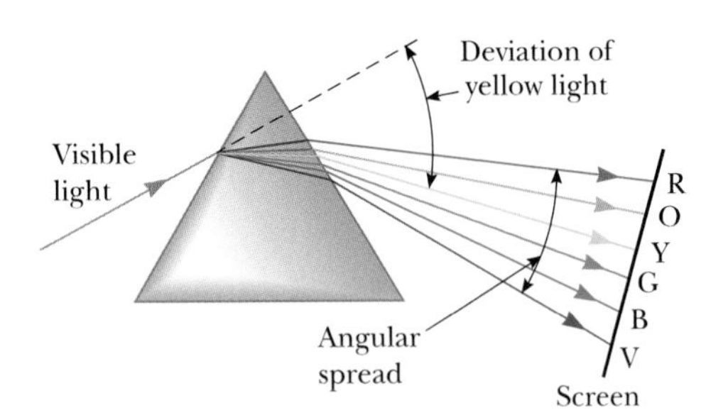

Figure P35.31

32. A narrow, white light beam is incident on a block of fused quartz at an angle of 30.0°. Find the angular spread of the light beam inside the quartz due to dispersion.

Section 35.8 Total Internal Reflection

33. For 589-nm light, calculate the critical angle for the following materials surrounded by air. (a) diamond (b) flint glass (c) ice

34. A glass fiber (n = 1.50) is submerged in water (n = 1.33). What is the critical angle for light to stay inside the optical fiber?

35. Consider a common mirage formed by superheated air immediately above a roadway. A truck driver whose eyes are 2.00 m above the road, where n = 1.000 3, looks forward. She perceives the illusion of a patch of water ahead on the road, where her line of sight makes an angle of 1.20° below the horizontal. Find the index of refraction of the air immediately above the road surface. *Suggestion:* Treat this problem as one about total internal reflection.

36. Determine the maximum angle θ for which the light rays incident on the end of the pipe in Figure P35.36 are subject to total internal reflection along the walls of the pipe. Assume the pipe has an index of refraction of 1.36 and the outside medium is air. Your answer defines the size of the *cone of acceptance* for the light pipe.

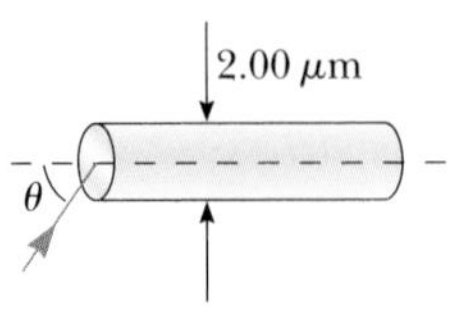

Figure P35.36

37. ● An optical fiber has index of refraction n and diameter d. It is surrounded by air. Light is sent into the fiber along its axis as shown in Figure P35.37. (a) Find the smallest outside radius R permitted for a bend in the fiber if no light is to escape. (b) **What If?** Does the result for part (a) predict reasonable behavior as d approaches zero? As n increases? As n approaches 1? (c) Evaluate R assuming the fiber diameter is 100 μm and its index of refraction is 1.40.

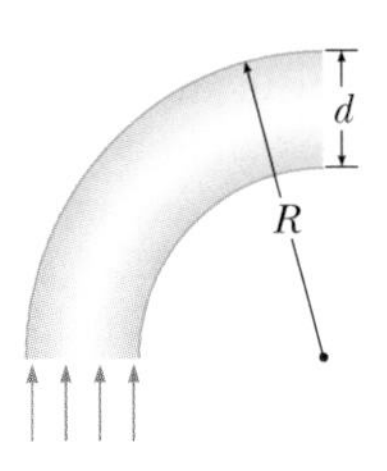

Figure P35.37

38. ● A room contains air in which the speed of sound is 343 m/s. The walls of the room are made of concrete in which the speed of sound is 1 850 m/s. (a) Find the critical angle for total internal reflection of sound at the concrete–air boundary. (b) In which medium must the sound be traveling if it is undergo total internal reflection? (c) "A bare concrete wall is a highly efficient mirror for sound." Give evidence for or against this statement.

39. ● Around 1965, engineers at the Toro Company invented a gasoline gauge for small engines diagrammed in Figure P35.39. The gauge has no moving parts. It consists of a flat slab of transparent plastic fitting vertically into a slot in the cap on the gas tank. None of the plastic has a reflective coating. The plastic projects from the horizontal top down nearly to the bottom of the opaque tank. Its lower edge is cut with facets making angles of 45° with the horizontal. A lawn mower operator looks down from above and sees a boundary between bright and dark on the gauge. The location of the boundary, across the width of the plastic, indicates the quantity of gasoline in the tank. Explain how the gauge works. Explain the design requirements, if any, for the index of refraction of the plastic.

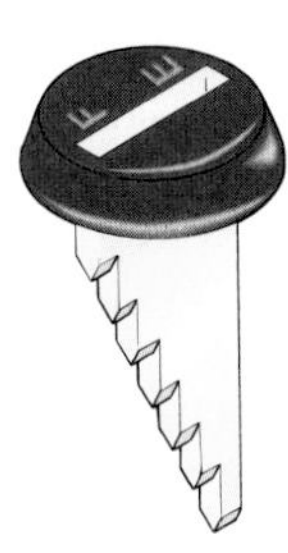

Figure P35.39

41. ● Figure P35.41a shows a desk ornament globe containing a photograph. The flat photograph is in air, inside a vertical slot located behind a water-filled compartment having the shape of one half of a cylinder. Suppose you are looking at the center of the photograph and then rotate the globe about a vertical axis. You find that the center of the photograph disappears when you rotate the globe beyond a certain maximum angle (Fig. P35.41b). Account for this phenomenon and calculate the maximum angle. Describe what you see when you turn the globe beyond this angle.

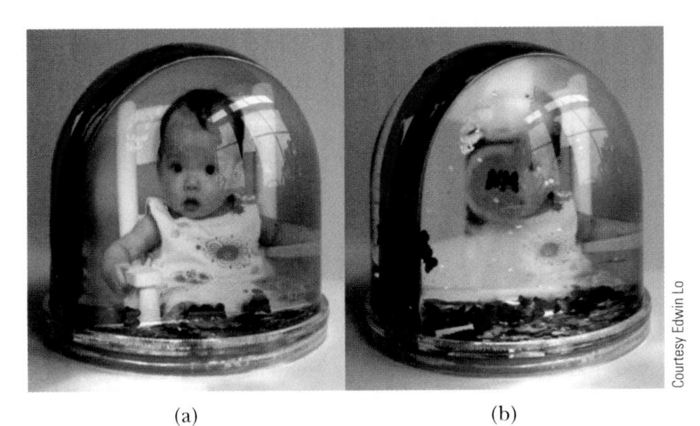

(a) (b)

Figure P35.41

Additional Problems

40. A digital videodisc records information in a spiral track approximately 1 μm wide. The track consists of a series of pits in the information layer (Fig. P35.40a) that scatter light from a laser beam sharply focused on them. The laser shines in through transparent plastic of thickness $t = 1.20$ mm and index of refraction 1.55 (Fig. P35.40b). Assume the width of the laser beam at the information layer must be $a = 1.00\ \mu$m to read from only one track and not from its neighbors. Assume the width of the beam as it enters the transparent plastic from below is $w = 0.700$ mm. A lens makes the beam converge into a cone with an apex angle $2\theta_1$ before it enters the videodisc. Find the incidence angle θ_1 of the light at the edge of the conical beam. This design is relatively immune to small dust particles degrading the video quality. Particles on the plastic surface would have to be as large as 0.7 mm to obscure the beam.

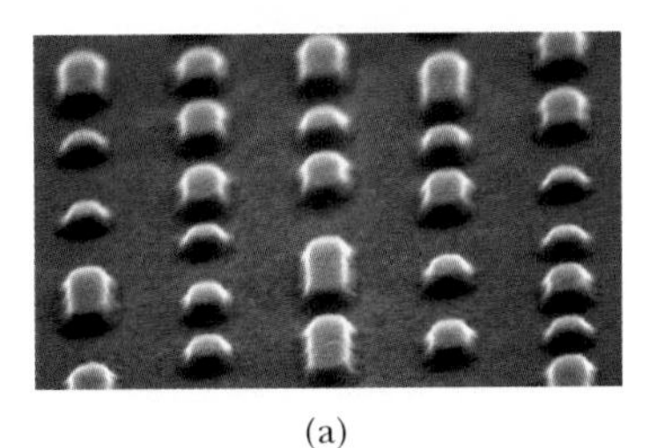

(a)

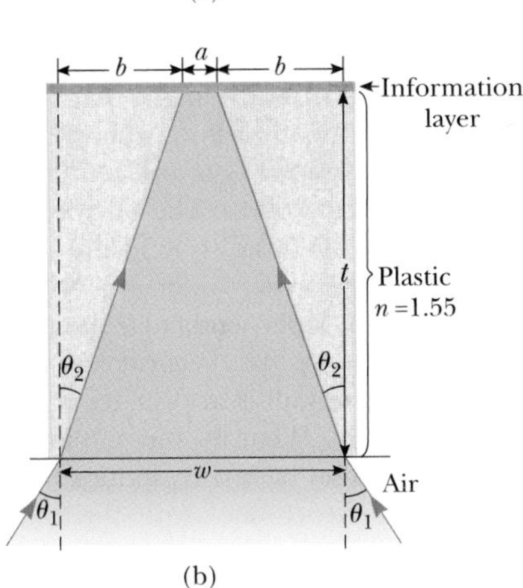

(b)

Figure P35.40

42. ● A light ray enters the atmosphere of a planet and descends vertically to the surface a distance h below. The index of refraction where the light enters the atmosphere is 1.000, and it increases linearly with distance to have the value n at the planet surface. (a) Over what time interval does the light traverse this path? (b) State how this travel time compares with the time interval required in the absence of an atmosphere.

43. A narrow beam of light is incident from air onto the surface of glass with index of refraction 1.56. Find the angle of incidence for which the corresponding angle of refraction is half the angle of incidence. *Suggestion:* You might want to use the trigonometric identity $\sin 2\theta = 2 \sin \theta \cos \theta$.

44. (a) Consider a horizontal interface between air above and glass of index 1.55 below. Draw a light ray incident from the air at angle of incidence 30.0°. Determine the angles of the reflected and refracted rays and show them on the diagram. (b) **What If?** Now suppose the light ray is incident from the glass at angle of incidence 30.0°. Determine the angles of the reflected and refracted rays and show all three rays on a new diagram. (c) For rays incident from the air onto the air–glass surface, determine and tabulate the angles of reflection and refraction for all the angles of incidence at 10.0° intervals from 0° to 90.0°.

(d) Do the same for light rays coming up to the interface through the glass.

45. ▲ A small light fixture on the bottom of a swimming pool is 1.00 m below the surface. The light emerging from the still water forms a circle on the water surface. What is the diameter of this circle?

46. The walls of a prison cell are perpendicular to the four cardinal compass directions. On the first day of spring, light from the rising Sun enters a rectangular window in the eastern wall. The light traverses 2.37 m horizontally to shine perpendicularly on the wall opposite the window. A young prisoner observes the patch of light moving across this western wall and for the first time forms his own understanding of the rotation of the Earth. (a) With what speed does the illuminated rectangle move? (b) The prisoner holds a small, square mirror flat against the wall at one corner of the rectangle of light. The mirror reflects light back to a spot on the eastern wall close beside the window. With what speed does the smaller square of light move across that wall? (c) Seen from a latitude of 40.0° north, the rising Sun moves through the sky along a line making a 50.0° angle with the southeastern horizon. In what direction does the rectangular patch of light on the western wall of the prisoner's cell move? (d) In what direction does the smaller square of light on the eastern wall move?

47. A hiker stands on an isolated mountain peak near sunset and observes a rainbow caused by water droplets in the air at a distance of 8.00 km along her line of sight. The valley is 2.00 km below the mountain peak and entirely flat. What fraction of the complete circular arc of the rainbow is visible to the hiker? (See Fig. 35.24.)

48. Figure P35.48 shows a top view of a square enclosure. The inner surfaces are plane mirrors. A ray of light enters a small hole in the center of one mirror. (a) At what angle θ must the ray enter if it exits through the hole after being reflected once by each of the other three mirrors? (b) **What If?** Are there other values of θ for which the ray can exit after multiple reflections? If so, sketch one of the ray's paths.

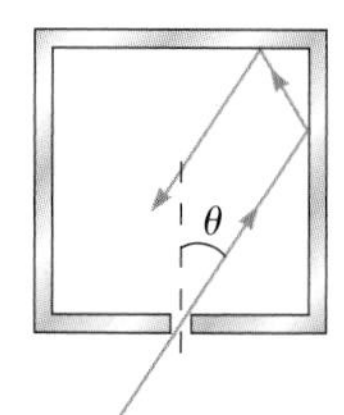

Figure P35.48

49. ▲ A laser beam strikes one end of a slab of material as shown in Figure P35.49. The index of refraction of the slab is 1.48. Determine the number of internal reflections of the beam before it emerges from the opposite end of the slab.

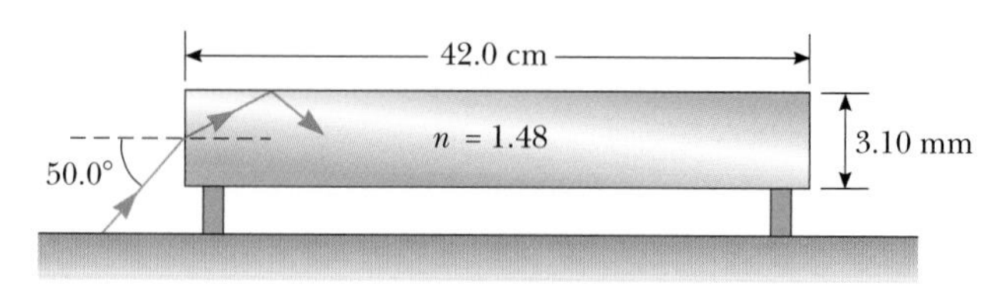

Figure P35.49

50. A 4.00-m-long pole stands vertically in a lake having a depth of 2.00 m. The Sun is 40.0° above the horizontal. Determine the length of the pole's shadow on the bottom of the lake. Take the index of refraction for water to be 1.33.

51. The light beam in Figure P35.51 strikes surface 2 at the critical angle. Determine the angle of incidence θ_1.

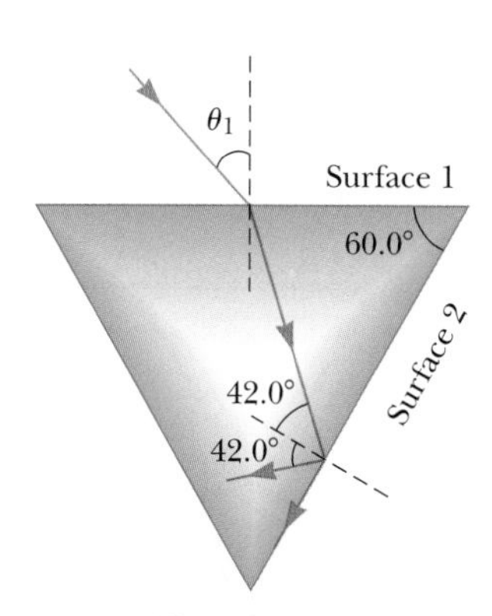

Figure P35.51

52. Builders use a leveling instrument in which the beam from a fixed helium–neon laser reflects in a horizontal plane from a small, flat mirror mounted on a vertical rotating shaft. The light is sufficiently bright and the rotation rate is sufficiently high that the reflected light appears as a horizontal line, wherever it falls on a wall. (a) Assume the mirror is at the center of a circular grain elevator of radius 3.00 m. The mirror spins with constant angular velocity 35.0 rad/s. Find the speed of the spot of laser light on the curved wall. (b) Now assume the spinning mirror is at a perpendicular distance of 3.00 m from point O on a long, flat, vertical wall. When the spot of laser light on the wall is at distance x from point O, what is its speed? (c) What is the minimum value for the speed? What value of x corresponds to it? How does the minimum speed compare with the speed you found in part (a)? (d) What is the maximum speed of the spot on the flat wall? (e) In what time interval does the spot change from its minimum to its maximum speed?

53. ▲ ● A light ray of wavelength 589 nm is incident at an angle θ on the top surface of a block of polystyrene as shown in Figure P35.53. (a) Find the maximum value of θ for which the refracted ray undergoes total internal reflection at the left vertical face of the block. **What If?** Repeat the calculation for the case in which the polystyrene block is immersed in (b) water and (c) carbon disulfide. You will need to explain your answers.

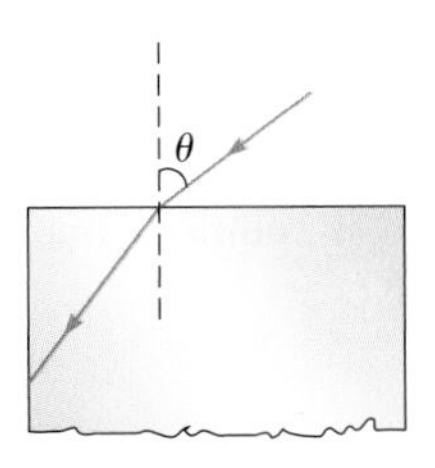

Figure P35.53

54. ● As sunlight enters the Earth's atmosphere, it changes direction due to the small difference between the speeds of light in vacuum and in air. The duration of an *optical* day is defined as the time interval between the instant when the top of the rising Sun is just visible above the horizon and the instant when the top of the Sun just disappears below the horizontal plane. The duration of the *geometric* day is defined as the time interval between the instant when a mathematically straight line between an observer and the top of the Sun just clears the horizon and the instant at which this line just dips below the horizon. (a) Explain which is longer, an optical day or a geometric day. (b) Find the difference between these two time intervals. Model the Earth's atmosphere as uniform, with index of refraction 1.000 293, a sharply defined upper surface, and depth 8 614 m. Assume the observer is at the Earth's equator so that the apparent path of the rising and setting Sun is perpendicular to the horizon.

55. A shallow glass dish is 4.00 cm wide at the bottom as shown in Figure P35.55. When an observer's eye is located as shown, the observer sees the edge of the bottom of the empty dish. When this dish is filled with water, the observer sees the center of the bottom of the dish. Find the height of the dish.

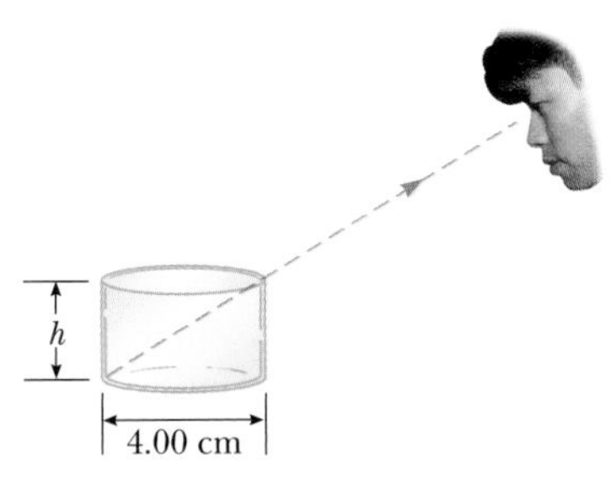

Figure P35.55

56. A ray of light passes from air into water. For its deviation angle $\delta = |\theta_1 - \theta_2|$ to be 10.0°, what must its angle of incidence be?

57. A material having an index of refraction n is surrounded by a vacuum and is in the shape of a quarter circle of radius R (Fig. P35.57). A light ray parallel to the base of the material is incident from the left at a distance L above the base and emerges from the material at the angle θ. Determine an expression for θ.

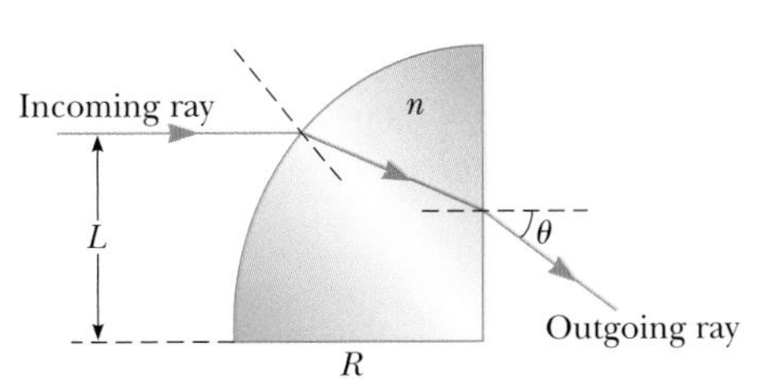

Figure P35.57

58. *Fermat's principle.* Pierre de Fermat (1601–1665) showed that whenever light travels from one point to another, its actual path is the path that requires the smallest time interval. The simplest example is for light propagating in a homogeneous medium. It moves in a straight line because a straight line is the shortest distance between two points. Derive Snell's law of refraction from Fermat's principle. Proceed as follows. In Figure P35.58, a light ray travels from point P in medium 1 to point Q in medium 2. The two points are respectively at perpendicular distances a and b from the interface. The displacement from P to Q has the component d parallel to the interface, and we let x represent the coordinate of the point where the ray enters the second medium. Let $t = 0$ be the instant at which the light starts from P. (a) Show that the time at which the light arrives at Q is

$$t = \frac{r_1}{v_1} + \frac{r_2}{v_2} = \frac{n_1\sqrt{a^2 + x^2}}{c} + \frac{n_2\sqrt{b^2 + (d - x)^2}}{c}$$

(b) To obtain the value of x for which t has its minimum value, differentiate t with respect to x and set the derivative equal to zero. Show that the result implies

$$\frac{n_1 x}{\sqrt{a^2 + x^2}} = \frac{n_2(d - x)}{\sqrt{b^2 + (d - x)^2}}$$

(c) Show that this expression in turn gives Snell's law

$$n_1 \sin\theta_1 = n_2 \sin\theta_2$$

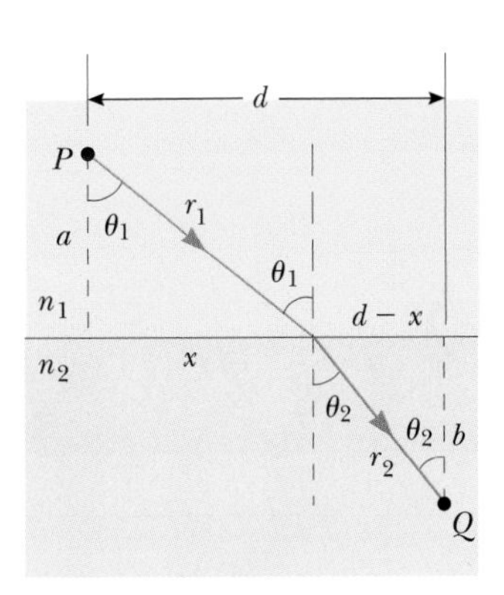

Figure P35.58

59. Refer to Problem 58 for the statement of Fermat's principle of least time. Derive the law of reflection (Eq. 35.2) from Fermat's principle.

60. A transparent cylinder of radius $R = 2.00$ m has a mirrored surface on its right half as shown in Figure P35.60. A light ray traveling in air is incident on the left side of the cylinder. The incident light ray and exiting light ray are parallel, and $d = 2.00$ m. Determine the index of refraction of the material.

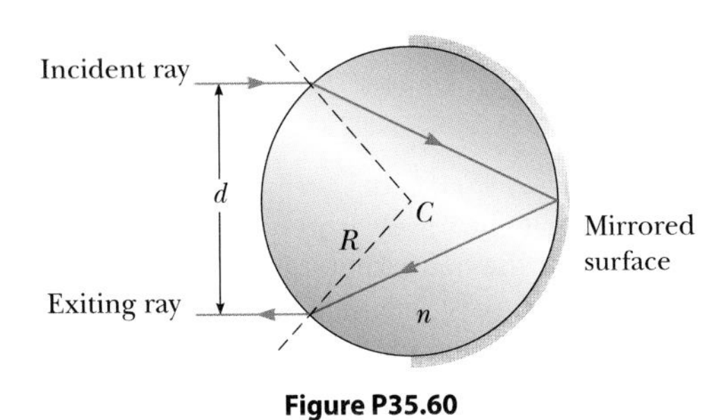

Figure P35.60

61. Suppose a luminous sphere of radius R_1 (such as the Sun) is surrounded by a uniform atmosphere of radius R_2 and index of refraction n. When the sphere is viewed from a location far away in vacuum, what is its apparent radius? You will need to distinguish between the two cases (a) $R_2 > nR_1$ and (b) $R_2 < nR_1$.

62. ● A. H. Pfund's method for measuring the index of refraction of glass is illustrated in Figure P35.62. One face of a slab of thickness t is painted white, and a small hole scraped clear at point P serves as a source of diverging rays when the slab is illuminated from below. Ray PBB' strikes the clear surface at the critical angle and is totally reflected as are rays such as PCC'. Rays such as PAA' emerge from the clear surface. On the painted surface, there appears a dark circle of diameter d surrounded by an illuminated region, or halo. (a) Derive an equation for n in terms of the measured quantities d and t. (b) What is the diameter of the dark circle if $n = 1.52$ for a slab 0.600 cm thick? (c) If white light is used, dispersion causes the critical angle to depend on color. Is the inner edge of the white halo tinged with red light or with violet light? Explain.

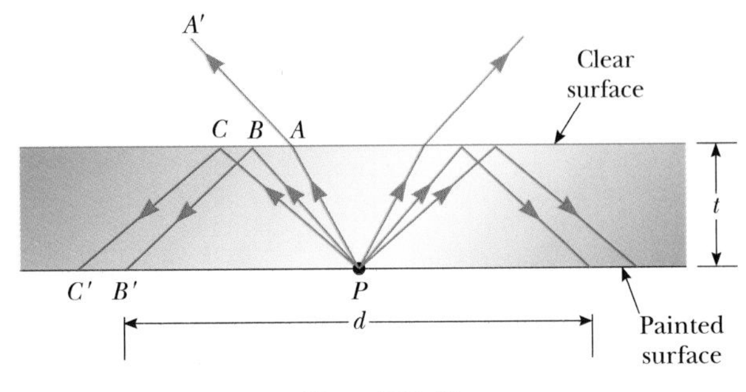

Figure P35.62

63. A light ray enters a rectangular block of plastic at an angle $\theta_1 = 45.0°$ and emerges at an angle $\theta_2 = 76.0°$ as shown in Figure P35.63. (a) Determine the index of refraction of the plastic. (b) If the light ray enters the plastic at a point $L = 50.0$ cm from the bottom edge, what time interval is required for the light ray to travel through the plastic?

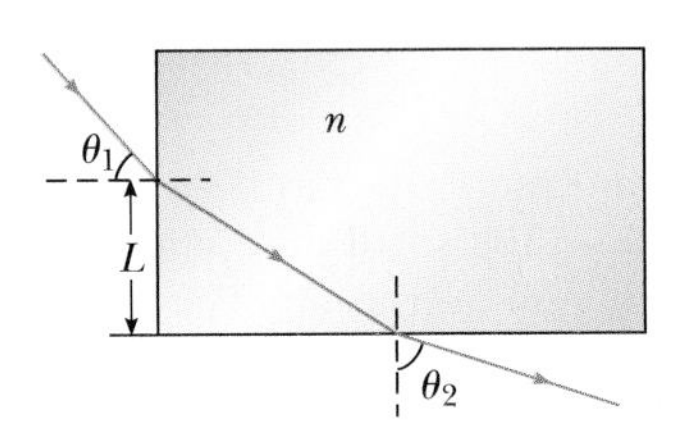

Figure P35.63

64. ● Students allow a narrow beam of laser light to strike a water surface. They measure the angle of refraction for selected angles of incidence and record the data shown in the accompanying table. Use the data to verify Snell's law of refraction by plotting the sine of the angle of incidence versus the sine of the angle of refraction. Explain what the shape of the graph demonstrates. Use the resulting plot to deduce the index of refraction of water, explaining how you do so.

Angle of Incidence (degrees)	Angle of Refraction (degrees)
10.0	7.5
20.0	15.1
30.0	22.3
40.0	28.7
50.0	35.2
60.0	40.3
70.0	45.3
80.0	47.7

65. **Review problem.** A mirror is often "silvered" with aluminum. By adjusting the thickness of the metallic film, one can make a sheet of glass into a mirror that reflects anything between, say, 3% and 98% of the incident light, transmitting the rest. Prove that it is impossible to construct a "one-way mirror" that would reflect 90% of the electromagnetic waves incident from one side and reflect 10% of those incident from the other side. *Suggestion:* Use Clausius's statement of the second law of thermodynamics.

Answers to Quick Quizzes

35.1 (d). The light rays from the actor's face must reflect from the mirror and into the camera. If these light rays are reversed, light from the camera reflects from the mirror into the eyes of the actor.

35.2 Beams ② and ④ are reflected; beams ③ and ⑤ are refracted.

35.3 (c). Because the light is entering a material in which the index of refraction is lower, the speed of light is higher and the light bends away from the normal.

35.4 (c). An ideal camera lens would have an index of refraction that does not vary with wavelength so that all colors would be bent through the same angle by the lens. Of the three choices, fused quartz has the least variation in n across the visible spectrum. A lens designer can do even better by stacking two lenses of different materials together to make an *achromatic doublet.*

35.5 **(i),** (b). The two bright rays exiting the bottom of the prism on the right in Figure 35.26 result from total internal reflection at the right face of the prism. Notice that there is no refracted light exiting the slanted side for these rays. The light from the other three rays is divided into reflected and refracted parts. **(ii),** (b). Counterclockwise rotation of the prism will cause the rays to strike the slanted side of the prism at a larger angle. When the five rays strike at an angle larger than the critical angle, they all undergo total internal reflection.

The light rays coming from the leaves in the background of this scene did not form a focused image on the film of the camera that took this photograph. Consequently, the background appears very blurry. Light rays passing though the raindrop, however, have been altered so as to form a focused image of the background leaves on the film. In this chapter, we investigate the formation of images as light rays reflect from mirrors and refract through lenses. (Don Hammond/CORBIS)

36 Image Formation

This chapter is concerned with the images that result when light rays encounter flat and curved surfaces. Images can be formed by either reflection or refraction, and we can design mirrors and lenses to form images with desired characteristics. We continue to use the ray approximation and assume light travels in straight lines. These two steps lead to valid predictions in the field called *geometric optics.* Subsequent chapters cover interference and diffraction effects, which are the objects of study in the field of *wave optics.*

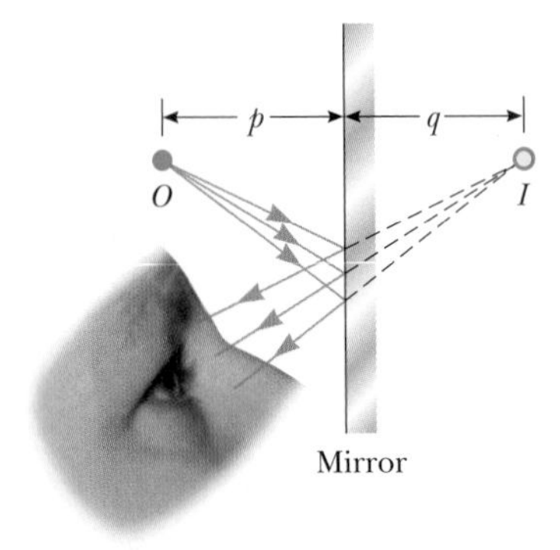

Figure 36.1 An image formed by reflection from a flat mirror. The image point I is located behind the mirror a perpendicular distance q from the mirror (the image distance). The image distance has the same magnitude as the object distance p.

36.1 Images Formed by Flat Mirrors

Image formation by mirrors can be understood through the analysis of light rays following the wave under reflection model. We begin by considering the simplest possible mirror, the flat mirror. Consider a point source of light placed at O in Figure 36.1, a distance p in front of a flat mirror. The distance p is called the **object distance.** Diverging light rays leave the source and are reflected from the mirror. Upon reflection, the rays continue to diverge. The dashed lines in Figure 36.1 are extensions of the diverging rays back to a point of intersection at I. The diverging rays appear to the viewer to originate at the point I behind the mirror. Point I, which is a distance q behind the mirror, is called the **image** of the object at O. The distance q is called the **image distance.** Regardless of the system under study, images can always be located by extending diverging rays back to a point at which they intersect. **Images are located either at a point from which rays of light *actually* diverge or at a point from which they *appear* to diverge.**

Images are classified as **real** or **virtual. A real image is formed when light rays pass through and diverge from the image point; a virtual image is formed when the light rays do not pass through the image point but only appear to diverge from that point.** The image formed by the mirror in Figure 36.1 is virtual. The image of an object seen in a flat mirror is *always* virtual. Real images can be displayed on a screen (as at a movie theater), but virtual images cannot be displayed on a screen. We shall see an example of a real image in Section 36.2.

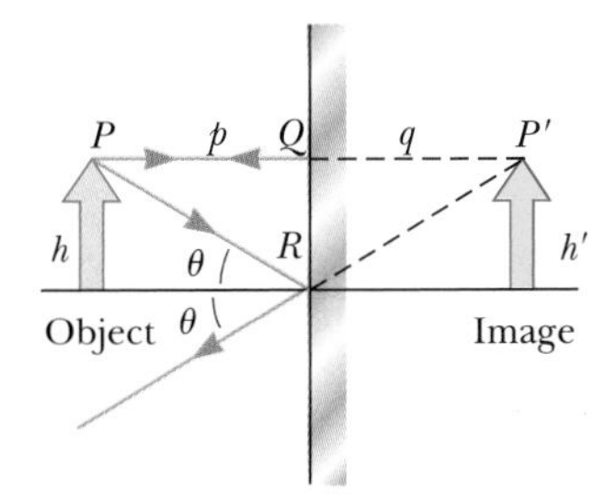

ACTIVE FIGURE 36.2

A geometric construction that is used to locate the image of an object placed in front of a flat mirror. Because the triangles PQR and $P'QR$ are congruent, $|p| = |q|$ and $h = h'$.

Sign in at www.thomsonedu.com and go to ThomsonNOW to move the object and see the effect on the image.

We can use the simple geometry in Active Figure 36.2 to examine the properties of the images of extended objects formed by flat mirrors. Even though there are an infinite number of choices of direction in which light rays could leave each point on the object (represented by a blue arrow), we need to choose only two rays to determine where an image is formed. One of those rays starts at P, follows a path perpendicular to the mirror, and reflects back on itself. The second ray follows the oblique path PR and reflects as shown in Active Figure 36.2 according to the law of reflection. An observer in front of the mirror would extend the two reflected rays back to the point at which they appear to have originated, which is point P' behind the mirror. A continuation of this process for points other than P on the object would result in a virtual image (represented by a yellow arrow) of the entire object behind the mirror. Because triangles PQR and $P'QR$ are congruent, $PQ = P'Q$, so that $|p| = |q|$. Therefore, **the image formed of an object placed in front of a flat mirror is as far behind the mirror as the object is in front of the mirror.**

The geometry in Active Figure 36.2 also reveals that the object height h equals the image height h'. Let us define **lateral magnification** M of an image as follows:

$$M \equiv \frac{\text{image height}}{\text{object height}} = \frac{h'}{h} \qquad \textbf{(36.1)}$$

◀ Lateral magnification

This general definition of the lateral magnification for an image from any type of mirror is also valid for images formed by lenses, which we study in Section 36.4. For a flat mirror, $M = +1$ for any image because $h' = h$. The positive value of the magnification signifies that the image is upright. (By upright we mean that if the object arrow points upward as in Active Figure 36.2, so does the image arrow.)

PITFALL PREVENTION 36.1

Magnification Does Not Necessarily Imply Enlargement

For optical elements other than flat mirrors, the magnification defined in Equation 36.1 can result in a number with a magnitude larger *or* smaller than 1. Therefore, despite the cultural usage of the word *magnification* to mean *enlargement,* the image could be smaller than the object.

A flat mirror produces an image that has an *apparent* left–right reversal. You can see this reversal by standing in front of a mirror and raising your right hand as shown in Figure 36.3. The image you see raises its left hand. Likewise, your hair appears to be parted on the side opposite your real part, and a mole on your right cheek appears to be on your left cheek.

This reversal is not *actually* a left–right reversal. Imagine, for example, lying on your left side on the floor with your body parallel to the mirror surface. Now your head is on the left and your feet are on the right. If you shake your feet, the image does not shake its head! If you raise your right hand, however, the image again raises its left hand. Therefore, the mirror again appears to produce a left–right reversal but in the up–down direction!

The reversal is actually a *front–back reversal,* caused by the light rays going forward toward the mirror and then reflecting back from it. An interesting exercise is to stand in front of a mirror while holding an overhead transparency in front of you so that you can read the writing on the transparency. You will also be able to read the writing on the image of the transparency. You may have had a similar experience if you have attached a transparent decal with words on it to the rear window of your car. If the decal can be read from outside the car, you can also read it when looking into your rearview mirror from inside the car.

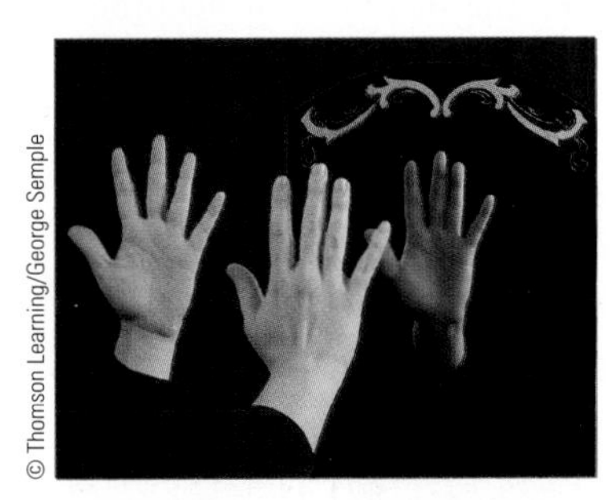

Figure 36.3 The image in the mirror of a person's right hand is reversed front to back, which makes the right hand appear to be a left hand. Notice that the thumb is on the left side of both real hands and on the left side of the image. That the thumb is not on the right side of the image indicates that there is no left-to-right reversal.

Quick Quiz 36.1 You are standing approximately 2 m away from a mirror. The mirror has water spots on its surface. True or False: It is possible for you to see the water spots and your image both in focus at the same time.

CONCEPTUAL EXAMPLE 36.1 Multiple Images Formed by Two Mirrors

Two flat mirrors are perpendicular to each other as in Figure 36.4, and an object is placed at point O. In this situation, multiple images are formed. Locate the positions of these images.

SOLUTION

The image of the object is at I_1 in mirror 1 (violet rays) and at I_2 in mirror 2 (blue rays). In addition, a third image is formed at I_3 (brown rays). This third image is the image of I_1 in mirror 2 or, equivalently, the image of I_2 in mirror 1. That is, the image at I_1 (or I_2) serves as the object for I_3. To form this image at I_3, the rays reflect twice after leaving the object at O.

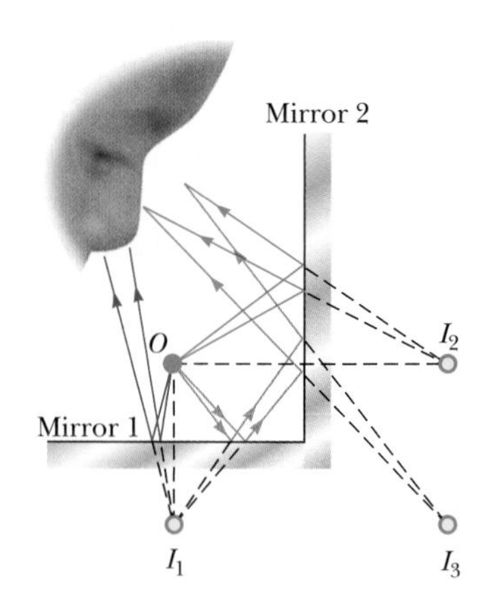

Figure 36.4 (Conceptual Example 36.1) When an object is placed in front of two mutually perpendicular mirrors as shown, three images are formed. Follow the different-colored light rays to understand the formation of each image.

CONCEPTUAL EXAMPLE 36.2 The Tilting Rearview Mirror

Most rearview mirrors in cars have a day setting and a night setting. The night setting greatly diminishes the intensity of the image so that lights from trailing vehicles do not temporarily blind the driver. How does such a mirror work?

SOLUTION

Figure 36.5 shows a cross-sectional view of a rearview mirror for each setting. The unit consists of a reflective coating on the back of a wedge of glass. In the day setting (Fig. 36.5a), the light from an object behind the car strikes the glass wedge at point 1. Most of the light enters the wedge, refracting as it crosses the front surface, and reflects from the back surface to return to the front surface, where it is refracted again as it re-enters the air as ray B (for *bright*). In addition, a small portion of the light is reflected at the front surface of the glass as indicated by ray D (for *dim*).

This dim reflected light is responsible for the image observed when the mirror is in the night setting (Fig. 36.5b). In that case, the wedge is rotated so that the path followed by the bright light (ray B) does not lead to the eye. Instead, the dim light reflected from the front surface of the wedge travels to the eye, and the brightness of trailing headlights does not become a hazard.

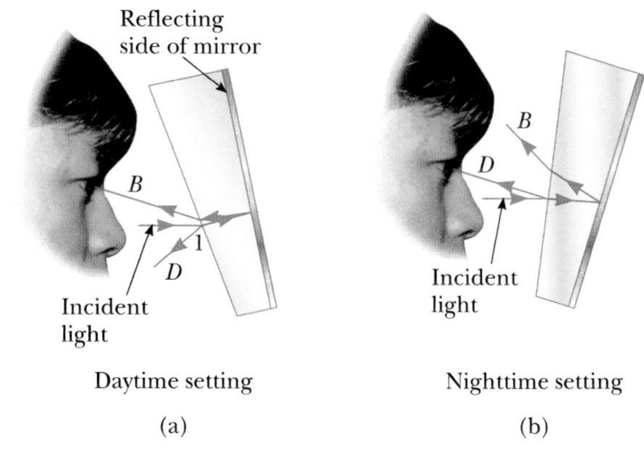

Figure 36.5 (Conceptual Example 36.2) Cross-sectional views of a rearview mirror. (a) With the day setting, the silvered back surface of the mirror reflects a bright ray B into the driver's eyes. (b) With the night setting, the glass of the unsilvered front surface of the mirror reflects a dim ray D into the driver's eyes.

36.2 Images Formed by Spherical Mirrors

In the preceding section, we considered images formed from flat mirrors. Now we study images formed by curved mirrors. Although a variety of curvatures are possible, we will restrict our investigation to spherical mirrors. As its name implies, a **spherical mirror** has the shape of a section of a sphere.

Concave Mirrors

We first consider reflection of light from the inner, concave surface of a spherical mirror as shown in Figure 36.6. This type of reflecting surface is called a **concave mirror.** Figure 36.6a shows that the mirror has a radius of curvature R, and its center of curvature is point C. Point V is the center of the spherical section, and a line through C and V is called the **principal axis** of the mirror. Figure 36.6a shows a

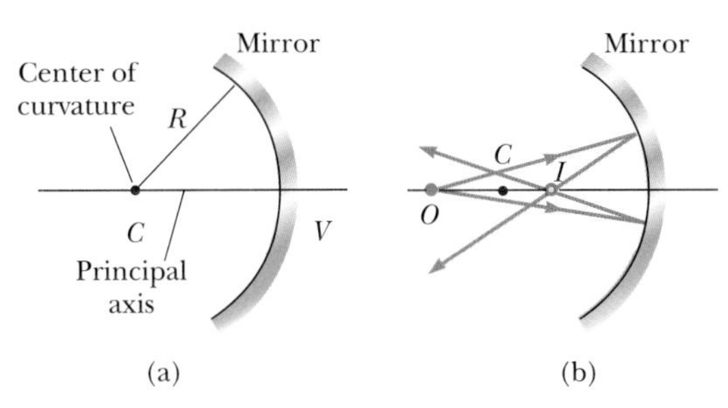

Figure 36.6 (a) A concave mirror of radius *R*. The center of curvature *C* is located on the principal axis. (b) A point object placed at *O* in front of a concave spherical mirror of radius *R*, where *O* is any point on the principal axis farther than *R* from the mirror surface, forms a real image at *I*. If the rays diverge from *O* at small angles, they all reflect through the same image point.

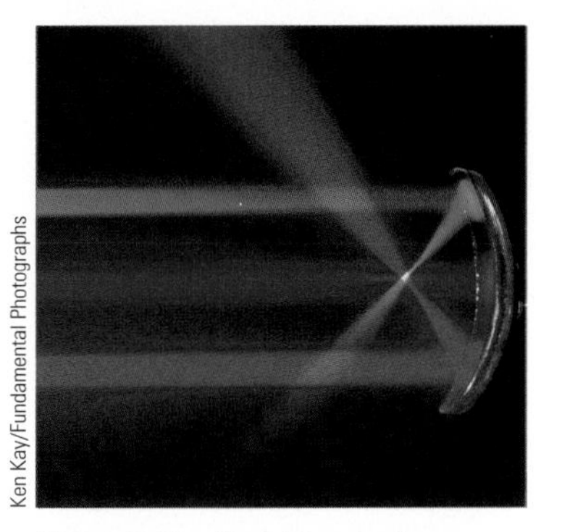

Figure 36.7 Red, blue, and green light rays are reflected by a curved mirror. Notice that the three colored beams meet at a point.

cross section of a spherical mirror, with its surface represented by the solid, curved black line. (The blue band represents the structural support for the mirrored surface, such as a curved piece of glass on which the silvered surface is deposited.) This type of mirror focuses incoming parallel rays to a point as demonstrated by the colored light rays in Figure 36.7.

Now consider a point source of light placed at point O in Figure 36.6b, where O is any point on the principal axis to the left of C. Two diverging light rays that originate at O are shown. After reflecting from the mirror, these rays converge and cross at the image point I. They then continue to diverge from I as if an object were there. As a result, the image at point I is real.

In this section, we shall consider only rays that diverge from the object and make a small angle with the principal axis. Such rays are called **paraxial rays.** All paraxial rays reflect through the image point as shown in Figure 36.6b. Rays that are far from the principal axis such as those shown in Figure 36.8 converge to other points on the principal axis, producing a blurred image. This effect, called *spherical aberration,* is present to some extent for any spherical mirror and is discussed in Section 36.5.

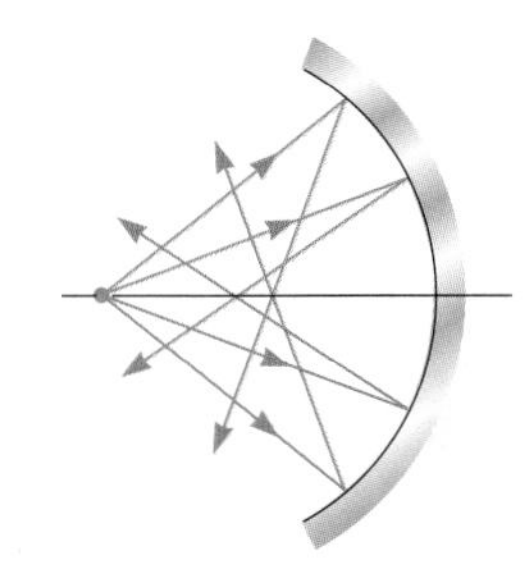

Figure 36.8 Rays diverging from the object at large angles from the principal axis reflect from a spherical concave mirror to intersect the principal axis at different points, resulting in a blurred image. This condition is called *spherical aberration.*

If the object distance p and radius of curvature R are known, we can use Figure 36.9 to calculate the image distance q. By convention, these distances are measured from point V. Figure 36.9 shows two rays leaving the tip of the object. One of these rays passes through the center of curvature C of the mirror, hitting the mirror perpendicular to the mirror surface and reflecting back on itself. The second ray strikes the mirror at its center (point V) and reflects as shown, obeying the law of reflection. The image of the tip of the arrow is located at the point where these two rays intersect. From the large, gold right triangle in Figure 36.9, we see that $\tan\theta = h/p$, and from the blue right triangle, we see that $\tan\theta = -h'/q$. The negative sign is introduced because the image is inverted, so h' is taken to be negative. Therefore, from Equation 36.1 and these results, we find that the magnification of the image is

$$M = \frac{h'}{h} = -\frac{q}{p} \qquad \textbf{(36.2)}$$

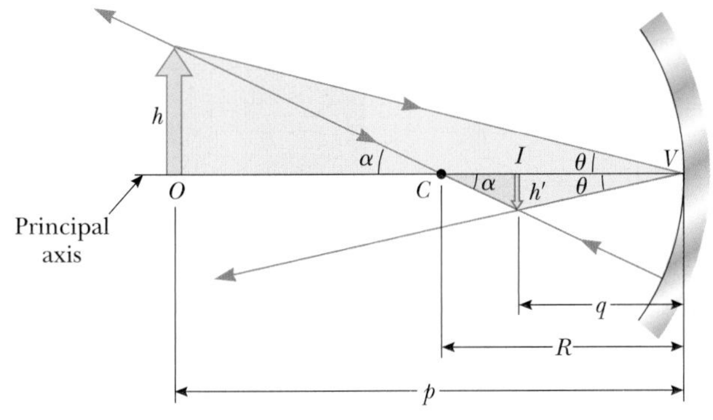

Figure 36.9 The image formed by a spherical concave mirror when the object *O* lies outside the center of curvature *C*. This geometric construction is used to derive Equation 36.4.

A satellite-dish antenna is a concave reflector for television signals from a satellite in orbit around the Earth. Because the satellite is so far away, the signals are carried by microwaves that are parallel when they arrive at the dish. These waves reflect from the dish and are focused on the receiver.

Also notice from the green right triangle in Figure 36.9 and the smaller gold right triangle that

$$\tan\alpha = \frac{-h'}{R-q} \quad \text{and} \quad \tan\alpha = \frac{h}{p-R}$$

from which it follows that

$$\frac{h'}{h} = -\frac{R-q}{p-R} \tag{36.3}$$

Comparing Equations 36.2 and 36.3 gives

$$\frac{R-q}{p-R} = \frac{q}{p}$$

Simple algebra reduces this expression to

Mirror equation in terms of radius of curvature ▶

$$\frac{1}{p} + \frac{1}{q} = \frac{2}{R} \tag{36.4}$$

which is called the *mirror equation.* We present a modified version of this equation shortly.

If the object is very far from the mirror—that is, if p is so much greater than R that p can be said to approach infinity—then $1/p \approx 0$, and Equation 36.4 shows that $q \approx R/2$. That is, when the object is very far from the mirror, the image point is halfway between the center of curvature and the center point on the mirror as shown in Figure 36.10a. The incoming rays from the object are essentially parallel in this figure because the source is assumed to be very far from the mirror. The image point in this special case is called the **focal point** F, and the image distance the **focal length** f, where

Focal length ▶

$$f = \frac{R}{2} \tag{36.5}$$

In Figure 36.7, the colored beams are traveling parallel to the principal axis and the mirror reflects all three beams to the focal point. Notice that the point at which the three beams intersect and the colors add is white.

Because the focal length is a parameter particular to a given mirror, it can be used to compare one mirror with another. Combining Equations 36.4 and 36.5, the **mirror equation** can be expressed in terms of the focal length:

Mirror equation in terms of focal length ▶

$$\frac{1}{p} + \frac{1}{q} = \frac{1}{f} \tag{36.6}$$

Notice that the focal length of a mirror depends only on the curvature of the mirror and not on the material from which the mirror is made because the formation of the image results from rays reflected from the surface of the material. The situ-

PITFALL PREVENTION 36.2

The *Focal* Point Is Not the *Focus* Point

The focal point *is usually not* the point at which the light rays focus to form an image. The focal point is determined solely by the curvature of the mirror; it does not depend on the location of the object. In general, an image forms at a point different from the focal point of a mirror (or a lens). The *only* exception is when the object is located infinitely far away from the mirror.

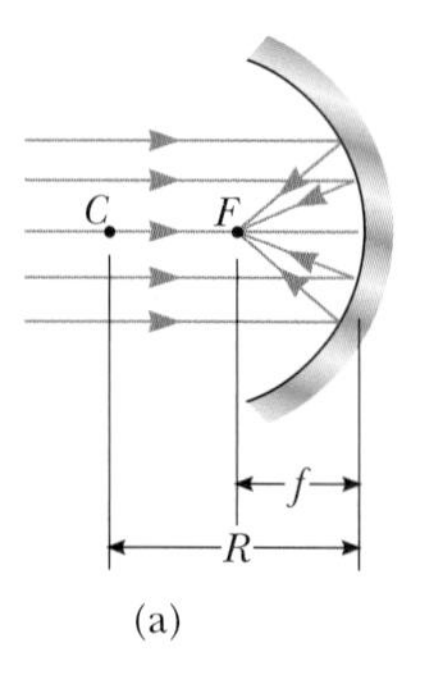

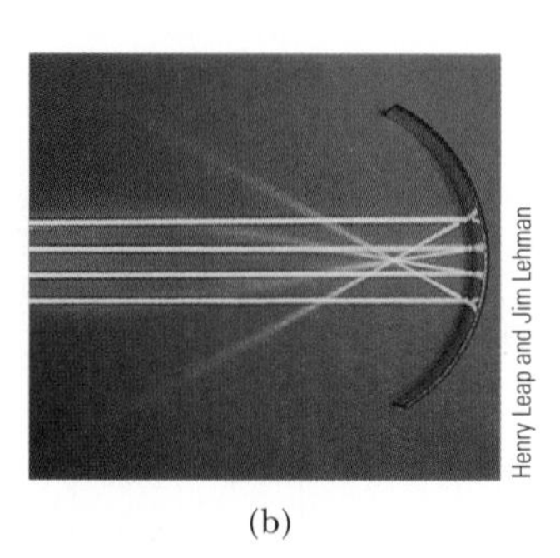

Figure 36.10 (a) Light rays from a distant object ($p \to \infty$) reflect from a concave mirror through the focal point F. In this case, the image distance $q \approx R/2 = f$, where f is the focal length of the mirror. (b) Reflection of parallel rays from a concave mirror.

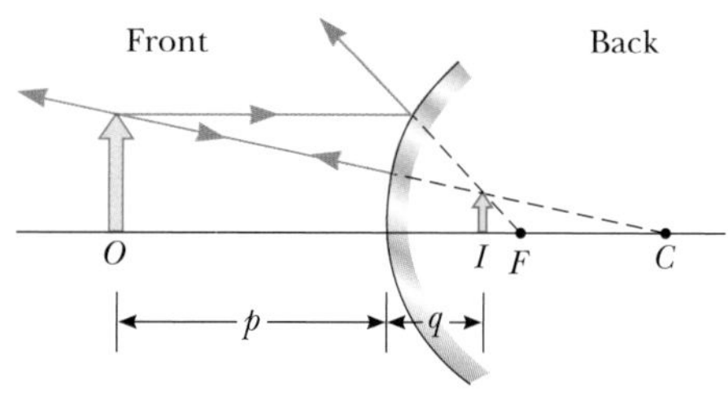

Figure 36.11 Formation of an image by a spherical convex mirror. The image formed by the object is virtual and upright.

ation is different for lenses; in that case, the light actually passes through the material and the focal length depends on the type of material from which the lens is made. (See Section 36.4.)

Convex Mirrors

Figure 36.11 shows the formation of an image by a **convex mirror**, that is, one silvered so that light is reflected from the outer, convex surface. It is sometimes called a **diverging mirror** because the rays from any point on an object diverge after reflection as though they were coming from some point behind the mirror. The image in Figure 36.11 is virtual because the reflected rays only appear to originate at the image point as indicated by the dashed lines. Furthermore, the image is always upright and smaller than the object. This type of mirror is often used in stores to foil shoplifters. A single mirror can be used to survey a large field of view because it forms a smaller image of the interior of the store.

We do not derive any equations for convex spherical mirrors because Equations 36.2, 36.4, and 36.6 can be used for either concave or convex mirrors if we adhere to the following procedure. We will refer to the region in which light rays originate and move toward the mirror as the *front side* of the mirror and the other side as the *back side.* For example, in Figures 36.9 and 36.11, the side to the left of the mirrors is the front side and the side to the right of the mirrors is the back side. Figure 36.12 states the sign conventions for object and image distances, and Table 36.1 summarizes the sign conventions for all quantities. One entry in the table, a *virtual object,* is formally introduced in Section 36.4.

Front, or real, side
Back, or virtual, side
p and q positive
p and q negative
Incident light
Reflected light
No light
Convex or concave mirror

Figure 36.12 Signs of p and q for convex and concave mirrors.

Ray Diagrams for Mirrors

The positions and sizes of images formed by mirrors can be conveniently determined with *ray diagrams.* These pictorial representations reveal the nature of the image and can be used to check results calculated from the mathematical representation using the mirror and magnification equations. To draw a ray diagram, you must know the position of the object and the locations of the mirror's focal point and center of curvature. You then draw three rays to locate the image as

TABLE 36.1

Sign Conventions for Mirrors

Quantity	Positive When . . .	Negative When . . .
Object location (p)	object is in front of mirror (real object).	object is in back of mirror (virtual object).
Image location (q)	image is in front of mirror (real image).	image is in back of mirror (virtual image).
Image height (h')	image is upright.	image is inverted.
Focal length (f) and radius (R)	mirror is concave.	mirror is convex.
Magnification (M)	image is upright.	image is inverted.

PITFALL PREVENTION 36.3

Watch Your Signs

Success in working mirror problems (as well as problems involving refracting surfaces and thin lenses) is largely determined by proper sign choices when substituting into the equations. The best way to success is to work a multitude of problems on your own.

PITFALL PREVENTION 36.4
Choose a Small Number of Rays

A *huge* number of light rays leave each point on an object (and pass through each point on an image). In a ray diagram, which displays the characteristics of the image, we choose only a few rays that follow simply stated rules. Locating the image by calculation complements the diagram.

shown by the examples in Active Figure 36.13. These rays all start from the same object point and are drawn as follows. You may choose any point on the object; here, let's choose the top of the object for simplicity. For concave mirrors (see Active Figs. 36.13a and 36.13b), draw the following three rays:

- Ray 1 is drawn from the top of the object parallel to the principal axis and is reflected through the focal point F.
- Ray 2 is drawn from the top of the object through the focal point (or as if coming from the focal point if $p < f$) and is reflected parallel to the principal axis.
- Ray 3 is drawn from the top of the object through the center of curvature C and is reflected back on itself.

The intersection of any two of these rays locates the image. The third ray serves as a check of the construction. The image point obtained in this fashion must always agree with the value of q calculated from the mirror equation. With concave mirrors, notice what happens as the object is moved closer to the mirror. The real, inverted image in Active Figure 36.13a moves to the left and becomes larger as the object approaches the focal point. When the object is at the focal point, the image is infinitely far to the left. When the object lies between the focal point and the mirror surface as shown in Active Figure 36.13b, however, the image is to the right, behind the object, and virtual, upright, and enlarged. This latter situation applies when you use a shaving mirror or a makeup mirror, both of which are concave. Your face is closer to the mirror than the focal point, and you see an upright, enlarged image of your face.

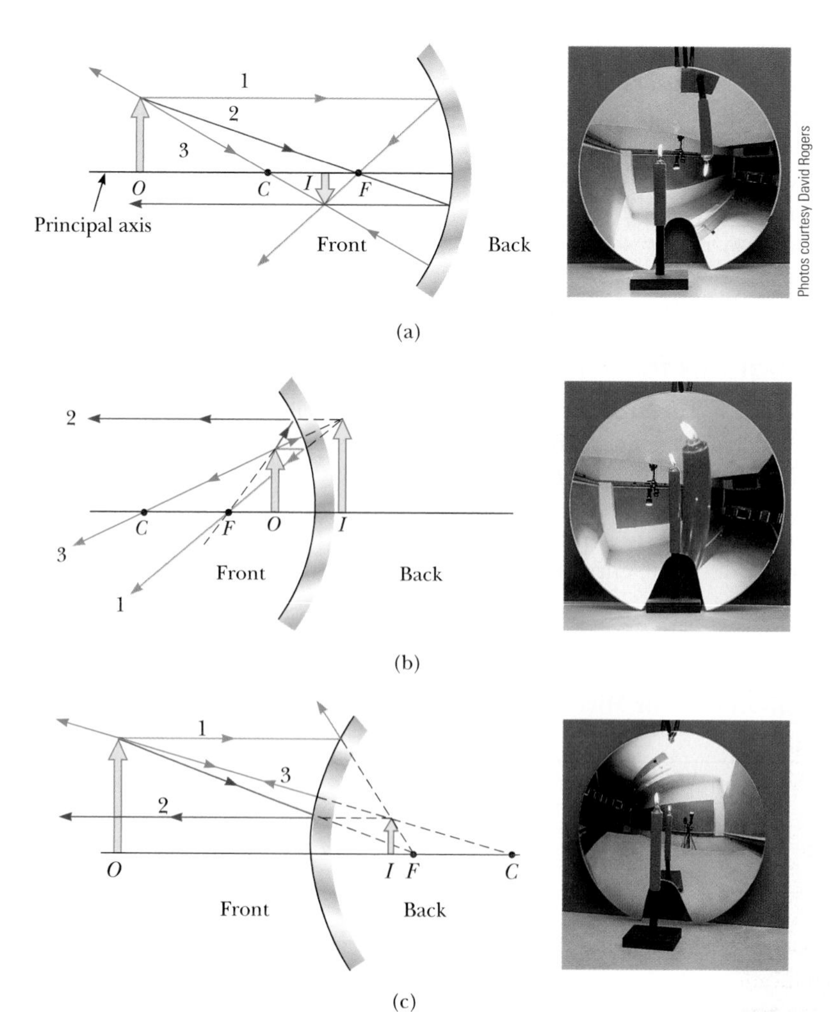

ACTIVE FIGURE 36.13

Ray diagrams for spherical mirrors along with corresponding photographs of the images of candles. (a) When the object is located so that the center of curvature lies between the object and a concave mirror surface, the image is real, inverted, and reduced in size. (b) When the object is located between the focal point and a concave mirror surface, the image is virtual, upright, and enlarged. (c) When the object is in front of a convex mirror, the image is virtual, upright, and reduced in size.

Sign in at www.thomsonedu.com and go to ThomsonNOW to move the objects and change the focal length of the mirrors to see the effect on the images.

For convex mirrors (see Active Fig. 36.13c), draw the following three rays:

- Ray 1 is drawn from the top of the object parallel to the principal axis and is reflected *away from* the focal point *F*.
- Ray 2 is drawn from the top of the object toward the focal point on the back side of the mirror and is reflected parallel to the principal axis.
- Ray 3 is drawn from the top of the object toward the center of curvature *C* on the back side of the mirror and is reflected back on itself.

In a convex mirror, the image of an object is always virtual, upright, and reduced in size as shown in Active Figure 36.13c. In this case, as the object distance decreases, the virtual image increases in size and moves away from the focal point toward the mirror as the object approaches the mirror. You should construct other diagrams to verify how image position varies with object position.

Quick Quiz 36.2 You wish to start a fire by reflecting sunlight from a mirror onto some paper under a pile of wood. Which would be the best choice for the type of mirror? (a) flat (b) concave (c) convex

Quick Quiz 36.3 Consider the image in the mirror in Figure 36.14. Based on the appearance of this image, would you conclude that (a) the mirror is concave and the image is real, (b) the mirror is concave and the image is virtual, (c) the mirror is convex and the image is real, or (d) the mirror is convex and the image is virtual?

NASA

Figure 36.14 (Quick Quiz 36.3) What type of mirror is shown here?

EXAMPLE 36.3 **The Image Formed by a Concave Mirror**

A spherical mirror has a focal length of +10.0 cm.

(A) Locate and describe the image for an object distance of 25.0 cm.

SOLUTION

Conceptualize Because the focal length of the mirror is positive, it is a concave mirror (see Table 36.1). We expect the possibilities of both real and virtual images.

Categorize Because the object distance in this part of the problem is larger than the focal length, we expect the image to be real. This situation is analogous to that in Active Figure 36.13a.

Analyze Find the image distance by using Equation 36.6:

$$\frac{1}{q} = \frac{1}{f} - \frac{1}{p}$$

$$\frac{1}{q} = \frac{1}{10.0 \text{ cm}} - \frac{1}{25.0 \text{ cm}}$$

$$q = 16.7 \text{ cm}$$

Find the magnification of the image from Equation 36.2:

$$M = -\frac{q}{p} = -\frac{16.7 \text{ cm}}{25.0 \text{ cm}} = -0.668$$

Finalize The absolute value of M is less than unity, so the image is smaller than the object, and the negative sign for M tells us that the image is inverted. Because q is positive, the image is located on the front side of the mirror and is real. Look into the bowl of a shiny spoon or stand far away from a shaving mirror to see this image.

(B) Locate and describe the image for an object distance of 10.0 cm.

SOLUTION

Categorize Because the object is at the focal point, we expect the image to be infinitely far away.

Analyze Find the image distance by using Equation 36.6:

$$\frac{1}{q} = \frac{1}{f} - \frac{1}{p}$$

$$\frac{1}{q} = \frac{1}{10.0 \text{ cm}} - \frac{1}{10.0 \text{ cm}}$$

$$q = \infty$$

Finalize This result means that rays originating from an object positioned at the focal point of a mirror are reflected so that the image is formed at an infinite distance from the mirror; that is, the rays travel parallel to one another after reflection. Such is the situation in a flashlight or an automobile headlight, where the bulb filament is placed at the focal point of a reflector, producing a parallel beam of light.

(C) Locate and describe the image for an object distance of 5.00 cm.

SOLUTION

Categorize Because the object distance is smaller than the focal length, we expect the image to be virtual. This situation is analogous to that in Active Figure 36.13b.

Analyze Find the image distance by using Equation 36.6:

$$\frac{1}{q} = \frac{1}{f} - \frac{1}{p}$$

$$\frac{1}{q} = \frac{1}{10.0 \text{ cm}} - \frac{1}{5.00 \text{ cm}}$$

$$q = -10.0 \text{ cm}$$

Find the magnification of the image from Equation 36.2:

$$M = -\frac{q}{p} = -\left(\frac{-10.0 \text{ cm}}{5.00 \text{ cm}}\right) = +2.00$$

Finalize The image is twice as large as the object, and the positive sign for M indicates that the image is upright (see Active Fig. 36.13b). The negative value of the image distance tells us that the image is virtual, as expected. Put your face close to a shaving mirror to see this type of image.

What If? Suppose you set up the candle and mirror apparatus illustrated in Active Figure 36.13a and described here in part (A). While adjusting the apparatus, you accidentally bump the candle and it begins to slide toward the mirror at velocity v_p. How fast does the image of the candle move?

Answer Solve the mirror equation, Equation 36.6, for q:

$$q = \frac{fp}{p - f}$$

Differentiate this equation with respect to time to find the velocity of the image:

$$(1) \quad v_q = \frac{dq}{dt} = \frac{d}{dt}\left(\frac{fp}{p - f}\right) = -\frac{f^2}{(p - f)^2}\frac{dp}{dt} = -\frac{f^2 v_p}{(p - f)^2}$$

Substitute numerical values from part (A):

$$v_q = -\frac{(10.0 \text{ cm})^2 v_p}{(25.0 \text{ cm} - 10.0 \text{ cm})^2} = -0.444 v_p$$

Therefore, the speed of the image is less than that of the object in this case.

We can see two interesting behaviors of the function for v_q in Equation (1). First, the velocity is negative regardless of the value of p or f. Therefore, if the object moves toward the mirror, the image moves toward the left in Active Figure 36.13 without regard for the side of the focal point at which the object is located or whether the mirror is concave or convex. Second, in the limit of $p \to 0$, the velocity v_q approaches $-v_p$. As the object moves very close to the mirror, the mirror looks like a plane mirror, the image is as far behind the mirror as the object is in front, and both the object and the image move with the same speed.

EXAMPLE 36.4 The Image Formed by a Convex Mirror

An automobile rearview mirror as shown in Figure 36.15 shows an image of a truck located 10.0 m from the mirror. The focal length of the mirror is -0.60 m.

(A) Find the position of the image of the truck.

Figure 36.15 (Example 36.4) An approaching truck is seen in a convex mirror on the right side of an automobile. Because the image is reduced in size, the truck appears to be farther away than it actually is. Notice also that the image of the truck is in focus, but the frame of the mirror is not, which demonstrates that the image is not at the same location as the mirror surface.

SOLUTION

Conceptualize This situation is depicted in Active Figure 36.13c.

Categorize Because the mirror is convex, we expect it to form an upright, reduced, virtual image for any object position.

Analyze Find the image distance by using Equation 36.6:

$$\frac{1}{q} = \frac{1}{f} - \frac{1}{p}$$

$$\frac{1}{q} = \frac{1}{-0.60\text{ m}} - \frac{1}{10.0\text{ m}}$$

$$q = -0.57\text{ m}$$

(B) Find the magnification of the image.

SOLUTION

Analyze Use Equation 36.2:

$$M = -\frac{q}{p} = -\left(\frac{-0.57\text{ m}}{10.0\text{ m}}\right) = +0.057$$

Finalize The negative value of q in part (A) indicates that the image is virtual, or behind the mirror, as shown in Active Figure 36.13c. The magnification in part (B) indicates that the image is much smaller than the truck and is upright because M is positive. Because of the image's small size, these mirrors carry the inscription, "Objects in this mirror are closer than they appear." Look into your rearview mirror or the back side of a shiny spoon to see an image of this type.

36.3 Images Formed by Refraction

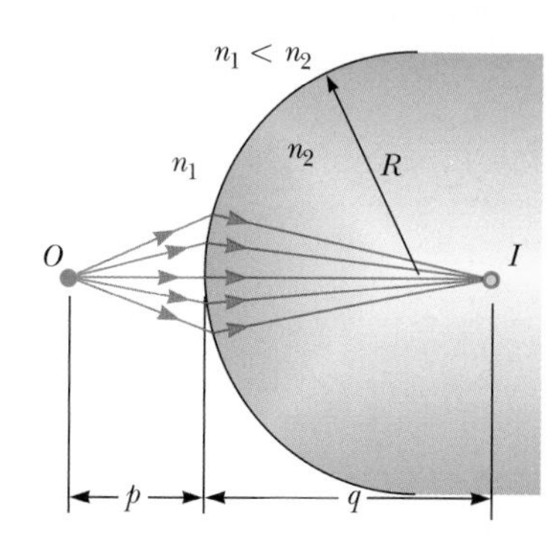

Figure 36.16 An image formed by refraction at a spherical surface. Rays making small angles with the principal axis diverge from a point object at O and are refracted through the image point I.

In this section, we describe how images are formed when light rays follow the wave under refraction model at the boundary between two transparent materials. Consider two transparent media having indices of refraction n_1 and n_2, where the boundary between the two media is a spherical surface of radius R (Fig. 36.16). We assume the object at O is in the medium for which the index of refraction is n_1. Let's consider the paraxial rays leaving O. As we shall see, all such rays are refracted at the spherical surface and focus at a single point I, the image point.

Figure 36.17 (page 1018) shows a single ray leaving point O and refracting to point I. Snell's law of refraction applied to this ray gives

$$n_1 \sin\theta_1 = n_2 \sin\theta_2$$

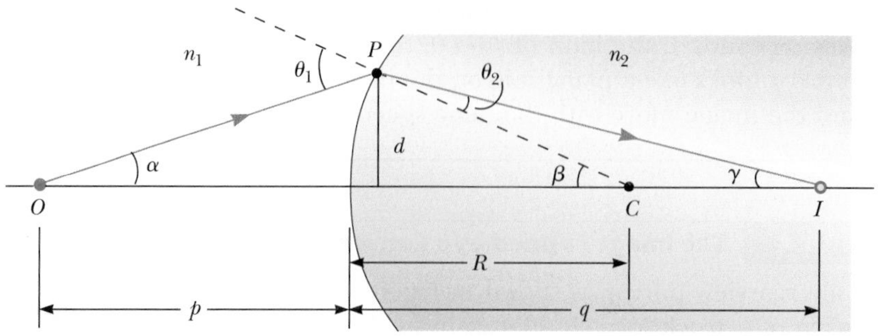

Figure 36.17 Geometry used to derive Equation 36.8, assuming that $n_1 < n_2$.

Because θ_1 and θ_2 are assumed to be small, we can use the small-angle approximation $\sin\theta \approx \theta$ (with angles in radians) and write Snell's law as

$$n_1\theta_1 = n_2\theta_2$$

We know that an exterior angle of any triangle equals the sum of the two opposite interior angles, so applying this rule to triangles *OPC* and *PIC* in Figure 36.17 gives

$$\theta_1 = \alpha + \beta$$

$$\beta = \theta_2 + \gamma$$

Combining all three expressions and eliminating θ_1 and θ_2 gives

$$n_1\alpha + n_2\gamma = (n_2 - n_1)\beta \tag{36.7}$$

Figure 36.17 shows three right triangles that have a common vertical leg of length d. For paraxial rays (unlike the relatively large-angle ray shown in Fig. 36.17), the horizontal legs of these triangles are approximately p for the triangle containing angle α, R for the triangle containing angle β, and q for the triangle containing angle γ. In the small-angle approximation, $\tan\theta \approx \theta$, so we can write the approximate relationships from these triangles as follows:

$$\tan\alpha \approx \alpha \approx \frac{d}{p} \qquad \tan\beta \approx \beta \approx \frac{d}{R} \qquad \tan\gamma \approx \gamma \approx \frac{d}{q}$$

Substituting these expressions into Equation 36.7 and dividing through by d gives

Relation between object and image distance for a refracting surface ▶

$$\frac{n_1}{p} + \frac{n_2}{q} = \frac{n_2 - n_1}{R} \tag{36.8}$$

For a fixed object distance p, the image distance q is independent of the angle the ray makes with the axis. This result tells us that all paraxial rays focus at the same point I.

As with mirrors, we must use a sign convention to apply Equation 36.8 to a variety of cases. We define the side of the surface in which light rays originate as the front side. The other side is called the back side. In contrast with mirrors, where real images are formed in front of the reflecting surface, real images are formed by refraction of light rays to the back of the surface. Because of the difference in location of real images, the refraction sign conventions for q and R are opposite the reflection sign conventions. For example, q and R are both positive in Figure 36.17. The sign conventions for spherical refracting surfaces are summarized in Table 36.2.

We derived Equation 36.8 from an assumption that $n_1 < n_2$ in Figure 36.17. This assumption is not necessary, however. Equation 36.8 is valid regardless of which index of refraction is greater.

TABLE 36.2

Sign Conventions for Refracting Surfaces

Quantity	Positive When . . .	Negative When . . .
Object location (p)	object is in front of surface (real object).	object is in back of surface (virtual object).
Image location (q)	image is in back of surface (real image).	image is in front of surface (virtual image).
Image height (h')	image is upright.	image is inverted.
Radius (R)	center of curvature is in back of surface.	center of curvature is in front of surface.

Flat Refracting Surfaces

If a refracting surface is flat, then R is infinite and Equation 36.8 reduces to

$$\frac{n_1}{p} = -\frac{n_2}{q}$$

$$q = -\frac{n_2}{n_1}p \qquad (36.9)$$

From this expression, we see that the sign of q is opposite that of p. Therefore, according to Table 36.2, **the image formed by a flat refracting surface is on the same side of the surface as the object** as illustrated in Active Figure 36.18 for the situation in which the object is in the medium of index n_1 and n_1 is greater than n_2. In this case, a virtual image is formed between the object and the surface. If n_1 is less than n_2, the rays on the back side diverge from one another at lesser angles than those in Active Figure 36.18. As a result, the virtual image is formed to the left of the object.

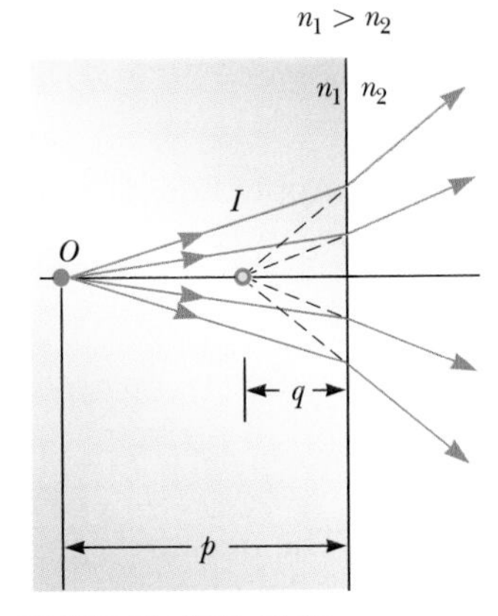

ACTIVE FIGURE 36.18

The image formed by a flat refracting surface is virtual and on the same side of the surface as the object. All rays are assumed to be paraxial.

Sign in at www.thomsonedu.com and go to ThomsonNOW to move the object and see the effect on the location of the image.

Quick Quiz 36.4 In Figure 36.16, what happens to the image point I as the object point O is moved to the right from very far away to very close to the refracting surface? (a) It is always to the right of the surface. (b) It is always to the left of the surface. (c) It starts off to the left, and at some position of O, I moves to the right of the surface. (d) It starts off to the right, and at some position of O, I moves to the left of the surface.

Quick Quiz 36.5 In Active Figure 36.18, what happens to the image point I as the object point O moves toward the right-hand surface of the material of index of refraction n_1? (a) It always remains between O and the surface, arriving at the surface just as O does. (b) It moves toward the surface more slowly than O so that eventually O passes I. (c) It approaches the surface and then moves to the right of the surface.

CONCEPTUAL EXAMPLE 36.5 **Let's Go Scuba Diving!**

Objects viewed under water with the naked eye appear blurred and out of focus. A scuba diver using a mask, however, has a clear view of underwater objects. Explain how that works, using the information that the indices of refraction of the cornea, water, and air are 1.376, 1.333, and 1.000 29, respectively.

SOLUTION

Because the cornea and water have almost identical indices of refraction, very little refraction occurs when a person under water views objects with the naked eye. In this case, light rays from an object focus behind the retina, resulting in a blurred image. When a mask is used, however, the air space between the eye and the mask surface provides the normal amount of refraction at the eye–air interface; consequently, the light from the object focuses on the retina.

EXAMPLE 36.6 Gaze into the Crystal Ball

A set of coins is embedded in a spherical plastic paperweight having a radius of 3.0 cm. The index of refraction of the plastic is $n_1 = 1.50$. One coin is located 2.0 cm from the edge of the sphere (Fig. 36.19). Find the position of the image of the coin.

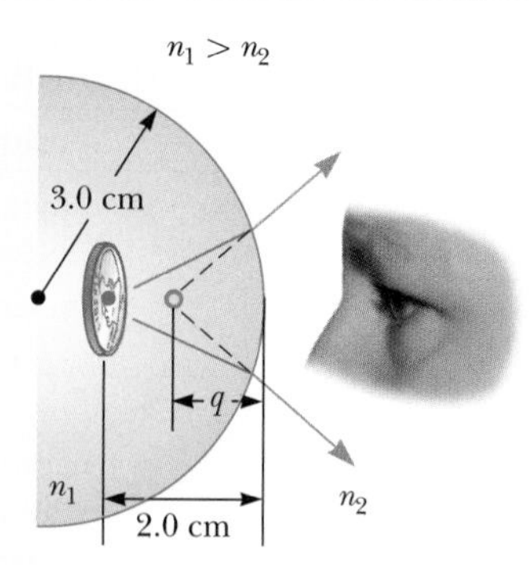

Figure 36.19 (Example 36.6) Light rays from a coin embedded in a plastic sphere form a virtual image between the surface of the object and the sphere surface. Because the object is inside the sphere, the front of the refracting surface is the *interior* of the sphere.

SOLUTION

Conceptualize Because $n_1 > n_2$, where $n_2 = 1.00$ is the index of refraction for air, the rays originating from the coin in Figure 36.19 are refracted away from the normal at the surface and diverge outward.

Categorize Because the light rays originate in one material and then pass through a curved surface into another material, this example involves an image formed by refraction.

Analyze Apply Equation 36.8, noting from Table 36.2 that R is negative:

$$\frac{n_2}{q} = \frac{n_2 - n_1}{R} - \frac{n_1}{p}$$

$$\frac{1}{q} = \frac{1.00 - 1.50}{-3.0 \text{ cm}} - \frac{1.50}{2.0 \text{ cm}}$$

$$q = -1.7 \text{ cm}$$

Finalize The negative sign for q indicates that the image is in front of the surface; in other words, it is in the same medium as the object as shown in Figure 36.19. Therefore, the image must be virtual. (See Table 36.2.) The coin appears to be closer to the paperweight surface than it actually is.

EXAMPLE 36.7 The One That Got Away

A small fish is swimming at a depth d below the surface of a pond (Fig. 36.20).

(A) What is the apparent depth of the fish as viewed from directly overhead?

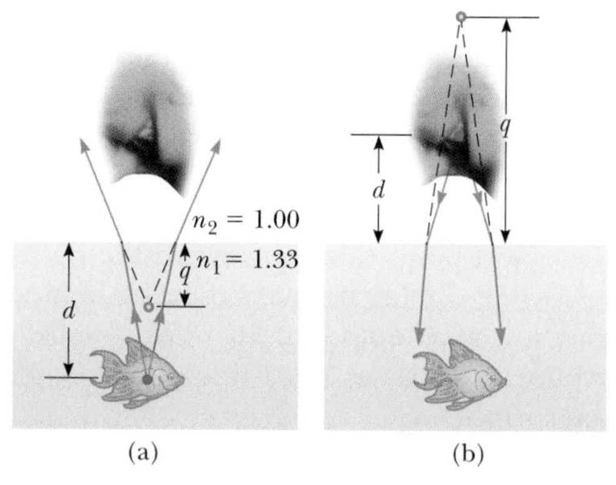

Figure 36.20 (Example 36.7) (a) The apparent depth q of the fish is less than the true depth d. All rays are assumed to be paraxial. (b) Your face appears to the fish to be higher above the surface than it is.

SOLUTION

Conceptualize Because $n_1 > n_2$, where $n_2 = 1.00$ is the index of refraction for air, the rays originating from the fish in Figure 36.20a are refracted away from the normal at the surface and diverge outward.

Categorize Because the refracting surface is flat, R is infinite. Hence, we can use Equation 36.9 to determine the location of the image with $p = d$.

Analyze Use the indices of refraction given in Figure 36.20a in Equation 36.9:

$$q = -\frac{n_2}{n_1}p = -\frac{1.00}{1.33}d = -0.752d$$

Finalize Because q is negative, the image is virtual as indicated by the dashed lines in Figure 36.20a. The apparent depth is approximately three-fourths the actual depth.

(B) If your face is a distance d above the water surface, at what apparent distance above the surface does the fish see your face?

SOLUTION

The light rays from your face are shown in Figure 36.20b.

Conceptualize Because the rays refract toward the normal, your face appears higher above the surface than it actually is.

Categorize Because the refracting surface is flat, R is infinite. Hence, we can use Equation 36.9 to determine the location of the image with $p = d$.

Analyze Use Equation 36.9 to find the image distance:

$$q = -\frac{n_2}{n_1}p = -\frac{1.33}{1.00}d = -1.33d$$

Finalize The negative sign for q indicates that the image is in the medium from which the light originated, which is the air above the water.

What If? What if you look more carefully at the fish and measure its apparent *height* from its upper fin to its lower fin? Is the apparent height h' of the fish different from the actual height h?

Answer Because all points on the fish appear to be fractionally closer to the observer, we expect the height to be smaller. Let the distance d in Figure 36.20a be measured to the top fin, and let the distance to the bottom fin be $d + h$. Then the images of the top and bottom of the fish are located at

$$q_{\text{top}} = -0.752d$$

$$q_{\text{bottom}} = -0.752(d + h)$$

The apparent height h' of the fish is

$$h' = q_{\text{top}} - q_{\text{bottom}} = -0.752d - [-0.752(d + h)] = 0.752h$$

Hence, the fish appears to be approximately three-fourths its actual height.

36.4 Thin Lenses

Lenses are commonly used to form images by refraction in optical instruments such as cameras, telescopes, and microscopes. Let's use what we just learned about images formed by refracting surfaces to help locate the image formed by a lens. Light passing through a lens experiences refraction at two surfaces. The development we shall follow is based on the notion that **the image formed by one refracting surface serves as the object for the second surface.** We shall analyze a thick lens first and then let the thickness of the lens be approximately zero.

Consider a lens having an index of refraction n and two spherical surfaces with radii of curvature R_1 and R_2 as in Figure 36.21 (page 1022). (Notice that R_1 is the radius of curvature of the lens surface the light from the object reaches first and R_2 is the radius of curvature of the other surface of the lens.) An object is placed at point O at a distance p_1 in front of surface 1.

Let's begin with the image formed by surface 1. Using Equation 36.8 and assuming $n_1 = 1$ because the lens is surrounded by air, we find that the image I_1 formed by surface 1 satisfies the equation

$$\frac{1}{p_1} + \frac{n}{q_1} = \frac{n-1}{R_1} \qquad \textbf{(36.10)}$$

where q_1 is the position of the image formed by surface 1. If the image formed by surface 1 is virtual (Fig. 36.21a), q_1 is negative; it is positive if the image is real (Fig. 36.21b).

Now let's apply Equation 36.8 to surface 2, taking $n_1 = n$ and $n_2 = 1$. (We make this switch in index because the light rays approaching surface 2 are *in the material*

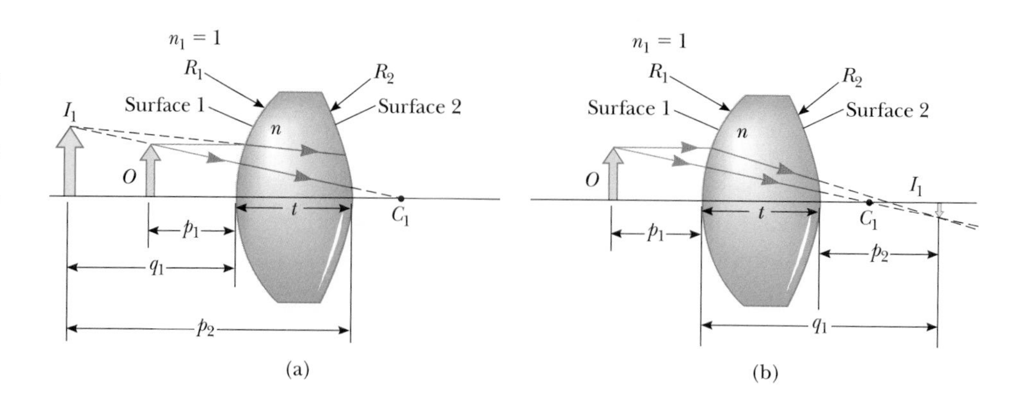

Figure 36.21 To locate the image formed by a lens, we use the virtual image at I_1 formed by surface 1 as the object for the image formed by surface 2. The point C_1 is the center of curvature of surface 1. (a) The image due to surface 1 is virtual, so I_1 is to the left of the surface. (b) The image due to surface 1 is real, so I_1 is to the right of the surface.

of the lens, and this material has index n.) Taking p_2 as the object distance for surface 2 and q_2 as the image distance gives

$$\frac{n}{p_2} + \frac{1}{q_2} = \frac{1 - n}{R_2} \tag{36.11}$$

We now introduce mathematically that the image formed by the first surface acts as the object for the second surface. If the image from surface 1 is virtual as in Figure 36.21a, we see that p_2, measured from surface 2, is related to q_1 as $p_2 = -q_1 + t$, where t is the thickness of the lens. Because q_1 is negative, p_2 is a positive number. Figure 36.21b shows the case of the image from surface 1 being real. In this situation, q_1 is positive and $p_2 = -q_1 + t$, where the image from surface 1 acts as a virtual object, so p_2 is negative. Regardless of the type of image from surface 1, the same equation describes the location of the object for surface 2 based on our sign convention. For a *thin* lens (one whose thickness is small compared with the radii of curvature), we can neglect t. In this approximation, $p_2 = -q_1$ for either type of image from surface 1. Hence, Equation 36.11 becomes

$$-\frac{n}{q_1} + \frac{1}{q_2} = \frac{1 - n}{R_2} \tag{36.12}$$

Adding Equations 36.10 and 36.12 gives

$$\frac{1}{p_1} + \frac{1}{q_2} = (n - 1)\left(\frac{1}{R_1} - \frac{1}{R_2}\right) \tag{36.13}$$

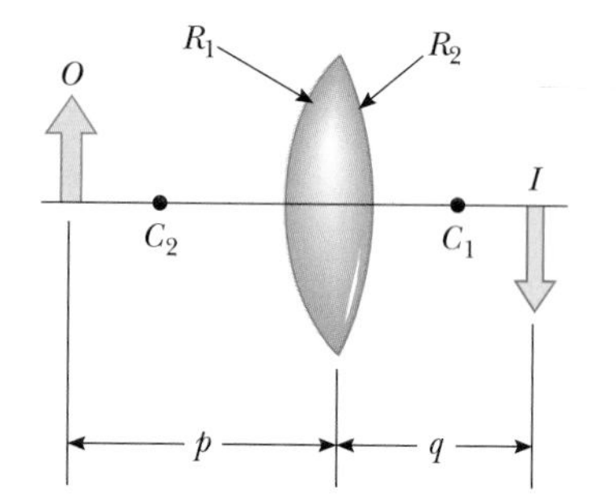

Figure 36.22 Simplified geometry for a thin lens.

For a thin lens, we can omit the subscripts on p_1 and q_2 in Equation 36.13 and call the object distance p and the image distance q, as in Figure 36.22. Hence, we can write Equation 36.13 as

$$\frac{1}{p} + \frac{1}{q} = (n - 1)\left(\frac{1}{R_1} - \frac{1}{R_2}\right) \tag{36.14}$$

This expression relates the image distance q of the image formed by a thin lens to the object distance p and to the lens properties (index of refraction and radii of curvature). It is valid only for paraxial rays and only when the lens thickness is much less than R_1 and R_2.

The **focal length** f of a thin lens is the image distance that corresponds to an infinite object distance, just as with mirrors. Letting p approach ∞ and q approach f in Equation 36.14, we see that the inverse of the focal length for a thin lens is

Lens-makers' equation ▶

$$\frac{1}{f} = (n - 1)\left(\frac{1}{R_1} - \frac{1}{R_2}\right) \tag{36.15}$$

This relationship is called the **lens-makers' equation** because it can be used to determine the values of R_1 and R_2 needed for a given index of refraction and a desired focal length f. Conversely, if the index of refraction and the radii of curvature of a lens are given, this equation can be used to find the focal length. If the

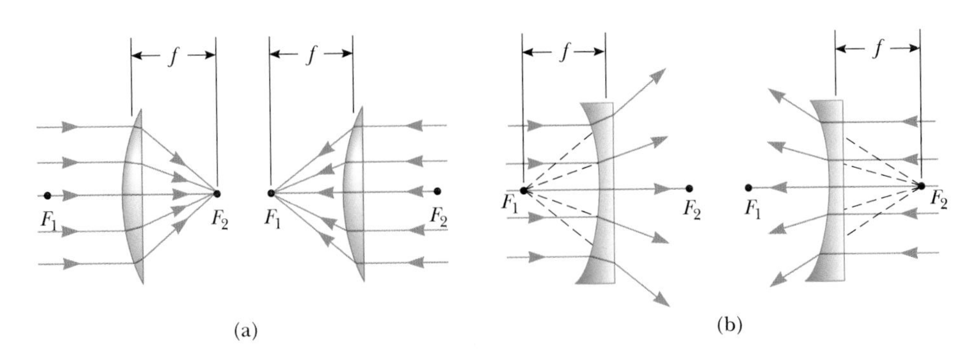

Figure 36.23 Parallel light rays pass through (a) a converging lens and (b) a diverging lens. The focal length is the same for light rays passing through a given lens in either direction. Both focal points F_1 and F_2 are the same distance from the lens.

lens is immersed in something other than air, this same equation can be used, with n interpreted as the *ratio* of the index of refraction of the lens material to that of the surrounding fluid.

Using Equation 36.15, we can write Equation 36.14 in a form identical to Equation 36.6 for mirrors:

$$\frac{1}{p} + \frac{1}{q} = \frac{1}{f} \quad \textbf{(36.16)}$$

This equation, called the **thin lens equation,** can be used to relate the image distance and object distance for a thin lens.

Because light can travel in either direction through a lens, each lens has two focal points, one for light rays passing through in one direction and one for rays passing through in the other direction. These two focal points are illustrated in Figure 36.23 for a plano-convex lens (a converging lens) and a plano-concave lens (a diverging lens).

Figure 36.24 is useful for obtaining the signs of p and q, and Table 36.3 gives the sign conventions for thin lenses. These sign conventions are the *same* as those for refracting surfaces (see Table 36.2).

Various lens shapes are shown in Figure 36.25. Notice that a converging lens is thicker at the center than at the edge, whereas a diverging lens is thinner at the center than at the edge.

PITFALL PREVENTION 36.5
A Lens Has Two Focal Points but Only One Focal Length

A lens has a focal point on each side, front and back. There is only one focal length, however; each of the two focal points is located the same distance from the lens (Fig. 36.23). As a result, the lens forms an image of an object at the same point if it is turned around. In practice, that might not happen because real lenses are not infinitesimally thin.

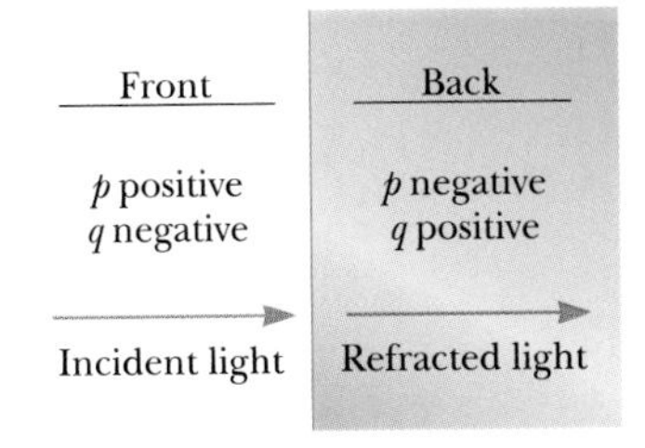

Figure 36.24 A diagram for obtaining the signs of p and q for a thin lens. (This diagram also applies to a refracting surface.)

Magnification of Images

Consider a thin lens through which light rays from an object pass. As with mirrors (Eq. 36.2), a geometric construction shows that the lateral magnification of the image is

$$M = \frac{h'}{h} = -\frac{q}{p} \quad \textbf{(36.17)}$$

From this expression, it follows that when M is positive, the image is upright and on the same side of the lens as the object. When M is negative, the image is inverted and on the side of the lens opposite the object.

TABLE 36.3
Sign Conventions for Thin Lenses

Quantity	Positive When . . .	Negative When . . .
Object location (p)	object is in front of lens (real object).	object is in back of lens (virtual object).
Image location (q)	image is in back of lens (real image).	image is in front of lens (virtual image).
Image height (h')	image is upright.	image is inverted.
R_1 and R_2	center of curvature is in back of lens.	center of curvature is in front of lens.
Focal length (f)	a converging lens.	a diverging lens.

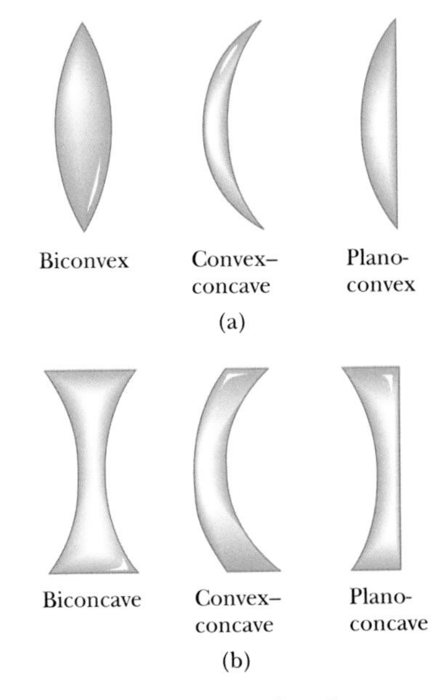

Figure 36.25 Various lens shapes. (a) Converging lenses have a positive focal length and are thickest at the middle. (b) Diverging lenses have a negative focal length and are thickest at the edges.

Ray Diagrams for Thin Lenses

Ray diagrams are convenient for locating the images formed by thin lenses or systems of lenses. They also help clarify our sign conventions. Active Figure 36.26 shows such diagrams for three single-lens situations.

To locate the image of a *converging* lens (Active Fig. 36.26a and b), the following three rays are drawn from the top of the object:

- Ray 1 is drawn parallel to the principal axis. After being refracted by the lens, this ray passes through the focal point on the back side of the lens.
- Ray 2 is drawn through the center of the lens and continues in a straight line.
- Ray 3 is drawn through the focal point on the front side of the lens (or as if coming from the focal point if $p < f$) and emerges from the lens parallel to the principal axis.

To locate the image of a *diverging* lens (Active Fig. 36.26c), the following three rays are drawn from the top of the object:

- Ray 1 is drawn parallel to the principal axis. After being refracted by the lens, this ray emerges directed away from the focal point on the front side of the lens.
- Ray 2 is drawn through the center of the lens and continues in a straight line.
- Ray 3 is drawn in the direction toward the focal point on the back side of the lens and emerges from the lens parallel to the principal axis.

For the converging lens in Active Figure 36.26a, where the object is to the left of the focal point ($p > f$), the image is real and inverted. When the object is between the focal point and the lens ($p < f$) as in Active Figure 36.26b, the image is virtual and upright. In that case, the lens acts as a magnifying glass, which we study in more detail in Section 36.8. For a diverging lens (Active Fig. 36.26c), the image is always virtual and upright, regardless of where the object is placed. These geometric constructions are reasonably accurate only if the distance between the rays and the principal axis is much less than the radii of the lens surfaces.

Notice that refraction occurs only at the surfaces of the lens. A certain lens design takes advantage of this behavior to produce the *Fresnel lens*, a powerful lens

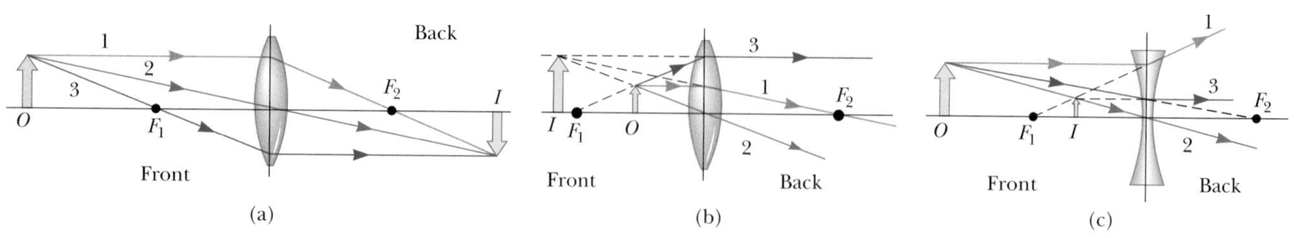

ACTIVE FIGURE 36.26

Ray diagrams for locating the image formed by a thin lens. (a) When the object is in front of and outside the focal point of a converging lens, the image is real, inverted, and on the back side of the lens. (b) When the object is between the focal point and a converging lens, the image is virtual, upright, larger than the object, and on the front side of the lens. (c) When an object is anywhere in front of a diverging lens, the image is virtual, upright, smaller than the object, and on the front side of the lens.

Sign in at www.thomsonedu.com and go to ThomsonNOW to move the objects and change the focal length of the lenses to see the effect on the images.

without great thickness. Because only the surface curvature is important in the refracting qualities of the lens, material in the middle of a Fresnel lens is removed as shown in the cross sections of lenses in Figure 36.27. Because the edges of the curved segments cause some distortion, Fresnel lenses are generally used only in situations in which image quality is less important than reduction of weight. A classroom overhead projector often uses a Fresnel lens; the circular edges between segments of the lens can be seen by looking closely at the light projected onto a screen.

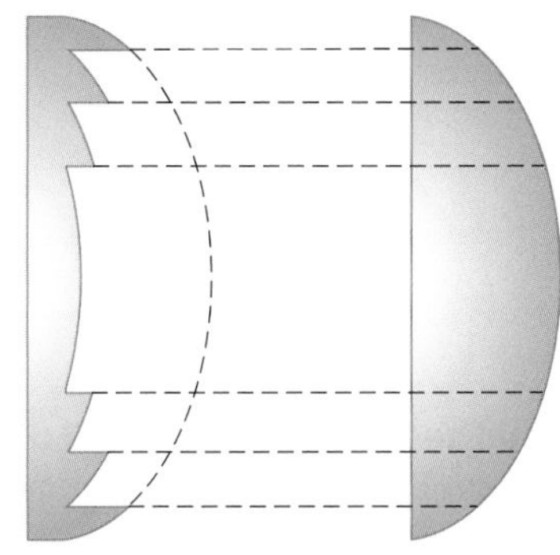

Figure 36.27 The Fresnel lens on the left has the same focal length as the thick lens on the right but is made of much less glass.

Quick Quiz 36.6 What is the focal length of a pane of window glass? (a) zero (b) infinity (c) the thickness of the glass (d) impossible to determine

---

EXAMPLE 36.8 Images Formed by a Converging Lens

A converging lens has a focal length of 10.0 cm.

(A) An object is placed 30.0 cm from the lens. Construct a ray diagram, find the image distance, and describe the image.

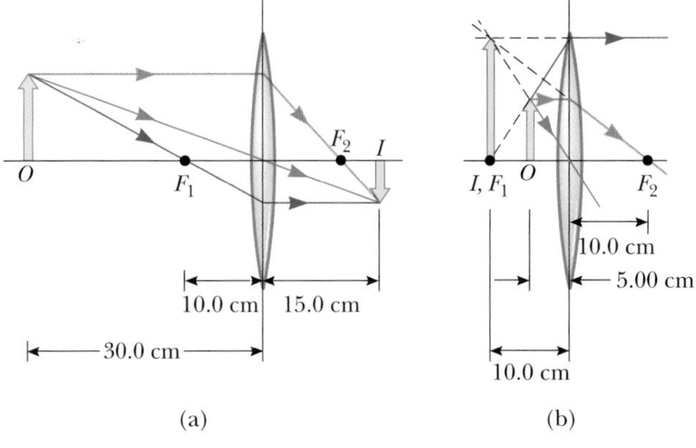

Figure 36.28 (Example 36.8) An image is formed by a converging lens. (a) The object is farther from the lens than the focal point. (b) The object is closer to the lens than the focal point.

SOLUTION

Conceptualize Because the lens is converging, the focal length is positive (see Table 36.3). We expect the possibilities of both real and virtual images.

Categorize Because the object distance is larger than the focal length, we expect the image to be real. The ray diagram for this situation is shown in Figure 36.28a.

Analyze Find the image distance by using Equation 36.16:

$$\frac{1}{q} = \frac{1}{f} - \frac{1}{p}$$

$$\frac{1}{q} = \frac{1}{10.0 \text{ cm}} - \frac{1}{30.0 \text{ cm}}$$

$$q = +15.0 \text{ cm}$$

Find the magnification of the image from Equation 36.17:

$$M = -\frac{q}{p} = -\frac{15.0 \text{ cm}}{30.0 \text{ cm}} = -0.500$$

Finalize The positive sign for the image distance tells us that the image is indeed real and on the back side of the lens. The magnification of the image tells us that the image is reduced in height by one half, and the negative sign for M tells us that the image is inverted.

(B) An object is placed 10.0 cm from the lens. Find the image distance and describe the image.

SOLUTION

Categorize Because the object is at the focal point, we expect the image to be infinitely far away.

Analyze Find the image distance by using Equation 36.16:

$$\frac{1}{q} = \frac{1}{f} - \frac{1}{p}$$

$$\frac{1}{q} = \frac{1}{10.0 \text{ cm}} - \frac{1}{10.0 \text{ cm}}$$

$$q = \infty$$

Finalize This result means that rays originating from an object positioned at the focal point of a lens are refracted so that the image is formed at an infinite distance from the lens; that is, the rays travel parallel to one another after refraction.

(C) An object is placed 5.00 cm from the lens. Construct a ray diagram, find the image distance, and describe the image.

SOLUTION

Categorize Because the object distance is smaller than the focal length, we expect the image to be virtual. The ray diagram for this situation is shown in Figure 36.28b.

Analyze Find the image distance by using Equation 36.16:

$$\frac{1}{q} = \frac{1}{f} - \frac{1}{p}$$

$$\frac{1}{q} = \frac{1}{10.0 \text{ cm}} - \frac{1}{5.00 \text{ cm}}$$

$$q = -10.0 \text{ cm}$$

Find the magnification of the image from Equation 36.17:

$$M = -\frac{q}{p} = -\left(\frac{-10.0 \text{ cm}}{5.00 \text{ cm}}\right) = +2.00$$

Finalize The negative image distance tells us that the image is virtual and formed on the side of the lens from which the light is incident, the front side. The image is enlarged, and the positive sign for M tells us that the image is upright.

What If? What if the object moves right up to the lens surface, so that $p \rightarrow 0$? Where is the image?

Answer In this case, because $p \ll R$, where R is either of the radii of the surfaces of the lens, the curvature of the lens can be ignored. The lens should appear to have the same effect as a flat piece of material, which suggests that the image is just on the front side of the lens, at $q = 0$. This conclusion can be verified mathematically by rearranging the thin lens equation:

$$\frac{1}{q} = \frac{1}{f} - \frac{1}{p}$$

If we let $p \rightarrow 0$, the second term on the right becomes very large compared with the first and we can neglect $1/f$. The equation becomes

$$\frac{1}{q} = -\frac{1}{p} \quad \rightarrow \quad q = -p = 0$$

Therefore, q is on the front side of the lens (because it has the opposite sign as p) and right at the lens surface.

EXAMPLE 36.9 Images Formed by a Diverging Lens

A diverging lens has a focal length of 10.0 cm.

(A) An object is placed 30.0 cm from the lens. Construct a ray diagram, find the image distance, and describe the image.

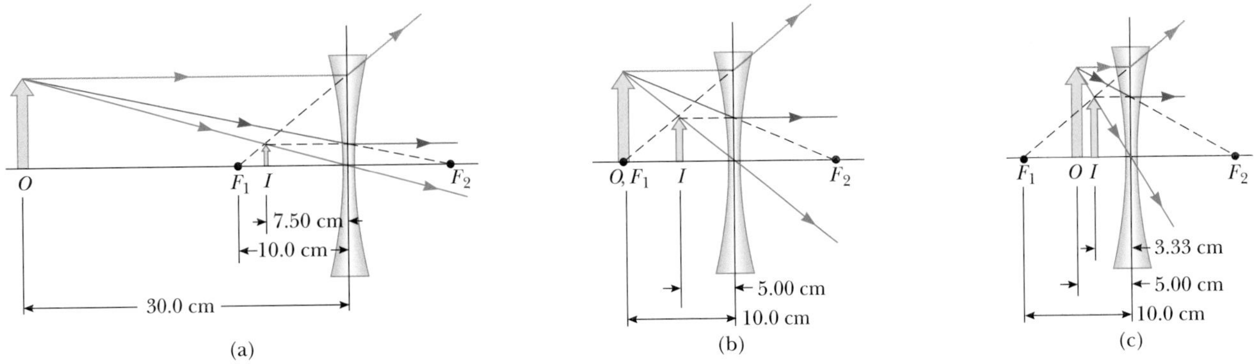

Figure 36.29 (Example 36.9) An image is formed by a diverging lens. (a) The object is farther from the lens than the focal point. (b) The object is at the focal point. (c) The object is closer to the lens than the focal point.

SOLUTION

Conceptualize Because the lens is diverging, the focal length is negative (see Table 36.3). The ray diagram for this situation is shown in Figure 36.29a.

Categorize Because the lens is diverging, we expect it to form an upright, reduced, virtual image for any object position.

Analyze Find the image distance by using Equation 36.16:

$$\frac{1}{q} = \frac{1}{f} - \frac{1}{p}$$

$$\frac{1}{q} = \frac{1}{-10.0 \text{ cm}} - \frac{1}{30.0 \text{ cm}}$$

$$q = -7.50 \text{ cm}$$

Find the magnification of the image from Equation 36.17:

$$M = -\frac{q}{p} = -\left(\frac{-7.50 \text{ cm}}{30.0 \text{ cm}}\right) = +0.250$$

Finalize This result confirms that the image is virtual, smaller than the object, and upright. Look through the diverging lens in a door peephole to see this type of image.

(B) An object is placed 10.0 cm from the lens. Construct a ray diagram, find the image distance, and describe the image.

SOLUTION

The ray diagram for this situation is shown in Figure 36.29b.

Analyze Find the image distance by using Equation 36.16:

$$\frac{1}{q} = \frac{1}{f} - \frac{1}{p}$$

$$\frac{1}{q} = \frac{1}{-10.0 \text{ cm}} - \frac{1}{10.0 \text{ cm}}$$

$$q = -5.00 \text{ cm}$$

Find the magnification of the image from Equation 36.17:

$$M = -\frac{q}{p} = -\left(\frac{-5.00 \text{ cm}}{10.0 \text{ cm}}\right) = +0.500$$

Finalize Notice the difference between this situation and that for a converging lens. For a diverging lens, an object at the focal point does not produce an image infinitely far away.

(C) An object is placed 5.00 cm from the lens. Construct a ray diagram, find the image distance, and describe the image.

SOLUTION

The ray diagram for this situation is shown in Figure 36.29c.

Analyze Find the image distance by using Equation 36.16:

$$\frac{1}{q} = \frac{1}{f} - \frac{1}{p}$$

$$\frac{1}{q} = \frac{1}{-10.0 \text{ cm}} - \frac{1}{5.00 \text{ cm}}$$

$$q = -3.33 \text{ cm}$$

Find the magnification of the image from Equation 36.17:

$$M = -\left(\frac{-3.33 \text{ cm}}{5.00 \text{ cm}}\right) = +0.667$$

Finalize For all three object positions, the image position is negative and the magnification is a positive number smaller than 1, which confirms that the image is virtual, smaller than the object, and upright.

Combination of Thin Lenses

If two thin lenses are used to form an image, the system can be treated in the following manner. First, the image formed by the first lens is located as if the second lens were not present. Then a ray diagram is drawn for the second lens, with the image formed by the first lens now serving as the object for the second lens. The second image formed is the final image of the system. If the image formed by the first lens lies on the back side of the second lens, that image is treated as a **virtual object** for the second lens (that is, in the thin lens equation, p is negative). The same procedure can be extended to a system of three or more lenses. Because the magnification due to the second lens is performed on the magnified image due to the first lens, the **overall magnification of the image due to the combination of lenses is the product of the individual magnifications:**

$$M = M_1 M_2 \qquad \textbf{(36.18)}$$

This equation can be used for combinations of any optical elements such as a lens and a mirror. For more than two optical elements, the magnifications due to all elements are multiplied together.

Let's consider the special case of a system of two lenses of focal lengths f_1 and f_2 in contact with each other. If $p_1 = p$ is the object distance for the combination, application of the thin lens equation (Eq. 36.16) to the first lens gives

$$\frac{1}{p} + \frac{1}{q_1} = \frac{1}{f_1}$$

where q_1 is the image distance for the first lens. Treating this image as the object for the second lens, we see that the object distance for the second lens must be $p_2 = -q_1$. (The distances are the same because the lenses are in contact and assumed to be infinitesimally thin. The object distance is negative because the object is virtual.) Therefore, for the second lens,

$$\frac{1}{p_2} + \frac{1}{q_2} = \frac{1}{f_2} \quad \rightarrow \quad -\frac{1}{q_1} + \frac{1}{q} = \frac{1}{f_2}$$

where $q = q_2$ is the final image distance from the second lens, which is the image distance for the combination. Adding the equations for the two lenses eliminates q_1 and gives

$$\frac{1}{p} + \frac{1}{q} = \frac{1}{f_1} + \frac{1}{f_2}$$

If the combination is replaced with a single lens that forms an image at the same location, its focal length must be related to the individual focal lengths by the expression

$$\frac{1}{f} = \frac{1}{f_1} + \frac{1}{f_2} \qquad (36.19)$$

◀ Focal length for a combination of two thin lenses in contact

Therefore, **two thin lenses in contact with each other are equivalent to a single thin lens having a focal length given by Equation 36.19.**

EXAMPLE 36.10 Where Is the Final Image?

Two thin converging lenses of focal lengths $f_1 = 10.0$ cm and $f_2 = 20.0$ cm are separated by 20.0 cm as illustrated in Figure 36.30. An object is placed 30.0 cm to the left of lens 1. Find the position and the magnification of the final image.

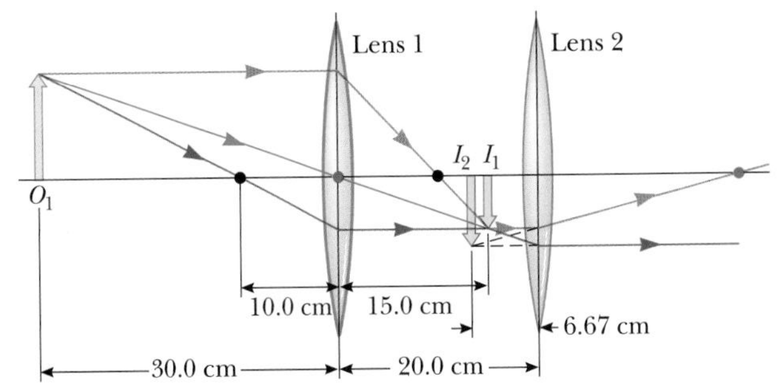

Figure 36.30 (Example 36.10) A combination of two converging lenses. The ray diagram shows the location of the final image due to the combination of lenses. The black dots are the focal points of lens 1 and the red dots are the focal points of lens 2.

SOLUTION

Conceptualize Imagine light rays passing through the first lens and forming a real image (because $p > f$) in the absence of a second lens. Figure 36.30 shows these light rays forming the inverted image I_1. Once the light rays converge to the image point, they do not stop. They continue through the image point and interact with the second lens. The rays leaving the image point behave in the same way as the rays leaving an object. Therefore, the image of the first lens serves as the object of the second lens.

Categorize We categorize this problem as one in which the thin lens equation is applied in a stepwise fashion to the two lenses.

Analyze Find the location of the image formed by lens 1 from the thin lens equation:

$$\frac{1}{q_1} = \frac{1}{f} - \frac{1}{p_1}$$

$$\frac{1}{q_1} = \frac{1}{10.0 \text{ cm}} - \frac{1}{30.0 \text{ cm}}$$

$$q_1 = +15.0 \text{ cm}$$

Find the magnification of the image from Equation 36.17:

$$M_1 = -\frac{q_1}{p_1} = -\frac{15.0 \text{ cm}}{30.0 \text{ cm}} = -0.500$$

The image formed by this lens acts as the object for the second lens. Therefore, the object distance for the second lens is 20.0 cm − 15.0 cm = 5.00 cm.

Find the location of the image formed by lens 2 from the thin lens equation:

$$\frac{1}{q_2} = \frac{1}{20.0 \text{ cm}} - \frac{1}{5.00 \text{ cm}}$$

$$q_2 = -6.67 \text{ cm}$$

Find the magnification of the image from Equation 36.17:

$$M_2 = -\frac{q_2}{p_2} = -\frac{(-6.67 \text{ cm})}{5.00 \text{ cm}} = +1.33$$

Find the overall magnification of the system from Equation 36.18:

$$M = M_1 M_2 = (-0.500)(1.33) = -0.667$$

Finalize The negative sign on the overall magnification indicates that the final image is inverted with respect to the initial object. Because the absolute value of the magnification is less than 1, the final image is smaller than the object. Because q_2 is negative, the final image is on the front, or left, side of lens 2. These conclusions are consistent with the ray diagram in Figure 36.30.

What If? Suppose you want to create an upright image with this system of two lenses. How must the second lens be moved?

Answer Because the object is farther from the first lens than the focal length of that lens, the first image is inverted. Consequently, the second lens must invert the image once again so that the final image is upright. An inverted image is only formed by a converging lens if the object is outside the focal point. Therefore, the image formed by the first lens must be to the left of the focal point of the second lens in Figure 36.30. To make that happen, you must move the second lens at least as far away from the first lens as the sum $q_1 + f_2 = 15.0 \text{ cm} + 20.0 \text{ cm} = 35.0 \text{ cm}$.

36.5 Lens Aberrations

Our analysis of mirrors and lenses assumes rays make small angles with the principal axis and the lenses are thin. In this simple model, all rays leaving a point source focus at a single point, producing a sharp image. Clearly, that is not always true. When the approximations used in this analysis do not hold, imperfect images are formed.

A precise analysis of image formation requires tracing each ray, using Snell's law at each refracting surface and the law of reflection at each reflecting surface. This procedure shows that the rays from a point object do not focus at a single point, with the result that the image is blurred. The departures of actual images from the ideal predicted by our simplified model are called **aberrations.**

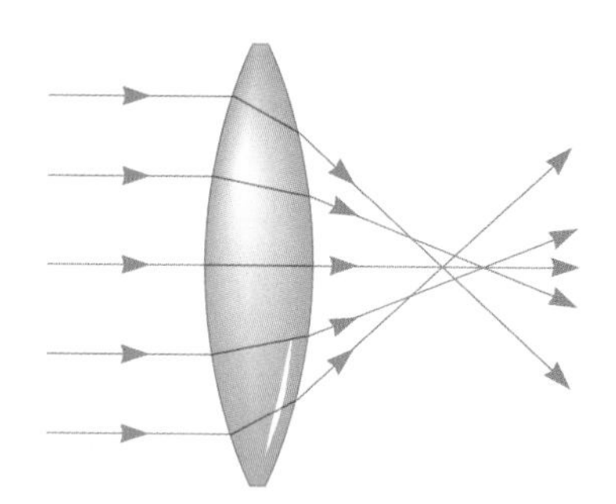

Figure 36.31 Spherical aberration caused by a converging lens. Does a diverging lens cause spherical aberration?

Spherical Aberration

Spherical aberration occurs because the focal points of rays far from the principal axis of a spherical lens (or mirror) are different from the focal points of rays of the same wavelength passing near the axis. Figure 36.31 illustrates spherical aberration for parallel rays passing through a converging lens. Rays passing through points near the center of the lens are imaged farther from the lens than rays passing through points near the edges. Figure 36.8 earlier in the chapter showed a similar situation for a spherical mirror.

Many cameras have an adjustable aperture to control light intensity and reduce spherical aberration. (An aperture is an opening that controls the amount of light passing through the lens.) Sharper images are produced as the aperture size is reduced; with a small aperture, only the central portion of the lens is exposed to the light and therefore a greater percentage of the rays are paraxial. At the same time, however, less light passes through the lens. To compensate for this lower light intensity, a longer exposure time is used.

In the case of mirrors, spherical aberration can be minimized through the use of a parabolic reflecting surface rather than a spherical surface. Parabolic surfaces are not used often, however, because those with high-quality optics are very expensive to make. Parallel light rays incident on a parabolic surface focus at a common point, regardless of their distance from the principal axis. Parabolic reflecting surfaces are used in many astronomical telescopes to enhance image quality.

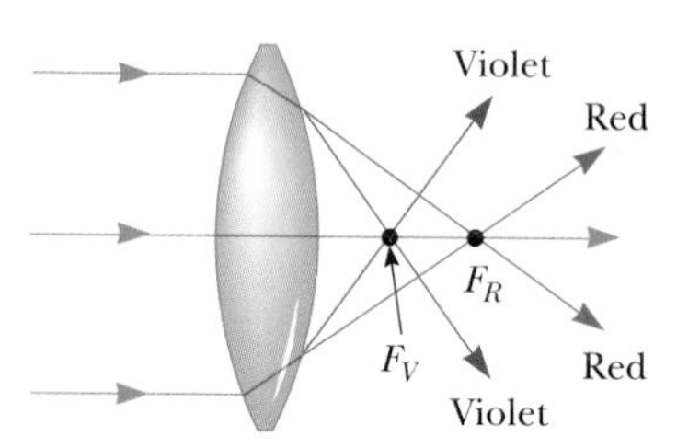

Figure 36.32 Chromatic aberration caused by a converging lens. Rays of different wavelengths focus at different points.

Chromatic Aberration

In Chapter 35, we described dispersion, whereby a material's index of refraction varies with wavelength. Because of this phenomenon, violet rays are refracted more than red rays when white light passes through a lens (Fig. 36.32). The figure shows that the focal length of a lens is greater for red light than for violet light. Other wavelengths (not shown in Fig. 36.32) have focal points intermediate between those of red and violet, which causes a blurred image and is called **chromatic aberration.**

Chromatic aberration for a diverging lens also results in a shorter focal length for violet light than for red light, but on the front side of the lens. Chromatic aberration can be greatly reduced by combining a converging lens made of one type of glass and a diverging lens made of another type of glass.

36.6 The Camera

The photographic **camera** is a simple optical instrument whose essential features are shown in Figure 36.33. It consists of a lighttight chamber, a converging lens that produces a real image, and a film behind the lens to receive the image.

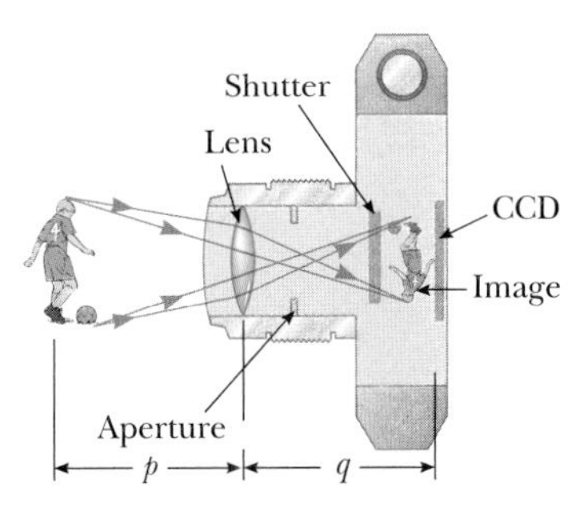

Figure 36.33 Cross-sectional view of a simple digital camera. The CCD is the light-sensitive component of the camera. In a nondigital camera, the light from the lens falls onto photographic film. In reality, $p \gg q$.

Digital cameras are similar to film cameras except that the light does not form an image on photographic film. The image in a digital camera is formed on a *charge-coupled device* (CCD), which digitizes the image, turning it into binary code as we discussed for sound in Section 17.5. (A CCD is described in Section 40.2.) The digital information is then stored on a memory chip for playback on the camera's display screen, or it can be downloaded to a computer. In the discussion that follows, we assume the camera is digital.

A camera is focused by varying the distance between the lens and the CCD. For proper focusing—which is necessary for the formation of sharp images—the lens-to-CCD distance depends on the object distance as well as the focal length of the lens.

The shutter, positioned behind the lens, is a mechanical device that is opened for selected time intervals, called *exposure times.* You can photograph moving objects by using short exposure times or photograph dark scenes (with low light levels) by using long exposure times. If this adjustment were not available, it would be impossible to take stop-action photographs. For example, a rapidly moving vehicle could move enough in the time interval during which the shutter is open to produce a blurred image. Another major cause of blurred images is the movement of the camera while the shutter is open. To prevent such movement, either short exposure times or a tripod should be used, even for stationary objects. Typical shutter speeds (that is, exposure times) are $\frac{1}{30}$ s, $\frac{1}{60}$ s, $\frac{1}{125}$ s, and $\frac{1}{250}$ s. In practice, stationary objects are normally shot with an intermediate shutter speed of $\frac{1}{60}$ s.

The intensity I of the light reaching the CCD is proportional to the area of the lens. Because this area is proportional to the square of the diameter D, it follows that I is also proportional to D^2. Light intensity is a measure of the rate at which energy is received by the CCD per unit area of the image. Because the area of the image is proportional to q^2 and $q \approx f$ (when $p \gg f$, so p can be approximated as infinite), we conclude that the intensity is also proportional to $1/f^2$ and therefore that $I \propto D^2/f^2$.

The ratio f/D is called the ***f*-number** of a lens:

$$f\text{-number} \equiv \frac{f}{D} \tag{36.20}$$

Hence, the intensity of light incident on the CCD varies according to the following proportionality:

$$I \propto \frac{1}{(f/D)^2} \propto \frac{1}{(f\text{-number})^2} \tag{36.21}$$

The *f*-number is often given as a description of the lens's "speed." The lower the *f*-number, the wider the aperture and the higher the rate at which energy from the light exposes the CCD; therefore, a lens with a low *f*-number is a "fast" lens. The conventional notation for an *f*-number is "*f*/" followed by the actual number. For example, "$f/4$" means an *f*-number of 4; it *does not* mean to divide f by 4! Extremely fast lenses, which have *f*-numbers as low as approximately $f/1.2$, are expensive because it is very difficult to keep aberrations acceptably small with light rays passing through a large area of the lens. Camera lens systems (that is, combinations of lenses with adjustable apertures) are often marked with multiple *f*-numbers, usually $f/2.8$, $f/4$, $f/5.6$, $f/8$, $f/11$, and $f/16$. Any one of these settings can be selected by adjusting the aperture, which changes the value of D. Increasing the setting from one *f*-number to the next higher value (for example, from $f/2.8$ to $f/4$) decreases the area of the aperture by a factor of 2. The lowest *f*-number setting on a camera lens corresponds to a wide-open aperture and the use of the maximum possible lens area.

Simple cameras usually have a fixed focal length and a fixed aperture size, with an *f*-number of about $f/11$. This high value for the *f*-number allows for a large **depth of field,** meaning that objects at a wide range of distances from the lens form reasonably sharp images on the CCD. In other words, the camera does not have to be focused.

Quick Quiz 36.7 A camera can be modeled as a simple converging lens that focuses an image on the CCD, acting as the screen. A camera is initially focused on a distant object. To focus the image of an object close to the camera, must the lens be (a) moved away from the CCD, (b) left where it is, or (c) moved toward the CCD?

EXAMPLE 36.11 Finding the Correct Exposure Time

The lens of a digital camera has a focal length of 55 mm and a speed (an *f*-number) of $f/1.8$. The correct exposure time for this speed under certain conditions is known to be $\frac{1}{500}$ s.

(A) Determine the diameter of the lens.

SOLUTION

Conceptualize Remember that the *f*-number for a lens relates its focal length to its diameter.

Categorize We evaluate results using equations developed in this section, so we categorize this example as a substitution problem.

Solve Equation 36.20 for D and substitute numerical values:

$$D = \frac{f}{f\text{-number}} = \frac{55 \text{ mm}}{1.8} = \boxed{31 \text{ mm}}$$

(B) Calculate the correct exposure time if the *f*-number is changed to $f/4$ under the same lighting conditions.

SOLUTION

The total light energy hitting the CCD is proportional to the product of the intensity and the exposure time. If I is the light intensity reaching the CCD, the energy per unit area received by the CCD in a time interval Δt is proportional to $I\,\Delta t$. Comparing the two situations, we require that $I_1\,\Delta t_1 = I_2\,\Delta t_2$, where Δt_1 is the correct exposure time for $f/1.8$ and Δt_2 is the correct exposure time for $f/4$.

Use this result and substitute for I from Equation 36.21:

$$I_1\,\Delta t_1 = I_2\,\Delta t_2 \rightarrow \frac{\Delta t_1}{(f_1\text{-number})^2} = \frac{\Delta t_2}{(f_2\text{-number})^2}$$

Solve for Δt_2 and substitute numerical values:

$$\Delta t_2 = \left(\frac{f_2\text{-number}}{f_1\text{-number}}\right)^2 \Delta t_1 = \left(\frac{4}{1.8}\right)^2 \left(\tfrac{1}{500}\text{ s}\right) \approx \boxed{\tfrac{1}{100}\text{ s}}$$

As the aperture size is reduced, the exposure time must increase.

36.7 The Eye

Like a camera, a normal eye focuses light and produces a sharp image. The mechanisms by which the eye controls the amount of light admitted and adjusts to produce correctly focused images, however, are far more complex, intricate, and effective than those in even the most sophisticated camera. In all respects, the eye is a physiological wonder.

Figure 36.34 shows the basic parts of the human eye. Light entering the eye passes through a transparent structure called the *cornea* (Fig. 36.35), behind which are a clear liquid (the *aqueous humor*), a variable aperture (the *pupil,* which is an opening in the *iris*), and the *crystalline lens.* Most of the refraction occurs at the outer surface of the eye, where the cornea is covered with a film of tears. Relatively little refraction occurs in the crystalline lens because the aqueous humor in contact with the lens has an average index of refraction close to that of the lens. The iris, which is the colored portion of the eye, is a muscular diaphragm that controls pupil size. The iris regulates the amount of light entering the eye by dilating, or opening, the pupil in low-light conditions and contracting, or closing, the pupil in high-light conditions. The *f*-number range of the human eye is approximately $f/2.8$ to $f/16$.

The cornea–lens system focuses light onto the back surface of the eye, the *retina,* which consists of millions of sensitive receptors called *rods* and *cones.* When stimulated by light, these receptors send impulses via the optic nerve to the brain, where an image is perceived. By this process, a distinct image of an object is observed when the image falls on the retina.

The eye focuses on an object by varying the shape of the pliable crystalline lens through a process called **accommodation.** The lens adjustments take place so swiftly that we are not even aware of the change. Accommodation is limited in that objects very close to the eye produce blurred images. The **near point** is the closest distance for which the lens can accommodate to focus light on the retina. This distance usually increases with age and has an average value of 25 cm. At age 10, the near point of the eye is typically approximately 18 cm. It increases to approximately 25 cm at age 20, to 50 cm at age 40, and to 500 cm or greater at age 60. The **far point** of the eye represents the greatest distance for which the lens of the relaxed eye can focus light on the retina. A person with normal vision can see very distant objects and therefore has a far point that can be approximated as infinity.

Recall that the light leaving the mirror in Figure 36.7 becomes white where it comes together but then diverges into separate colors again. Because nothing but air exists at the point where the rays cross (and hence nothing exists to cause the colors to separate again), seeing white light as a result of a combination of colors must be a visual illusion. In fact, that is the case. Only three types of color-sensitive

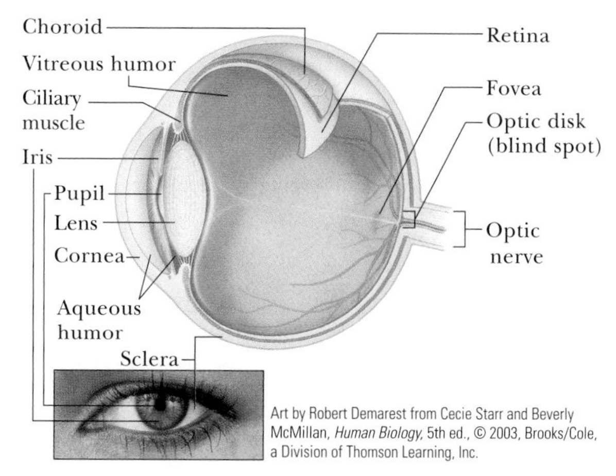

Figure 36.34 Important parts of the eye.

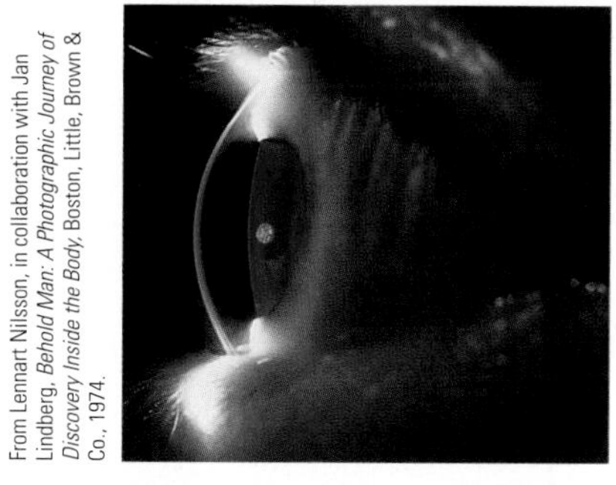

Figure 36.35 Close-up photograph of the cornea of the human eye.

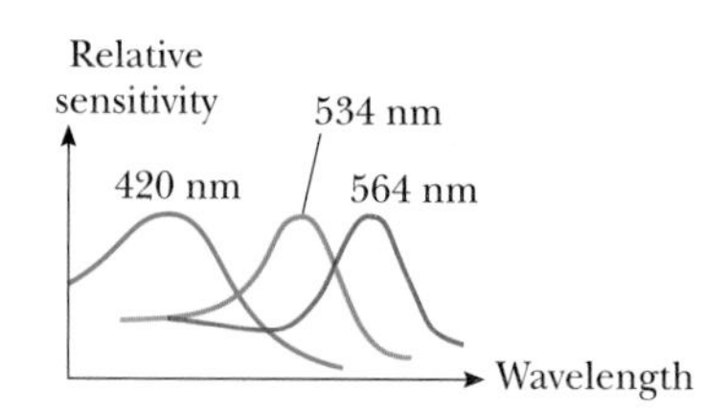

Figure 36.36 Approximate color sensitivity of the three types of cones in the retina.

cells are present in the retina. They are called red, green, and blue cones because of the peaks of the color ranges to which they respond (Fig. 36.36). If the red and green cones are stimulated simultaneously (as would be the case if yellow light were shining on them), the brain interprets what is seen as yellow. If all three types of cones are stimulated by the separate colors red, blue, and green as in Figure 36.7, white light is seen. If all three types of cones are stimulated by light that contains *all* colors, such as sunlight, again white light is seen.

Color televisions take advantage of this visual illusion by having only red, green, and blue dots on the screen. With specific combinations of brightness in these three primary colors, our eyes can be made to see any color in the rainbow. Therefore, the yellow lemon you see in a television commercial is not actually yellow, it is red and green! The paper on which this page is printed is made of tiny, matted, translucent fibers that scatter light in all directions, and the resultant mixture of colors appears white to the eye. Snow, clouds, and white hair are not actually white. In fact, there is no such thing as a white pigment. The appearance of these things is a consequence of the scattering of light containing all colors, which we interpret as white.

Conditions of the Eye

When the eye suffers a mismatch between the focusing range of the lens–cornea system and the length of the eye, with the result that light rays from a near object reach the retina before they converge to form an image as shown in Figure 36.37a, the condition is known as **farsightedness** (or *hyperopia*). A farsighted person can usually see faraway objects clearly but not nearby objects. Although the near point of a normal eye is approximately 25 cm, the near point of a farsighted person is much farther away. The refracting power in the cornea and lens is insufficient to focus the light from all but distant objects satisfactorily. The condition can be corrected by placing a converging lens in front of the eye as shown in Figure 36.37b. The lens refracts the incoming rays more toward the principal axis before entering the eye, allowing them to converge and focus on the retina.

A person with **nearsightedness** (or *myopia*), another mismatch condition, can focus on nearby objects but not on faraway objects. The far point of the nearsighted eye is not infinity and may be less than 1 m. The maximum focal length of the nearsighted eye is insufficient to produce a sharp image on the retina, and rays from a distant object converge to a focus in front of the retina. They then continue past that point, diverging before they finally reach the retina and causing blurred vision (Fig. 36.38a). Nearsightedness can be corrected with a diverging lens as shown in Figure 36.38b. The lens refracts the rays away from the principal axis before they enter the eye, allowing them to focus on the retina.

Beginning in middle age, most people lose some of their accommodation ability as their visual muscles weaken and the lens hardens. Unlike farsightedness, which is a mismatch between focusing power and eye length, **presbyopia** (literally, "old-age vision") is due to a reduction in accommodation ability. The cornea and

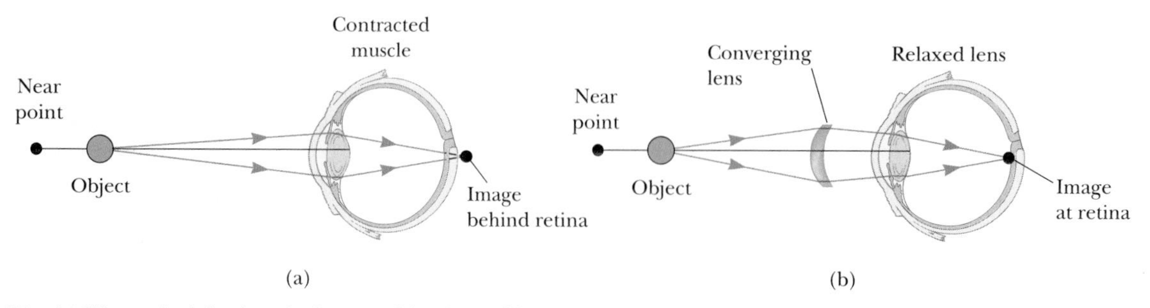

Figure 36.37 (a) When a farsighted eye looks at an object located between the near point and the eye, the image point is behind the retina, resulting in blurred vision. The eye muscle contracts to try to bring the object into focus. (b) Farsightedness is corrected with a converging lens.

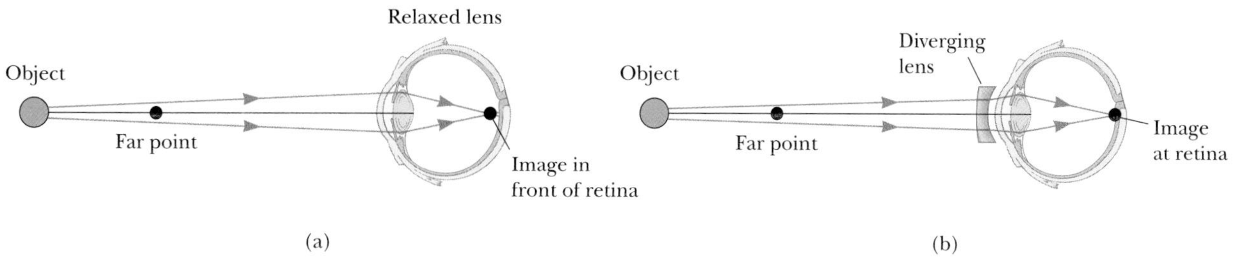

Figure 36.38 (a) When a nearsighted eye looks at an object that lies beyond the eye's far point, the image is formed in front of the retina, resulting in blurred vision. (b) Nearsightedness is corrected with a diverging lens.

lens do not have sufficient focusing power to bring nearby objects into focus on the retina. The symptoms are the same as those of farsightedness, and the condition can be corrected with converging lenses.

In eyes having a defect known as **astigmatism,** light from a point source produces a line image on the retina. This condition arises when either the cornea, the lens, or both are not perfectly symmetric. Astigmatism can be corrected with lenses that have different curvatures in two mutually perpendicular directions.

Optometrists and ophthalmologists usually prescribe lenses[1] measured in **diopters:** the **power** P of a lens in diopters equals the inverse of the focal length in meters: $P = 1/f$. For example, a converging lens of focal length +20 cm has a power of +5.0 diopters, and a diverging lens of focal length −40 cm has a power of −2.5 diopters.

Quick Quiz 36.8 Two campers wish to start a fire during the day. One camper is nearsighted, and one is farsighted. Whose glasses should be used to focus the Sun's rays onto some paper to start the fire? (a) either camper (b) the nearsighted camper (c) the farsighted camper

36.8 The Simple Magnifier

The simple magnifier, or magnifying glass, consists of a single converging lens. This device increases the apparent size of an object.

Suppose an object is viewed at some distance p from the eye as illustrated in Figure 36.39. The size of the image formed at the retina depends on the angle θ subtended by the object at the eye. As the object moves closer to the eye, θ increases and a larger image is observed. An average normal human eye, however, cannot focus on an object closer than about 25 cm, the near point (Fig. 36.40a, page 1036). Therefore, θ is maximum at the near point.

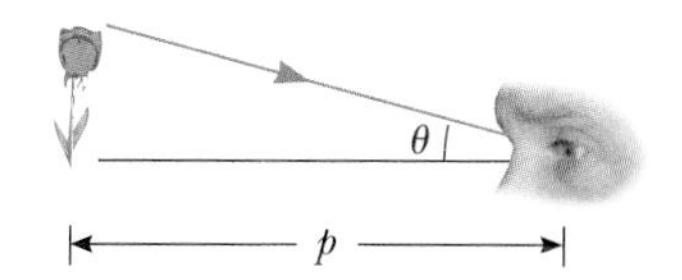

Figure 36.39 The size of the image formed on the retina depends on the angle θ subtended at the eye.

To further increase the apparent angular size of an object, a converging lens can be placed in front of the eye as in Figure 36.40b, with the object located at point O, immediately inside the focal point of the lens. At this location, the lens forms a virtual, upright, enlarged image. We define **angular magnification** m as the ratio of the angle subtended by an object with a lens in use (angle θ in Fig. 36.40b) to the angle subtended by the object placed at the near point with no lens in use (angle θ_0 in Fig. 36.40a):

$$m \equiv \frac{\theta}{\theta_0} \quad \textbf{(36.22)}$$

[1] The word *lens* comes from *lentil,* the name of an Italian legume. (You may have eaten lentil soup.) Early eyeglasses were called "glass lentils" because the biconvex shape of their lenses resembled the shape of a lentil. The first lenses for farsightedness and presbyopia appeared around 1280; concave eyeglasses for correcting nearsightedness did not appear until more than 100 years later.

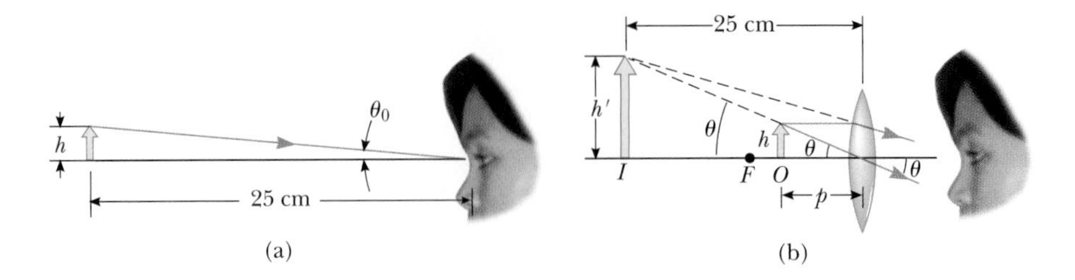

Figure 36.40 (a) An object placed at the near point of the eye (p = 25 cm) subtends an angle $\theta_0 \approx h/25$ at the eye. (b) An object placed near the focal point of a converging lens produces a magnified image that subtends an angle $\theta \approx h'/25$ at the eye.

The angular magnification is a maximum when the image is at the near point of the eye, that is, when $q = -25$ cm. The object distance corresponding to this image distance can be calculated from the thin lens equation:

$$\frac{1}{p} + \frac{1}{-25 \text{ cm}} = \frac{1}{f} \quad \rightarrow \quad p = \frac{25f}{25 + f}$$

where f is the focal length of the magnifier in centimeters. If we make the small-angle approximations

$$\tan \theta_0 \approx \theta_0 \approx \frac{h}{25} \quad \text{and} \quad \tan \theta \approx \theta \approx \frac{h}{p} \qquad \textbf{(36.23)}$$

Equation 36.22 becomes

$$m_{\text{max}} = \frac{\theta}{\theta_0} = \frac{h/p}{h/25} = \frac{25}{p} = \frac{25}{25f/(25 + f)}$$

$$m_{\text{max}} = 1 + \frac{25 \text{ cm}}{f} \qquad \textbf{(36.24)}$$

Although the eye can focus on an image formed anywhere between the near point and infinity, it is most relaxed when the image is at infinity. For the image formed by the magnifying lens to appear at infinity, the object has to be at the focal point of the lens. In this case, Equations 36.23 become

$$\theta_0 \approx \frac{h}{25} \quad \text{and} \quad \theta \approx \frac{h}{f}$$

and the magnification is

$$m_{\text{min}} = \frac{\theta}{\theta_0} = \frac{25 \text{ cm}}{f} \qquad \textbf{(36.25)}$$

With a single lens, it is possible to obtain angular magnifications up to about 4 without serious aberrations. Magnifications up to about 20 can be achieved by using one or two additional lenses to correct for aberrations.

George Semple

A simple magnifier, also called a magnifying glass, is used to view an enlarged image of a portion of a map.

EXAMPLE 36.12 Magnification of a Lens

What is the maximum magnification that is possible with a lens having a focal length of 10 cm, and what is the magnification of this lens when the eye is relaxed?

SOLUTION

Conceptualize Study Figure 36.40b for the situation in which a magnifying glass forms an enlarged image of an object placed inside the focal point. The maximum magnification occurs when the image is located at the near point of the eye. When the eye is relaxed, the image is at infinity.

Categorize We evaluate results using equations developed in this section, so we categorize this example as a substitution problem.

Evaluate the maximum magnification from Equation 36.24:

$$m_{max} = 1 + \frac{25 \text{ cm}}{f} = 1 + \frac{25 \text{ cm}}{10 \text{ cm}} = 3.5$$

Evaluate the minimum magnification, when the eye is relaxed, from Equation 36.25:

$$m_{min} = \frac{25 \text{ cm}}{f} = \frac{25 \text{ cm}}{10 \text{ cm}} = 2.5$$

36.9 The Compound Microscope

A simple magnifier provides only limited assistance in inspecting minute details of an object. Greater magnification can be achieved by combining two lenses in a device called a **compound microscope** shown in Active Figure 36.41a. It consists of one lens, the *objective,* that has a very short focal length $f_o < 1$ cm and a second lens, the *eyepiece,* that has a focal length f_e of a few centimeters. The two lenses are separated by a distance L that is much greater than either f_o or f_e. The object, which is placed just outside the focal point of the objective, forms a real, inverted image at I_1, and this image is located at or close to the focal point of the eyepiece. The eyepiece, which serves as a simple magnifier, produces at I_2 a virtual, enlarged image of I_1. The lateral magnification M_1 of the first image is $-q_1/p_1$. Notice from Active Figure 36.41a that q_1 is approximately equal to L and that the object is very close to the focal point of the objective: $p_1 \approx f_o$. Therefore, the lateral magnification by the objective is

$$M_o \approx -\frac{L}{f_o}$$

The angular magnification by the eyepiece for an object (corresponding to the image at I_1) placed at the focal point of the eyepiece is, from Equation 36.25,

$$m_e = \frac{25 \text{ cm}}{f_e}$$

The overall magnification of the image formed by a compound microscope is defined as the product of the lateral and angular magnifications:

$$M = M_o m_e = -\frac{L}{f_o}\left(\frac{25 \text{ cm}}{f_e}\right) \qquad \textbf{(36.26)}$$

The negative sign indicates that the image is inverted.

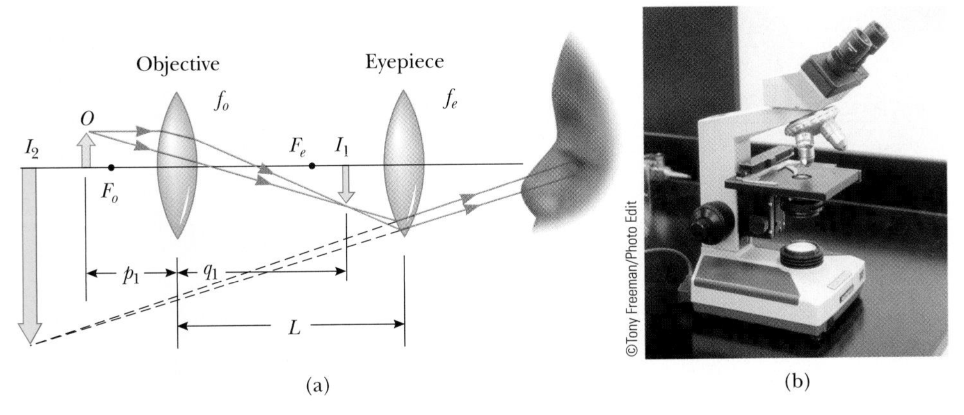

ACTIVE FIGURE 36.41

(a) Diagram of a compound microscope, which consists of an objective lens and an eyepiece lens. (b) A compound microscope. The three-objective turret allows the user to choose from several powers of magnification. Combinations of eyepieces with different focal lengths and different objectives can produce a wide range of magnifications.

Sign in at www.thomsonedu.com and go to ThomsonNOW to adjust the focal lengths of the objective and eyepiece lenses and see the effect on the final image.

The microscope has extended human vision to the point where we can view previously unknown details of incredibly small objects. The capabilities of this instrument have steadily increased with improved techniques for precision grinding of lenses. A question often asked about microscopes is, "If one were extremely patient and careful, would it be possible to construct a microscope that would enable the human eye to see an atom?" The answer is no, as long as light is used to illuminate the object. For an object under an optical microscope (one that uses visible light) to be seen, the object must be at least as large as a wavelength of light. Because the diameter of any atom is many times smaller than the wavelengths of visible light, the mysteries of the atom must be probed using other types of "microscopes."

36.10 The Telescope

Two fundamentally different types of **telescopes** exist; both are designed to aid in viewing distant objects, such as the planets in our solar system. The **refracting telescope** uses a combination of lenses to form an image, and the **reflecting telescope** uses a curved mirror and a lens.

Like the compound microscope, the refracting telescope shown in Active Figure 36.42a has an objective and an eyepiece. The two lenses are arranged so that the objective forms a real, inverted image of a distant object very near the focal point of the eyepiece. Because the object is essentially at infinity, this point at which I_1 forms is the focal point of the objective. The eyepiece then forms, at I_2, an enlarged, inverted image of the image at I_1. To provide the largest possible magnification, the image distance for the eyepiece is infinite. The light rays exit the eyepiece lens parallel to the principal axis, and the image due to the objective lens must form at the focal point of the eyepiece. Hence, the two lenses are separated by a distance $f_o + f_e$, which corresponds to the length of the telescope tube.

The angular magnification of the telescope is given by θ/θ_o, where θ_o is the angle subtended by the object at the objective and θ is the angle subtended by the final image at the viewer's eye. Consider Active Figure 36.42a, in which the object is a very great distance to the left of the figure. The angle θ_o (to the *left* of the objective) subtended by the object at the objective is the same as the angle (to the *right* of the objective) subtended by the first image at the objective. Therefore,

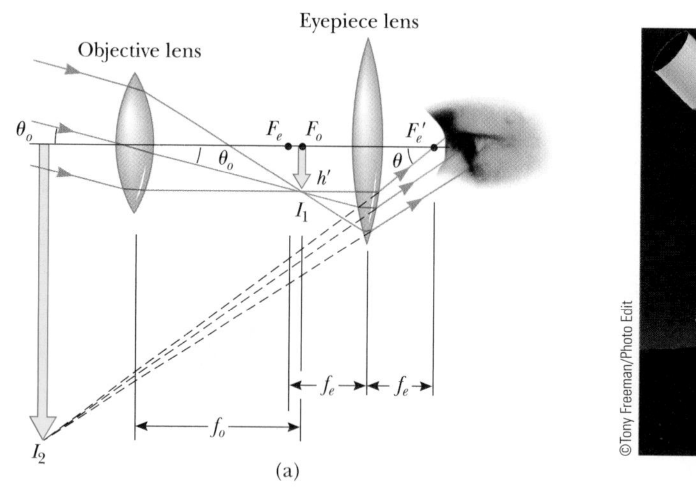

ACTIVE FIGURE 36.42

(a) Lens arrangement in a refracting telescope, with the object at infinity. (b) A refracting telescope.

Sign in at www.thomsonedu.com and go to ThomsonNOW to adjust the focal lengths of the objective and eyepiece lenses and see the effect on the final image.

$$\tan \theta_o \approx \theta_o \approx -\frac{h'}{f_o}$$

where the negative sign indicates that the image is inverted.

The angle θ subtended by the final image at the eye is the same as the angle that a ray coming from the tip of I_1 and traveling parallel to the principal axis makes with the principal axis after it passes through the lens. Therefore,

$$\tan \theta \approx \theta \approx \frac{h'}{f_e}$$

We have not used a negative sign in this equation because the final image is not inverted; the object creating this final image I_2 is I_1, and both it and I_2 point in the same direction. Therefore, the angular magnification of the telescope can be expressed as

$$m = \frac{\theta}{\theta_o} = \frac{h'/f_e}{-h'/f_o} = -\frac{f_o}{f_e} \quad \textbf{(36.27)}$$

This result shows that the angular magnification of a telescope equals the ratio of the objective focal length to the eyepiece focal length. The negative sign indicates that the image is inverted.

When you look through a telescope at such relatively nearby objects as the Moon and the planets, magnification is important. Individual stars in our galaxy, however, are so far away that they always appear as small points of light no matter how great the magnification. To gather as much light as possible, large research telescopes used to study very distant objects must have a large diameter. It is difficult and expensive to manufacture large lenses for refracting telescopes. Another difficulty with large lenses is that their weight leads to sagging, which is an additional source of aberration.

These problems associated with large lenses can be partially overcome by replacing the objective with a concave mirror, which results in a reflecting telescope. Because light is reflected from the mirror and does not pass through a lens, the mirror can have rigid supports on the back side. Such supports eliminate the problem of sagging.

Figure 36.43a shows the design for a typical reflecting telescope. The incoming light rays are reflected by a parabolic mirror at the base. These reflected rays converge toward point *A* in the figure, where an image would be formed. Before this image is formed, however, a small, flat mirror M reflects the light toward an opening in the tube's side and it passes into an eyepiece. This particular design is said to have a Newtonian focus because Newton developed it. Figure 36.43b shows such a telescope. Notice that the light never passes through glass (except through the

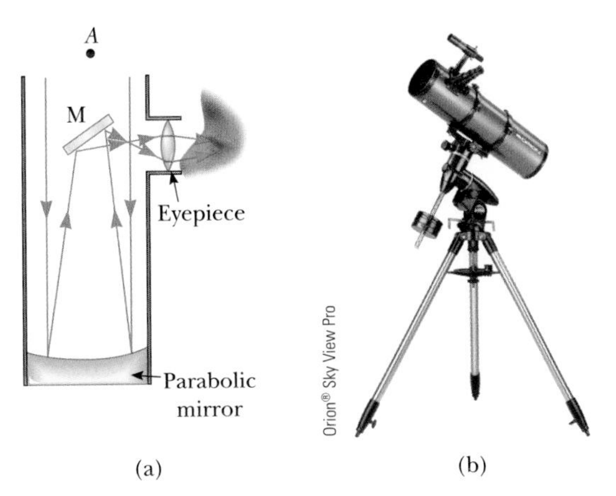

Figure 36.43 (a) A Newtonian-focus reflecting telescope. (b) A reflecting telescope. This type of telescope is shorter than that in Figure 36.42b.

small eyepiece) in the reflecting telescope. As a result, problems associated with chromatic aberration are virtually eliminated. The reflecting telescope can be made even shorter by orienting the flat mirror so that it reflects the light back toward the objective mirror and the light enters an eyepiece in a hole in the middle of the mirror.

The largest reflecting telescopes in the world are at the Keck Observatory on Mauna Kea, Hawaii. The site includes two telescopes with diameters of 10 m, each containing 36 hexagonally shaped, computer-controlled mirrors that work together to form a large reflecting surface. Discussions and plans have been initiated for telescopes with different mirrors working together, as at the Keck Observatory, resulting in an effective diameter up to 21 m. In contrast, the largest refracting telescope in the world, at the Yerkes Observatory in Williams Bay, Wisconsin, has a diameter of only 1 m.

Summary

DEFINITIONS

The **lateral magnification** M of the image due to a mirror or lens is defined as the ratio of the image height h' to the object height h. It is equal to the negative of the ratio of the image distance q to the object distance p:

$$M \equiv \frac{\text{image height}}{\text{object height}} = \frac{h'}{h} = -\frac{q}{p} \qquad \textbf{(36.1, 36.2, 36.17)}$$

The **angular magnification** m is the ratio of the angle subtended by an object with a lens in use (angle θ in Fig. 36.40b) to the angle subtended by the object placed at the near point with no lens in use (angle θ_0 in Fig. 36.40a):

$$m \equiv \frac{\theta}{\theta_0} \qquad \textbf{(36.22)}$$

The ratio of the focal length of a camera lens to the diameter of the lens is called the ***f*-number** of the lens:

$$f\text{-number} \equiv \frac{f}{D} \qquad \textbf{(36.20)}$$

CONCEPTS AND PRINCIPLES

In the paraxial ray approximation, the object distance p and image distance q for a spherical mirror of radius R are related by the **mirror equation:**

$$\frac{1}{p} + \frac{1}{q} = \frac{2}{R} = \frac{1}{f} \qquad \textbf{(36.4, 36.6)}$$

where $f = R/2$ is the **focal length** of the mirror.

An image can be formed by refraction from a spherical surface of radius R. The object and image distances for refraction from such a surface are related by

$$\frac{n_1}{p} + \frac{n_2}{q} = \frac{n_2 - n_1}{R} \qquad \textbf{(36.8)}$$

where the light is incident in the medium for which the index of refraction is n_1 and is refracted in the medium for which the index of refraction is n_2.

(continued)

The inverse of the **focal length** f of a thin lens surrounded by air is given by the **lens-makers' equation:**

$$\frac{1}{f} = (n - 1)\left(\frac{1}{R_1} - \frac{1}{R_2}\right) \quad \textbf{(36.15)}$$

Converging lenses have positive focal lengths, and **diverging lenses** have negative focal lengths.

For a thin lens, and in the paraxial ray approximation, the object and image distances are related by the **thin lens equation:**

$$\frac{1}{p} + \frac{1}{q} = \frac{1}{f} \quad \textbf{(36.16)}$$

The maximum magnification of a single lens of focal length f used as a simple magnifier is

$$m_{\max} = 1 + \frac{25 \text{ cm}}{f} \quad \textbf{(36.24)}$$

The overall magnification of the image formed by a compound microscope is:

$$M = -\frac{L}{f_o}\left(\frac{25 \text{ cm}}{f_e}\right) \quad \textbf{(36.26)}$$

where f_o and f_e are the focal lengths of the objective and eyepiece lenses, respectively, and L is the distance between the lenses.

The angular magnification of a refracting telescope can be expressed as

$$m = -\frac{f_o}{f_e} \quad \textbf{(36.27)}$$

where f_o and f_e are the focal lengths of the objective and eyepiece lenses, respectively. The angular magnification of a reflecting telescope is given by the same expression where f_o is the focal length of the objective mirror.

Questions

☐ denotes answer available in *Student Solutions Manual/Study Guide;* **O** denotes objective question

1. Consider a concave spherical mirror with a real object. Is the image always inverted? Is the image always real? Give conditions for your answers.

2. Repeat Question 1 for a convex spherical mirror.

3. **O** **(i)** What is the focal length of a plane mirror? (a) 0 (b) 1 (c) −1 (d) ∞ (e) equal to the mirror height (f) Neither the focal length nor its reciprocal can be defined. **(ii)** What magnification does a plane mirror produce? (a) 0 (b) 1 (c) −1 (d) ∞ (e) Neither the magnification nor its reciprocal can be defined.

4. Do the equations $1/p + 1/q = 1/f$ and $M = -q/p$ apply to the image formed by a flat mirror? Explain your answer.

5. **O** Lulu looks at her image in a makeup mirror. It is enlarged when she is close to the mirror. As she backs away, the image becomes larger, then impossible to identify when she is 30 cm from the mirror, then upside down when she is beyond 30 cm, and finally small, clear, and upside down when she is much farther from the mirror. **(i)** Is the mirror (a) convex, (b) plane, or (c) concave? **(ii)** What is the magnitude of its focal length? (a) 0 (b) 15 cm (c) 30 cm (d) 60 cm (e) ∞

6. Consider a spherical concave mirror with the object located to the left of the mirror beyond the focal point. Using ray diagrams, show that the image moves to the left as the object approaches the focal point.

7. **O** **(i)** Consider the mirror in Figure 36.11. What are the signs of the following? (a) the object distance (b) the image distance (c) the mirror radius (d) the focal length (e) the object height (f) the image height (g) the magnification **(ii)** Consider the objective lens in Active Figure 36.41a. What are the signs of the following? (a) the object distance (b) the image distance (c) the focal length (d) the object height (e) the image height (f) the magnification **(iii)** Answer the same questions (a) through (f) as in part (ii) for the eyepiece in Active Figure 36.41a.

8. **O** A person spearfishing from a boat sees a stationary fish a few meters away in a direction about 30° below the horizontal. To spear the fish, should the person (a) aim above where he sees the fish, (b) aim precisely at the fish, or (c) aim below the fish? Assume the dense spear does not change direction when it enters the water.

9. **O** A single converging lens can be used to constitute a scale model of each of the following devices in use simply by changing the distance from the lens to a candle representing the object. Rank the cases according to the distance from the object to the lens from the largest to the smallest. (a) a movie projector (b) Batman's signal, used to project an image on clouds high above Gotham City (c) a magnifying glass (d) a burning glass, used to make a sharp image of the Sun on tinder (e) an astronomical refracting telescope, used to make a sharp image of stars on an electronic detector (f) a searchlight, used to produce a beam of parallel rays from a point source. (g) a camera lens, used to photograph a soccer game.

10. In Active Figure 36.26a, assume the blue object arrow is replaced by one that is much taller than the lens. How many rays from the top of the object will strike the lens? How many principal rays can be drawn in a ray diagram?

11. **O** A converging lens in a vertical plane receives light from an object and forms an inverted image on a screen. An opaque card is then placed next to the lens, covering only the upper half of the lens. What happens to the image on the screen? (a) The upper half of the image disappears. (b) The lower half of the image disappears. (c) The entire image disappears. (d) The entire image is still visible, but is dimmer. (e) Half of the image disappears and the rest is dimmer. (f) No change in the image occurs.

12. **O** A converging lens of focal length 8 cm forms a sharp image of an object on a screen. What is the smallest possible distance between the object and the screen? (a) 0 (b) 4 cm (c) 8 cm (d) 16 cm (e) 32 cm (f) ∞

13. Explain this statement: "The focal point of a lens is the location of the image of a point object at infinity." Discuss the notion of infinity in real terms as it applies to object distances. Based on this statement, can you think of a simple method for determining the focal length of a converging lens?

14. Discuss the proper position of a photographic slide relative to the lens in a slide projector. What type of lens must the slide projector have?

15. **O** In this chapter's opening photograph, a water drop functions as a biconvex lens with radii of curvature of small magnitude. What is the location of the image photographed? (a) inside the water drop (b) on the back surface of the drop, farthest from the camera (c) somewhat beyond the back surface of the drop (d) on the front surface of the drop, closest to the camera (e) somewhat closer to the camera than the front surface of the drop

16. Explain why a mirror cannot give rise to chromatic aberration.

17. Can a converging lens be made to diverge light if it is placed into a liquid? **What If?** What about a converging mirror?

18. Explain why a fish in a spherical goldfish bowl appears larger than it really is.

19. Why do some emergency vehicles have the symbol ƎƆИA⅃UᙠMA written on the front?

20. Lenses used in eyeglasses, whether converging or diverging, are always designed so that the middle of the lens curves away from the eye like the center lenses of Figures 36.25a and 36.25b. Why?

21. **O** The faceplate of a diving mask can be a corrective lens for a diver who does not have perfect vision and who needs essentially the same prescription for both eyes. Then the diver does not have to wear glasses or contact lenses. The proper design allows the person to see clearly both under water and in the air. Normal eyeglasses have lenses with both the front and back surfaces curved. Should the lens of a diving mask be curved (a) on the outer surface only, (b) on the inner surface only, or (c) on both surfaces?

22. In Figures Q36.22a and Q36.22b, which glasses correct nearsightedness and which correct farsightedness?

(a)

(b)

Figure Q36.22 Questions 22 and 23.

23. A child tries on either his hyperopic grandfather's or his myopic brother's glasses and complains, "Everything looks blurry." Why do the eyes of a person wearing glasses not look blurry? (See Figure Q36.22.)

24. In a Jules Verne novel, a piece of ice is shaped to form a magnifying lens to focus sunlight to start a fire. Is that possible?

25. A solar furnace can be constructed by using a concave mirror to reflect and focus sunlight into a furnace enclosure. What factors in the design of the reflecting mirror would guarantee very high temperatures?

26. Figure Q36.26 shows a lithograph by M. C. Escher titled *Hand with Reflection Sphere (Self-Portrait in Spherical Mirror).* Escher said about the work:

> The picture shows a spherical mirror, resting on a left hand. But as a print is the reverse of the original drawing on stone, it was my right hand that you see depicted. (Being left-handed, I needed my left hand to make the drawing.) Such a globe reflection collects almost one's whole surroundings in one disk-shaped image. The whole room, four walls, the floor, and the ceiling, everything, albeit distorted, is compressed into that one small circle. Your own head, or more exactly the point between your eyes, is the absolute center. No matter how you turn or twist yourself, you can't get out of that central point. You are immovably the focus, the unshakable core, of your world.

Comment on the accuracy of Escher's description.

Figure Q36.26

27. A converging lens of short focal length can take light diverging from a small source and refract it into a beam of parallel rays. A Fresnel lens as shown in Figure 36.27 is used in a lighthouse for this purpose. A concave mirror can take light diverging from a small source and reflect it into a beam of parallel rays. Is it possible to make a Fresnel mirror? Is this idea original, or has it already been done? *Suggestion:* Look at the walls and ceiling of an auditorium.

Problems

WebAssign The Problems from this chapter may be assigned online in WebAssign.

ThomsonNOW Sign in at **www.thomsonedu.com** and go to ThomsonNOW to assess your understanding of this chapter's topics with additional quizzing and conceptual questions.

1, 2, 3 denotes straightforward, intermediate, challenging; □ denotes full solution available in *Student Solutions Manual/Study Guide;* ▲ denotes coached solution with hints available at **www.thomsonedu.com;** denotes developing symbolic reasoning; ● denotes asking for qualitative reasoning; denotes computer useful in solving problem

Section 36.1 Images Formed by Flat Mirrors

1. Does your bathroom mirror show you older or younger than you actually are? Compute an order-of-magnitude estimate for the age difference based on data you specify.

2. In a church choir loft, two parallel walls are 5.30 m apart. The singers stand against the north wall. The organist faces the south wall, sitting 0.800 m away from it. To enable her to see the choir, a flat mirror 0.600 m wide is mounted on the south wall, straight in front of her. What width of the north wall can the organist see? *Suggestion:* Draw a top-view diagram to justify your answer.

3. Determine the minimum height of a vertical flat mirror in which a person 5 ft 10 in. in height can see his or her full image. (A ray diagram would be helpful.)

4. A person walks into a room that has two flat mirrors on opposite walls. The mirrors produce multiple images of the person. When the person is 5.00 ft from the mirror on the left wall and 10.0 ft from the mirror on the right wall, find the distance from the person to the first three images seen in the mirror on the left.

5. A periscope (Fig. P36.5) is useful for viewing objects that cannot be seen directly. It can be used in submarines and when watching golf matches or parades from behind a crowd of people. Suppose the object is a distance p_1 from the upper mirror and the two flat mirrors are separated by a distance h. (a) What is the distance of the final image from the lower mirror? (b) Is the final image real or virtual? (c) Is it upright or inverted? (d) What is its magnification? (e) Does it appear to be left–right reversed?

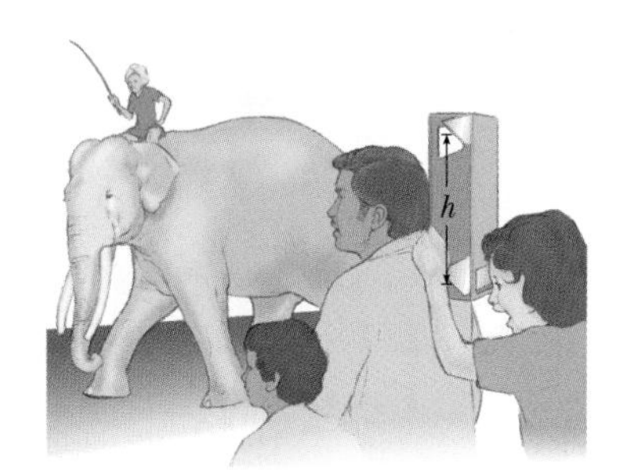

Figure P36.5

Section 36.2 Images Formed by Spherical Mirrors

6. A concave spherical mirror has a radius of curvature of 20.0 cm. Find the location of the image for object distances of (a) 40.0 cm, (b) 20.0 cm, and (c) 10.0 cm. For each case, state whether the image is real or virtual and upright or inverted. Find the magnification in each case.

7. ▲ A spherical convex mirror has a radius of curvature with a magnitude of 40.0 cm. Determine the position of the virtual image and the magnification for object distances of (a) 30.0 cm and (b) 60.0 cm. (c) Are the images upright or inverted?

8. At an intersection of hospital hallways, a convex mirror is mounted high on a wall to help people avoid collisions. The magnitude of the mirror's radius of curvature is 0.550 m. Locate and describe the image of a patient 10.0 m from the mirror. Determine the magnification of the image.

9. A concave mirror has a radius of curvature of 60.0 cm. Calculate the image position and magnification of an object placed in front of the mirror at distances of (a) 90.0 cm and (b) 20.0 cm. (c) Draw ray diagrams to obtain the image characteristics in each case.

10. A large church has a niche in one wall. On the floor plan, the niche appears as a semicircular indentation of radius 2.50 m. A worshiper stands on the centerline of the niche, 2.00 m out from its deepest point, and whispers a prayer. Where is the sound concentrated after reflection from the back wall of the niche?

11. A dentist uses a mirror to examine a tooth. The tooth is 1.00 cm in front of the mirror, and the image is formed 10.0 cm behind the mirror. Determine (a) the mirror's radius of curvature and (b) the magnification of the image.

12. A certain Christmas tree ornament is a silver sphere having a diameter of 8.50 cm. Determine an object location for which the size of the reflected image is three-fourths the object's size. Use a principal-ray diagram to arrive at a description of the image.

13. (a) A concave mirror forms an inverted image four times larger than the object. Find the focal length of the mirror, assuming the distance between object and image is 0.600 m. (b) A convex mirror forms a virtual image half the size of the object. Assuming the distance between image and object is 20.0 cm, determine the radius of curvature of the mirror.

14. To fit a contact lens to a patient's eye, a *keratometer* can be used to measure the curvature of the eye's front surface, the cornea. This instrument places an illuminated object of known size at a known distance p from the cornea. The cornea reflects some light from the object, forming an image of the object. The magnification M of the image is measured by using a small viewing telescope that allows comparison of the image formed by the cornea with a second calibrated image projected into the field of view by a prism arrangement. Determine the radius of curvature of the cornea for the case $p = 30.0$ cm and $M = 0.013\ 0$.

15. An object 10.0 cm tall is placed at the zero mark of a meterstick. A spherical mirror located at some point on the meterstick creates an image of the object that is upright, 4.00 cm tall, and located at the 42.0-cm mark of the meterstick. (a) Is the mirror convex or concave? (b) Where is the mirror? (c) What is the mirror's focal length?

16. A dedicated sports car enthusiast polishes the inside and outside surfaces of a hubcap that is a section of a sphere. When she looks into one side of the hubcap, she sees an image of her face 30.0 cm in back of the hubcap. She then flips the hubcap over and sees another image of her face 10.0 cm in back of the hubcap. (a) How far is her face from the hubcap? (b) What is the radius of curvature of the hubcap?

17. A spherical mirror is to be used to form, on a screen located 5.00 m from the object, an image five times the size of the object. (a) Describe the type of mirror

required. (b) Where should the mirror be positioned relative to the object?

18. You unconsciously estimate the distance to an object from the angle it subtends in your field of view. This angle θ in radians is related to the linear height of the object h and to the distance d by $\theta = h/d$. Assume you are driving a car and another car, 1.50 m high, is 24.0 m behind you. (a) Suppose your car has a flat passenger-side rearview mirror, 1.55 m from your eyes. How far from your eyes is the image of the car following you? (b) What angle does the image subtend in your field of view? (c) **What If?** Now suppose your car has a convex rearview mirror with a radius of curvature of magnitude 2.00 m (as suggested in Fig. 36.15). How far from your eyes is the image of the car behind you? (d) What angle does the image subtend at your eyes? (e) Based on its angular size, how far away does the following car appear to be?

19. ● **Review problem.** A ball is dropped at $t = 0$ from rest 3.00 m directly above the vertex of a concave mirror that has a radius of curvature of 1.00 m and lies in a horizontal plane. (a) Describe the motion of the ball's image in the mirror. (b) At what instant or instants do the ball and its image coincide?

Section 36.3 Images Formed by Refraction

20. A flint glass plate ($n = 1.66$) rests on the bottom of an aquarium tank. The plate is 8.00 cm thick (vertical dimension) and is covered with a layer of water ($n = 1.33$) 12.0 cm deep. Calculate the apparent thickness of the plate as viewed from straight above the water.

21. A cubical block of ice 50.0 cm on a side is placed over a speck of dust on a level floor. Find the location of the image of the speck as viewed from above. The index of refraction of ice is 1.309.

22. One end of a long glass rod ($n = 1.50$) is formed into a convex surface with a radius of curvature of 6.00 cm. An object is located in air along the axis of the rod. Find the image positions corresponding to object distances of (a) 20.0 cm, (b) 10.0 cm, and (c) 3.00 cm from the end of the rod.

23. A glass sphere ($n = 1.50$) with a radius of 15.0 cm has a tiny air bubble 5.00 cm above its center. The sphere is viewed looking down along the extended radius containing the bubble. What is the apparent depth of the bubble below the surface of the sphere?

24. Figure P36.24 shows a curved surface separating a material with index of refraction n_1 from a material with index n_2. The surface forms an image I of object O. The ray shown in blue passes through the surface along a radial line. Its angles of incidence and refraction are both zero, so its direction does not change at the surface. For the ray shown in brown, the direction changes according to $n_1 \sin \theta_1 = n_2 \sin \theta_2$. For paraxial rays, we assume θ_1 and θ_2 are small, so we may write $n_1 \tan \theta_1 = n_2 \tan \theta_2$. The magnification is defined as $M = h'/h$. Prove that the magnification is given by $M = -n_1 q/n_2 p$.

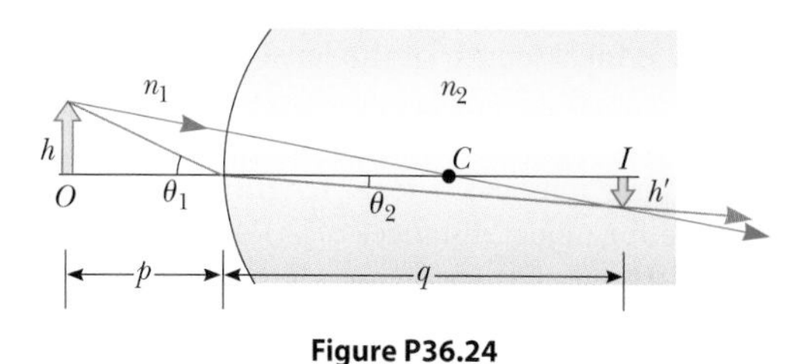

Figure P36.24

25. ● As shown in Figure P36.25, a water tank containing lobsters has a curved front made of plastic with uniform thickness and a radius of curvature of magnitude 80.0 cm. Locate and describe the images of lobsters (a) 30.0 cm and (b) 90.0 cm from the base of the front wall. (c) Find the magnification of each image. You may use the result of Problem 24. (d) The lobsters are both 9.00 cm in height. Find the height of each image. (e) Explain why you do not need to know the index of refraction of the plastic to solve this problem.

Alexandra Héder

Figure P36.25

26. A goldfish is swimming at 2.00 cm/s toward the front wall of a rectangular aquarium. What is the apparent speed of the fish measured by an observer looking in from outside the front wall of the tank? The index of refraction of water is 1.33.

Section 36.4 Thin Lenses

27. ▲ The left face of a biconvex lens has a radius of curvature of magnitude 12.0 cm, and the right face has a radius

of curvature of magnitude 18.0 cm. The index of refraction of the glass is 1.44. (a) Calculate the focal length of the lens. (b) **What If?** Calculate the focal length the lens has after it is turned around to interchange the radii of curvature of the two faces.

28. A contact lens is made of plastic with an index of refraction of 1.50. The lens has an outer radius of curvature of +2.00 cm and an inner radius of curvature of +2.50 cm. What is the focal length of the lens?

29. A converging lens has a focal length of 20.0 cm. Locate the image for object distances of (a) 40.0 cm, (b) 20.0 cm, and (c) 10.0 cm. For each case, state whether the image is real or virtual and upright or inverted. Find the magnification in each case.

30. An object located 32.0 cm in front of a lens forms an image on a screen 8.00 cm behind the lens. (a) Find the focal length of the lens. (b) Determine the magnification. (c) Is the lens converging or diverging?

31. ▲ The nickel's image in Figure P36.31 has twice the diameter of the nickel and is 2.84 cm from the lens. Determine the focal length of the lens.

Figure P36.31

32. Suppose an object has thickness dp so that it extends from object distance p to $p + dp$. Prove that the thickness dq of its image is given by $(-q^2/p^2)\,dp$. Then the longitudinal magnification is $dq/dp = -M^2$, where M is the lateral magnification.

33. An object is located 20.0 cm to the left of a diverging lens having a focal length $f = -32.0$ cm. Determine (a) the location and (b) the magnification of the image. (c) Construct a ray diagram for this arrangement.

34. The projection lens in a certain slide projector is a single thin lens. A slide 24.0 mm high is to be projected so that its image fills a screen 1.80 m high. The slide-to-screen distance is 3.00 m. (a) Determine the focal length of the projection lens. (b) How far from the slide should the lens of the projector be placed so as to form the image on the screen?

35. The use of a lens in a certain situation is described by the equation

$$\frac{1}{p} + \frac{1}{-3.50p} = \frac{1}{7.50\text{ cm}}$$

Determine (a) the object distance and (b) the image distance. (c) Use a ray diagram to obtain a description of the image. (d) Identify a practical device described by the given equation and write the statement of a problem for which the equation appears in the solution.

36. An antelope is at a distance of 20.0 m from a converging lens of focal length 30.0 cm. The lens forms an image of the animal. If the antelope runs away from the lens at a speed of 5.00 m/s, how fast does the image move? Does the image move toward or away from the lens?

37. ● An object is at a distance d to the left of a flat screen. A converging lens with focal length $f < d/4$ is placed between object and screen. (a) Show that two lens positions exist that form an image on the screen and determine how far these positions are from the object. (b) How do the two images differ from each other?

38. ● In Figure P36.38, a thin converging lens of focal length 14.0 cm forms an image of the square $abcd$, which is $h_c = h_b = 10.0$ cm high and lies between distances of $p_d = 20.0$ cm and $p_a = 30.0$ cm from the lens. (a) Let a', b', c', and d' represent the respective corners of the image. Let q_a represent the image distance for points a' and b', q_d represent the image distance for points c' and d', h'_b represent the distance from point b' to the axis, and h'_c represent the height of c'. Evaluate each of these quantities. Make a sketch of the image. (b) The area of the object is 100 cm^2. By carrying out the following steps, you will evaluate the area of the image. Let q represent the image distance of any point between a' and d', for which the object distance is p. Let h' represent the distance from the axis to the point at the edge of the image between b' and c' at image distance q. Demonstrate that

$$|h'| = (10\text{ cm})q\left(\frac{1}{14\text{ cm}} - \frac{1}{q}\right)$$

(c) Explain why the geometric area of the image is given by

$$\int_{q_a}^{q_d} |h'|\,dq$$

Carry out the integration to find the area of the image.

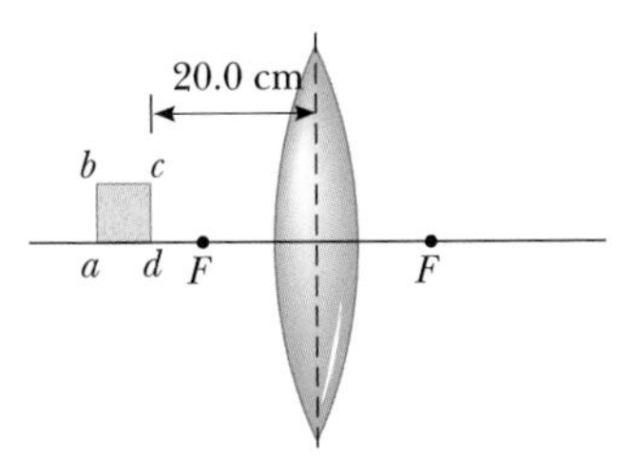

Figure P36.38

39. Figure 36.33 diagrams a cross section of a camera. It has a single lens of focal length 65.0 mm that is to form an image on the CCD at the back of the camera. Suppose the position of the lens has been adjusted to focus the image of a distant object. How far and in what direction must the lens be moved to form a sharp image of an object that is 2.00 m away?

Section 36.5 Lens Aberrations

40. The magnitudes of the radii of curvature are 32.5 cm and 42.5 cm for the two faces of a biconcave lens. The glass has index of refraction 1.53 for violet light and 1.51 for red light. For a very distant object, locate and describe (a) the image formed by violet light and (b) the image formed by red light.

41. Two rays traveling parallel to the principal axis strike a large plano-convex lens having an index of refraction of 1.60 (Fig. P36.41). If the convex face is spherical, a ray near the edge does not pass through the focal point (spherical aberration occurs). Assume this face has a radius of curvature of 20.0 cm and the two rays are at distances $h_1 = 0.500$ cm and $h_2 = 12.0$ cm from the principal axis. Find the difference Δx in the positions where each crosses the principal axis.

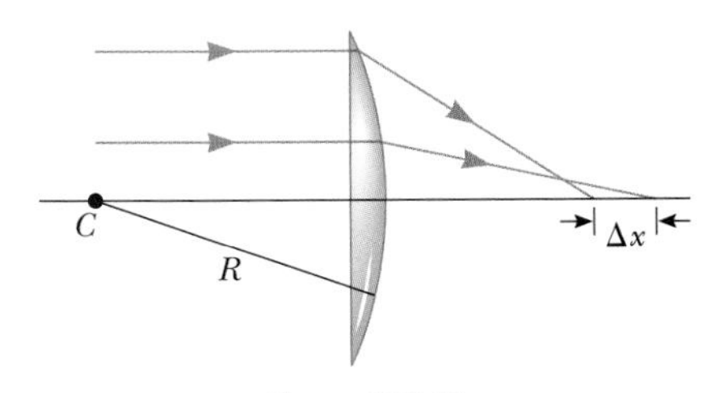

Figure P36.41

Section 36.6 The Camera

42. A camera is being used with a correct exposure at $f/4$ and a shutter speed of $\frac{1}{16}$ s. To photograph a rapidly moving subject, the shutter speed is changed to $\frac{1}{128}$ s. Find the new f-number setting needed to maintain satisfactory exposure.

Section 36.7 The Eye

43. A nearsighted person cannot see objects clearly beyond 25.0 cm (her far point). If she has no astigmatism and contact lenses are prescribed for her, what power and type of lens are required to correct her vision?

44. The accommodation limits for nearsighted Nick's eyes are 18.0 cm and 80.0 cm. When he wears his glasses, he can see faraway objects clearly. At what minimum distance is he able to see objects clearly?

Section 36.8 The Simple Magnifier

Section 36.9 The Compound Microscope

Section 36.10 The Telescope

45. A lens that has a focal length of 5.00 cm is used as a magnifying glass. (a) To obtain maximum magnification, where should the object be placed? (b) What is the magnification?

46. The distance between eyepiece and objective lens in a certain compound microscope is 23.0 cm. The focal length of the eyepiece is 2.50 cm and that of the objective is 0.400 cm. What is the overall magnification of the microscope?

47. The refracting telescope at the Yerkes Observatory has a 1.00-m diameter objective lens of focal length 20.0 m. Assume it is used with an eyepiece of focal length 2.50 cm. (a) Determine the magnification of Mars as seen through this telescope. (b) Are the Martian polar caps right side up or upside down?

48. ● Astronomers often take photographs with the objective lens or mirror of a telescope alone, without an eyepiece. (a) Show that the image size h' for such a telescope is given by $h' = fh/(f - p)$, where h is the object size, f is the objective focal length, and p is the object distance. (b) **What If?** Simplify the expression in part (a) for the case in which the object distance is much greater than objective focal length. (c) The "wingspan" of the International Space Station is 108.6 m, the overall width of its solar panel configuration. Find the width of the image formed by a telescope objective of focal length 4.00 m when the station is orbiting at an altitude of 407 km.

49. A certain telescope has an objective mirror with an aperture diameter of 200 mm and a focal length of 2 000 mm. It captures the image of a nebula on photographic film at its prime focus with an exposure time of 1.50 min. To produce the same light energy per unit area on the film,

what is the required exposure time to photograph the same nebula with a smaller telescope that has an objective with a diameter of 60.0 mm and a focal length of 900 mm?

Additional Problems

50. A *zoom lens* system is a combination of lenses that produces a variable magnification of a fixed object as it maintains a fixed image position. The magnification is varied by moving one or more lenses along the axis. Multiple lenses are used in practice to obtain high-quality images, but the effect of zooming in on an object can be demonstrated with a simple two-lens system. An object, two converging lenses, and a screen are mounted on an optical bench. The first lens, which is to the right of the object, has a focal length of 5.00 cm, and the second lens, which is to the right of the first lens, has a focal length of 10.0 cm. The screen is to the right of the second lens. Initially, an object is situated at a distance of 7.50 cm to the left of the first lens, and the image formed on the screen has a magnification of +1.00. (a) Find the distance between the object and the screen. (b) Both lenses are now moved along their common axis, while the object and the screen maintain fixed positions, until the image formed on the screen has a magnification of +3.00. Find the displacement of each lens from its initial position in part (a). Can the lenses be displaced in more than one way?

51. The distance between an object and its upright image is 20.0 cm. If the magnification is 0.500, what is the focal length of the lens being used to form the image?

52. The distance between an object and its upright image is d. If the magnification is M, what is the focal length of the lens being used to form the image?

53. A real object is located at the zero end of a meterstick. A large concave mirror at the 100-cm end of the meterstick forms an image of the object at the 70.0-cm position. A small convex mirror placed at the 20.0-cm position forms a final image at the 10.0-cm point. What is the radius of curvature of the convex mirror?

54. The lens and mirror in Figure P36.54 have focal lengths of +80.0 cm and −50.0 cm, respectively. An object is placed 1.00 m to the left of the lens as shown. Locate the final image, formed by light that has gone through the lens twice. State whether the image is upright or inverted and determine the overall magnification.

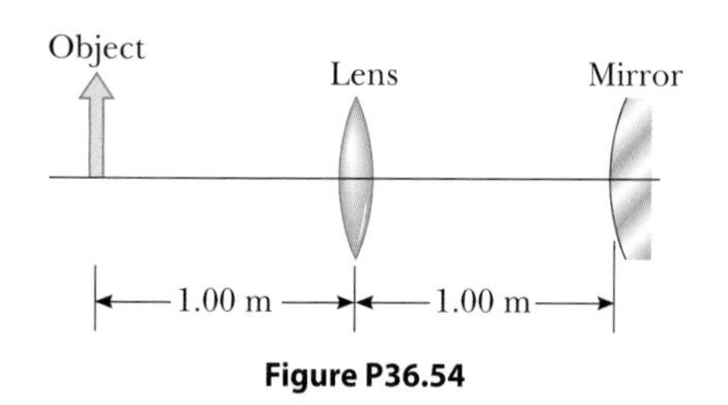

Figure P36.54

55. ● An object is originally at the x_i = 0 cm position of a meterstick located on the x axis. A converging lens of focal length 26.0 cm is fixed at the position 32.0 cm. Then we gradually slide the object to the position x_f = 12.0 cm. Find the location x' of the object's image as a function of the object position x. Describe the pattern of the motion of the image with reference to a graph or a table of values. As the object moves 12 cm to the right, how far does the image move? In what direction or directions?

56. The object in Figure P36.56 is midway between the lens and the mirror. The mirror's radius of curvature is 20.0 cm, and the lens has a focal length of −16.7 cm. Considering only the light that leaves the object and travels first toward the mirror, locate the final image formed by this system. Is this image real or virtual? Is it upright or inverted? What is the overall magnification?

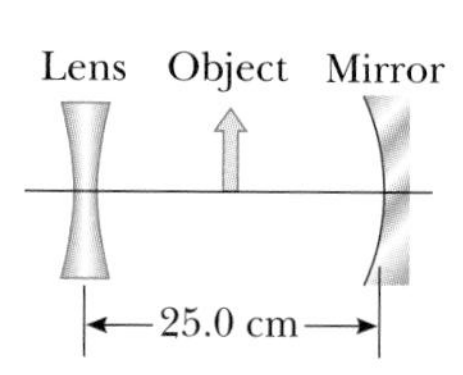

Figure P36.56

57. ● In many applications, it is necessary to expand or decrease the diameter of a beam of parallel rays of light. This change can be made by using a converging lens and a diverging lens in combination. Suppose you have a converging lens of focal length 21.0 cm and a diverging lens of focal length −12.0 cm. How can you arrange these lenses to increase the diameter of a beam of parallel rays? By what factor will the diameter increase?

58. The lens-makers' equation applies to a lens immersed in a liquid if n in the equation is replaced by n_2/n_1. Here n_2 refers to the index of refraction of the lens material and n_1 is that of the medium surrounding the lens. (a) A certain lens has focal length 79.0 cm in air and index of refraction 1.55. Find its focal length in water. (b) A certain mirror has focal length 79.0 cm in air. Find its focal length in water.

59. ▲ A parallel beam of light enters a glass hemisphere perpendicular to the flat face as shown in Figure P36.59. The

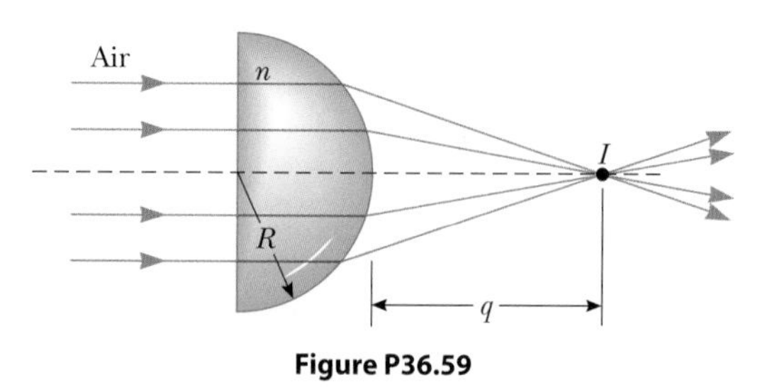

Figure P36.59

magnitude of the radius is 6.00 cm, and the index of refraction is 1.560. Determine the point at which the beam is focused. (Assume paraxial rays.)

60. **Review problem.** A spherical lightbulb of diameter 3.20 cm radiates light equally in all directions, with power 4.50 W. (a) Find the light intensity at the surface of the lightbulb. (b) Find the light intensity 7.20 m away from the center of the lightbulb. (c) At this 7.20-m distance, a lens is set up with its axis pointing toward the lightbulb. The lens has a circular face with a diameter 15.0 cm and has a focal length of 35.0 cm. Find the diameter of the image of the lightbulb. (d) Find the light intensity at the image.

61. An object is placed 12.0 cm to the left of a diverging lens of focal length −6.00 cm. A converging lens of focal length 12.0 cm is placed a distance d to the right of the diverging lens. Find the distance d so that the final image is at infinity. Draw a ray diagram for this case.

62. Assume the intensity of sunlight is 1.00 kW/m^2 at a particular location. A highly reflecting concave mirror is to be pointed toward the Sun to produce a power of at least 350 W at the image. (a) Find the required radius R_a of the circular face area of the mirror. (b) Now suppose the light intensity is to be at least 120 kW/m^2 at the image. Find the required relationship between R_a and the radius of curvature R of the mirror. The disk of the Sun subtends an angle of 0.533° at the Earth.

63. ▲ The disk of the Sun subtends an angle of 0.533° at the Earth. What are the position and diameter of the solar image formed by a concave spherical mirror with a radius of curvature of 3.00 m?

64. ● Figure P36.64 shows a thin converging lens for which the radii of curvature are $R_1 = 9.00$ cm and $R_2 = -11.0$ cm. The lens is in front of a concave spherical mirror with the radius of curvature $R = 8.00$ cm. (a) Assume its focal points F_1 and F_2 are 5.00 cm from the center of the lens. Determine its index of refraction. (b) The lens and mirror are 20.0 cm apart, and an object is placed 8.00 cm to the left of the lens. Determine the position of the final image and its magnification as seen by the eye in the figure. (c) Is the final image inverted or upright? Explain.

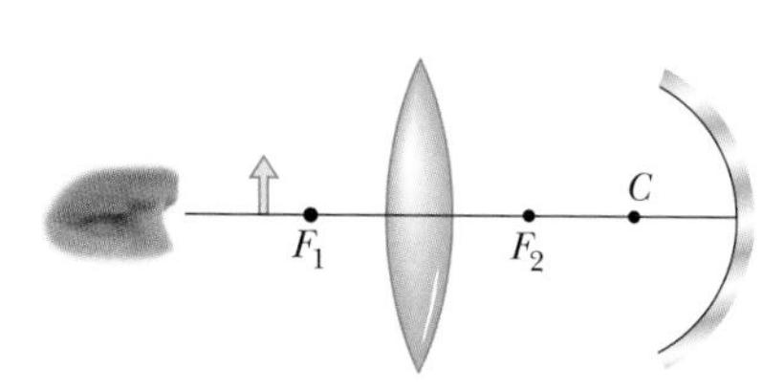

Figure P36.64

65. In a darkened room, a burning candle is placed 1.50 m from a white wall. A lens is placed between candle and wall at a location that causes a larger, inverted image to form on the wall. When the lens is moved 90.0 cm toward the wall, another image of the candle is formed. Find (a) the two object distances that produce the specified images and (b) the focal length of the lens. (c) Characterize the second image.

66. ● A floating strawberry illusion is achieved with two parabolic mirrors, each having a focal length 7.50 cm, facing each other so that their centers are 7.50 cm apart (Fig. P36.66). If a strawberry is placed on the lower mirror, an image of the strawberry is formed at the small opening at the center of the top mirror. Show that the final image is formed at that location and describe its characteristics. *Note:* A very startling effect is to shine a flashlight beam on this image. Even at a glancing angle, the incoming light beam is seemingly reflected from the image! Do you understand why?

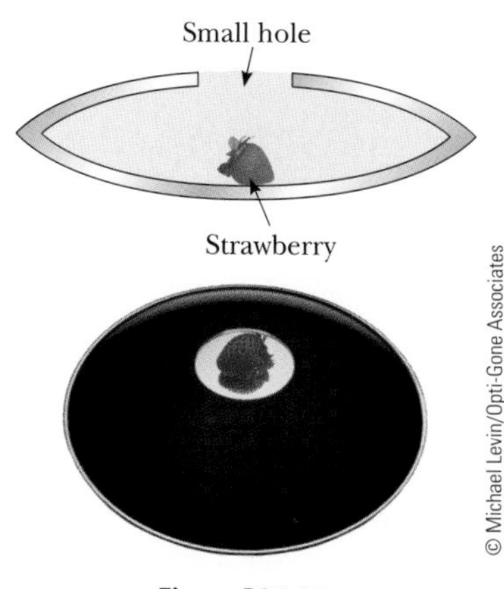

Figure P36.66

67. An object 2.00 cm high is placed 40.0 cm to the left of a converging lens having a focal length of 30.0 cm. A diverging lens with a focal length of −20.0 cm is placed 110 cm to the right of the converging lens. (a) Determine the position and magnification of the final image. (b) Is the image upright or inverted? (c) **What If?** Repeat parts (a) and (b) for the case in which the second lens is a converging lens having a focal length of +20.0 cm.

68. Two lenses made of kinds of glass having different indices of refraction n_1 and n_2 are cemented together to form an *optical doublet.* Optical doublets are often used to correct chromatic aberrations in optical devices. The first lens of a certain doublet has one flat side and one concave side with a radius of curvature of magnitude R. The second lens has two convex sides with radii of curvature also of magnitude R. Show that the doublet can be modeled as a single thin lens with a focal length described by

$$\frac{1}{f} = \frac{2n_2 - n_1 - 1}{R}$$

Answers to Quick Quizzes

36.1 False. The water spots are 2 m away from you, and your image is 4 m away. You cannot focus your eyes on both at the same time.

36.2 (b). A concave mirror focuses the light from a large area of the mirror onto a small area of the paper, resulting in a very high power input to the paper.

36.3 (b). A convex mirror always forms an image with a magnification less than 1, so the mirror must be concave. In a concave mirror, only virtual images are upright. This particular photograph is of the Hubble Space Telescope primary mirror. The scientists acting as the object for the image are to the left of the photograph and not visible to us.

36.4 (d). When O is far away, the rays refract into the material of index n_2 and converge to form a real image as in Figure 36.16. For certain combinations of R and n_2 as O moves very close to the refracting surface, the incident angle of the rays increases so much that rays are no longer refracted back toward the principal axis. The result is a virtual image as shown in the next column.

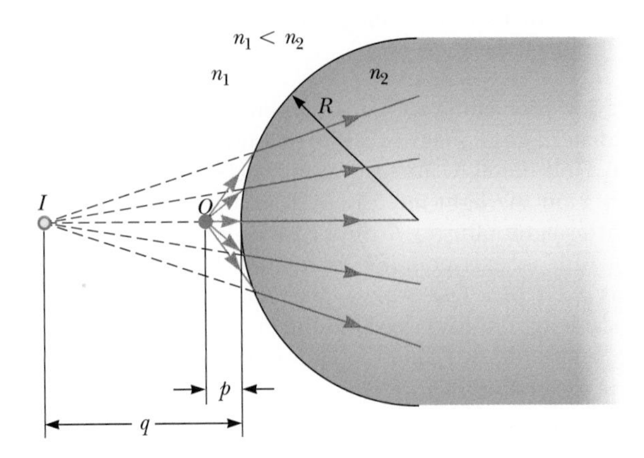

36.5 (a). No matter where O is, the rays refract into the air away from the normal and form a virtual image between O and the surface.

36.6 (b). Because the flat surfaces of the plane have infinite radii of curvature, Equation 36.15 indicates that the focal length is also infinite. Parallel rays striking the plane focus at infinity, which means that they remain parallel after passing through the glass.

36.7 (a). If the object is brought closer to the lens, the image moves farther away from the lens, behind the plane of the CCD. To bring the image back up to the CCD, the lens is moved toward the object and away from the CCD.

36.8 (c). The Sun's rays must converge onto the paper. A farsighted person wears converging lenses.

The colors in many of a hummingbird's feathers are not due to pigment. The *iridescence* that makes the brilliant colors that often appear on the bird's throat and belly is due to an interference effect caused by structures in the feathers. The colors will vary with the viewing angle. (RO-MA/Index Stock Imagery)

37 Interference of Light Waves

In Chapter 36, we studied light rays passing through a lens or reflecting from a mirror to describe the formation of images. This discussion completed our study of *geometric optics*. In this chapter and in Chapter 38, we are concerned with *wave optics* or *physical optics*, the study of interference, diffraction, and polarization of light. These phenomena cannot be adequately explained with the ray optics used in Chapters 35 and 36. We now learn how treating light as waves rather than as rays leads to a satisfying description of such phenomena.

37.1 Conditions for Interference

In Chapter 18, we studied the waves in interference model and found that the superposition of two mechanical waves can be constructive or destructive. In constructive interference, the amplitude of the resultant wave is greater than that of either individual wave, whereas in destructive interference, the resultant amplitude is less than that of the larger wave. Light waves also interfere with one another. Fundamentally, all interference associated with light waves arises when the electromagnetic fields that constitute the individual waves combine.

If two lightbulbs are placed side by side so that light from both bulbs combines, no interference effects are observed because the light waves from one bulb are emitted independently of those from the other bulb. The emissions from the two lightbulbs do not maintain a constant phase relationship with each other over time. Light waves from an ordinary source such as a lightbulb undergo random phase changes in time intervals of less than a nanosecond. Therefore, the conditions for constructive interference, destructive interference, or some intermediate state are maintained only for such short time intervals. Because the eye cannot follow such rapid changes, no interference effects are observed. Such light sources are said to be **incoherent.**

To observe interference of waves from two sources, the following conditions must be met:

Conditions for interference ▶

- The sources must be **coherent**; that is, **they must maintain a constant phase with respect to each other.**
- The sources should be **monochromatic**; that is, they should be of a single wavelength.

As an example, single-frequency sound waves emitted by two side-by-side loudspeakers driven by a single amplifier can interfere with each other because the two speakers are coherent. In other words, they respond to the amplifier in the same way at the same time.

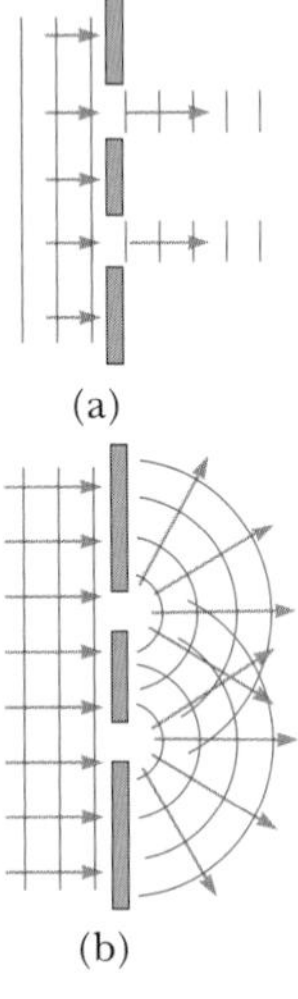

Figure 37.1 (a) If light waves did not spread out after passing through the slits, no interference would occur. (b) The light waves from the two slits overlap as they spread out, filling what we expect to be shadowed regions with light and producing interference fringes on a screen placed to the right of the slits.

37.2 Young's Double-Slit Experiment

A common method for producing two coherent light sources is to use a monochromatic source to illuminate a barrier containing two small openings, usually in the shape of slits. The light emerging from the two slits is coherent because a single source produces the original light beam and the two slits serve only to separate the original beam into two parts (which, after all, is what is done to the sound signal from two side-by-side loudspeakers). Any random change in the light emitted by the source occurs in both beams at the same time. As a result, interference effects can be observed when the light from the two slits arrives at a viewing screen.

If the light traveled only in its original direction after passing through the slits as shown in Figure 37.1a, the waves would not overlap and no interference pattern would be seen. Instead, as we have discussed in our treatment of Huygens's principle (Section 35.6), the waves spread out from the slits as shown in Figure 37.1b. In other words, the light deviates from a straight-line path and enters the region that

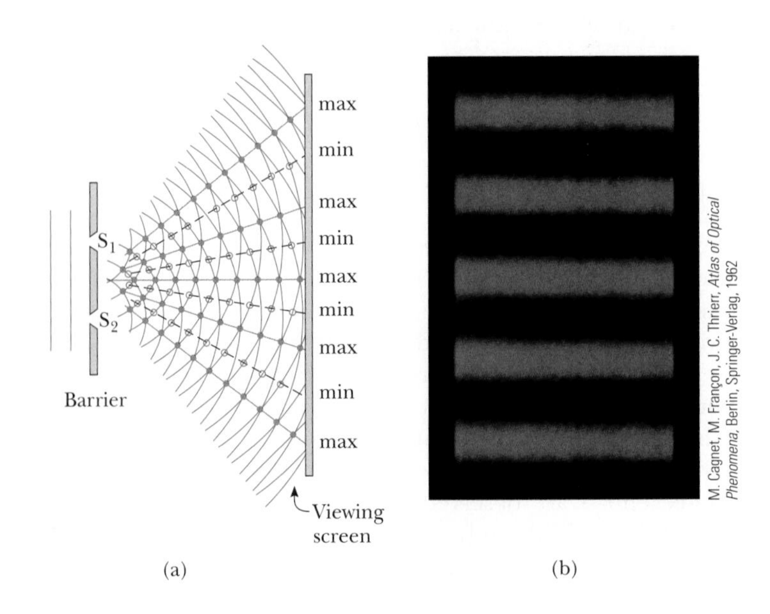

ACTIVE FIGURE 37.2

(a) Schematic diagram of Young's double-slit experiment. Slits S_1 and S_2 behave as coherent sources of light waves that produce an interference pattern on the viewing screen (drawing not to scale). (b) An enlargement of the center of a fringe pattern formed on the viewing screen.

Sign in at www.thomsonedu.com and go to ThomsonNOW to adjust the slit separation and the wavelength of the light and see the effect on the interference pattern.

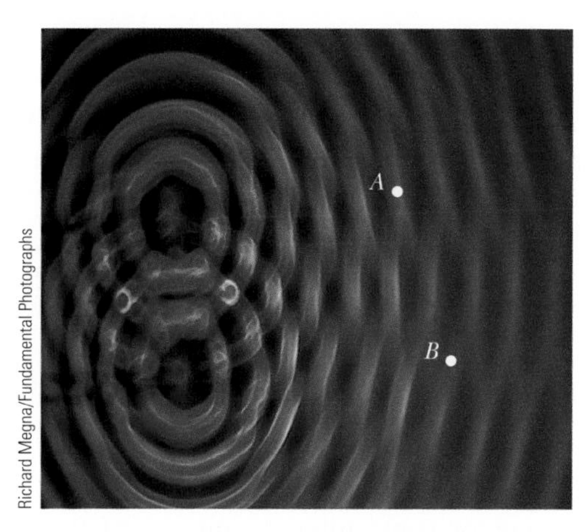

Figure 37.3 An interference pattern involving water waves is produced by two vibrating sources at the water's surface. The pattern is analogous to that observed in Young's double-slit experiment. Notice the regions of constructive (A) and destructive (B) interference.

would otherwise be shadowed. As noted in Section 35.3, this divergence of light from its initial line of travel is called **diffraction.**

Interference in light waves from two sources was first demonstrated by Thomas Young in 1801. A schematic diagram of the apparatus Young used is shown in Active Figure 37.2a. Plane light waves arrive at a barrier that contains two parallel slits S_1 and S_2. The light from S_1 and S_2 produces on a viewing screen a visible pattern of bright and dark parallel bands called **fringes** (Active Fig. 37.2b). When the light from S_1 and that from S_2 both arrive at a point on the screen such that constructive interference occurs at that location, a bright fringe appears. When the light from the two slits combines destructively at any location on the screen, a dark fringe results. Figure 37.3 is a photograph of an interference pattern produced by two coherent vibrating sources in a water tank.

Figure 37.4 shows some of the ways in which two waves can combine at the screen. In Figure 37.4a, the two waves, which leave the two slits in phase, strike the screen at the central point O. Because both waves travel the same distance, they arrive at O in phase. As a result, constructive interference occurs at this location and a bright fringe is observed. In Figure 37.4b, the two waves also start in phase, but here the lower wave has to travel one wavelength farther than the upper wave to reach point P. Because the lower wave falls behind the upper one by exactly one wavelength, they still arrive in phase at P and a second bright fringe appears at this location. At point R in Figure 37.4c, however, between points O and P, the lower wave has fallen half a wavelength behind the upper wave and a trough of the upper wave overlaps a crest of the lower wave, giving rise to destructive interference at point R. A dark fringe is therefore observed at this location.

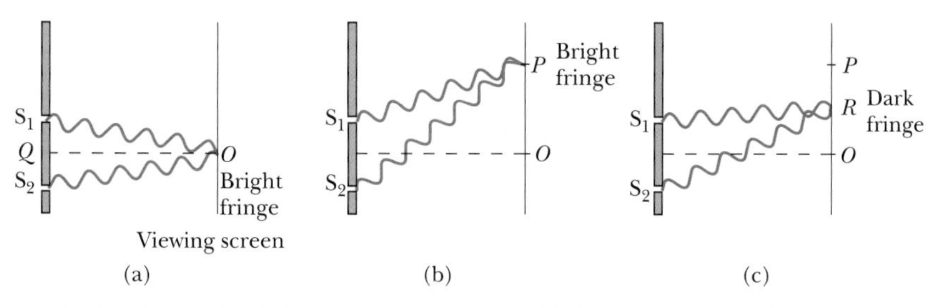

Figure 37.4 (a) Constructive interference occurs at point O when the waves combine. (b) Constructive interference also occurs at point P. (c) Destructive interference occurs at point R when the two waves combine because the lower wave falls one-half a wavelength behind the upper wave. (All figures not to scale.)

37.3 Light Waves in Interference

We can describe Young's experiment quantitatively with the help of Figure 37.5. The viewing screen is located a perpendicular distance L from the barrier containing two slits, S_1 and S_2 (Fig. 37.5a). These slits are separated by a distance d, and the source is monochromatic. To reach any arbitrary point P in the upper half of the screen, a wave from the lower slit must travel farther than a wave from the upper slit by a distance $d \sin \theta$ (Fig. 37.5b). This distance is called the **path difference** δ (Greek letter delta). If we assume the rays labeled r_1 and r_2 are parallel, which is approximately true if L is much greater than d, then δ is given by

Path difference ▶

$$\delta = r_2 - r_1 = d \sin \theta \quad \textbf{(37.1)}$$

The value of δ determines whether the two waves are in phase when they arrive at point P. If δ is either zero or some integer multiple of the wavelength, the two waves are in phase at point P and constructive interference results. Therefore, the condition for bright fringes, or **constructive interference,** at point P is

Conditions for constructive interference ▶

$$d \sin \theta_{\text{bright}} = m\lambda \quad (m = 0, \pm 1, \pm 2, \cdots) \quad \textbf{(37.2)}$$

The number m is called the **order number.** For constructive interference, the order number is the same as the number of wavelengths that represents the path difference between the waves from the two slits. The central bright fringe at $\theta_{\text{bright}} = 0$ is called the *zeroth-order maximum.* The first maximum on either side, where $m = \pm 1$, is called the *first-order maximum,* and so forth.

When δ is an odd multiple of $\lambda/2$, the two waves arriving at point P are 180° out of phase and give rise to destructive interference. Therefore, the condition for dark fringes, or **destructive interference,** at point P is

Conditions for destructive interference ▶

$$d \sin \theta_{\text{dark}} = (m + \tfrac{1}{2})\lambda \quad (m = 0, \pm 1, \pm 2, \cdots) \quad \textbf{(37.3)}$$

These equations provide the *angular* positions of the fringes. It is also useful to obtain expressions for the *linear* positions measured along the screen from O to P. From the triangle OPQ in Figure 37.5a, we see that

$$\tan \theta = \frac{y}{L} \quad \textbf{(37.4)}$$

Using this result, the linear positions of bright and dark fringes are given by

$$y_{\text{bright}} = L \tan \theta_{\text{bright}} \quad \textbf{(37.5)}$$

$$y_{\text{dark}} = L \tan \theta_{\text{dark}} \quad \textbf{(37.6)}$$

where θ_{bright} and θ_{dark} are given by Equations 37.2 and 37.3.

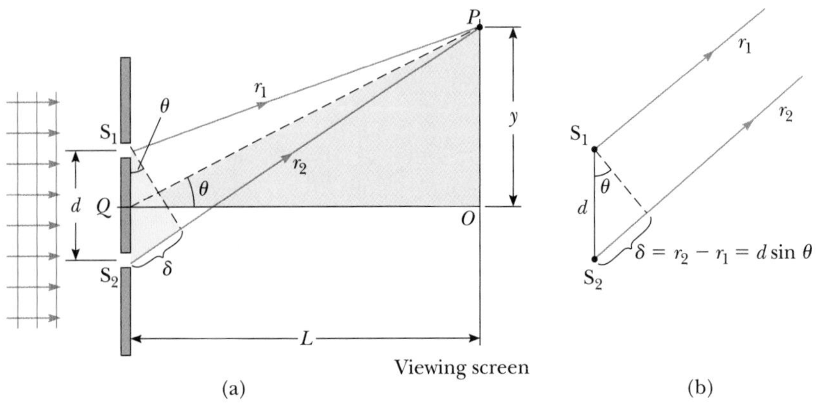

Figure 37.5 (a) Geometric construction for describing Young's double-slit experiment (not to scale). (b) When we assume r_1 is parallel to r_2, the path difference between the two rays is $r_2 - r_1 = d \sin \theta$. For this approximation to be valid, it is essential that $L \gg d$.

When the angles to the fringes are small, the positions of the fringes are linear near the center of the pattern. This can be verified by noting that for small angles, $\tan\theta \approx \sin\theta$, so Equation 37.5 gives the positions of the bright fringes as $y_{\text{bright}} = L\sin\theta_{\text{bright}}$. Incorporating Equation 37.2 gives

$$y_{\text{bright}} = L\left(\frac{m\lambda}{d}\right) \quad \text{(small angles)} \qquad \textbf{(37.7)}$$

This result shows that y_{bright} is linear in the order number m, so the fringes are equally spaced.

As demonstrated in Example 37.1, Young's double-slit experiment provides a method for measuring the wavelength of light. In fact, Young used this technique to do precisely that. In addition, his experiment gave the wave model of light a great deal of credibility. It was inconceivable that particles of light coming through the slits could cancel one another in a way that would explain the dark fringes.

The principles discussed in this section are the basis of the **waves in interference** analysis model. This model was applied to mechanical waves in one dimension in Chapter 18. Here we see the details of applying this model in three dimensions to light.

The faint pastel-colored bows beneath the main rainbow are called *supernumerary bows.* They are formed by interference between rays of light leaving raindrops at angles slightly smaller than the angle of maximum intensity. (See Section 35.7 for a discussion of the rainbow.)

Quick Quiz 37.1 Which of the following causes the fringes in a two-slit interference pattern to move farther apart? (a) decreasing the wavelength of the light (b) decreasing the screen distance L (c) decreasing the slit spacing d (d) immersing the entire apparatus in water

EXAMPLE 37.1 Measuring the Wavelength of a Light Source

A viewing screen is separated from a double slit by 1.2 m. The distance between the two slits is 0.030 mm. Monochromatic light is directed toward the double slit and forms an interference pattern on the screen. The second-order bright fringe ($m = 2$) is 4.5 cm from the center line on the screen.

(A) Determine the wavelength of the light.

SOLUTION

Conceptualize Study Figure 37.5 to be sure you understand the phenomenon of interference of light waves.

Categorize We evaluate results using equations developed in this section, so we categorize this example as a substitution problem.

Solve Equation 37.7 for the wavelength and substitute numerical values:

$$\lambda = \frac{y_{\text{bright}}d}{mL} = \frac{(4.5 \times 10^{-2}\text{ m})(3.0 \times 10^{-5}\text{ m})}{2(1.2\text{ m})}$$

$$= 5.6 \times 10^{-7}\text{ m} = 560\text{ nm}$$

(B) Calculate the distance between adjacent bright fringes.

SOLUTION

Find the distance between adjacent bright fringes from Equation 37.7 and the results of part (A):

$$y_{m+1} - y_m = L\frac{(m+1)\lambda}{d} - L\left(\frac{m\lambda}{d}\right)$$

$$= L\left(\frac{\lambda}{d}\right) = 1.2\text{ m}\left(\frac{5.6 \times 10^{-7}\text{ m}}{3.0 \times 10^{-5}\text{ m}}\right)$$

$$= 2.2 \times 10^{-2}\text{ m} = 2.2\text{ cm}$$

EXAMPLE 37.2 Separating Double-Slit Fringes of Two Wavelengths

A light source emits visible light of two wavelengths: $\lambda = 430$ nm and $\lambda' = 510$ nm. The source is used in a double-slit interference experiment in which $L = 1.50$ m and $d = 0.025\ 0$ mm. Find the separation distance between the third-order bright fringes for the two wavelengths.

SOLUTION

Conceptualize In Figure 37.5a, imagine light of two wavelengths incident on the slits and forming two interference patterns on the screen.

Categorize We evaluate results using equations developed in this section, so we categorize this example as a substitution problem.

Use Equation 37.7, with $m = 3$, to find the fringe positions corresponding to these two wavelengths:

$$y_{\text{bright}} = L\left(\frac{m\lambda}{d}\right) = L\left(\frac{3\lambda}{d}\right) = 1.50\text{ m}\left[\frac{3(430 \times 10^{-9}\text{ m})}{0.025\ 0 \times 10^{-3}\text{ m}}\right]$$

$$= 7.74 \times 10^{-2}\text{ m}$$

$$y'_{\text{bright}} = L\left(\frac{m\lambda'}{d}\right) = L\left(\frac{3\lambda'}{d}\right) = 1.50\text{ m}\left[\frac{3(510 \times 10^{-9}\text{ m})}{0.025\ 0 \times 10^{-3}\text{ m}}\right]$$

$$= 9.18 \times 10^{-2}\text{ m}$$

Evaluate the separation distance between the two fringes:

$$\Delta y = 9.18 \times 10^{-2}\text{ m} - 7.74 \times 10^{-2}\text{ m}$$

$$= 1.44 \times 10^{-2}\text{ m} = 1.44\text{ cm}$$

What If? What if we examine the entire interference pattern due to the two wavelengths and look for overlapping fringes? Are there any locations on the screen where the bright fringes from the two wavelengths overlap exactly?

Answer Find such a location by setting the location of any bright fringe due to λ equal to one due to λ', using Equation 37.7:

$$L\left(\frac{m\lambda}{d}\right) = L\left(\frac{m'\lambda'}{d}\right) \rightarrow \frac{m'}{m} = \frac{\lambda}{\lambda'}$$

Substitute the wavelengths:

$$\frac{m'}{m} = \frac{430\text{ nm}}{510\text{ nm}} = \frac{43}{51}$$

Use Equation 37.7 to find the value of y for these fringes:

$$y = 1.50\text{ m}\left[\frac{51(430 \times 10^{-9}\text{ m})}{0.025\ 0 \times 10^{-3}\text{ m}}\right] = 1.32\text{ m}$$

This value of y is comparable to L, so the small-angle approximation used for Equation 37.7 is *not* valid. This conclusion suggests we should not expect Equation 37.7 to give us the correct result. If you use Equation 37.5, you can show that the bright fringes do indeed overlap when the same condition, $m'/m = \lambda/\lambda'$, is met (see Problem 38). Therefore, the 51st fringe of the 430-nm light does overlap with the 43rd fringe of the 510-nm light, but not at the location of 1.32 m. You are asked to find the correct location as part of Problem 38.

37.4 Intensity Distribution of the Double-Slit Interference Pattern

Notice that the edges of the bright fringes in Active Figure 37.2b are not sharp; rather, there is a gradual change from bright to dark. So far, we have discussed the locations of only the centers of the bright and dark fringes on a distant screen. Let's now direct our attention to the intensity of the light at other points between the positions of maximum constructive and destructive interference. In other words, we now calculate the distribution of light intensity associated with the double-slit interference pattern.

Again, suppose the two slits represent coherent sources of sinusoidal waves such that the two waves from the slits have the same angular frequency ω and are in phase. The total magnitude of the electric field at point P on the screen in Figure 37.6 is the superposition of the two waves. Assuming that the two waves have the same amplitude E_0, we can write the magnitude of the electric field at point P due to each wave separately as

$$E_1 = E_0 \sin \omega t \quad \text{and} \quad E_2 = E_0 \sin (\omega t + \phi) \qquad (37.8)$$

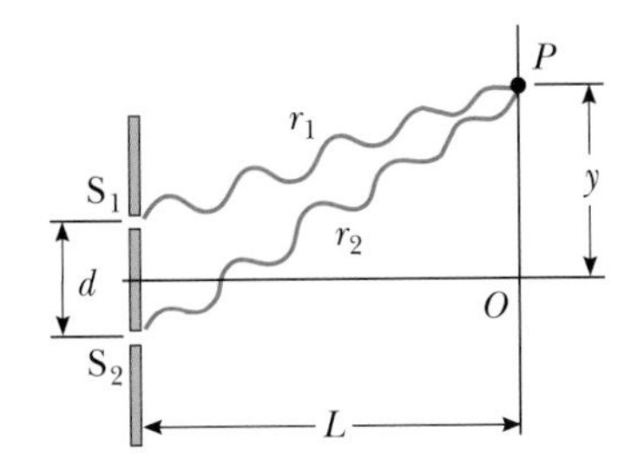

Figure 37.6 Construction for analyzing the double-slit interference pattern. A bright fringe, or intensity maximum, is observed at O.

Although the waves are in phase at the slits, *their phase difference ϕ at P depends on the path difference* $\delta = r_2 - r_1 = d \sin \theta$. A path difference of λ (for constructive interference) corresponds to a phase difference of 2π rad. A path difference of δ is the same fraction of λ as the phase difference ϕ is of 2π. We can describe this fraction mathematically with the ratio

$$\frac{\delta}{\lambda} = \frac{\phi}{2\pi}$$

which gives

$$\phi = \frac{2\pi}{\lambda} \delta = \frac{2\pi}{\lambda} d \sin \theta \qquad (37.9)$$

◀ Phase difference

This equation shows how the phase difference ϕ depends on the angle θ in Figure 37.5.

Using the superposition principle and Equation 37.8, we obtain the following expression for the magnitude of the resultant electric field at point P:

$$E_P = E_1 + E_2 = E_0[\sin \omega t + \sin (\omega t + \phi)] \qquad (37.10)$$

We can simplify this expression by using the trigonometric identity

$$\sin A + \sin B = 2 \sin \left(\frac{A + B}{2}\right) \cos \left(\frac{A - B}{2}\right)$$

Taking $A = \omega t + \phi$ and $B = \omega t$, Equation 37.10 becomes

$$E_P = 2E_0 \cos \left(\frac{\phi}{2}\right) \sin \left(\omega t + \frac{\phi}{2}\right) \qquad (37.11)$$

This result indicates that the electric field at point P has the same frequency ω as the light at the slits but that the amplitude of the field is multiplied by the factor $2 \cos (\phi/2)$. To check the consistency of this result, note that if $\phi = 0, 2\pi, 4\pi, \ldots$, the magnitude of the electric field at point P is $2E_0$, corresponding to the condition for maximum constructive interference. These values of ϕ are consistent with Equation 37.2 for constructive interference. Likewise, if $\phi = \pi, 3\pi, 5\pi, \ldots$, the magnitude of the electric field at point P is zero, which is consistent with Equation 37.3 for total destructive interference.

Finally, to obtain an expression for the light intensity at point P, recall from Section 34.4 that *the intensity of a wave is proportional to the square of the resultant electric field magnitude at that point* (Eq. 34.24). Using Equation 37.11, we can therefore express the light intensity at point P as

$$I \propto E_P^2 = 4E_0^2 \cos^2 \left(\frac{\phi}{2}\right) \sin^2 \left(\omega t + \frac{\phi}{2}\right)$$

Most light-detecting instruments measure time-averaged light intensity, and the time-averaged value of $\sin^2 (\omega t + \phi/2)$ over one cycle is $\frac{1}{2}$. (See Fig. 33.5.) Therefore, we can write the average light intensity at point P as

$$I = I_{\text{max}} \cos^2 \left(\frac{\phi}{2}\right) \qquad (37.12)$$

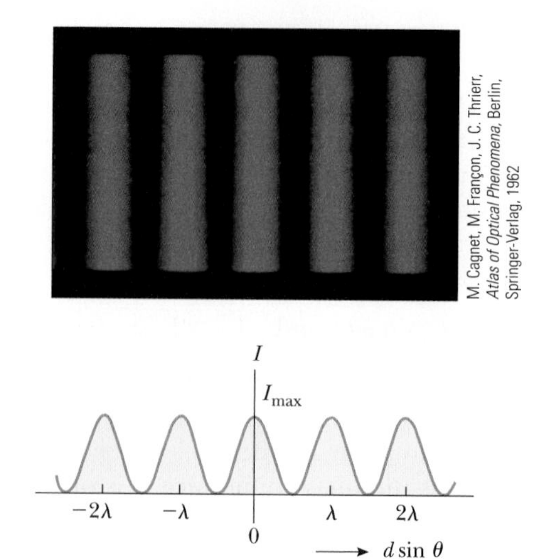

Figure 37.7 Light intensity versus $d \sin \theta$ for a double-slit interference pattern when the screen is far from the two slits ($L \gg d$).

where I_{max} is the maximum intensity on the screen and the expression represents the time average. Substituting the value for ϕ given by Equation 37.9 into this expression gives

$$I = I_{\text{max}} \cos^2 \left(\frac{\pi d \sin \theta}{\lambda} \right) \tag{37.13}$$

Alternatively, because $\sin \theta \approx y/L$ for small values of θ in Figure 37.5, we can write Equation 37.13 in the form

$$I = I_{\text{max}} \cos^2 \left(\frac{\pi d}{\lambda L} y \right) \tag{37.14}$$

Constructive interference, which produces light intensity maxima, occurs when the quantity $\pi \, dy/\lambda L$ is an integral multiple of π, corresponding to $y = (\lambda L/d)\, m$. This result is consistent with Equation 37.7.

A plot of light intensity versus $d \sin \theta$ is given in Figure 37.7. The interference pattern consists of equally spaced fringes of equal intensity. Remember, however, that this result is valid only if the slit-to-screen distance L is much greater than the slit separation and only for small values of θ.

Figure 37.8 shows similar plots of light intensity versus $d \sin \theta$ for light passing through multiple slits. For more than two slits, the pattern contains primary and secondary maxima. For three slits, notice that the primary maxima are nine times more intense than the secondary maxima as measured by the height of the curve because the intensity varies as E^2. For N slits, the intensity of the primary maxima is N^2 times greater than that due to a single slit. As the number of slits increases, the primary maxima increase in intensity and become narrower, while the secondary maxima decrease in intensity relative to the primary maxima. Figure 37.8 also shows that as the number of slits increases, the number of secondary maxima also increases. In fact, the number of secondary maxima is always $N - 2$, where N is the number of slits. In Section 38.4, we shall investigate the pattern for a very large number of slits in a device called a *diffraction grating.*

Quick Quiz 37.2 Using Figure 37.8 as a model, sketch the interference pattern from six slits.

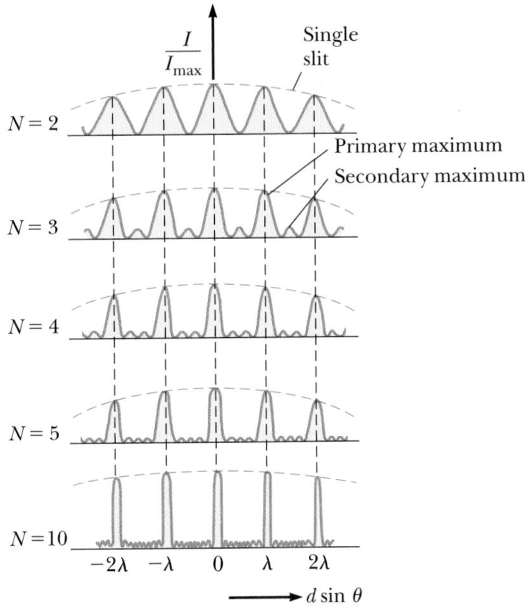

Figure 37.8 Multiple-slit interference patterns. As N, the number of slits, is increased, the primary maxima (the tallest peaks in each graph) become narrower but remain fixed in position and the number of secondary maxima increases. For any value of N, the decrease in intensity in maxima to the left and right of the central maximum, indicated by the blue dashed arcs, is due to *diffraction patterns* from the individual slits, which are discussed in Chapter 38.

37.5 Change of Phase Due to Reflection

Young's method for producing two coherent light sources involves illuminating a pair of slits with a single source. Another simple, yet ingenious, arrangement for producing an interference pattern with a single light source is known as *Lloyd's mirror*[1] (Fig. 37.9). A point light source S is placed close to a mirror, and a viewing screen is positioned some distance away and perpendicular to the mirror. Light waves can reach point P on the screen either directly from S to P or by the path involving reflection from the mirror. The reflected ray can be treated as a ray originating from a virtual source S$'$. As a result, we can think of this arrangement as a double-slit source with the distance between sources S and S$'$ comparable to length d in Figure 37.5. Hence, at observation points far from the source ($L \gg d$), we expect waves from S and S$'$ to form an interference pattern exactly like the one formed by two real coherent sources. An interference pattern is indeed observed. The positions of the dark and bright fringes, however, are reversed relative to the pattern created by two real coherent sources (Young's experiment). Such a reversal can only occur if the coherent sources S and S$'$ differ in phase by 180°.

To illustrate further, consider point P', the point where the mirror intersects the screen. This point is equidistant from sources S and S$'$. If path difference alone were responsible for the phase difference, we would see a bright fringe at P' (because the path difference is zero for this point), corresponding to the central bright fringe of the two-slit interference pattern. Instead, a dark fringe is observed at P'. We therefore conclude that a 180° phase change must be produced by reflection from the mirror. In general, **an electromagnetic wave undergoes a phase change of 180° upon reflection from a medium that has a higher index of refraction than the one in which the wave is traveling.**

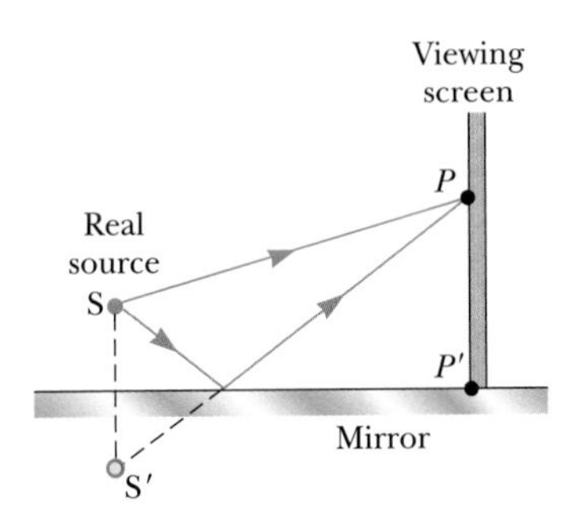

Figure 37.9 Lloyd's mirror. An interference pattern is produced at point P on the screen as a result of the combination of the direct ray (blue) and the reflected ray (brown). The reflected ray undergoes a phase change of 180°.

It is useful to draw an analogy between reflected light waves and the reflections of a transverse wave pulse on a stretched string (Section 16.4). The reflected pulse on a string undergoes a phase change of 180° when reflected from the boundary

[1] Developed in 1834 by Humphrey Lloyd (1800–1881), Professor of Natural and Experimental Philosophy, Trinity College, Dublin.

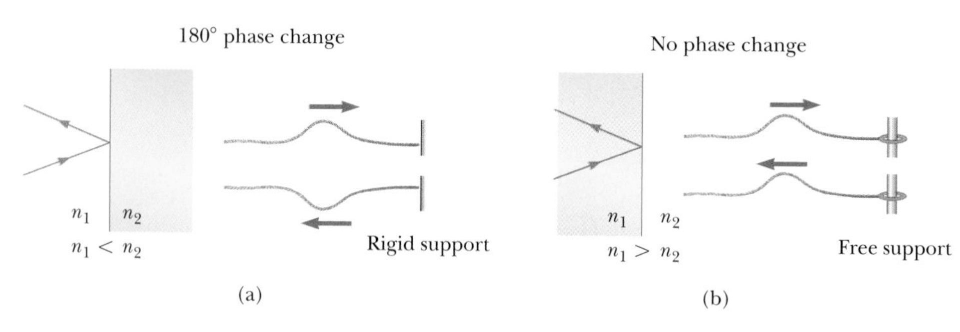

Figure 37.10 (a) For $n_1 < n_2$, a light ray traveling in medium 1 when reflected from the surface of medium 2 undergoes a 180° phase change. The same thing happens with a reflected pulse traveling along a string fixed at one end. (b) For $n_1 > n_2$, a light ray traveling in medium 1 undergoes no phase change when reflected from the surface of medium 2. The same is true of a reflected wave pulse on a string whose supported end is free to move.

of a denser medium, but no phase change occurs when the pulse is reflected from the boundary of a less dense medium. Similarly, an electromagnetic wave undergoes a 180° phase change when reflected from a boundary leading to an optically denser medium (defined as a medium with a higher index of refraction), but no phase change occurs when the wave is reflected from a boundary leading to a less dense medium. These rules, summarized in Figure 37.10, can be deduced from Maxwell's equations, but the treatment is beyond the scope of this text.

37.6 Interference in Thin Films

Interference effects are commonly observed in thin films, such as thin layers of oil on water or the thin surface of a soap bubble. The varied colors observed when white light is incident on such films result from the interference of waves reflected from the two surfaces of the film.

Consider a film of uniform thickness t and index of refraction n as shown in Figure 37.11. Let's assume the light rays traveling in air are nearly normal to the two surfaces of the film. The wavelength of light λ_n in the film (see Section 35.5) is

$$\lambda_n = \frac{\lambda}{n}$$

where λ is the wavelength of the light in free space and n is the index of refraction of the film material.

180° phase change
No phase change
1
2
Air
A
Film
t
B
Air
3
4

Figure 37.11 Interference in light reflected from a thin film is due to a combination of rays 1 and 2 reflected from the upper and lower surfaces of the film. Rays 3 and 4 lead to interference effects for light transmitted through the film.

Reflected ray 1, which is reflected from the upper surface (A) in Figure 37.11, undergoes a phase change of 180° with respect to the incident wave. Reflected ray 2, which is reflected from the lower film surface (B), undergoes no phase change because it is reflected from a medium (air) that has a lower index of refraction. Therefore, ray 1 is 180° out of phase with ray 2, which is equivalent to a path difference of $\lambda_n/2$. We must also consider, however, that ray 2 travels an extra distance $2t$ before the waves recombine in the air above surface A. (Remember that we are considering light rays that are close to normal to the surface. If the rays are not close to normal, the path difference is larger than $2t$.) If $2t = \lambda_n/2$, rays 1 and 2 recombine in phase and the result is constructive interference. In general, the condition for *constructive* interference in thin films is[2]

$$2t = (m + \tfrac{1}{2})\lambda_n \quad (m = 0, 1, 2, \ldots) \qquad \textbf{(37.15)}$$

This condition takes into account two factors: (1) the difference in path length for the two rays (the term $m\lambda_n$) and (2) the 180° phase change upon reflection (the term $\frac{1}{2}\lambda_n$). Because $\lambda_n = \lambda/n$, we can write Equation 37.15 as

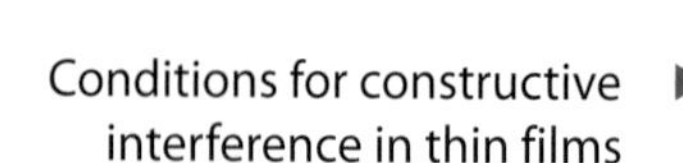

$$2nt = (m + \tfrac{1}{2})\lambda \quad (m = 0, 1, 2, \ldots) \qquad \textbf{(37.16)}$$

[2] The full interference effect in a thin film requires an analysis of an infinite number of reflections back and forth between the top and bottom surfaces of the film. We focus here only on a single reflection from the bottom of the film, which provides the largest contribution to the interference effect.

If the extra distance $2t$ traveled by ray 2 corresponds to a multiple of λ_n, the two waves combine out of phase and the result is destructive interference. The general equation for *destructive* interference in thin films is

$$2nt = m\lambda \quad (m = 0, 1, 2, \dots) \qquad \textbf{(37.17)}$$

◀ Conditions for destructive interference in thin films

The foregoing conditions for constructive and destructive interference are valid when the medium above the top surface of the film is the same as the medium below the bottom surface or, if there are different media above and below the film, the index of refraction of both is less than n. If the film is placed between two different media, one with $n < n_{\text{film}}$ and the other with $n > n_{\text{film}}$, the conditions for constructive and destructive interference are reversed. In that case, either there is a phase change of 180° for both ray 1 reflecting from surface A and ray 2 reflecting from surface B or there is no phase change for either ray; hence, the net change in relative phase due to the reflections is zero.

Rays 3 and 4 in Figure 37.11 lead to interference effects in the light transmitted through the thin film. The analysis of these effects is similar to that of the reflected light. You are asked to explore the transmitted light in Problems 23, 29, and 30.

PITFALL PREVENTION 37.1
Be Careful with Thin Films

Be sure to include *both* effects—path length and phase change—when analyzing an interference pattern resulting from a thin film. The possible phase change is a new feature we did not need to consider for double-slit interference. Also think carefully about the material on either side of the film. You may have a situation in which there is a 180° phase change at *both* surfaces or at *neither* surface, if there are different materials on either side of the film.

Quick Quiz 37.3 One microscope slide is placed on top of another with their left edges in contact and a human hair under the right edge of the upper slide. As a result, a wedge of air exists between the slides. An interference pattern results when monochromatic light is incident on the wedge. What is at the left edges of the slides? (a) a dark fringe (b) a bright fringe (c) impossible to determine

Newton's Rings

Another method for observing interference in light waves is to place a plano-convex lens on top of a flat glass surface as shown in Figure 37.12a. With this arrangement, the air film between the glass surfaces varies in thickness from zero at the point of contact to some value t at point P. If the radius of curvature R of the lens is much greater than the distance r and the system is viewed from above, a pattern of light and dark rings is observed as shown in Figure 37.12b. These circular fringes, discovered by Newton, are called **Newton's rings.**

The interference effect is due to the combination of ray 1, reflected from the flat plate, with ray 2, reflected from the curved surface of the lens. Ray 1 undergoes a phase change of 180° upon reflection (because it is reflected from a medium of higher index of refraction), whereas ray 2 undergoes no phase change (because it is reflected from a medium of lower index of refraction). Hence, the conditions for constructive and destructive interference are given by Equations 37.16 and 37.17, respectively, with $n = 1$ because the film is air. Because there is

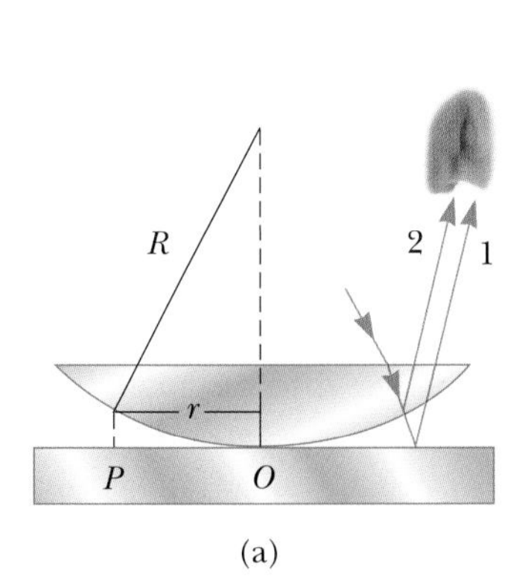

(a)

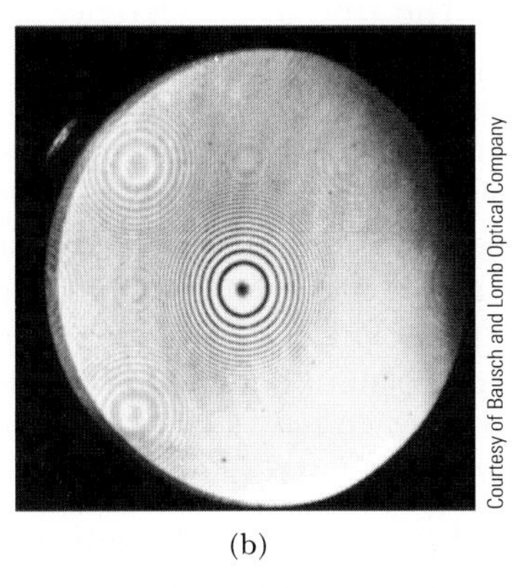

(b)

Figure 37.12 (a) The combination of rays reflected from the flat plate and the curved lens surface gives rise to an interference pattern known as Newton's rings. (b) Photograph of Newton's rings.

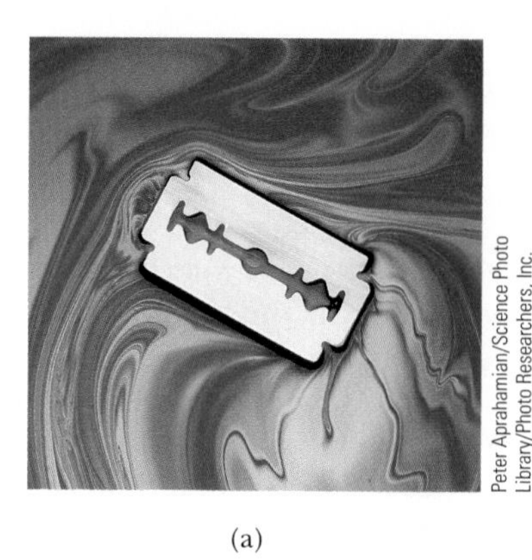

(a)

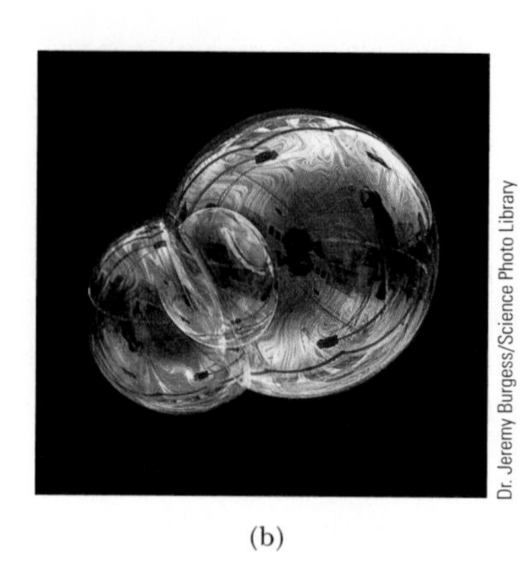

(b)

(a) A thin film of oil floating on water displays interference, shown by the pattern of colors when white light is incident on the film. Variations in film thickness produce the interesting color pattern. The razor blade gives you an idea of the size of the colored bands. (b) Interference in soap bubbles. The colors are due to interference between light rays reflected from the front and back surfaces of the thin film of soap making up the bubble. The color depends on the thickness of the film, ranging from black, where the film is thinnest, to magenta, where it is thickest.

no path difference and the total phase change is due only to the 180° phase change upon reflection, the contact point at O is dark as seen in Figure 37.12b.

Using the geometry shown in Figure 37.12a, we can obtain expressions for the radii of the bright and dark bands in terms of the radius of curvature R and wavelength λ. For example, the dark rings have radii given by the expression $r \approx \sqrt{m\lambda R/n}$. The details are left as a problem (see Problem 60). We can obtain the wavelength of the light causing the interference pattern by measuring the radii of the rings, provided R is known. Conversely, we can use a known wavelength to obtain R.

One important use of Newton's rings is in the testing of optical lenses. A circular pattern like that pictured in Figure 37.12b is obtained only when the lens is ground to a perfectly symmetric curvature. Variations from such symmetry produce a pattern with fringes that vary from a smooth, circular shape. These variations indicate how the lens must be reground and repolished to remove imperfections.

PROBLEM-SOLVING STRATEGY **Thin-Film Interference**

The following features should be kept in mind when working thin-film interference problems.

1. *Conceptualize.* Think about what is going on physically in the problem. Identify the light source and the location of the observer.

2. *Categorize.* Confirm that you should use the techniques for thin-film interference by identifying the thin film causing the interference.

3. *Analyze.* The type of interference that occurs is determined by the phase relationship between the portion of the wave reflected at the upper surface of the film and the portion reflected at the lower surface. Phase differences between the two portions of the wave have two causes: differences in the distances traveled by the two portions and phase changes occurring on reflection. *Both* causes must be considered when determining which type of interference occurs. If the media above and below the film both have index of refraction larger than that of the film or if both indices are smaller, use Equation 37.16 for constructive interference and Equation 37.17 for destructive interference. If the film is located between two different media, one with $n < n_{\text{film}}$ and the other with $n > n_{\text{film}}$, reverse these two equations for constructive and destructive interference.

4. *Finalize.* Inspect your final results to see if they make sense physically and are of an appropriate size.

EXAMPLE 37.3 Interference in a Soap Film

Calculate the minimum thickness of a soap-bubble film that results in constructive interference in the reflected light if the film is illuminated with light whose wavelength in free space is $\lambda = 600$ nm. The index of refraction of the soap film is 1.33.

SOLUTION

Conceptualize Imagine that the film in Figure 37.11 is soap, with air on both sides.

Categorize We evaluate the result using an equation from this section, so we categorize this example as a substitution problem.

The minimum film thickness for constructive interference in the reflected light corresponds to $m = 0$ in Equation 37.16. Solve this equation for t and substitute numerical values:

$$t = \frac{(0 + \frac{1}{2})\lambda}{2n} = \frac{\lambda}{4n} = \frac{(600 \text{ nm})}{4(1.33)} = 113 \text{ nm}$$

What If? What if the film is twice as thick? Does this situation produce constructive interference?

Answer Using Equation 37.16, we can solve for the thicknesses at which constructive interference occurs:

$$t = (m + \tfrac{1}{2})\frac{\lambda}{2n} = (2m + 1)\frac{\lambda}{4n} \qquad (m = 0, 1, 2, \ldots)$$

The allowed values of m show that constructive interference occurs for *odd* multiples of the thickness corresponding to $m = 0$, $t = 113$ nm. Therefore, constructive interference does *not* occur for a film that is twice as thick.

EXAMPLE 37.4 Nonreflective Coatings for Solar Cells

Solar cells—devices that generate electricity when exposed to sunlight—are often coated with a transparent, thin film of silicon monoxide (SiO, $n = 1.45$) to minimize reflective losses from the surface. Suppose a silicon solar cell ($n = 3.5$) is coated with a thin film of silicon monoxide for this purpose (Fig. 37.13a). Determine the minimum film thickness that produces the least reflection at a wavelength of 550 nm, near the center of the visible spectrum.

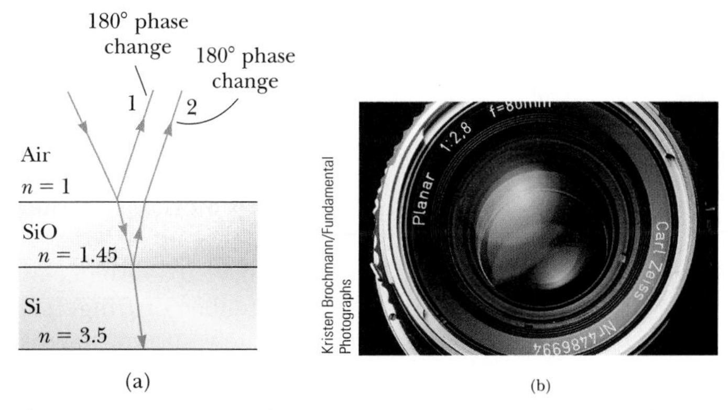

Figure 37.13 (Example 37.4) (a) Reflective losses from a silicon solar cell are minimized by coating the surface of the cell with a thin film of silicon monoxide. (b) The reflected light from a coated camera lens often has a reddish-violet appearance.

SOLUTION

Conceptualize Figure 37.13a helps us visualize the path of the rays in the SiO film that result in interference in the reflected light.

Categorize Based on the geometry of the SiO layer, we categorize this example as a thin-film interference problem.

Analyze The reflected light is a minimum when rays 1 and 2 in Figure 37.13a meet the condition of destructive interference. In this situation, *both* rays undergo a 180° phase change upon reflection: ray 1 from the upper SiO surface, and ray 2 from the lower SiO surface. The net change in phase due to reflection is therefore zero, and the condition for a reflection minimum requires a path difference of $\lambda_n/2$, where λ_n is the wavelength of the light in SiO. Hence, $2nt = \lambda/2$, where λ is the wavelength in air and n is the index of refraction of SiO.

Solve the equation $2nt = \lambda/2$ for t and substitute numerical values:

$$t = \frac{\lambda}{4n} = \frac{550 \text{ nm}}{4(1.45)} = 94.8 \text{ nm}$$

Finalize A typical uncoated solar cell has reflective losses as high as 30%, but a coating of SiO can reduce this value to about 10%. This significant decrease in reflective losses increases the cell's efficiency because less reflection means that more sunlight enters the silicon to create charge carriers in the cell. No coating can ever be made perfectly nonreflecting because the required thickness is wavelength-dependent and the incident light covers a wide range of wavelengths.

Glass lenses used in cameras and other optical instruments are usually coated with a transparent thin film to reduce or eliminate unwanted reflection and to enhance the transmission of light through the lenses. The camera lens in Figure 37.13b has several coatings (of different thicknesses) to minimize reflection of light waves having wavelengths near the center of the visible spectrum. As a result, the small amount of light that is reflected by the lens has a greater proportion of the far ends of the spectrum and often appears reddish violet.

37.7 The Michelson Interferometer

The **interferometer,** invented by American physicist A. A. Michelson (1852–1931), splits a light beam into two parts and then recombines the parts to form an interference pattern. The device can be used to measure wavelengths or other lengths with great precision because a large and precisely measurable displacement of one of the mirrors is related to an exactly countable number of wavelengths of light.

A schematic diagram of the interferometer is shown in Active Figure 37.14. A ray of light from a monochromatic source is split into two rays by mirror M_0, which is inclined at 45° to the incident light beam. Mirror M_0, called a *beam splitter,* transmits half the light incident on it and reflects the rest. One ray is reflected from M_0 vertically upward toward mirror M_1, and the second ray is transmitted horizontally through M_0 toward mirror M_2. Hence, the two rays travel separate paths L_1 and L_2. After reflecting from M_1 and M_2, the two rays eventually recombine at M_0 to produce an interference pattern, which can be viewed through a telescope.

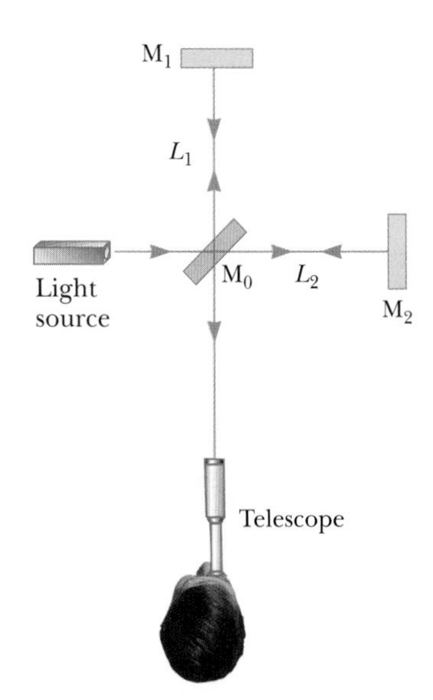

ACTIVE FIGURE 37.14

Diagram of the Michelson interferometer. A single ray of light is split into two rays by mirror M_0, which is called a beam splitter. The path difference between the two rays is varied with the adjustable mirror M_1. As M_1 is moved, an interference pattern changes in the field of view.

Sign in at www.thomsonedu.com and go to ThomsonNOW to move the mirror and see the effect on the interference pattern and use the interferometer to measure the wavelength of light.

The interference condition for the two rays is determined by the difference in their path length. When the two mirrors are exactly perpendicular to each other, the interference pattern is a target pattern of bright and dark circular fringes, similar to Newton's rings. As M_1 is moved, the fringe pattern collapses or expands, depending on the direction in which M_1 is moved. For example, if a dark circle appears at the center of the target pattern (corresponding to destructive interference) and M_1 is then moved a distance $\lambda/4$ toward M_0, the path difference changes by $\lambda/2$. What was a dark circle at the center now becomes a bright circle. As M_1 is moved an additional distance $\lambda/4$ toward M_0, the bright circle becomes a dark circle again. Therefore, the fringe pattern shifts by one-half fringe each time M_1 is moved a distance $\lambda/4$. The wavelength of light is then measured by counting the number of fringe shifts for a given displacement of M_1. If the wavelength is accurately known, mirror displacements can be measured to within a fraction of the wavelength.

We will see an important historical use of the Michelson interferometer in our discussion of relativity in Chapter 39. Modern uses include the following two applications, Fourier transform infrared spectroscopy and the laser interferometer gravitational-wave observatory.

Fourier Transform Infrared Spectroscopy

Spectroscopy is the study of the wavelength distribution of radiation from a sample that can be used to identify the characteristics of atoms or molecules in the sample. Infrared spectroscopy is particularly important to organic chemists when analyzing organic molecules. Traditional spectroscopy involves the use of an optical element, such as a prism (Section 35.5) or a diffraction grating (Section 38.4), which spreads out various wavelengths in a complex optical signal from the sample into different angles. In this way, the various wavelengths of radiation and their intensities in the signal can be determined. These types of devices are limited in their resolution and effectiveness because they must be scanned through the various angular deviations of the radiation.

The technique of *Fourier transform infrared* (FTIR) *spectroscopy* is used to create a higher-resolution spectrum in a time interval of 1 second that may have required 30 minutes with a standard spectrometer. In this technique, the radiation from a sample enters a Michelson interferometer. The movable mirror is swept through the zero-path-difference condition, and the intensity of radiation at the viewing position is recorded. The result is a complex set of data relating light intensity as a function of mirror position, called an *interferogram*. Because there is a relationship between mirror position and light intensity for a given wavelength, the interferogram contains information about all wavelengths in the signal.

In Section 18.8, we discussed Fourier analysis of a waveform. The waveform is a function that contains information about all the individual frequency components that make up the waveform.[3] Equation 18.13 shows how the waveform is generated from the individual frequency components. Similarly, the interferogram can be analyzed by computer, in a process called a *Fourier transform*, to provide all of the wavelength components. This information is the same as that generated by traditional spectroscopy, but the resolution of FTIR spectroscopy is much higher.

Laser Interferometer Gravitational-Wave Observatory

Einstein's general theory of relativity (Section 39.10) predicts the existence of *gravitational waves*. These waves propagate from the site of any gravitational disturbance, which could be periodic and predictable, such as the rotation of a double star around a center of mass, or unpredictable, such as the supernova explosion of a massive star.

In Einstein's theory, gravitation is equivalent to a distortion of space. Therefore, a gravitational disturbance causes an additional distortion that propagates through space in a manner similar to mechanical or electromagnetic waves. When gravitational waves from a disturbance pass by the Earth, they create a distortion of the local space. The laser interferometer gravitational-wave observatory (LIGO) apparatus is designed to detect this distortion. The apparatus employs a Michelson interferometer that uses laser beams with an effective path length of several kilometers. At the end of an arm of the interferometer, a mirror is mounted on a massive pendulum. When a gravitational wave passes by, the pendulum and the attached mirror move and the interference pattern due to the laser beams from the two arms changes.

Two sites for interferometers have been developed in the United States—in Richland, Washington, and in Livingston, Louisiana—to allow coincidence studies of gravitational waves. Figure 37.15 shows the Washington site. The two arms of

Figure 37.15 The Laser Interferometer Gravitational-Wave Observatory (LIGO) near Richland, Washington. Notice the two perpendicular arms of the Michelson interferometer.

[3] In acoustics, it is common to talk about the components of a complex signal in terms of frequency. In optics, it is more common to identify the components by wavelength.

the Michelson interferometer are evident in the photograph. Five data runs have been performed as of 2007. These runs have been coordinated with other gravitational wave detectors, such as GEO in Hannover, Germany, TAMA in Mitaka, Japan, and VIRGO in Cascina, Italy. So far, gravitational waves have not yet been detected, but the data runs have provided critical information for modifications and design features for the next generation of detectors.

Summary

ThomsonNOW™ Sign in at **www.thomsonedu.com** and go to ThomsonNOW to take a practice test for this chapter.

CONCEPTS AND PRINCIPLES

Interference in light waves occurs whenever two or more waves overlap at a given point. An interference pattern is observed if (1) the sources are coherent and (2) the sources have identical wavelengths.

The **intensity** at a point in a double-slit interference pattern is

$$I = I_{\max} \cos^2\left(\frac{\pi d \sin\theta}{\lambda}\right) \quad \textbf{(37.13)}$$

where $I_{\max}$ is the maximum intensity on the screen and the expression represents the time average.

A wave traveling from a medium of index of refraction n_1 toward a medium of index of refraction n_2 undergoes a 180° phase change upon reflection when $n_2 > n_1$ and undergoes no phase change when $n_2 < n_1$.

The condition for constructive interference in a film of thickness t and index of refraction n surrounded by air is

$$2nt = (m + \tfrac{1}{2})\lambda \quad (m = 0, 1, 2, \ldots) \quad \textbf{(37.16)}$$

where λ is the wavelength of the light in free space.

Similarly, the condition for destructive interference in a thin film surrounded by air is

$$2nt = m\lambda \quad (m = 0, 1, 2, \ldots) \quad \textbf{(37.17)}$$

ANALYSIS MODEL FOR PROBLEM SOLVING

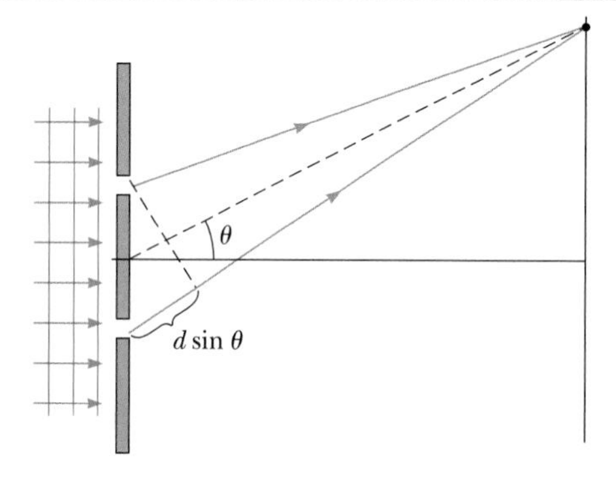

Waves in Interference. Young's double-slit experiment serves as a prototype for interference phenomena involving electromagnetic radiation. In this experiment, two slits separated by a distance d are illuminated by a single-wavelength light source. The condition for bright fringes **(constructive interference)** is

$$d \sin\theta_{\text{bright}} = m\lambda \quad (m = 0, \pm 1, \pm 2, \ldots) \quad \textbf{(37.2)}$$

The condition for dark fringes **(destructive interference)** is

$$d \sin\theta_{\text{dark}} = (m + \tfrac{1}{2})\lambda \quad (m = 0, \pm 1, \pm 2, \ldots) \quad \textbf{(37.3)}$$

The number m is called the **order number** of the fringe.

Questions

☐ denotes answer available in *Student Solutions Manual/Study Guide;* **O** denotes objective question

Question 4 in Chapter 18 may be assigned with this chapter.

☐ **1.** What is the necessary condition on the path length difference between two waves that interfere (a) constructively and (b) destructively?

2. Explain why two flashlights held close together do not produce an interference pattern on a distant screen.

3. **O** Four trials of Young's double-slit experiment are conducted. (a) In the first trial, blue light passes through two fine slits 400 μm apart and forms an interference pattern on a screen 4 m away. (b) In a second trial, red light passes through the same slits and falls on the same screen. (c) A third trial is performed with red light and the same screen, but with slits 800 μm apart. (d) A final trial is performed with red light, slits 800 μm apart, and a screen 8 m away. **(i)** Rank the trials (a) through (d) from largest to smallest value of the angle between the central maximum and the first-order side maximum. In your ranking, note any cases of equality. **(ii)** Rank the same trials according to the distance between the central maximum and the first-order side maximum on the screen.

4. Suppose you blow smoke into the space between the barrier and the viewing screen in Young's double-slit experiment, shown in Active Figure 37.2a. Would the smoke show evidence of interference within this space? Explain your answer.

5. **O** Suppose Young's double-slit experiment is performed in air using red light and then the apparatus is immersed in water. What happens to the interference pattern on the screen? (a) It disappears. (b) The bright and dark fringes stay in the same locations, but the contrast is reduced. (c) The bright fringes are closer together. (d) The color shifts toward blue. (e) The bright fringes are farther apart. (f) The bright fringes are in continuous motion. (g) No change happens in the interference pattern.

☐ **6.** In Young's double-slit experiment, why do we use monochromatic light? If white light is used, how would the pattern change?

7. **O** Suppose you perform Young's double-slit experiment with the slit separation slightly smaller than the wavelength of the light. As a screen, you use a large half-cylinder with its axis along the midline between the slits. What interference pattern will you see on the interior surface of the cylinder? (a) bright and dark fringes so closely spaced as to be indistinguishable (b) one central bright fringe and two dark fringes only (c) a completely bright screen with no dark fringes (d) one central dark fringe and two bright fringes only (e) a completely dark screen with no bright fringes

8. As a soap bubble evaporates, it appears black immediately before it breaks, as at the top of the circular film shown in Figure Q37.8. Explain this phenomenon in terms of the phase changes that occur on reflection from the two surfaces of the soap film.

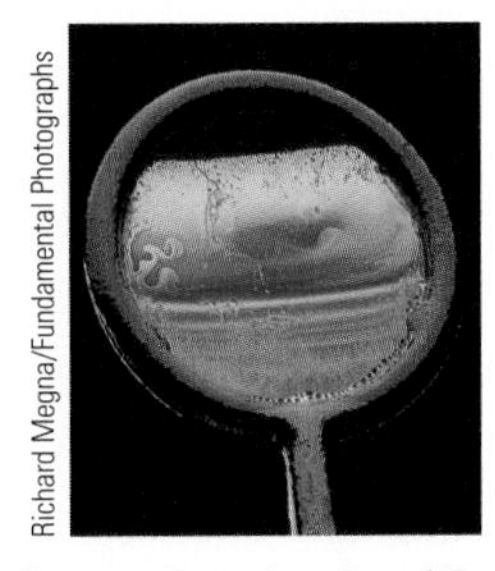

Figure Q37.8 Question 8 and Problem 63.

9. **O** A film of oil on a puddle in a parking lot shows a variety of bright colors in swirled patches. What can you say about the thickness of the oil film? (a) It is much less than the wavelength of visible light. (b) It is of the same order of magnitude as the wavelength of visible light. (c) It is much greater than the wavelength of visible light. (d) It might have any relationship to the wavelength of visible light.

10. **O** Assume the index of refraction of flint glass is 1.66 and the index of refraction of crown glass is 1.52. **(i)** A film formed by one drop of sassafras oil, on a horizontal surface of a flint glass block, is viewed by reflected light. The film appears brightest at its outer margin, where it is thinnest. A film of the same oil on crown glass appears dark at its outer margin. What can you say about the index of refraction of the oil? (a) It must be less than 1.52. (b) It must be between 1.52 and 1.66. (c) It must be greater than 1.66. (d) None of statements (a) through (c) is necessarily true. **(ii)** Could a very thin film of some other liquid appear bright by reflected light on both of the glass blocks? **(iii)** Could it appear dark on both?

(iv) Could it appear dark on crown glass and bright on flint glass? Experiments described by Thomas Young suggested this question.

11. A lens with outer radius of curvature R and index of refraction n rests on a flat glass plate. The combination is illuminated with white light from above and observed from above. Is there a dark spot or a light spot at the center of the lens? What does it mean if the observed rings are noncircular?

12. Why is the lens on a good-quality camera coated with a thin film?

13. O Green light has a wavelength of 500 nm in air. **(i)** Assume green light is reflected from a mirror with angle of incidence 0°. The incident and reflected waves together constitute a standing wave with what distance from one node to the next antinode? (a) 1 000 nm (b) 500 nm (c) 250 nm (d) 125 nm (e) 62.5 nm **(ii)** The green light is sent into a Michelson interferometer that is adjusted to produce a central bright circle. How far must the interferometer's moving mirror be shifted to change the center of the pattern into a dark circle? Choose from the same possibilities. **(iii)** The light is reflected perpendicularly from a thin film of a plastic with index of refraction 2.00. The film appears bright in the reflected light. How much additional thickness would make the film appear dark?

14. O Using a Michelson interferometer, shown in Active Figure 37.14, you are viewing a dark circle at the center of the interference pattern. As you gradually move the light source toward the central mirror M_0, through a distance $\lambda/2$, what do you see? (a) There is no change in the pattern. (b) The dark circle changes into a bright circle. (c) The dark circle changes into a bright circle and then back into a dark circle. (d) The dark circle changes into a bright circle, then into a dark circle, and then into a bright circle.

Problems

WebAssign The Problems from this chapter may be assigned online in WebAssign.

ThomsonNOW Sign in at **www.thomsonedu.com** and go to ThomsonNOW to assess your understanding of this chapter's topics with additional quizzing and conceptual questions.

1, 2, 3 denotes straightforward, intermediate, challenging; □ denotes full solution available in *Student Solutions Manual/Study Guide;* ▲ denotes coached solution with hints available at **www.thomsonedu.com;** denotes developing symbolic reasoning; ● denotes asking for qualitative reasoning; denotes computer useful in solving problem

Section 37.1 Conditions for Interference

Section 37.2 Young's Double-Slit Experiment

Section 37.3 Light Waves in Interference

Note: Problems 4, 5, 6, 7, 8, and 10 in Chapter 18 can be assigned with this section.

1. A laser beam (λ = 632.8 nm) is incident on two slits 0.200 mm apart. How far apart are the bright interference fringes on a screen 5.00 m away from the double slits?

2. A Young's interference experiment is performed with monochromatic light. The separation between the slits is 0.500 mm, and the interference pattern on a screen 3.30 m away shows the first side maximum 3.40 mm from the center of the pattern. What is the wavelength?

3. ▲ Two radio antennas separated by 300 m as shown in Figure P37.3 simultaneously broadcast identical signals at the same wavelength. A radio in a car traveling due north receives the signals. (a) If the car is at the position of the second maximum, what is the wavelength of the signals? (b) How much farther must the car travel to encounter the next minimum in reception? *Note:* Do not use the small-angle approximation in this problem.

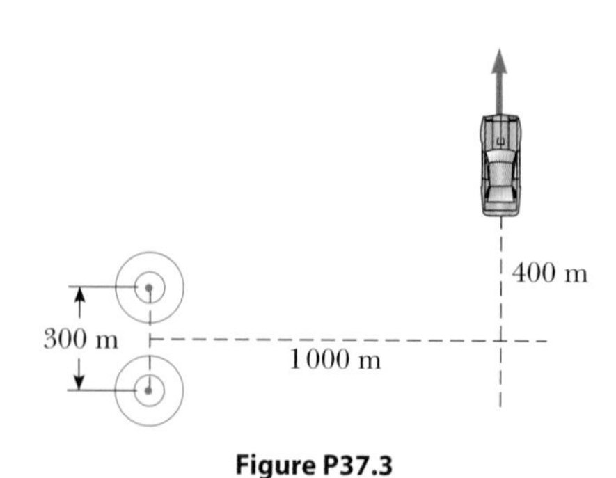

Figure P37.3

4. In a location where the speed of sound is 354 m/s, a 2 000-Hz sound wave impinges on two slits 30.0 cm apart. (a) At what angle is the first maximum located? (b) **What If?** If the sound wave is replaced by 3.00-cm microwaves, what slit separation gives the same angle for the first maximum? (c) **What If?** If the slit separation is 1.00 μm, what frequency of light gives the same first maximum angle?

5. ▲ Young's double-slit experiment is performed with 589-nm light and a distance of 2.00 m between the slits and the screen. The tenth interference minimum is observed 7.26 mm from the central maximum. Determine the spacing of the slits.

6. ● Write the statement of a problem, including data, for which the following equations appear in the solution.

$$\lambda = \frac{343 \text{ m/s}}{1\,620/\text{s}} \qquad (35.0 \text{ cm}) \sin \theta_0 = 0\lambda$$

$$(35.0 \text{ cm}) \sin \theta_{1\,\text{soft}} = 0.5\lambda \qquad (35.0 \text{ cm}) \sin \theta_{1\,\text{loud}} = 1\lambda$$

$$(35.0 \text{ cm}) \sin \theta_{2\,\text{soft}} = 1.5\lambda \qquad (35.0 \text{ cm}) \sin \theta_{2\,\text{loud}} = 2\lambda$$

State the solution to the problem, including values for each quantity that appears as an unknown. State what you can conclude from the last of the set of six equations. Does this equation describe an angle $\theta_{2\,\text{loud}}$ that is larger than 90°?

7. Two narrow, parallel slits separated by 0.250 mm are illuminated by green light (λ = 546.1 nm). The interference pattern is observed on a screen 1.20 m away from the plane of the slits. Calculate the distance (a) from the central maximum to the first bright region on either side of the central maximum and (b) between the first and second dark bands.

8. A riverside warehouse has two open doors as shown in Figure P37.8. Its walls are lined with sound-absorbing material. A boat on the river sounds its horn. To person A, the sound is loud and clear. To person B, the sound is barely audible. The principal wavelength of the sound waves is 3.00 m. Assuming person B is at the position of the first minimum, determine the distance between the doors, center to center.

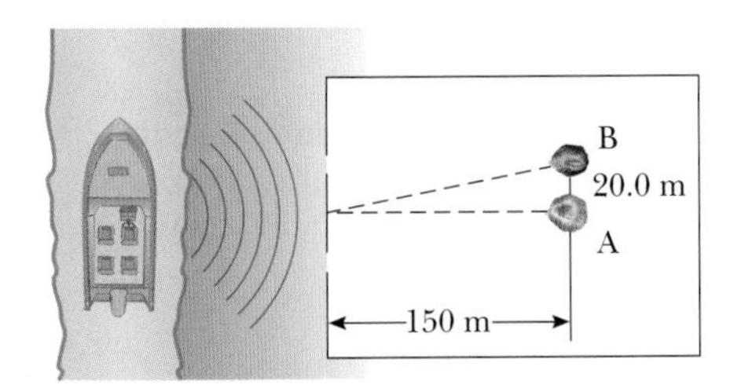

Figure P37.8

9. Light with wavelength 442 nm passes through a double-slit system that has a slit separation d = 0.400 mm. Determine how far away a screen must be placed so that dark fringes appear directly opposite both slits, with only one bright fringe between them.

10. Two slits are separated by 0.320 mm. A beam of 500-nm light strikes the slits, producing an interference pattern. Determine the number of maxima observed in the angular range $-30.0° < \theta < 30.0°$.

11. ● Young's double-slit experiment underlies the *instrument landing system* used to guide aircraft to safe landings when the visibility is poor. Although real systems are more complicated than the example described here, they operate on the same principles. A pilot is trying to align her plane with a runway as suggested in Figure P37.11a. Two radio antennas A_1 and A_2 are positioned adjacent to the runway, separated by 40.0 m. The antennas broadcast unmodulated coherent radio waves at 30.0 MHz. (a) Find the wavelength of the waves. The pilot "locks onto" the strong signal radiated along an interference maximum, and steers the plane to keep the received signal strong. If she has found the central maximum, the plane will have precisely the right heading to land when it reaches the runway. (b) **What If?** Suppose the plane is flying along the first side maximum instead (Fig. P37.11b). How far to the side of the runway centerline will the plane be when it is 2.00 km from the antennas? (c) It is possible to tell the pilot that she is on the wrong maximum by sending out two signals from each antenna and equipping the aircraft with a two-channel receiver. The ratio of the two frequencies must not be the ratio of small integers (such as $\frac{3}{4}$). Explain how this two-frequency system would work and

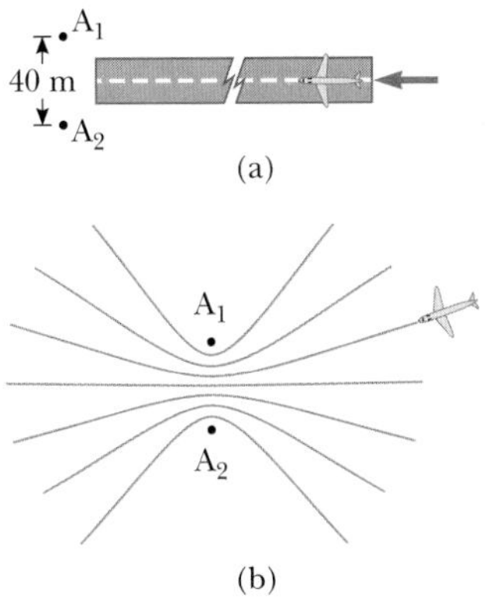

Figure P37.11

why it would not necessarily work if the frequencies were related by an integer ratio.

12. A student holds a laser that emits light of wavelength 633 nm. The beam passes though a pair of slits separated by 0.300 mm, in a glass plate attached to the front of the laser. The beam then falls perpendicularly on a screen, creating an interference pattern on it. The student begins to walk directly toward the screen at 3.00 m/s. The central maximum on the screen is stationary. Find the speed of the first-order maxima on the screen.

13. In Figure 37.5, let L = 1.20 m and d = 0.120 mm and assume the slit system is illuminated with monochromatic 500-nm light. Calculate the phase difference between the two wave fronts arriving at P when (a) $\theta = 0.500°$ and (b) y = 5.00 mm. (c) What is the value of θ for which the phase difference is 0.333 rad? (d) What is the value of θ for which the path difference is $\lambda/4$?

14. Coherent light rays of wavelength λ strike a pair of slits separated by distance d at an angle θ_1 as shown in Figure P37.14. Assume an interference maximum is formed at an angle θ_2 a great distance from the slits. Show that $d(\sin\theta_2 - \sin\theta_1) = m\lambda$, where m is an integer.

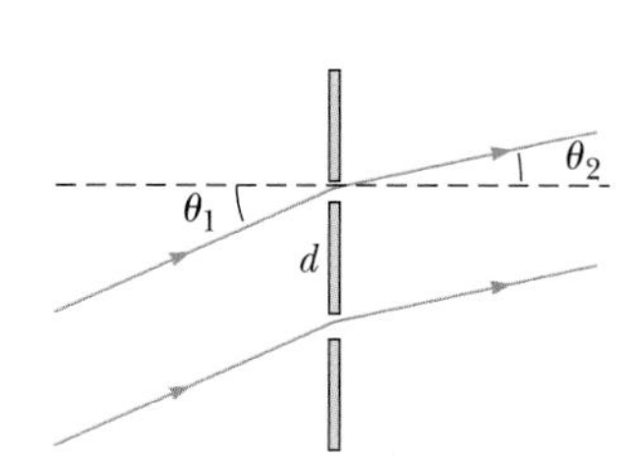

Figure P37.14

15. ● In a double-slit arrangement of Figure 37.5, d = 0.150 mm, L = 140 cm, λ = 643 nm, and y = 1.80 cm. (a) What is the path difference δ for the rays from the two slits arriving at P? (b) Express this path difference in terms of λ. (c) Does P correspond to a maximum, a minimum, or an intermediate condition? Give evidence for your answer.

Section 37.4 Intensity Distribution of the Double-Slit Interference Pattern

16. The intensity on the screen at a certain point in a double-slit interference pattern is 64.0% of the maximum value. (a) What minimum phase difference (in radians) between sources produces this result? (b) Express this phase difference as a path difference for 486.1-nm light.

17. ▲ In Figure 37.5, let L = 120 cm and d = 0.250 cm. The slits are illuminated with coherent 600-nm light. Calculate the distance y above the central maximum for which the average intensity on the screen is 75.0% of the maximum.

18. Two slits are separated by 0.180 mm. An interference pattern is formed on a screen 80.0 cm away by 656.3-nm light. Calculate the fraction of the maximum intensity 0.600 cm above the central maximum.

19. ▲ Show that the two waves with wave functions E_1 = 6.00 sin $(100\pi t)$ and E_2 = 8.00 sin $(100\pi t + \pi/2)$ add to give a wave with the wave function E_R sin $(100\pi t + \phi)$. Find the required values for E_R and ϕ.

20. Make a graph of I/I_{max} as a function of θ for the interference pattern produced by the arrangement described in Problem 7. Let θ range over the interval from $-0.3°$ to $+0.3°$.

21. Two narrow, parallel slits separated by 0.850 mm are illuminated by 600-nm light, and the viewing screen is 2.80 m away from the slits. (a) What is the phase difference between the two interfering waves on a screen at a point 2.50 mm from the central bright fringe? (b) What is the ratio of the intensity at this point to the intensity at the center of a bright fringe?

22. ● Monochromatic coherent light of amplitude E_0 and angular frequency ω passes through three parallel slits each separated by a distance d from its neighbor. (a) Show that the time-averaged intensity as a function of the angle θ is

$$I(\theta) = I_{max}\left[1 + 2\cos\left(\frac{2\pi d \sin\theta}{\lambda}\right)\right]^2$$

(b) Explain how this expression describes both the primary and the secondary maxima. Determine the ratio of the intensities of the primary and secondary maxima.

Section 37.5 Change of Phase Due to Reflection

Section 37.6 Interference in Thin Films

23. ● An oil film (n = 1.45) floating on water is illuminated by white light at normal incidence. The film is 280 nm

thick. Find (a) the color of the light in the visible spectrum most strongly reflected and (b) the color of the light in the spectrum most strongly transmitted. Explain your reasoning.

24. A soap bubble ($n = 1.33$) is floating in air. If the thickness of the bubble wall is 115 nm, what is the wavelength of the light that is most strongly reflected?

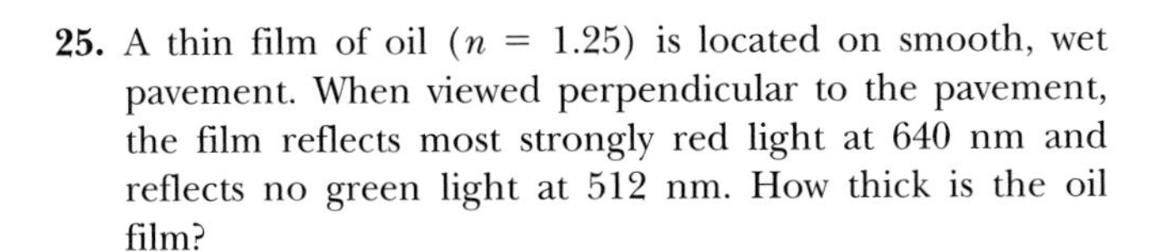

25. A thin film of oil ($n = 1.25$) is located on smooth, wet pavement. When viewed perpendicular to the pavement, the film reflects most strongly red light at 640 nm and reflects no green light at 512 nm. How thick is the oil film?

26. A possible means for making an airplane invisible to radar is to coat the plane with an antireflective polymer. If radar waves have a wavelength of 3.00 cm and the index of refraction of the polymer is $n = 1.50$, how thick would you make the coating?

27. A material having an index of refraction of 1.30 is used as an antireflective coating on a piece of glass ($n = 1.50$). What should the minimum thickness of this film be to minimize reflection of 500-nm light?

28. A film of MgF_2 ($n = 1.38$) having thickness 1.00×10^{-5} cm is used to coat a camera lens. Are any wavelengths in the visible spectrum intensified in the reflected light?

29. ● Astronomers observe the chromosphere of the Sun with a filter that passes the red hydrogen spectral line of wavelength 656.3 nm, called the H_α line. The filter consists of a transparent dielectric of thickness d held between two partially aluminized glass plates. The filter is held at a constant temperature. (a) Find the minimum value of d that produces maximum transmission of perpendicular H_α light if the dielectric has an index of refraction of 1.378. (b) **What If?** If the temperature of the filter increases above the normal value, what happens to the transmitted wavelength? (The index of refraction of the filter does not change significantly.) (c) The dielectric will also pass what near-visible wavelength? One of the glass plates is colored red to absorb this light.

30. A beam of 580-nm light passes through two closely spaced glass plates as shown in Figure P37.30. For what minimum nonzero value of the plate separation d is the transmitted light bright?

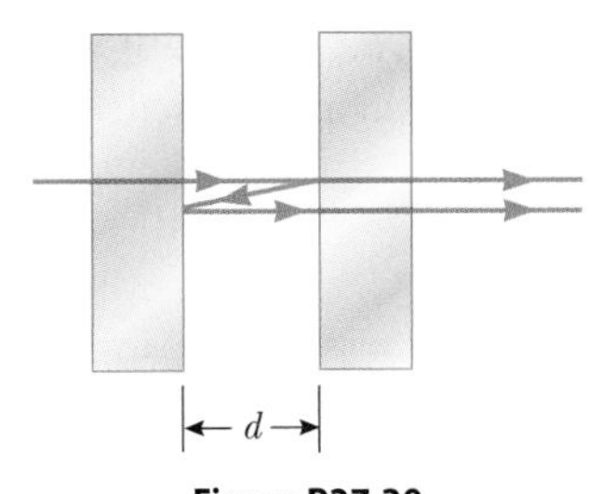

Figure P37.30

31. ▲ An air wedge is formed between two glass plates separated at one edge by a very fine wire as shown in Figure P37.31. When the wedge is illuminated from above by 600-nm light and viewed from above, 30 dark fringes are observed. Calculate the radius of the wire.

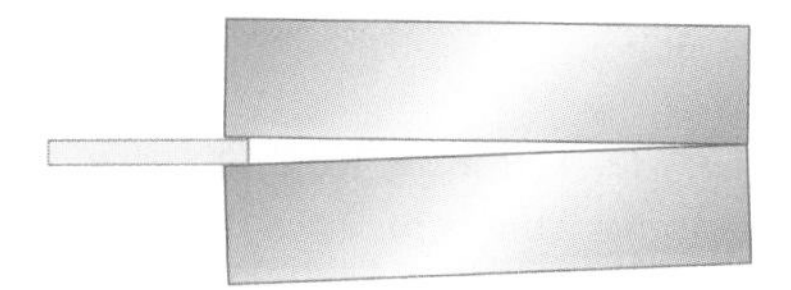

Figure P37.31 Problems 31 and 33.

32. When a liquid is introduced into the air space between the lens and the plate in a Newton's-rings apparatus, the diameter of the tenth ring changes from 1.50 to 1.31 cm. Find the index of refraction of the liquid.

33. Two glass plates 10.0 cm long are in contact at one end and separated at the other end by a thread 0.050 0 mm in diameter (Fig. P37.31). Light containing the two wavelengths 400 nm and 600 nm is incident perpendicularly and viewed by reflection. At what distance from the contact point is the next dark fringe?

Section 37.7 The Michelson Interferometer

34. Monochromatic light is beamed into a Michelson interferometer. The movable mirror is displaced 0.382 mm, causing the interferometer pattern to reproduce itself 1 700 times. Determine the wavelength of the light. What color is it?

35. Mirror M_1 in Active Figure 37.14 is moved through a displacement ΔL. During this displacement, 250 fringe

reversals (formation of successive dark or bright bands) are counted. The light being used has a wavelength of 632.8 nm. Calculate the displacement ΔL.

36. One leg of a Michelson interferometer contains an evacuated cylinder of length L, having glass plates on each end. A gas is slowly leaked into the cylinder until a pressure of 1 atm is reached. If N bright fringes pass on the screen during this process when light of wavelength λ is used, what is the index of refraction of the gas?

Figure P37.40

Additional Problems

37. In an experiment similar to that of Example 37.1, green light with wavelength 560 nm, sent through a pair of slits 30.0 μm apart, produces bright fringes 2.24 cm apart on a screen 1.20 m away. Calculate the fringe separation for this same arrangement assuming that the apparatus is submerged in a tank containing a sugar solution with index of refraction 1.38.

38. In the **What If?** section of Example 37.2, it was claimed that overlapping fringes in a two-slit interference pattern for two different wavelengths obey the following relationship even for large values of the angle θ:

$$\frac{m'}{m} = \frac{\lambda}{\lambda'}$$

(a) Prove this assertion. (b) Using the data in Example 37.2, find the nonzero value of y on the screen at which the fringes from the two wavelengths first coincide.

39. One radio transmitter A operating at 60.0 MHz is 10.0 m from another similar transmitter B that is 180° out of phase with A. How far must an observer move from A toward B along the line connecting the two transmitters to reach the nearest point where the two beams are in phase?

40. **Review problem.** This problem extends the result of Problem 10 in Chapter 18. Figure P37.40 shows two adjacent vibrating balls dipping into a pan of water. At distant points, they produce an interference pattern of water waves as shown in Figure 37.3. Let λ represent the wavelength of the ripples. Show that the two sources produce a standing wave along the line segment, of length d, between them. In terms of λ and d, find the number of nodes and the number of antinodes in the standing wave. Find the number of zones of constructive and of destructive interference in the interference pattern far away from the sources. Each line of destructive interference springs from a node in the standing wave, and each line of constructive interference springs from an antinode.

41. Raise your hand and hold it flat. Think of the space between your index finger and your middle finger as one slit and think of the space between middle finger and ring finger as a second slit. (a) Consider the interference resulting from sending coherent visible light perpendicularly through this pair of openings. Compute an order-of-magnitude estimate for the angle between adjacent zones of constructive interference. (b) To make the angles in the interference pattern easy to measure with a plastic protractor, you should use an electromagnetic wave with frequency of what order of magnitude? How is this wave classified on the electromagnetic spectrum?

42. Two coherent waves, coming from sources at different locations, move along the x axis. Their wave functions are

$$E_1 = (860 \text{ V/m}) \sin \left[\frac{2\pi x_1}{650 \text{ nm}} - 2\pi(462 \text{ THz})t + \frac{\pi}{6} \right]$$

and

$$E_2 = (860 \text{ V/m}) \sin \left[\frac{2\pi x_2}{650 \text{ nm}} - 2\pi(462 \text{ THz})t + \frac{\pi}{8} \right]$$

Determine the relationship between x_1 and x_2 that produces constructive interference when the two waves are superposed.

43. In a Young's interference experiment, the two slits are separated by 0.150 mm and the incident light includes two wavelengths: $\lambda_1 = 540$ nm (green) and $\lambda_2 = 450$ nm (blue). The overlapping interference patterns are observed on a screen 1.40 m from the slits. Calculate the minimum distance from the center of the screen to a point where a bright fringe of the green light coincides with a bright fringe of the blue light.

44. In a Young's double-slit experiment using light of wavelength λ, a thin piece of Plexiglas having index of refraction n covers one of the slits. If the center point on the

screen is a dark spot instead of a bright spot, what is the minimum thickness of the Plexiglas?

45. **Review problem.** A flat piece of glass is held stationary and horizontal above the flat top end of a 10.0-cm-long vertical metal rod that has its lower end rigidly fixed. The thin film of air between the rod and glass is observed to be bright by reflected light when it is illuminated by light of wavelength 500 nm. As the temperature is slowly increased by 25.0°C, the film changes from bright to dark and back to bright 200 times. What is the coefficient of linear expansion of the metal?

46. A certain crude oil has an index of refraction of 1.25. A ship dumps 1.00 m^3 of this oil into the ocean, and the oil spreads into a thin uniform slick. If the film produces a first-order maximum of light of wavelength 500 nm normally incident on it, how much surface area of the ocean does the oil slick cover? Assume the index of refraction of the ocean water is 1.34.

47. Astronomers observe a 60.0-MHz radio source both directly and by reflection from the sea. If the receiving dish is 20.0 m above sea level, what is the angle of the radio source above the horizon at first maximum?

48. Interference effects are produced at point P on a screen as a result of direct rays from a 500-nm source and reflected rays from the mirror as shown in Figure P37.48. Assume the source is 100 m to the left of the screen and 1.00 cm above the mirror. Find the distance y to the first dark band above the mirror.

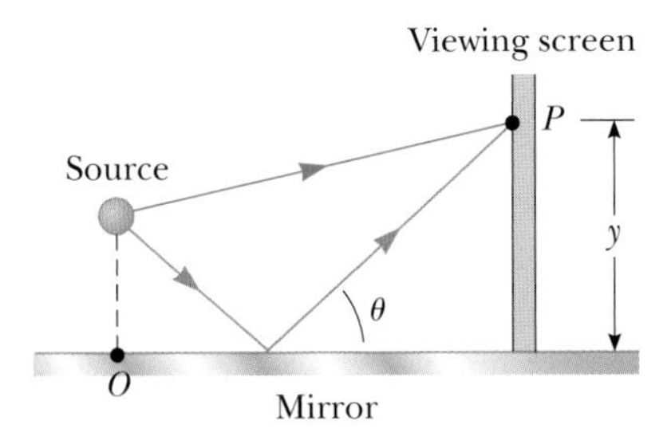

Figure P37.48

49. The waves from a radio station can reach a home receiver by two paths. One is a straight-line path from transmitter to home, a distance of 30.0 km. The second path is by reflection from the ionosphere (a layer of ionized air molecules high in the atmosphere). Assume this reflection takes place at a point midway between receiver and transmitter and the wavelength broadcast by the radio station is 350 m. Find the minimum height of the ionospheric layer that could produce destructive interference between the direct and reflected beams. Assume no phase change occurs on reflection.

50. Many cells are transparent and colorless. Structures of great interest in biology and medicine can be practically invisible to ordinary microscopy. To indicate the size and shape of cell structures, an *interference microscope* reveals a difference in index of refraction as a shift in interference fringes. The idea is exemplified in the following problem. An air wedge is formed between two glass plates in contact along one edge and slightly separated at the opposite edge. When the plates are illuminated with monochromatic light from above, the reflected light has 85 dark fringes. Calculate the number of dark fringes that appear if water (n = 1.33) replaces the air between the plates.

51. Measurements are made of the intensity distribution within the central bright fringe in a Young's interference pattern (see Fig. 37.7). At a particular value of y, it is found that I/I_{max} = 0.810 when 600-nm light is used. What wavelength of light should be used to reduce the relative intensity at the same location to 64.0% of the maximum intensity?

52. Our discussion of the techniques for determining constructive and destructive interference by reflection from a thin film in air has been confined to rays striking the film at nearly normal incidence. **What If?** Assume a ray is incident at an angle of 30.0° (relative to the normal) on a film with index of refraction 1.38. Calculate the minimum thickness for constructive interference of sodium light with a wavelength of 590 nm.

53. The condition for constructive interference by reflection from a thin film in air as developed in Section 37.6 assumes nearly normal incidence. **What If?** Show that if the light is incident on the film at a nonzero angle ϕ_1 (relative to the normal), the condition for constructive interference is $2nt \cos \theta_2 = (m + \frac{1}{2})\lambda$, where θ_2 is the angle of refraction.

54. ● The quantity δ in Equation 37.1 is called the path difference. Its size in comparison to the wavelength controls the character of the interference between two beams in vacuum by controlling the phase difference between the beams. The analogous quantity nt in Equations 37.16 and 37.17 is called the *optical path length* corresponding to the geometrical distance t. The optical

path length is proportional to n because a larger index of refraction shortens the wavelength, so more cycles of a wave fit into a particular geometrical distance. (a) Assume a mixture of corn syrup and water is prepared in a tank, with its index of refraction n increasing uniformly from 1.33 at $y = 20.0$ cm at the top to 1.90 at $y = 0$. Write the index of refraction $n(y)$ as a function of y. (b) Compute the optical path length corresponding to the 20-cm height of the tank by calculating

$$\int_0^{20\text{ cm}} n(y)\,dy$$

(c) Suppose a narrow beam of light is directed into the mixture with its original direction between horizontal and vertically upward. Qualitatively describe its path.

55. (a) Both sides of a uniform film that has index of refraction n and thickness d are in contact with air. For normal incidence of light, an intensity minimum is observed in the reflected light at λ_2 and an intensity maximum is observed at λ_1, where $\lambda_1 > \lambda_2$. Assuming that no intensity minima are observed between λ_1 and λ_2, show that the integer m in Equations 37.16 and 37.17 is given by $m = \lambda_1/2(\lambda_1 - \lambda_2)$. (b) Determine the thickness of the film, assuming $n = 1.40$, $\lambda_1 = 500$ nm, and $\lambda_2 = 370$ nm.

56. Figure P37.56 shows a radio-wave transmitter and a receiver separated by a distance d and both a distance h above the ground. The receiver can receive signals both directly from the transmitter and indirectly from signals that reflect from the ground. Assume the ground is level between the transmitter and receiver and a 180° phase shift occurs upon reflection. Determine the longest wavelengths that interfere (a) constructively and (b) destructively.

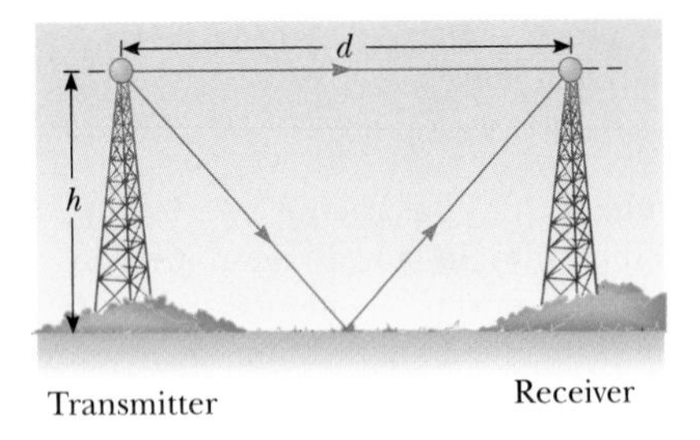

Figure P37.56

57. Consider the double-slit arrangement shown in Figure P37.57, where the slit separation is d and the distance from the slit to the screen is L. A sheet of transparent plastic having an index of refraction n and thickness t is placed over the upper slit. As a result, the central maximum of the interference pattern moves upward a distance y'. Find y'.

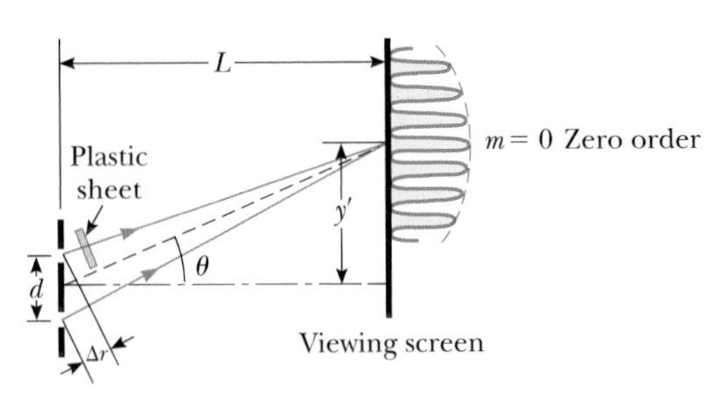

Figure P37.57

58. A piece of transparent material having an index of refraction n is cut into the shape of a wedge as shown in Figure P37.58. The angle of the wedge is small. Monochromatic light of wavelength λ is normally incident from above and is viewed from above. Let h represent the height of the wedge and ℓ its width. Show that bright fringes occur at the positions $x = \lambda\ell(m + \frac{1}{2})/2hn$ and dark fringes occur at the positions $x = \lambda\ell m/2hn$, where $m = 0, 1, 2, \ldots$ and x is measured as shown.

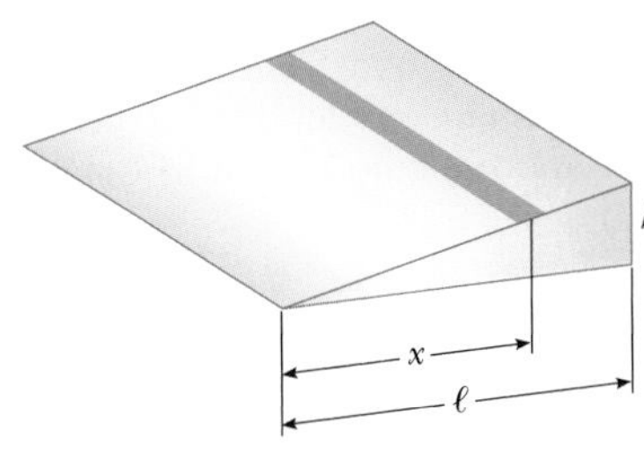

Figure P37.58

59. In a Newton's-rings experiment, a plano-convex glass ($n = 1.52$) lens having diameter 10.0 cm is placed on a flat plate as shown in Figure 37.12a. When 650-nm light is incident normally, 55 bright rings are observed, with the last one precisely on the edge of the lens. (a) What is the radius of curvature of the convex surface of the lens? (b) What is the focal length of the lens?

60. A plano-convex lens has index of refraction n. The curved side of the lens has radius of curvature R and rests on a flat glass surface of the same index of refraction, with a film of index n_{film} between them, as shown in Fig. 37.12a. The lens is illuminated from above by light of wavelength λ. Show that the dark Newton's rings have radii given approximately by

$$r \approx \sqrt{\frac{m\lambda R}{n_{\text{film}}}}$$

where m is an integer and r is much less than R.

61. A plano-concave lens having index of refraction 1.50 is placed on a flat glass plate as shown in Figure P37.61. Its curved surface, with radius of curvature 8.00 m, is on the bottom. The lens is illuminated from above with yellow sodium light of wavelength 589 nm, and a series of concentric bright and dark rings is observed by reflection. The interference pattern has a dark spot at the center, surrounded by 50 dark rings, the largest of which is at the outer edge of the lens. (a) What is the thickness of the air layer at the center of the interference pattern? (b) Calculate the radius of the outermost dark ring. (c) Find the focal length of the lens.

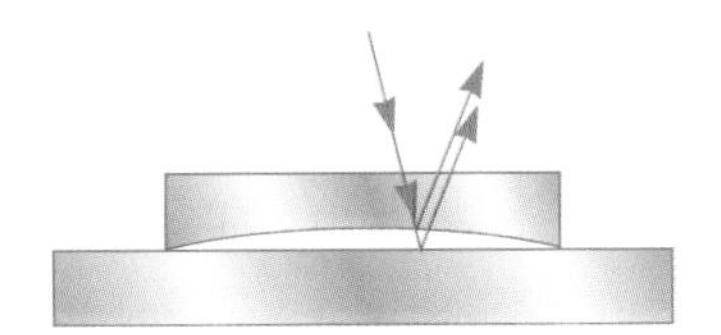

Figure P37.61

62. A plano-convex lens having a radius of curvature of r = 4.00 m is placed on a concave glass surface whose radius of curvature is R = 12.0 m as shown in Figure P37.62. Determine the radius of the 100th bright ring, assuming 500-nm light is incident normal to the flat surface of the lens.

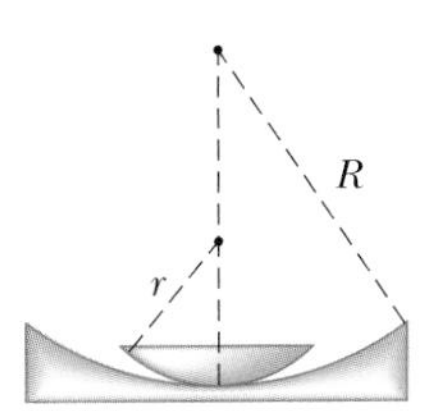

Figure P37.62

63. Figure Q37.8 shows an unbroken soap film in a circular frame. The film thickness increases from top to bottom, slowly at first and then rapidly. As a simpler model, consider a soap film (n = 1.33) contained within a rectangular wire frame. The frame is held vertically so that the film drains downward and forms a wedge with flat faces. The thickness of the film at the top is essentially zero. The film is viewed in reflected white light with near-normal incidence, and the first violet (λ = 420 nm) interference band is observed 3.00 cm from the top edge of the film. (a) Locate the first red (λ = 680 nm) interference band. (b) Determine the film thickness at the positions of the violet and red bands. (c) What is the wedge angle of the film?

64. Compact disc (CD) and digital videodisc (DVD) players use interference to generate strong signals from tiny bumps, shown in Figure P35.40. A pit's depth is chosen to be one-quarter of the wavelength of the laser light used to read the disc. Then light reflected from the pit and light reflected from the adjoining flat surface differ in path length traveled by one-half wavelength, interfering destructively at the detector. As the disc rotates, the light intensity drops significantly every time light is reflected from near a pit edge. The space between the leading and trailing edges of a pit determines the time interval between the fluctuations. The series of time intervals is decoded into a series of zeros and ones that carries the stored information. Assume infrared light with a wavelength of 780 nm in vacuum is used in a CD player. The disc is coated with plastic having an index of refraction of 1.50. What should the depth of each pit be? A DVD player uses light of a shorter wavelength, and the pit dimensions are correspondingly smaller. This reduction is one factor resulting in a DVD's greater storage capacity compared with that of a CD.

65. Interference fringes are produced using Lloyd's mirror and a 606-nm source as shown in Figure 37.9. Fringes 1.20 mm apart are formed on a screen 2.00 m from the real source S. Find the vertical distance h of the source above the reflecting surface.

66. Slit 1 of a double slit is wider than slit 2 so that the light from slit 1 has an amplitude 3.00 times that of the light from slit 2. Show that Equation 37.12 is replaced by the equation $I = (4I_{max}/9)(1 + 3\cos^2 \phi/2)$ for this situation.

67. Monochromatic light of wavelength 620 nm passes through a very narrow slit S and then strikes a screen in which are two parallel slits, S_1 and S_2, as shown in Figure P37.67. Slit S_1 is directly in line with S and at a distance of L = 1.20 m away from S, whereas S_2 is displaced a distance d to one side. The light is detected at point P on a second screen, equidistant from S_1 and S_2. When either slit S_1 or S_2 is open, equal light intensities are measured at point P. When both slits are open, the intensity is three times larger. Find the minimum possible value for the slit separation d.

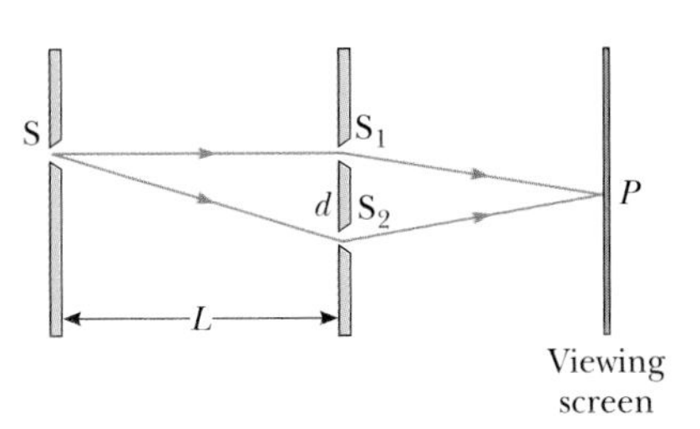

Figure P37.67

Answers to Quick Quizzes

37.1 (c). Equation 37.7 shows that decreasing λ or L will bring the fringes closer together. Immersing the apparatus in water decreases the wavelength so that the fringes move closer together.

37.2 The graph is shown below. The width of the primary maxima is slightly narrower than the $N = 5$ primary width but wider than the $N = 10$ primary width. Because $N = 6$, the secondary maxima are $\frac{1}{36}$ as intense as the primary maxima.

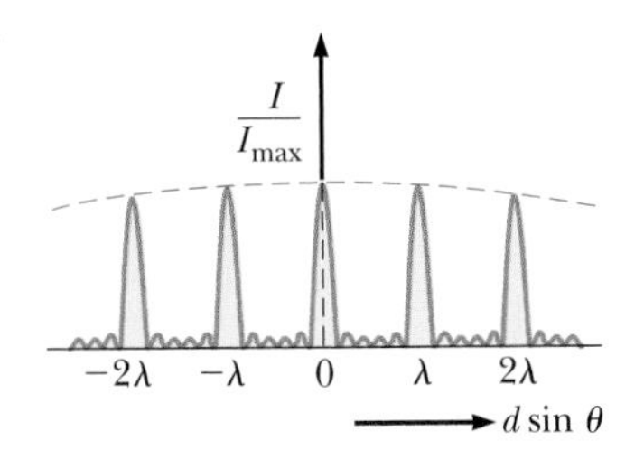

37.3 (a). At the left edge, the air wedge has zero thickness and the only contribution to the interference is the 180° phase shift as the light reflects from the upper surface of the glass slide.

The Hubble Space Telescope does its viewing above the atmosphere and does not suffer from the atmospheric blurring, caused by air turbulence, that plagues ground-based telescopes. Despite this advantage, it does have limitations due to diffraction effects. In this chapter, we show how the wave nature of light limits the ability of any optical system to distinguish between closely spaced objects. (© Denis Scott/CORBIS)

38 Diffraction Patterns and Polarization

When plane light waves pass through a small aperture in an opaque barrier, the aperture acts as if it were a point source of light, with waves entering the shadow region behind the barrier. This phenomenon, known as diffraction, can be described only with a wave model for light as discussed in Section 35.3. In this chapter, we investigate the features of the *diffraction pattern* that occurs when the light from the aperture is allowed to fall upon a screen.

In Chapter 34, we learned that electromagnetic waves are transverse. That is, the electric and magnetic field vectors associated with electromagnetic waves are perpendicular to the direction of wave propagation. In this chapter, we show that under certain conditions these transverse waves with electric field vectors in all possible transverse directions can be *polarized* in various ways. In other words, only certain directions of the electric field vectors are present in the polarized wave.

38.1 Introduction to Diffraction Patterns

In Section 35.3, we discussed that light of wavelength comparable to or larger than the width of a slit spreads out in all forward directions upon passing through the slit. This phenomenon is called *diffraction*. When light passes through a narrow slit, it spreads beyond the narrow path defined by the slit into regions that would be in shadow if light traveled in straight lines. Other waves, such as sound waves and

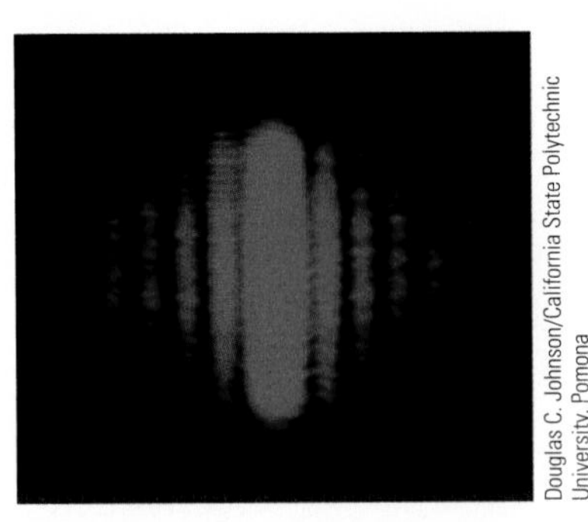

Douglas C. Johnson/California State Polytechnic University, Pomona

Figure 38.1 The diffraction pattern that appears on a screen when light passes through a narrow vertical slit. The pattern consists of a broad central fringe and a series of less intense and narrower side fringes.

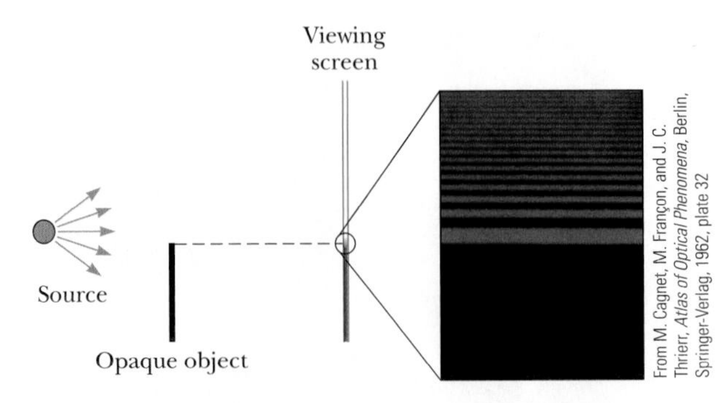

From M. Cagnet, M. Françon, and J. C. Thrierr, *Atlas of Optical Phenomena*, Berlin, Springer-Verlag, 1962, plate 32

Figure 38.2 Light from a small source passes by the edge of an opaque object and continues on to a screen. A diffraction pattern consisting of bright and dark fringes appears on the screen in the region above the edge of the object.

water waves, also have this property of spreading when passing through apertures or by sharp edges.

You might expect that the light passing through a small opening would simply result in a broad region of light on a screen due to the spreading of the light as it passes through the opening. We find something more interesting, however. A **diffraction pattern** consisting of light and dark areas is observed, somewhat similar to the interference patterns discussed earlier. For example, when a narrow slit is placed between a distant light source (or a laser beam) and a screen, the light produces a diffraction pattern like that shown in Figure 38.1. The pattern consists of a broad, intense central band (called the **central maximum**) flanked by a series of narrower, less intense additional bands (called **side maxima** or **secondary maxima**) and a series of intervening dark bands (or **minima**). Figure 38.2 shows a diffraction pattern associated with light passing by the edge of an object. Again we see bright and dark fringes, which is reminiscent of an interference pattern.

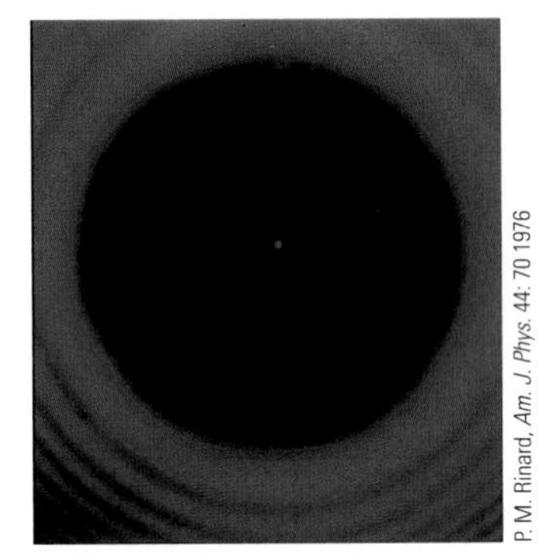

P. M. Rinard, *Am. J. Phys.* 44: 70 1976

Figure 38.3 Diffraction pattern created by the illumination of a penny, with the penny positioned midway between screen and light source. Note the bright spot at the center.

Figure 38.3 shows a diffraction pattern associated with the shadow of a penny. A bright spot occurs at the center, and circular fringes extend outward from the shadow's edge. We can explain the central bright spot by using the wave theory of light, which predicts constructive interference at this point. From the viewpoint of geometric optics (in which light is viewed as rays traveling in straight lines), we expect the center of the shadow to be dark because that part of the viewing screen is completely shielded by the penny.

Shortly before the central bright spot was first observed, one of the supporters of geometric optics, Simeon Poisson, argued that if Augustin Fresnel's wave theory of light were valid, a central bright spot should be observed in the shadow of a circular object illuminated by a point source of light. To Poisson's astonishment, the spot was observed by Dominique Arago shortly thereafter. Therefore, Poisson's prediction reinforced the wave theory rather than disproving it.

PITFALL PREVENTION 38.1
Diffraction Versus Diffraction Pattern

Diffraction refers to the general behavior of waves spreading out as they pass through a slit. We used diffraction in explaining the existence of an interference pattern in Chapter 37. A *diffraction pattern* is actually a misnomer, but is deeply entrenched in the language of physics. The diffraction pattern seen on a screen when a single slit is illuminated is actually another interference pattern. The interference is between parts of the incident light illuminating different regions of the slit.

38.2 Diffraction Patterns from Narrow Slits

Let's consider a common situation, that of light passing through a narrow opening modeled as a slit and projected onto a screen. To simplify our analysis, we assume the observing screen is far from the slit and the rays reaching the screen are approximately parallel. (This situation can also be achieved experimentally by using a converging lens to focus the parallel rays on a nearby screen.) In this model, the pattern on the screen is called a **Fraunhofer diffraction pattern.**[1]

Active Figure 38.4a shows light entering a single slit from the left and diffracting as it propagates toward a screen. Active Figure 38.4b is a photograph of a single-slit Fraunhofer diffraction pattern. A bright fringe is observed along the axis at

[1] If the screen is brought close to the slit (and no lens is used), the pattern is a *Fresnel* diffraction pattern. The Fresnel pattern is more difficult to analyze, so we shall restrict our discussion to Fraunhofer diffraction.

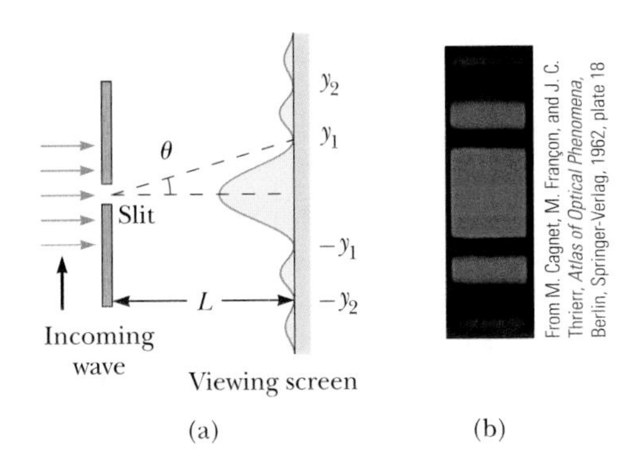

ACTIVE FIGURE 38.4

(a) Fraunhofer diffraction pattern of a single slit. The pattern consists of a central bright fringe flanked by much weaker maxima alternating with dark fringes. (Drawing not to scale.) The labels y indicate positions of dark fringes on the screen. (b) Photograph of a single-slit Fraunhofer diffraction pattern.

Sign in at www.thomsonedu.com and go to ThomsonNOW to adjust the slit width and the wavelength of the light to see the effect on the diffraction pattern.

$\theta = 0$, with alternating dark and bright fringes on each side of the central bright fringe.

Until now, we have assumed slits are point sources of light. In this section, we abandon that assumption and see how the finite width of slits is the basis for understanding Fraunhofer diffraction. We can explain some important features of this phenomenon by examining waves coming from various portions of the slit as shown in Figure 38.5. According to Huygens's principle, **each portion of the slit acts as a source of light waves.** Hence, light from one portion of the slit can interfere with light from another portion, and the resultant light intensity on a viewing screen depends on the direction θ. Based on this analysis, we recognize that a diffraction pattern is actually an interference pattern in which the different sources of light are different portions of the single slit!

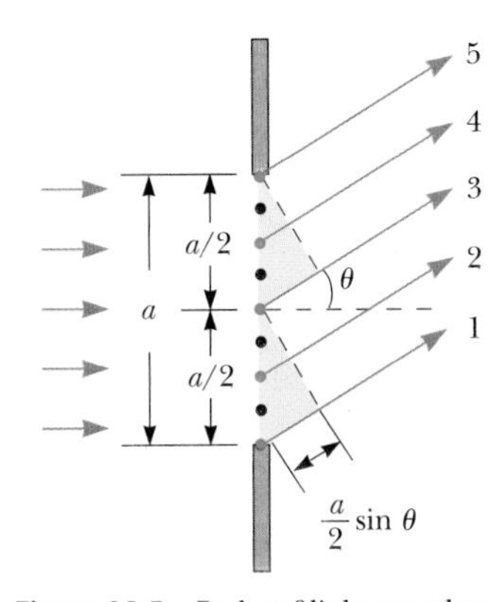

Figure 38.5 Paths of light rays that encounter a narrow slit of width a and diffract toward a screen in the direction described by angle θ. Each portion of the slit acts as a point source of light waves. The path difference between rays 1 and 3, rays 2 and 4, or rays 3 and 5 is $(a/2)\sin\theta$. (Drawing not to scale.)

To analyze the diffraction pattern, let's divide the slit into two halves as shown in Figure 38.5. Keeping in mind that all the waves are in phase as they leave the slit, consider rays 1 and 3. As these two rays travel toward a viewing screen far to the right of the figure, ray 1 travels farther than ray 3 by an amount equal to the path difference $(a/2)\sin\theta$, where a is the width of the slit. Similarly, the path difference between rays 2 and 4 is also $(a/2)\sin\theta$, as is that between rays 3 and 5. If this path difference is exactly half a wavelength (corresponding to a phase difference of 180°), the pairs of waves cancel each other and destructive interference results. This cancellation occurs for any two rays that originate at points separated by half the slit width because the phase difference between two such points is 180°. Therefore, waves from the upper half of the slit interfere destructively with waves from the lower half when

$$\frac{a}{2}\sin\theta = \pm\frac{\lambda}{2}$$

or when

$$\sin\theta = \pm\frac{\lambda}{a}$$

Dividing the slit into four equal parts and using similar reasoning, we find that the viewing screen is also dark when

$$\sin\theta = \pm 2\frac{\lambda}{a}$$

Likewise, dividing the slit into six equal parts shows that darkness occurs on the screen when

$$\sin\theta = \pm 3\frac{\lambda}{a}$$

Therefore, the general condition for destructive interference is

Condition for destructive interference for a single slit ▶

$$\sin \theta_{\text{dark}} = m\frac{\lambda}{a} \quad m = \pm 1, \pm 2, \pm 3, \ldots \tag{38.1}$$

This equation gives the values of θ_{dark} for which the diffraction pattern has zero light intensity, that is, when a dark fringe is formed. It tells us nothing, however, about the variation in light intensity along the screen. The general features of the intensity distribution are shown in Active Figure 38.4. A broad, central bright fringe is observed; this fringe is flanked by much weaker bright fringes alternating with dark fringes. The various dark fringes occur at the values of θ_{dark} that satisfy Equation 38.1. Each bright-fringe peak lies approximately halfway between its bordering dark-fringe minima. Notice that the central bright maximum is twice as wide as the secondary maxima.

PITFALL PREVENTION 38.2

Similar Equation Warning!

Equation 38.1 has exactly the same form as Equation 37.2, with d, the slit separation, used in Equation 37.2 and a, the slit width, used in Equation 38.1. Equation 37.2, however, describes the *bright* regions in a two-slit interference pattern, whereas Equation 38.1 describes the *dark* regions in a single-slit diffraction pattern. Furthermore, $m = 0$ does not represent a dark fringe in the diffraction pattern.

Quick Quiz 38.1 Suppose the slit width in Active Figure 38.4 is made half as wide. Does the central bright fringe (a) become wider, (b) remain the same, or (c) become narrower?

EXAMPLE 38.1 Where Are the Dark Fringes?

Light of wavelength 580 nm is incident on a slit having a width of 0.300 mm. The viewing screen is 2.00 m from the slit. Find the positions of the first dark fringes and the width of the central bright fringe.

SOLUTION

Conceptualize Based on the problem statement, we imagine a single-slit diffraction pattern similar to that in Active Figure 38.4.

Categorize We categorize this example as a straightforward application of our discussion of single-slit diffraction patterns.

Analyze Evaluate Equation 38.1 for the two dark fringes that flank the central bright fringe, which correspond to $m = \pm 1$:

$$\sin \theta_{\text{dark}} = \pm\frac{\lambda}{a} = \pm\frac{5.80 \times 10^{-7}\text{ m}}{0.300 \times 10^{-3}\text{ m}} = \pm 1.933 \times 10^{-3}$$

From the triangle in Active Figure 38.4a, notice that $\tan \theta_{\text{dark}} = y_1/L$. Because θ_{dark} is very small, we can use the approximation $\sin \theta_{\text{dark}} \approx \tan \theta_{\text{dark}}$; therefore, $\sin \theta_{\text{dark}} \approx y_1/L$.

Use this result to find the positions of the first minima measured from the central axis:

$$y_1 \approx L \sin \theta_{\text{dark}} = (2.00\text{ m})(\pm 1.933 \times 10^{-3})$$
$$= \pm 3.866 \times 10^{-3}\text{ m}$$

Find the width of the central bright fringe:

$$2|y_1| = 7.73 \times 10^{-3}\text{ m} = 7.73\text{ mm}$$

Finalize Notice that this value is much greater than the width of the slit. Let's explore what happens if we change the slit width.

What If? What if the slit width is increased by an order of magnitude to 3.00 mm? What happens to the diffraction pattern?

Answer Based on Equation 38.1, we expect that the angles at which the dark bands appear will decrease as a increases. Therefore, the diffraction pattern narrows.

From Equation 38.1, find the sines of the angles θ_{dark} for the $m = \pm 1$ dark fringes:

$$\sin \theta_{\text{dark}} = \pm\frac{\lambda}{a} = \pm\frac{5.80 \times 10^{-7}\text{ m}}{3.00 \times 10^{-3}\text{ m}} = \pm 1.933 \times 10^{-4}$$

Use this result to find the positions of the first minima measured from the central axis:

$$y_1 \approx L \sin \theta_{\text{dark}} = (2.00 \text{ m})(\pm 1.933 \times 10^{-4})$$
$$= \pm 3.866 \times 10^{-4} \text{ m}$$

Find the width of the central bright fringe:

$$2|y_1| = 7.73 \times 10^{-4} \text{ m} = 0.773 \text{ mm}$$

Notice that this result is *smaller* than the width of the slit. In general, for large values of a, the various maxima and minima are so closely spaced that only a large, central bright area resembling the geometric image of the slit is observed. This concept is very important in the performance of optical instruments such as telescopes.

Intensity of Single-Slit Diffraction Patterns

Analysis of the intensity variation in a diffraction pattern from a single slit of width a shows that the intensity is given by

$$I = I_{\text{max}}\left[\frac{\sin(\pi a \sin \theta/\lambda)}{\pi a \sin \theta/\lambda}\right]^2 \quad \textbf{(38.2)}$$

◀ Intensity of a single-slit Fraunhofer diffraction pattern

where I_{max} is the intensity at $\theta = 0$ (the central maximum) and λ is the wavelength of light used to illuminate the slit. This expression shows that *minima* occur when

$$\frac{\pi a \sin \theta_{\text{dark}}}{\lambda} = m\pi$$

or

$$\sin \theta_{\text{dark}} = m\frac{\lambda}{a} \qquad m = \pm 1, \pm 2, \pm 3, \ldots$$

◀ Condition for intensity minima for a single slit

in agreement with Equation 38.1.

Figure 38.6a represents a plot of Equation 38.2, and Figure 38.6b is a photograph of a single-slit Fraunhofer diffraction pattern. Notice that most of the light intensity is concentrated in the central bright fringe.

Intensity of Two-Slit Diffraction Patterns

When more than one slit is present, we must consider not only diffraction patterns due to the individual slits but also the interference patterns due to the waves coming from different slits. Notice the curved dashed lines in Figure 37.8, which indicate a decrease in intensity of the interference maxima as θ increases. This decrease is due to a diffraction pattern. To determine the effects of both two-slit

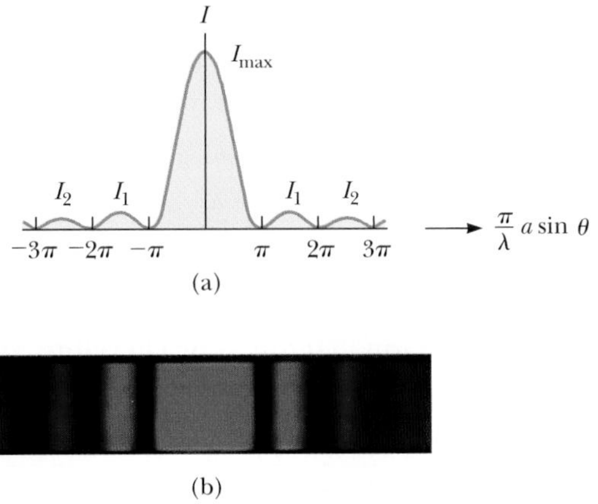

I I_{max} I_2 I_1 I_1 I_2 -3π -2π $-\pi$ π 2π 3π $\frac{\pi}{\lambda} a \sin \theta$

(a)

(b)

Figure 38.6 (a) A plot of light intensity I versus $(\pi/\lambda)\,a \sin \theta$ for the single-slit Fraunhofer diffraction pattern. (b) Photograph of a single-slit Fraunhofer diffraction pattern.

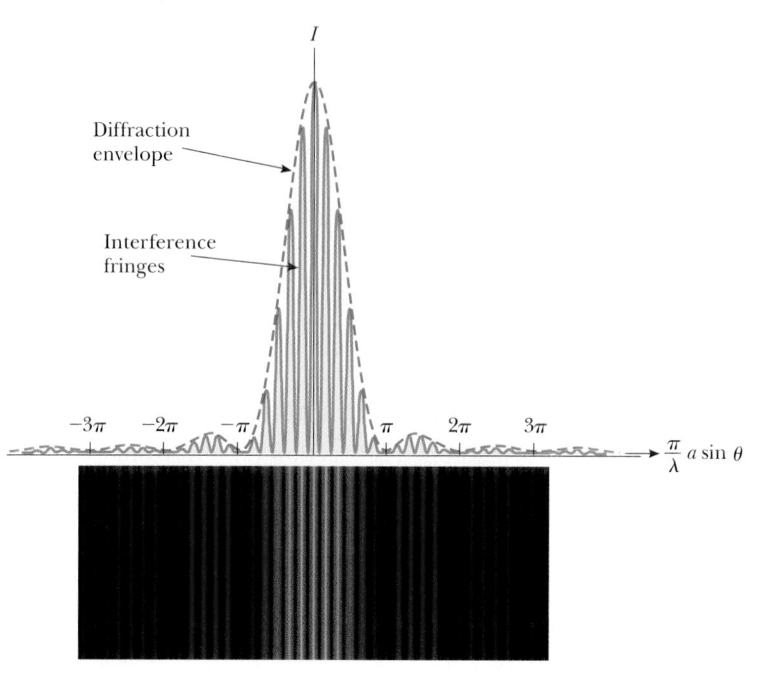

ACTIVE FIGURE 38.7

The combined effects of two-slit and single-slit interference. This pattern is produced when 650-nm light waves pass through two 3.0-μm slits that are 18 μm apart. Notice how the diffraction pattern acts as an "envelope" and controls the intensity of the regularly spaced interference maxima.

Sign in at www.thomsonedu.com and go to ThomsonNOW to adjust the slit width, slit separation, and the wavelength of the light to see the effect on the interference pattern.

interference and a single-slit diffraction pattern from each slit, we combine Equations 37.12 and 38.2:

$$I = I_{\max} \cos^2\left(\frac{\pi d \sin\theta}{\lambda}\right)\left[\frac{\sin(\pi a \sin\theta/\lambda)}{\pi a \sin\theta/\lambda}\right]^2 \quad \textbf{(38.3)}$$

Although this expression looks complicated, it merely represents the single-slit diffraction pattern (the factor in square brackets) acting as an "envelope" for a two-slit interference pattern (the cosine-squared factor) as shown in Active Figure 38.7. The broken blue curve in Active Figure 38.7 represents the factor in square brackets in Equation 38.3. The cosine-squared factor by itself would give a series of peaks all with the same height as the highest peak of the brown curve in Active Figure 38.7. Because of the effect of the square-bracket factor, however, these peaks vary in height as shown.

Equation 37.2 indicates the conditions for interference maxima as $d \sin\theta = m\lambda$, where d is the distance between the two slits. Equation 38.1 specifies that the first diffraction minimum occurs when $a \sin\theta = \lambda$, where a is the slit width. Dividing Equation 37.2 by Equation 38.1 (with $m = 1$) allows us to determine which interference maximum coincides with the first diffraction minimum:

$$\frac{d \sin\theta}{a \sin\theta} = \frac{m\lambda}{\lambda}$$

$$\frac{d}{a} = m \quad \textbf{(38.4)}$$

In Active Figure 38.7, $d/a = 18\ \mu\text{m}/3.0\ \mu\text{m} = 6$. Therefore, the sixth interference maximum (if we count the central maximum as $m = 0$) is aligned with the first diffraction minimum and cannot be seen.

Quick Quiz 38.2 Consider the central peak in the diffraction envelope in Active Figure 38.7. Suppose the wavelength of the light is changed to 450 nm. What happens to this central peak? (a) The width of the peak decreases, and the number of interference fringes it encloses decreases. (b) The width of the peak decreases, and the number of interference fringes it encloses increases. (c) The width of the peak decreases, and the number of interference fringes it encloses remains the same. (d) The width of the peak increases, and the number of interference fringes it encloses decreases. (e) The width of the peak increases, and the number of interference fringes it encloses increases. (f) The width of the peak increases, and the number of interference fringes it encloses remains the same. (g) The width of the peak remains the same and the number of interference fringes it encloses decreases. (h) The width of the peak remains the same and the number of interference fringes it encloses increases. (i) The width of the peak remains the same and the number of interference fringes it encloses remains the same.

38.3 Resolution of Single-Slit and Circular Apertures

The ability of optical systems to distinguish between closely spaced objects is limited because of the wave nature of light. To understand this limitation, consider Figure 38.8, which shows two light sources far from a narrow slit of width a. The sources can be two noncoherent point sources S_1 and S_2; for example, they could be two distant stars. If no interference occurred between light passing through different parts of the slit, two distinct bright spots (or images) would be observed on the viewing screen. Because of such interference, however, each source is imaged as a bright central region flanked by weaker bright and dark fringes, a diffraction pattern. What is observed on the screen is the sum of two diffraction patterns: one from S_1 and the other from S_2.

If the two sources are far enough apart to keep their central maxima from overlapping as in Figure 38.8a, their images can be distinguished and are said to be *resolved.* If the sources are close together as in Figure 38.8b, however, the two central maxima overlap and the images are not resolved. To determine whether two images are resolved, the following condition is often used:

When the central maximum of one image falls on the first minimum of another image, the images are said to be just resolved. This limiting condition of resolution is known as **Rayleigh's criterion.**

From Rayleigh's criterion, we can determine the minimum angular separation $\theta_{\min}$ subtended by the sources at the slit in Figure 38.8 for which the images are just resolved. Equation 38.1 indicates that the first minimum in a single-slit diffraction pattern occurs at the angle for which

$$\sin \theta = \frac{\lambda}{a}$$

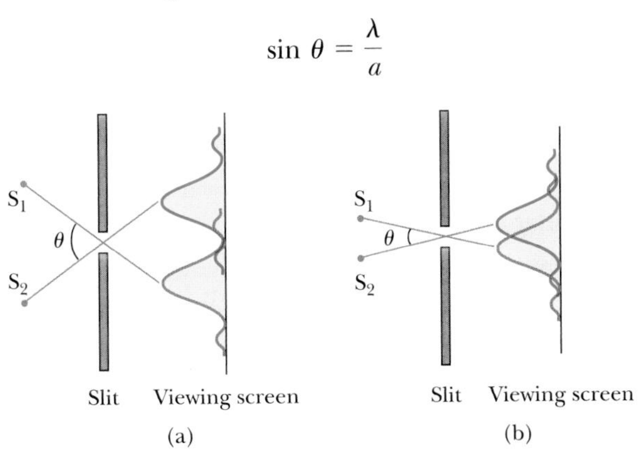

Figure 38.8 Two point sources far from a narrow slit each produce a diffraction pattern. (a) The angle subtended by the sources at the slit is large enough for the diffraction patterns to be distinguishable. (b) The angle subtended by the sources is so small that their diffraction patterns overlap, and the images are not well resolved. (Notice that the angles are greatly exaggerated. The drawing is not to scale.)

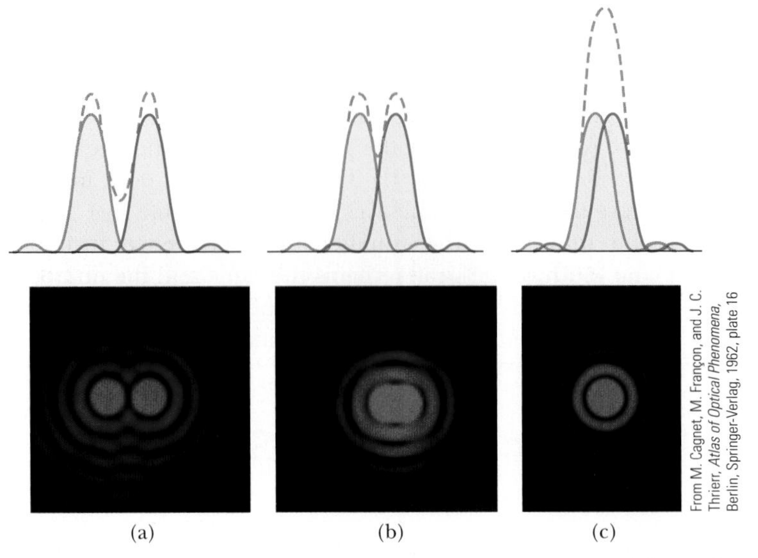

From M. Cagnet, M. Françon, and J. C. Thrierr, *Atlas of Optical Phenomena*, Berlin, Springer-Verlag, 1962, plate 16
(a)
(b)
(c)

Figure 38.9 Individual diffraction patterns of two point sources (solid curves) and the resultant patterns (dashed curves) for various angular separations of the sources as the light passes through a circular aperture. In each case, the dashed curve is the sum of the two solid curves. (a) The sources are far apart, and the patterns are well resolved. (b) The sources are closer together such that the angular separation just satisfies Rayleigh's criterion, and the patterns are just resolved. (c) The sources are so close together that the patterns are not resolved.

where a is the width of the slit. According to Rayleigh's criterion, this expression gives the smallest angular separation for which the two images are resolved. Because $\lambda \ll a$ in most situations, $\sin\theta$ is small and we can use the approximation $\sin\theta \approx \theta$. Therefore, the limiting angle of resolution for a slit of width a is

$$\theta_{\text{min}} = \frac{\lambda}{a} \qquad \textbf{(38.5)}$$

where θ_{min} is expressed in radians. Hence, the angle subtended by the two sources at the slit must be greater than λ/a if the images are to be resolved.

Many optical systems use circular apertures rather than slits. The diffraction pattern of a circular aperture as shown in the photographs of Figure 38.9 consists of a central circular bright disk surrounded by progressively fainter bright and dark rings. Figure 38.9 shows diffraction patterns for three situations in which light from two point sources passes through a circular aperture. When the sources are far apart, their images are well resolved (Fig. 38.9a). When the angular separation of the sources satisfies Rayleigh's criterion, the images are just resolved (Fig. 38.9b). Finally, when the sources are close together, the images are said to be unresolved (Fig. 38.9c).

Analysis shows that the limiting angle of resolution of the circular aperture is

Limiting angle of resolution for a circular aperture ▶

$$\theta_{\text{min}} = 1.22\,\frac{\lambda}{D} \qquad \textbf{(38.6)}$$

where D is the diameter of the aperture. This expression is similar to Equation 38.5 except for the factor 1.22, which arises from a mathematical analysis of diffraction from the circular aperture.

Quick Quiz 38.3 Cat's eyes have pupils that can be modeled as vertical slits. At night, would cats be more successful in resolving (a) headlights on a distant car or (b) vertically separated lights on the mast of a distant boat?

Quick Quiz 38.4 Suppose you are observing a binary star with a telescope and are having difficulty resolving the two stars. You decide to use a colored filter to maximize the resolution. (A filter of a given color transmits only that color of light.) What color filter should you choose? (a) blue (b) green (c) yellow (d) red

---

EXAMPLE 38.2 Resolution of the Eye

Light of wavelength 500 nm, near the center of the visible spectrum, enters a human eye. Although pupil diameter varies from person to person, estimate a daytime diameter of 2 mm.

(A) Estimate the limiting angle of resolution for this eye, assuming its resolution is limited only by diffraction.

SOLUTION

Conceptualize In Figure 38.9, identify the aperture through which the light travels as the pupil of the eye. Light passing through this small aperture causes diffraction patterns to occur on the retina.

Categorize We evaluate the result using equations developed in this section, so we categorize this example as a substitution problem.

Use Equation 38.6, taking $\lambda = 500$ nm and $D = 2$ mm:

$$\theta_{\min} = 1.22\frac{\lambda}{D} = 1.22\left(\frac{5.00 \times 10^{-7}\text{ m}}{2 \times 10^{-3}\text{ m}}\right)$$

$$\approx \boxed{3 \times 10^{-4}\text{ rad}} \approx \boxed{1\text{ min of arc}}$$

(B) Determine the minimum separation distance d between two point sources that the eye can distinguish if the point sources are a distance $L = 25$ cm from the observer (Fig. 38.10).

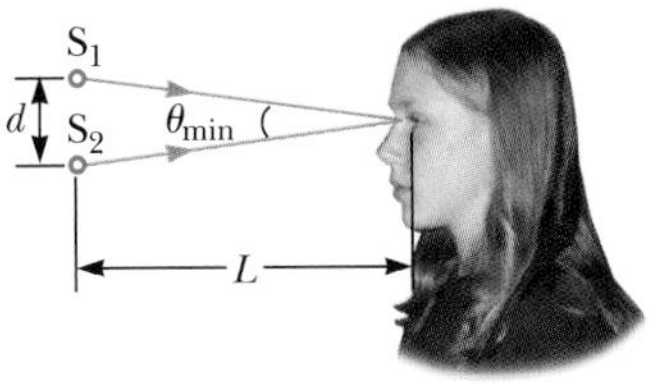

Figure 38.10 (Example 38.2) Two point sources separated by a distance d as observed by the eye.

SOLUTION

Noting that $\theta_{\min}$ is small, find d:

$$\sin\theta_{\min} \approx \theta_{\min} \approx \frac{d}{L} \quad \rightarrow \quad d = L\theta_{\min}$$

Substitute numerical values:

$$d = (25\text{ cm})(3 \times 10^{-4}\text{ rad}) = \boxed{8 \times 10^{-3}\text{ cm}}$$

This result is approximately equal to the thickness of a human hair.

EXAMPLE 38.3 Resolution of a Telescope

The Keck telescope at Mauna Kea, Hawaii, has an effective diameter of 10 m. What is its limiting angle of resolution for 600-nm light?

SOLUTION

Conceptualize In Figure 38.9, identify the aperture through which the light travels as the opening of the telescope. Light passing through this aperture causes diffraction patterns to occur in the final image.

Categorize We evaluate the result using equations developed in this section, so we categorize this example as a substitution problem.

Use Equation 38.6, taking $\lambda = 6.00 \times 10^{-7}$ m and $D =$ 10 m:

$$\theta_{\min} = 1.22\frac{\lambda}{D} = 1.22\left(\frac{6.00 \times 10^{-7}\text{ m}}{10\text{ m}}\right)$$

$$= \boxed{7.3 \times 10^{-8}\text{ rad}} \approx \boxed{0.015\text{ s of arc}}$$

Any two stars that subtend an angle greater than or equal to this value are resolved (if atmospheric conditions are ideal).

What If? What if we consider radio telescopes? They are much larger in diameter than optical telescopes, but do they have better angular resolutions than optical telescopes? For example, the radio telescope at Arecibo, Puerto Rico, has a diameter of 305 m and is designed to detect radio waves of 0.75-m wavelength. How does its resolution compare with that of the Keck telescope?

Answer The increase in diameter might suggest that radio telescopes would have better resolution than the Keck telescope, but Equation 38.6 shows that $\theta_{\min}$ depends on *both* diameter and wavelength. Calculating the minimum angle of resolution for the radio telescope, we find

$$\theta_{\min} = 1.22\frac{\lambda}{D} = 1.22\left(\frac{0.75\text{ m}}{305\text{ m}}\right)$$

$$= 3.0 \times 10^{-3}\text{ rad} \approx 10\text{ min of arc}$$

This limiting angle of resolution is measured in *minutes* of arc rather than the *seconds* of arc for the optical telescope. Therefore, the change in wavelength more than compensates for the increase in diameter. The limiting angle of resolution for the Arecibo radio telescope is more than 40 000 times larger (that is, *worse*) than the Keck minimum.

The Keck telescope discussed in Example 38.3 can never reach its diffraction limit because the limiting angle of resolution is always set by atmospheric blurring at optical wavelengths. This seeing limit is usually about 1 s of arc and is never smaller than about 0.1 s of arc. The atmospheric blurring is caused by variations in index of refraction with temperature variations in the air. This blurring is one reason for the superiority of photographs from the Hubble Space Telescope, which views celestial objects from an orbital position above the atmosphere.

As an example of the effects of atmospheric blurring, consider telescopic images of Pluto and its moon, Charon. Figure 38.11a, an image taken in 1978, represents the discovery of Charon. In this photograph, taken from an Earth-based telescope, atmospheric turbulence causes the image of Charon to appear only as a bump on the edge of Pluto. In comparison, Figure 38.11b shows a photograph taken with the Hubble Space Telescope. Without the problems of atmospheric turbulence, Pluto and its moon are clearly resolved.

38.4 The Diffraction Grating

The **diffraction grating,** a useful device for analyzing light sources, consists of a large number of equally spaced parallel slits. A *transmission grating* can be made by cutting parallel grooves on a glass plate with a precision ruling machine. The spaces between the grooves are transparent to the light and hence act as separate slits. A *reflection grating* can be made by cutting parallel grooves on the surface of a

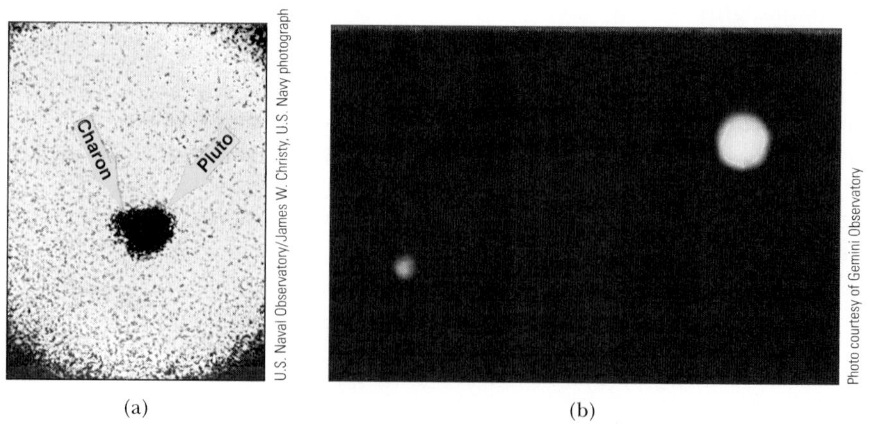

Figure 38.11 (a) The photograph on which Charon, the moon of Pluto, was discovered in 1978. From an Earth-based telescope, atmospheric blurring results in Charon appearing only as a subtle bump on the edge of Pluto. (b) A Hubble Space Telescope photo of Pluto and Charon, clearly resolving the two objects.

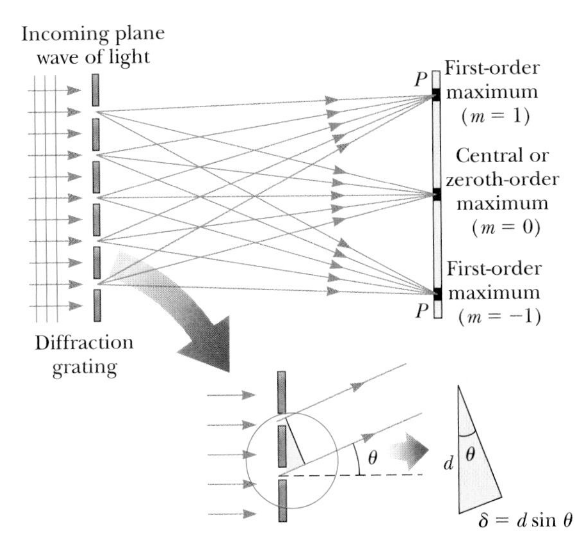

Figure 38.12 Side view of a diffraction grating. The slit separation is d, and the path difference between adjacent slits is $d \sin \theta$.

reflective material. The reflection of light from the spaces between the grooves is specular, and the reflection from the grooves cut into the material is diffuse. Therefore, the spaces between the grooves act as parallel sources of reflected light like the slits in a transmission grating. Current technology can produce gratings that have very small slit spacings. For example, a typical grating ruled with 5 000 grooves/cm has a slit spacing $d = (1/5\ 000)\ \text{cm} = 2.00 \times 10^{-4}\ \text{cm}$.

A section of a diffraction grating is illustrated in Figure 38.12. A plane wave is incident from the left, normal to the plane of the grating. The pattern observed on the screen far to the right of the grating is the result of the combined effects of interference and diffraction. Each slit produces diffraction, and the diffracted beams interfere with one another to produce the final pattern.

The waves from all slits are in phase as they leave the slits. For an arbitrary direction θ measured from the horizontal, however, the waves must travel different path lengths before reaching the screen. Notice in Figure 38.12 that the path difference δ between rays from any two adjacent slits is equal to $d \sin \theta$. If this path difference equals one wavelength or some integral multiple of a wavelength, waves from all slits are in phase at the screen and a bright fringe is observed. Therefore, the condition for *maxima* in the interference pattern at the angle θ_{bright} is

$$d \sin \theta_{\text{bright}} = m\lambda \quad m = 0, \pm 1, \pm 2, \pm 3, \ldots \tag{38.7}$$

◀ Condition for interference maxima for a grating

We can use this expression to calculate the wavelength if we know the grating spacing d and the angle θ_{bright}. If the incident radiation contains several wavelengths, the mth-order maximum for each wavelength occurs at a specific angle. All wavelengths are seen at $\theta = 0$, corresponding to $m = 0$, the zeroth-order maximum. The first-order maximum ($m = 1$) is observed at an angle that satisfies the relationship $\sin \theta_{\text{bright}} = \lambda/d$, the second-order maximum ($m = 2$) is observed at a larger angle θ_{bright}, and so on. For the small values of d typical in a diffraction grating, the angles θ_{bright} are large, as we see in Example 38.5.

The intensity distribution for a diffraction grating obtained with the use of a monochromatic source is shown in Active Figure 38.13. Notice the sharpness of the principal maxima and the broadness of the dark areas compared with the broad bright fringes characteristic of the two-slit interference pattern (see Fig. 37.7). You should also review Figure 37.8, which shows that the width of the intensity maxima decreases as the number of slits increases. Because the principal maxima are so sharp, they are much brighter than two-slit interference maxima.

Quick Quiz 38.5 Ultraviolet light of wavelength 350 nm is incident on a diffraction grating with slit spacing d and forms an interference pattern on a screen

PITFALL PREVENTION 38.3
A Diffraction Grating Is an Interference Grating

As with *diffraction pattern*, *diffraction grating* is a misnomer, but is deeply entrenched in the language of physics. The diffraction grating depends on diffraction in the same way as the double slit, spreading the light so that light from different slits can interfere. It would be more correct to call it an *interference grating*, but *diffraction grating* is the name in use.

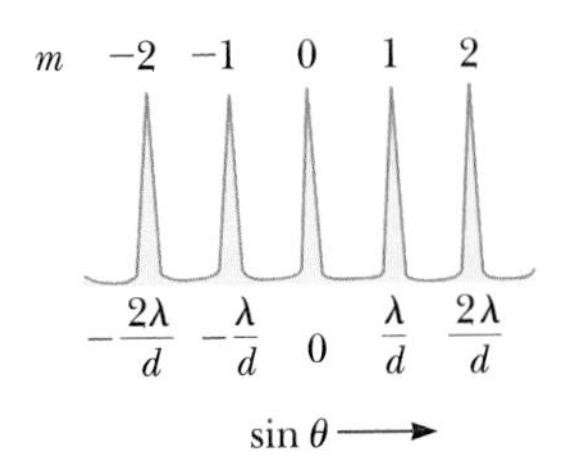

ACTIVE FIGURE 38.13

Intensity versus $\sin \theta$ for a diffraction grating. The zeroth-, first-, and second-order maxima are shown.

Sign in at www.thomsonedu.com and go to ThomsonNOW to choose the number of slits to be illuminated and see the effect on the interference pattern.

a distance L away. The angular positions θ_{bright} of the interference maxima are large. The locations of the bright fringes are marked on the screen. Now red light of wavelength 700 nm is used with a diffraction grating to form another diffraction pattern on the screen. Will the bright fringes of this pattern be located at the marks on the screen if (a) the screen is moved to a distance $2L$ from the grating, (b) the screen is moved to a distance $L/2$ from the grating, (c) the grating is replaced with one of slit spacing $2d$, (d) the grating is replaced with one of slit spacing $d/2$, or (e) nothing is changed?

CONCEPTUAL EXAMPLE 38.4 A Compact Disc Is a Diffraction Grating

Light reflected from the surface of a compact disc is multicolored, as shown in Figure 38.14. The colors and their intensities depend on the orientation of the CD relative to the eye and relative to the light source. Explain how this works.

Figure 38.14 (Conceptual Example 38.4) A compact disc observed under white light. The colors observed in the reflected light and their intensities depend on the orientation of the CD relative to the eye and relative to the light source.

SOLUTION

The surface of a CD has a spiral grooved track (with adjacent grooves having a separation on the order of 1 μm). Therefore, the surface acts as a reflection grating. The light reflecting from the regions between these closely spaced grooves interferes constructively only in certain directions that depend on the wavelength and the direction of the incident light. Any section of the CD serves as a diffraction grating for white light, sending different colors in different directions. The different colors you see upon viewing one section change when the light source, the CD, or you change position. This change in position causes the angle of incidence or the angle of the diffracted light to be altered.

EXAMPLE 38.5 The Orders of a Diffraction Grating

Monochromatic light from a helium–neon laser (λ = 632.8 nm) is incident normally on a diffraction grating containing 6 000 grooves per centimeter. Find the angles at which the first- and second-order maxima are observed.

SOLUTION

Conceptualize Study Figure 38.12 and imagine that the light coming from the left originates from the helium–neon laser.

Categorize We evaluate results using equations developed in this section, so we categorize this example as a substitution problem.

Calculate the slit separation as the inverse of the number of grooves per centimeter:

$$d = \frac{1}{6\,000}\text{ cm} = 1.667 \times 10^{-4}\text{ cm} = 1\,667\text{ nm}$$

Solve Equation 38.7 for $\sin\theta$ and substitute numerical values for the first-order maximum ($m = 1$) to find θ_1:

$$\sin\theta_1 = \frac{(1)\lambda}{d} = \frac{632.8\text{ nm}}{1\,667\text{ nm}} = 0.379\,7$$

$$\theta_1 = 22.31°$$

Repeat for the second-order maximum ($m = 2$):

$$\sin\theta_2 = \frac{(2)\lambda}{d} = \frac{2(632.8\text{ nm})}{1\,667\text{ nm}} = 0.759\,4$$

$$\theta_2 = 49.41°$$

What If? What if you looked for the third-order maximum? Would you find it?

Answer For $m = 3$, we find $\sin \theta_3 = 1.139$. Because $\sin \theta$ cannot exceed unity, this result does not represent a realistic solution. Hence, only zeroth-, first-, and second-order maxima can be observed for this situation.

Applications of Diffraction Gratings

A schematic drawing of a simple apparatus used to measure angles in a diffraction pattern is shown in Active Figure 38.15. This apparatus is a *diffraction grating spectrometer.* The light to be analyzed passes through a slit, and a collimated beam of light is incident on the grating. The diffracted light leaves the grating at angles that satisfy Equation 38.7, and a telescope is used to view the image of the slit. The wavelength can be determined by measuring the precise angles at which the images of the slit appear for the various orders.

The spectrometer is a useful tool in *atomic spectroscopy,* in which the light from an atom is analyzed to find the wavelength components. These wavelength components can be used to identify the atom. We shall investigate atomic spectra in Chapter 42 of the extended version of this text.

Another application of diffraction gratings is the *grating light valve* (GLV), which may compete in the near future in video projection with the digital micromirror devices (DMDs) discussed in Section 35.4. A GLV is a silicon microchip fitted with an array of parallel silicon nitride ribbons coated with a thin layer of aluminum (Fig. 38.16). Each ribbon is approximately 20 μm long and 5 μm wide and is separated from the silicon substrate by an air gap on the order of 100 nm. With no voltage applied, all ribbons are at the same level. In this situation, the array of ribbons acts as a flat surface, specularly reflecting incident light.

When a voltage is applied between a ribbon and the electrode on the silicon substrate, an electric force pulls the ribbon downward, closer to the substrate. Alternate ribbons can be pulled down, while those in between remain in an elevated configuration. As a result, the array of ribbons acts as a diffraction grating such that the constructive interference for a particular wavelength of light can be directed toward a screen or other optical display system. By using three such devices—one each for red, blue, and green light—full-color display is possible.

A GLV tends to be simpler to fabricate and higher in resolution than comparable DMDs. On the other hand, DMDs have already made an entry into the market. It will be interesting to watch this technology competition in future years.

Another interesting application of diffraction gratings is **holography,** the production of three-dimensional images of objects. The physics of holography was developed by Dennis Gabor (1900–1979) in 1948 and resulted in the Nobel Prize

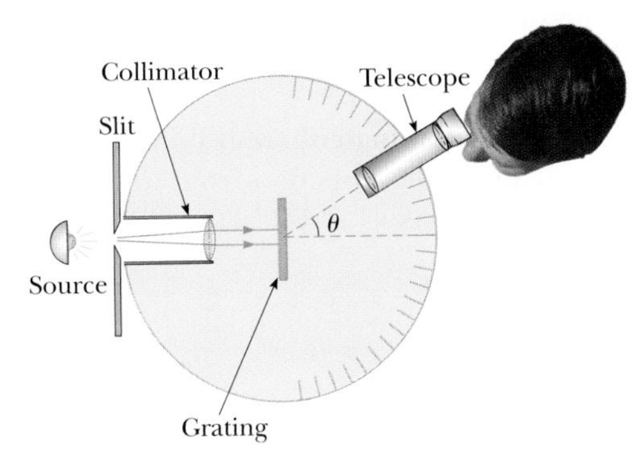

ACTIVE FIGURE 38.15

Diagram of a diffraction grating spectrometer. The collimated beam incident on the grating is spread into its various wavelength components with constructive interference for a particular wavelength occurring at the angles θ_{bright} that satisfy the equation $d \sin \theta_{\text{bright}} = m\lambda$, where $m = 0, \pm 1, \pm 2, \ldots$.

Sign in at www.thomsonedu.com and go to ThomsonNOW to use the spectrometer and observe constructive interference for various wavelengths.

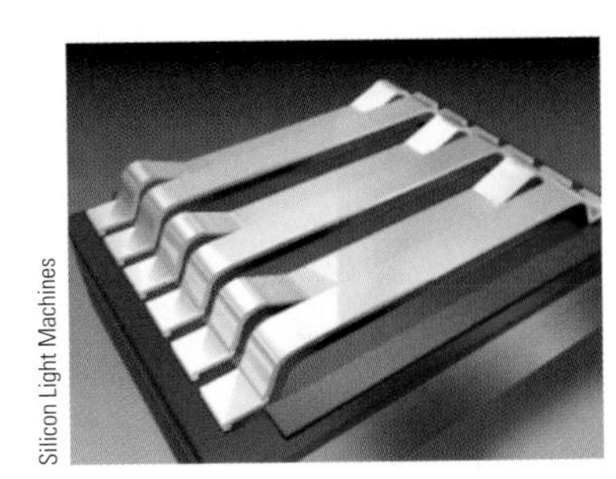

Silicon Light Machines

Figure 38.16 A small portion of a grating light valve. The alternating reflective ribbons at different levels act as a diffraction grating, offering very high-speed control of the direction of light toward a digital display device.

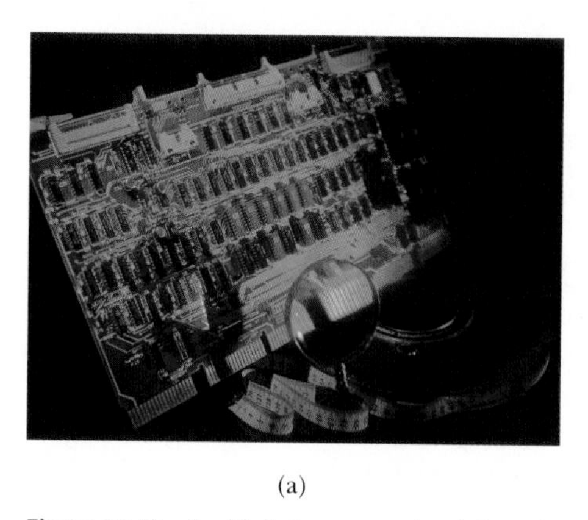

(a)

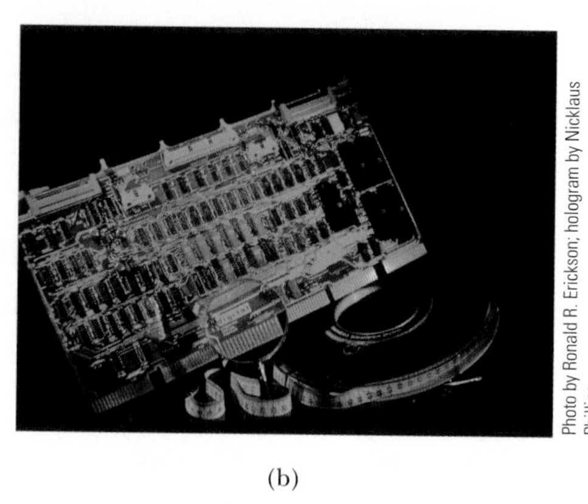

(b)

Figure 38.17 In this hologram, a circuit board is shown from two different views. Notice the difference in the appearance of the measuring tape and the view through the magnifying lens in (a) and (b).

in Physics for Gabor in 1971. The requirement of coherent light for holography delayed the realization of holographic images from Gabor's work until the development of lasers in the 1960s. Figure 38.17 shows a hologram and the three-dimensional character of its image. Notice in particular the difference in the view through the magnifying glass in Figures 38.17a and 38.17b.

Figure 38.18 shows how a hologram is made. Light from the laser is split into two parts by a half-silvered mirror at *B*. One part of the beam reflects off the object to be photographed and strikes an ordinary photographic film. The other half of the beam is diverged by lens L_2, reflects from mirrors M_1 and M_2, and finally strikes the film. The two beams overlap to form an extremely complicated interference pattern on the film. Such an interference pattern can be produced only if the phase relationship of the two waves is constant throughout the exposure of the film. This condition is met by illuminating the scene with light coming through a pinhole or with coherent laser radiation. The hologram records not only the intensity of the light scattered from the object (as in a conventional photograph), but also the phase difference between the reference beam and the beam scattered from the object. Because of this phase difference, an interference pattern is formed that produces an image in which all three-dimensional information available from the perspective of any point on the hologram is preserved.

In a normal photographic image, a lens is used to focus the image so that each point on the object corresponds to a single point on the film. Notice that there is no lens used in Figure 38.18 to focus the light onto the film. Therefore, light from each point on the object reaches *all* points on the film. As a result, each region of the photographic film on which the hologram is recorded contains information about all illuminated points on the object, which leads to a remarkable result: if a small section of the hologram is cut from the film, the complete image can be formed from the small piece! (The quality of the image is reduced, but the entire image is present.)

A hologram is best viewed by allowing coherent light to pass through the developed film as one looks back along the direction from which the beam comes. The interference pattern on the film acts as a diffraction grating. Figure 38.19 shows

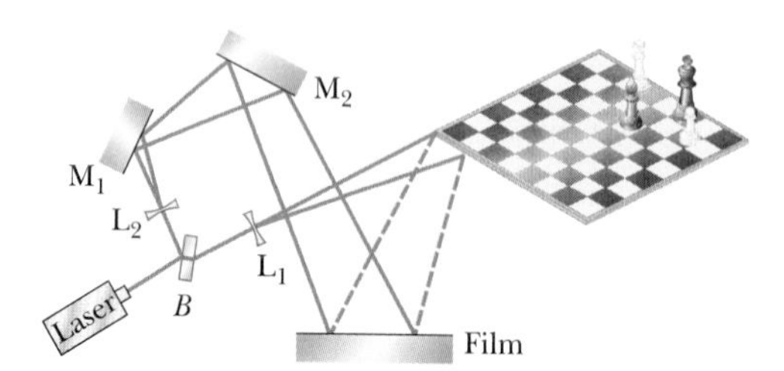

Figure 38.18 Experimental arrangement for producing a hologram.

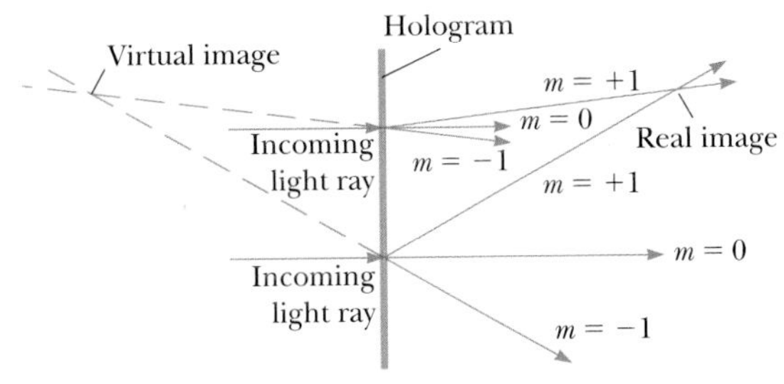

Figure 38.19 Two light rays strike a hologram at normal incidence. For each ray, outgoing rays corresponding to $m = 0$ and $m = \pm 1$ are shown. If the $m = -1$ rays are extended backward, a virtual image of the object photographed in the hologram exists on the front side of the hologram.

two rays of light striking and passing through the film. For each ray, the $m = 0$ and $m = \pm 1$ rays in the diffraction pattern are shown emerging from the right side of the film. The $m = +1$ rays converge to form a real image of the scene, which is not the image that is normally viewed. By extending the light rays corresponding to $m = -1$ behind the film, we see that there is a virtual image located there, with light coming from it in exactly the same way that light came from the actual object when the film was exposed. This image is what one sees when looking through the holographic film.

Holograms are finding a number of applications. You may have a hologram on your credit card. This special type of hologram is called a *rainbow hologram* and is designed to be viewed in reflected white light.

38.5 Diffraction of X-Rays by Crystals

In principle, the wavelength of any electromagnetic wave can be determined if a grating of the proper spacing (on the order of λ) is available. X-rays, discovered by Wilhelm Roentgen (1845–1923) in 1895, are electromagnetic waves of very short wavelength (on the order of 0.1 nm). It would be impossible to construct a grating having such a small spacing by the cutting process described at the beginning of Section 38.4. The atomic spacing in a solid is known to be about 0.1 nm, however. In 1913, Max von Laue (1879–1960) suggested that the regular array of atoms in a crystal could act as a three-dimensional diffraction grating for x-rays. Subsequent experiments confirmed this prediction. The diffraction patterns from crystals are complex because of the three-dimensional nature of the crystal structure. Nevertheless, x-ray diffraction has proved to be an invaluable technique for elucidating these structures and for understanding the structure of matter.

Figure 38.20 shows one experimental arrangement for observing x-ray diffraction from a crystal. A collimated beam of monochromatic x-rays is incident on a crystal. The diffracted beams are very intense in certain directions, corresponding

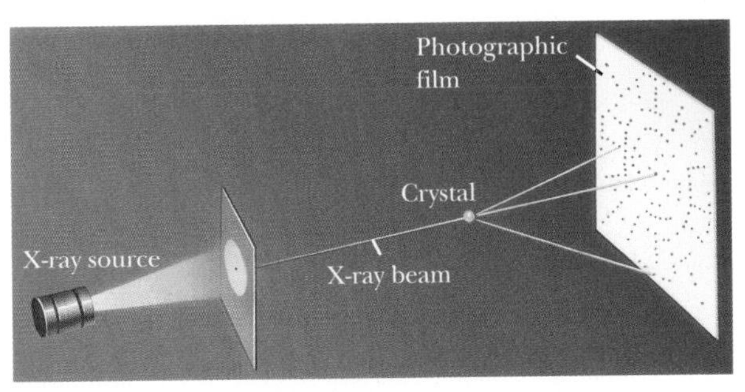

Figure 38.20 Schematic diagram of the technique used to observe the diffraction of x-rays by a crystal. The array of spots formed on the film is called a Laue pattern.

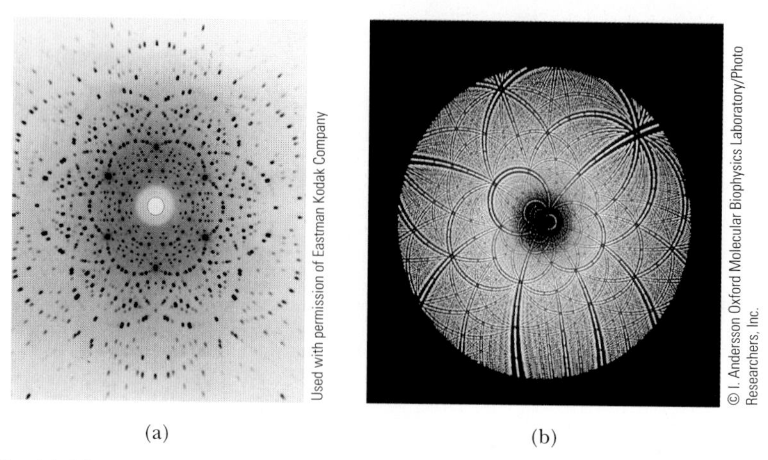

Figure 38.21 (a) A Laue pattern of a single crystal of the mineral beryl (beryllium aluminum silicate). Each dot represents a point of constructive interference. (b) A Laue pattern of the enzyme Rubisco, produced with a wideband x-ray spectrum. This enzyme is present in plants and takes part in the process of photosynthesis. The Laue pattern is used to determine the crystal structure of Rubisco.

to constructive interference from waves reflected from layers of atoms in the crystal. The diffracted beams, which can be detected by a photographic film, form an array of spots known as a *Laue pattern* as in Figure 38.21a. One can deduce the crystalline structure by analyzing the positions and intensities of the various spots in the pattern. Figure 38.21b shows a Laue pattern from a crystalline enzyme, using a wide range of wavelengths so that a swirling pattern results.

PITFALL PREVENTION 38.4
Different Angles

Notice in Figure 38.23 that the angle θ is measured from the reflecting surface rather than from the normal as in the case of the law of reflection in Chapter 35. With slits and diffraction gratings, we also measured the angle θ from the normal to the array of slits. Because of historical tradition, the angle is measured differently in Bragg diffraction, so interpret Equation 38.8 with care.

The arrangement of atoms in a crystal of sodium chloride (NaCl) is shown in Figure 38.22. Each unit cell (the geometric solid that repeats throughout the crystal) is a cube having an edge length a. A careful examination of the NaCl structure shows that the ions lie in discrete planes (the shaded areas in Fig. 38.22). Now suppose an incident x-ray beam makes an angle θ with one of the planes as in Figure 38.23. The beam can be reflected from both the upper plane and the lower one, but the beam reflected from the lower plane travels farther than the beam reflected from the upper plane. The effective path difference is $2d \sin \theta$. The two beams reinforce each other (constructive interference) when this path difference equals some integer multiple of λ. The same is true for reflection from the entire family of parallel planes. Hence, the condition for *constructive* interference (maxima in the reflected beam) is

Bragg's law ▶

$$2d \sin \theta = m\lambda \quad m = 1, 2, 3, \ldots \tag{38.8}$$

This condition is known as **Bragg's law,** after W. L. Bragg (1890–1971), who first derived the relationship. If the wavelength and diffraction angle are measured, Equation 38.8 can be used to calculate the spacing between atomic planes.

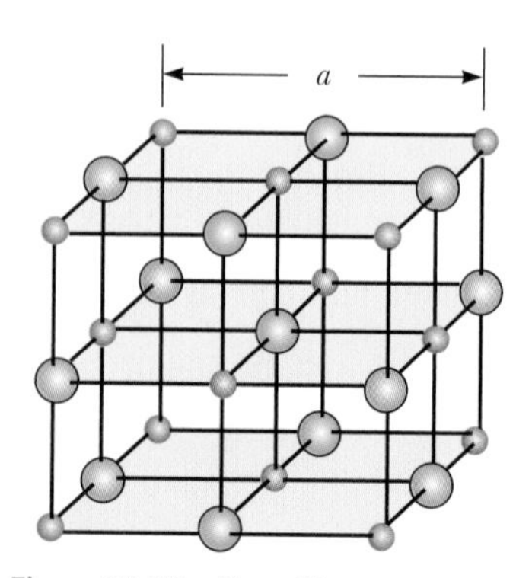

Figure 38.22 Crystalline structure of sodium chloride (NaCl). The blue spheres represent Cl^- ions, and the red spheres represent Na^+ ions. The length of the cube edge is $a = 0.562\,737$ nm.

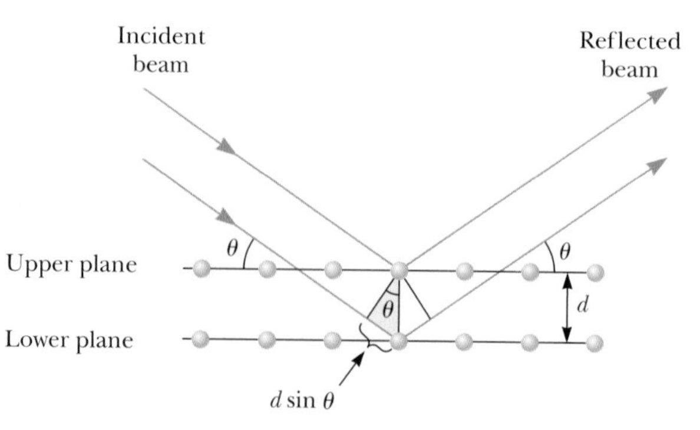

Figure 38.23 A two-dimensional description of the reflection of an x-ray beam from two parallel crystalline planes separated by a distance d. The beam reflected from the lower plane travels farther than the beam reflected from the upper plane by a distance $2d \sin \theta$.

38.6 Polarization of Light Waves

In Chapter 34, we described the transverse nature of light and all other electromagnetic waves. Polarization, discussed in this section, is firm evidence of this transverse nature.

An ordinary beam of light consists of a large number of waves emitted by the atoms of the light source. Each atom produces a wave having some particular orientation of the electric field vector $\vec{\mathbf{E}}$, corresponding to the direction of atomic vibration. The *direction of polarization* of each individual wave is defined to be the direction in which the electric field is vibrating. In Figure 38.24, this direction happens to lie along the y axis. An individual electromagnetic wave, however, could have its $\vec{\mathbf{E}}$ vector in the yz plane, making any possible angle with the y axis. Because all directions of vibration from a wave source are possible, the resultant electromagnetic wave is a superposition of waves vibrating in many different directions. The result is an **unpolarized** light beam, represented in Figure 38.25a. The direction of wave propagation in this figure is perpendicular to the page. The arrows show a few possible directions of the electric field vectors for the individual waves making up the resultant beam. At any given point and at some instant of time, all these individual electric field vectors add to give one resultant electric field vector.

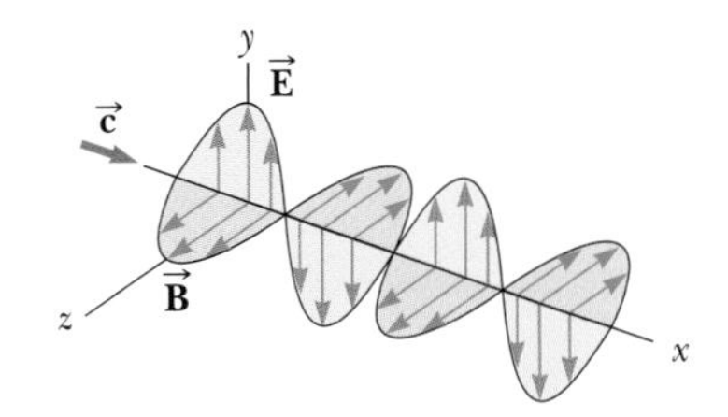

Figure 38.24 Schematic diagram of an electromagnetic wave propagating at velocity $\vec{\mathbf{c}}$ in the x direction. The electric field vibrates in the xy plane, and the magnetic field vibrates in the xz plane.

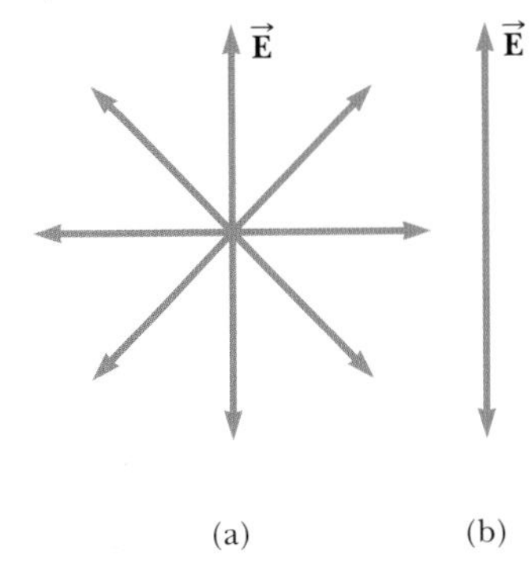

Figure 38.25 (a) A representation of an unpolarized light beam viewed along the direction of propagation (perpendicular to the page). The transverse electric field can vibrate in any direction in the plane of the page with equal probability. (b) A linearly polarized light beam with the electric field vibrating in the vertical direction.

As noted in Section 34.3, a wave is said to be **linearly polarized** if the resultant electric field $\vec{\mathbf{E}}$ vibrates in the same direction *at all times* at a particular point as shown in Figure 38.25b. (Sometimes, such a wave is described as *plane-polarized,* or simply *polarized.*) The plane formed by $\vec{\mathbf{E}}$ and the direction of propagation is called the *plane of polarization* of the wave. If the wave in Figure 38.24 represents the resultant of all individual waves, the plane of polarization is the xy plane.

A linearly polarized beam can be obtained from an unpolarized beam by removing all waves from the beam except those whose electric field vectors oscillate in a single plane. We now discuss four processes for producing polarized light from unpolarized light.

Polarization by Selective Absorption

The most common technique for producing polarized light is to use a material that transmits waves whose electric fields vibrate in a plane parallel to a certain direction and that absorbs waves whose electric fields vibrate in all other directions.

In 1938, E. H. Land (1909–1991) discovered a material, which he called *Polaroid,* that polarizes light through selective absorption. This material is fabricated in thin sheets of long-chain hydrocarbons. The sheets are stretched during manufacture so that the long-chain molecules align. After a sheet is dipped into a solution containing iodine, the molecules become good electrical conductors. Conduction takes place primarily along the hydrocarbon chains because electrons can move easily only along the chains. If light whose electric field vector is parallel to the chains is incident on the material, the electric field accelerates electrons along the chains and energy is absorbed from the radiation. Therefore, the light does not pass through the material. Light whose electric field vector is perpendicular to the chains passes through the material because electrons cannot move from one molecule to the next. As a result, when unpolarized light is incident on the material, the exiting light is polarized perpendicular to the molecular chains.

It is common to refer to the direction perpendicular to the molecular chains as the *transmission axis.* In an ideal polarizer, all light with $\vec{\mathbf{E}}$ parallel to the transmission axis is transmitted and all light with $\vec{\mathbf{E}}$ perpendicular to the transmission axis is absorbed.

Active Figure 38.26 (page 1094) represents an unpolarized light beam incident on a first polarizing sheet, called the *polarizer.* Because the transmission axis is oriented vertically in the figure, the light transmitted through this sheet is polarized vertically. A second polarizing sheet, called the *analyzer,* intercepts the beam. In

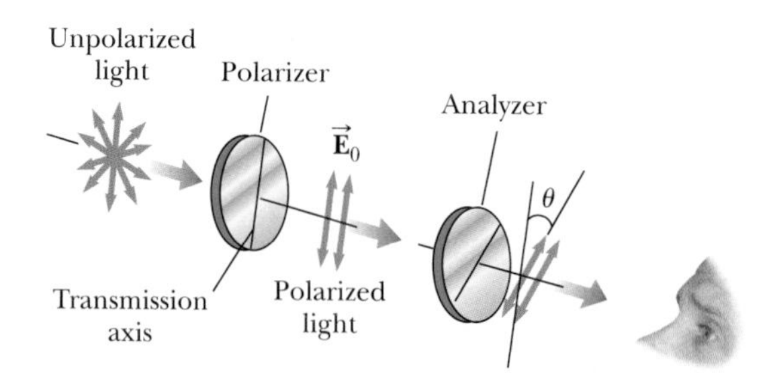

ACTIVE FIGURE 38.26

Two polarizing sheets whose transmission axes make an angle θ with each other. Only a fraction of the polarized light incident on the analyzer is transmitted through it.

Sign in at www.thomsonedu.com and go to ThomsonNOW to rotate the analyzer and see the effect on the transmitted light.

Active Figure 38.26, the analyzer transmission axis is set at an angle θ to the polarizer axis. We call the electric field vector of the first transmitted beam $\vec{\mathbf{E}}_0$. The component of $\vec{\mathbf{E}}_0$ perpendicular to the analyzer axis is completely absorbed. The component of $\vec{\mathbf{E}}_0$ parallel to the analyzer axis, which is transmitted through the analyzer, is $E_0 \cos \theta$. Because the intensity of the transmitted beam varies as the square of its magnitude, we conclude that the intensity I of the (polarized) beam transmitted through the analyzer varies as

Malus's law ▶

$$I = I_{\max} \cos^2 \theta \tag{38.9}$$

where $I_{\max}$ is the intensity of the polarized beam incident on the analyzer. This expression, known as **Malus's law,**[2] applies to any two polarizing materials whose transmission axes are at an angle θ to each other. This expression shows that the intensity of the transmitted beam is maximum when the transmission axes are parallel ($\theta = 0$ or $180°$) and is zero (complete absorption by the analyzer) when the transmission axes are perpendicular to each other. This variation in transmitted intensity through a pair of polarizing sheets is illustrated in Figure 38.27.

Polarization by Reflection

When an unpolarized light beam is reflected from a surface, the reflected light may be completely polarized, partially polarized, or unpolarized, depending on the angle of incidence. If the angle of incidence is $0°$, the reflected beam is unpolarized. For other angles of incidence, the reflected light is polarized to some extent, and for one particular angle of incidence, the reflected light is completely polarized. Let's now investigate reflection at that special angle.

Suppose an unpolarized light beam is incident on a surface as in Figure 38.28a. Each individual electric field vector can be resolved into two components: one parallel to the surface (and perpendicular to the page in Fig. 38.28, represented by

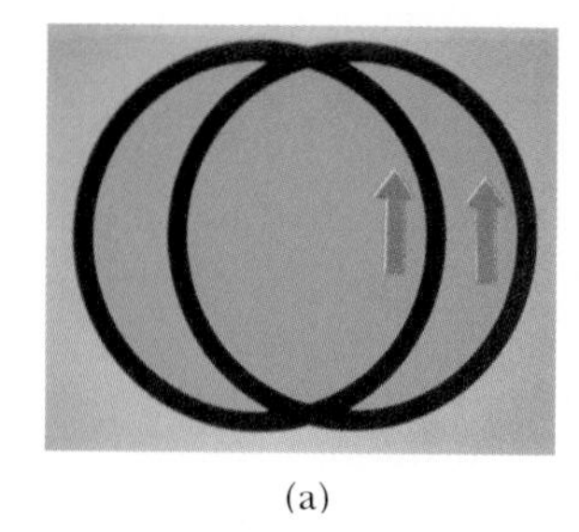
(a)

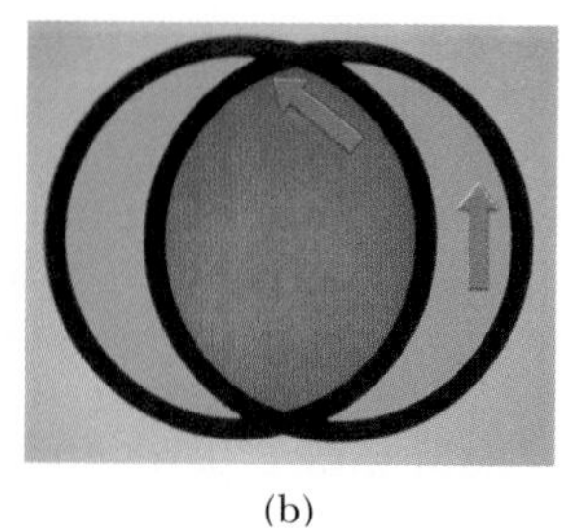
(b)

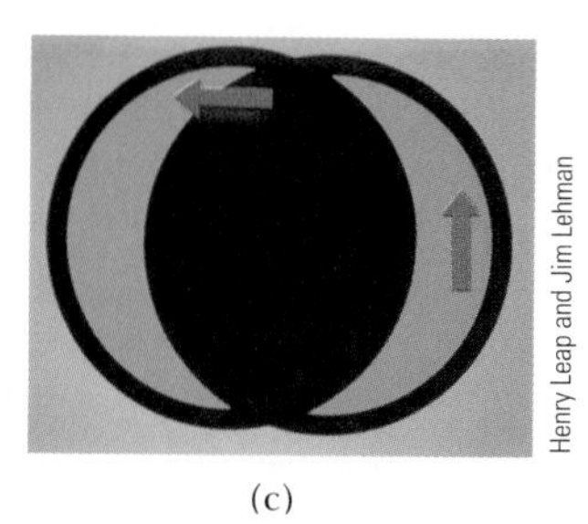
(c)

Henry Leap and Jim Lehman

Figure 38.27 The intensity of light transmitted through two polarizers depends on the relative orientation of their transmission axes. (a) The transmitted light has maximum intensity when the transmission axes are aligned with each other. (b) The transmitted light has lesser intensity when the transmission axes are at an angle of $45°$ with each other. (c) The transmitted light intensity is a minimum when the transmission axes are perpendicular to each other.

[2] Named after its discoverer, E. L. Malus (1775–1812). Malus discovered that reflected light was polarized by viewing it through a calcite ($CaCO_3$) crystal.

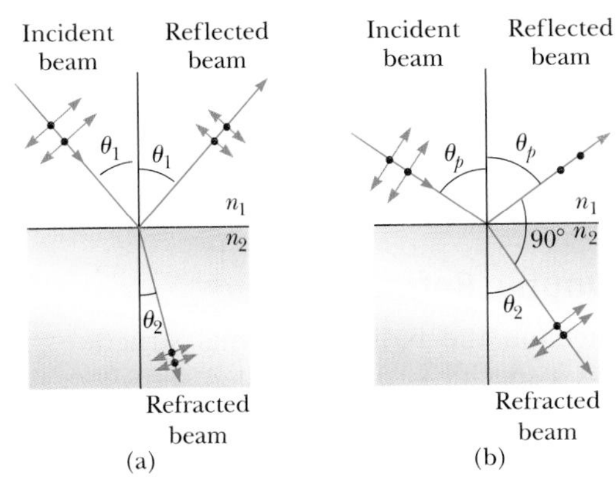

Figure 38.28 (a) When unpolarized light is incident on a reflecting surface, the reflected and refracted beams are partially polarized. (b) The reflected beam is completely polarized when the angle of incidence equals the polarizing angle θ_p, which satisfies the equation $n = \tan\theta_p$. At this incident angle, the reflected and refracted rays are perpendicular to each other.

the dots) and the other (represented by the brown arrows) perpendicular both to the first component and to the direction of propagation. Therefore, the polarization of the entire beam can be described by two electric field components in these directions. It is found that the parallel component reflects more strongly than the perpendicular component, resulting in a partially polarized reflected beam. Furthermore, the refracted beam is also partially polarized.

Now suppose the angle of incidence θ_1 is varied until the angle between the reflected and refracted beams is 90° as in Figure 38.28b. At this particular angle of incidence, the reflected beam is completely polarized (with its electric field vector parallel to the surface) and the refracted beam is still only partially polarized. The angle of incidence at which this polarization occurs is called the **polarizing angle** θ_p.

We can obtain an expression relating the polarizing angle to the index of refraction of the reflecting substance by using Figure 38.28b. From this figure, we see that $\theta_p + 90° + \theta_2 = 180°$; therefore, $\theta_2 = 90° - \theta_p$. Using Snell's law of refraction (Eq. 35.8) gives

$$\frac{n_2}{n_1} = \frac{\sin\theta_1}{\sin\theta_2} = \frac{\sin\theta_p}{\sin\theta_2}$$

Because $\sin\theta_2 = \sin(90° - \theta_p) = \cos\theta_p$, we can write this expression as $n_2/n_1 = \sin\theta_p/\cos\theta_p$, which means that

$$\tan\theta_p = \frac{n_2}{n_1} \qquad \textbf{(38.10)}$$

◀ Brewster's law

This expression is called **Brewster's law,** and the polarizing angle θ_p is sometimes called **Brewster's angle,** after its discoverer, David Brewster (1781–1868). Because n varies with wavelength for a given substance, Brewster's angle is also a function of wavelength.

We can understand polarization by reflection by imagining that the electric field in the incident light sets electrons at the surface of the material in Figure 38.28b into oscillation. The component directions of oscillation are (1) parallel to the arrows shown on the refracted beam of light and (2) perpendicular to the page. The oscillating electrons act as antennas radiating light with a polarization parallel to the direction of oscillation. For the oscillations in direction 1, there is no radiation in the perpendicular direction, which is along the reflected ray (see the $\theta = 90°$ direction in Fig. 34.10). For oscillations in direction 2, the electrons radiate light with a polarization perpendicular to the page (the $\theta = 0$ direction in Fig. 34.10). Therefore, the light reflected from the surface at this angle is completely polarized parallel to the surface.

Polarization by reflection is a common phenomenon. Sunlight reflected from water, glass, and snow is partially polarized. If the surface is horizontal, the electric field vector of the reflected light has a strong horizontal component. Sunglasses made of polarizing material reduce the glare of reflected light. The transmission axes of such lenses are oriented vertically so that they absorb the strong horizontal component of the reflected light. If you rotate sunglasses through 90°, they are not as effective at blocking the glare from shiny horizontal surfaces.

Polarization by Double Refraction

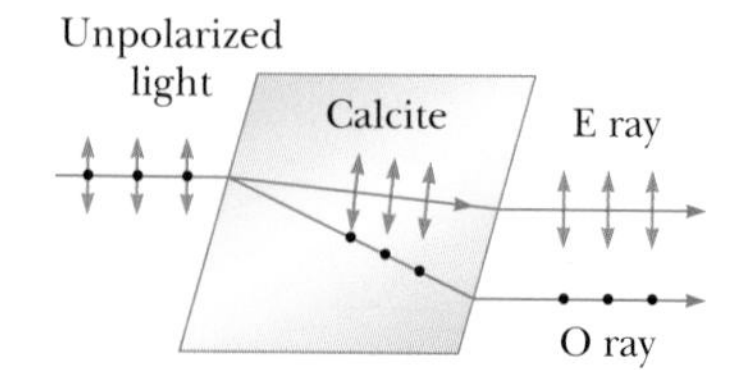

Figure 38.29 Unpolarized light incident at an angle to the optic axis in a calcite crystal splits into an ordinary (O) ray and an extraordinary (E) ray. These two rays are polarized in mutually perpendicular directions. (Drawing not to scale.)

Solids can be classified on the basis of internal structure. Those in which the atoms are arranged in a specific order are called *crystalline;* the NaCl structure of Figure 38.22 is one example of a crystalline solid. Those solids in which the atoms are distributed randomly are called *amorphous.* When light travels through an amorphous material such as glass, it travels with a speed that is the same in all directions. That is, glass has a single index of refraction. In certain crystalline materials such as calcite and quartz, however, the speed of light is not the same in all directions. In these materials, the speed of light depends on the direction of propagation *and* on the plane of polarization of the light. Such materials are characterized by two indices of refraction. Hence, they are often referred to as **double-refracting** or **birefringent** materials.

When unpolarized light enters a birefringent material, it may split into an **ordinary (O) ray** and an **extraordinary (E) ray.** These two rays have mutually perpendicular polarizations and travel at different speeds through the material. The two speeds correspond to two indices of refraction, n_O for the ordinary ray and n_E for the extraordinary ray.

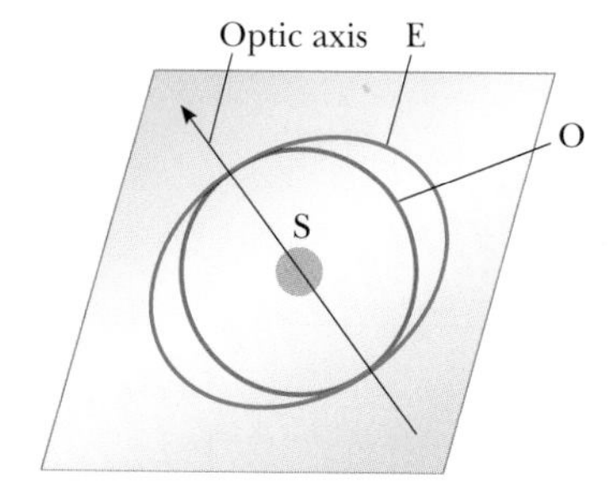

Figure 38.30 A point source S inside a double-refracting crystal produces a spherical wave front corresponding to the ordinary (O) ray and an elliptical wave front corresponding to the extraordinary (E) ray. The two waves propagate with the same velocity along the optic axis.

There is one direction, called the **optic axis,** along which the ordinary and extraordinary rays have the same speed. If light enters a birefringent material at an angle to the optic axis, however, the different indices of refraction will cause the two polarized rays to split and travel in different directions as shown in Figure 38.29.

The index of refraction n_O for the ordinary ray is the same in all directions. If one could place a point source of light inside the crystal as in Figure 38.30, the ordinary waves would spread out from the source as spheres. The index of refraction n_E varies with the direction of propagation. A point source sends out an extraordinary wave having wave fronts that are elliptical in cross section. The difference in speed for the two rays is a maximum in the direction perpendicular to the optic axis. For example, in calcite, $n_O = 1.658$ at a wavelength of 589.3 nm, and n_E varies from 1.658 along the optic axis to 1.486 perpendicular to the optic axis. Values for n_O and the extreme value of n_E for various double-refracting crystals are given in Table 38.1.

If you place a calcite crystal on a sheet of paper and then look through the crystal at any writing on the paper, you would see two images as shown in Figure 38.31. As can be seen from Figure 38.29, these two images correspond to one formed by the ordinary ray and one formed by the extraordinary ray. If the two images are viewed through a sheet of rotating polarizing glass, they alternately appear and dis-

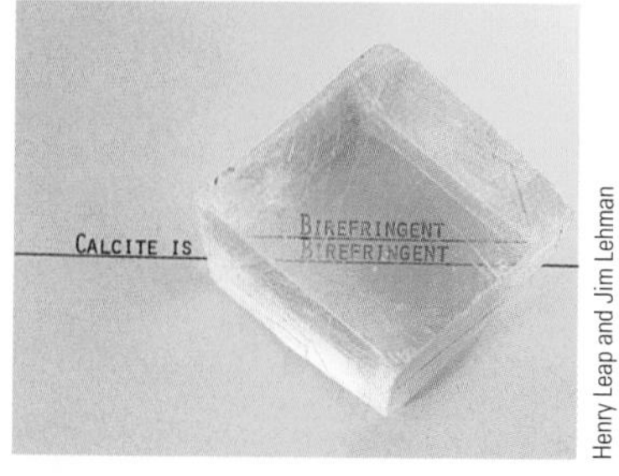

Henry Leap and Jim Lehman

Figure 38.31 A calcite crystal produces a double image because it is a birefringent (double-refracting) material.

TABLE 38.1

Indices of Refraction for Some Double-Refracting Crystals at a Wavelength of 589.3 nm

Crystal	n_O	n_E	n_O/n_E
Calcite ($CaCO_3$)	1.658	1.486	1.116
Quartz (SiO_2)	1.544	1.553	0.994
Sodium nitrate ($NaNO_3$)	1.587	1.336	1.188
Sodium sulfite ($NaSO_3$)	1.565	1.515	1.033
Zinc chloride ($ZnCl_2$)	1.687	1.713	0.985
Zinc sulfide (ZnS)	2.356	2.378	0.991

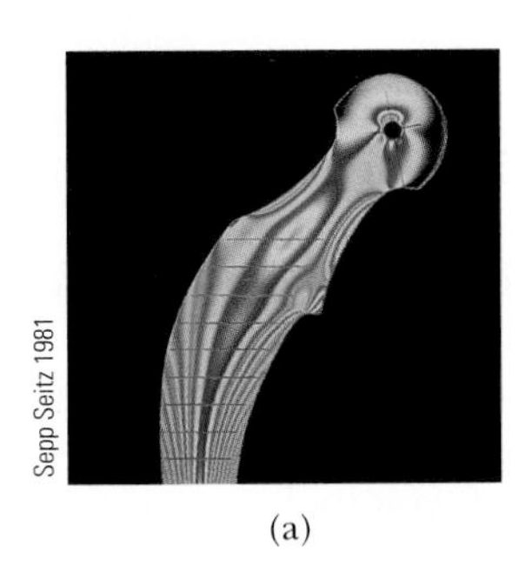

Sepp Seitz 1981

(a)

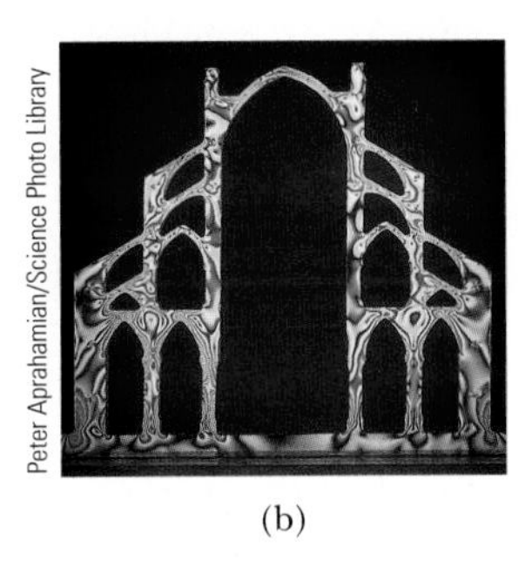

Peter Aprahamian/Science Photo Library

(b)

Figure 38.32 (a) Strain distribution in a plastic model of a hip replacement used in a medical research laboratory. The pattern is produced when the plastic model is viewed between a polarizer and analyzer oriented perpendicular to each other. (b) A plastic model of an arch structure under load conditions observed between perpendicular polarizers. Such patterns are useful in the optimal design of architectural components.

appear because the ordinary and extraordinary rays are plane-polarized along mutually perpendicular directions.

Some materials such as glass and plastic become birefringent when stressed. Suppose an unstressed piece of plastic is placed between a polarizer and an analyzer so that light passes from polarizer to plastic to analyzer. When the plastic is unstressed and the analyzer axis is perpendicular to the polarizer axis, none of the polarized light passes through the analyzer. In other words, the unstressed plastic has no effect on the light passing through it. If the plastic is stressed, however, regions of greatest stress become birefringent and the polarization of the light passing through the plastic changes. Hence, a series of bright and dark bands is observed in the transmitted light, with the bright bands corresponding to regions of greatest stress.

Engineers often use this technique, called *optical stress analysis,* in designing structures ranging from bridges to small tools. They build a plastic model and analyze it under different load conditions to determine regions of potential weakness and failure under stress. Two examples of plastic models under stress are shown in Figure 38.32.

Polarization by Scattering

When light is incident on any material, the electrons in the material can absorb and reradiate part of the light. Such absorption and reradiation of light by electrons in the gas molecules that make up air is what causes sunlight reaching an observer on the Earth to be partially polarized. You can observe this effect—called **scattering**—by looking directly up at the sky through a pair of sunglasses whose lenses are made of polarizing material. Less light passes through at certain orientations of the lenses than at others.

Figure 38.33 illustrates how sunlight becomes polarized when it is scattered. The phenomenon is similar to that creating completely polarized light upon reflection from a surface at Brewster's angle. An unpolarized beam of sunlight traveling in the horizontal direction (parallel to the ground) strikes a molecule of one of the gases that make up air, setting the electrons of the molecule into vibration. These vibrating charges act like the vibrating charges in an antenna. The horizontal component of the electric field vector in the incident wave results in a horizontal component of the vibration of the charges, and the vertical component of the vector results in a vertical component of vibration. If the observer in Figure 38.33 is looking straight up (perpendicular to the original direction of propagation of the light), the vertical oscillations of the charges send no radiation toward the observer. Therefore, the observer sees light that is completely polarized in the horizontal direction as indicated by the brown arrows. If the observer looks in other directions, the light is partially polarized in the horizontal direction.

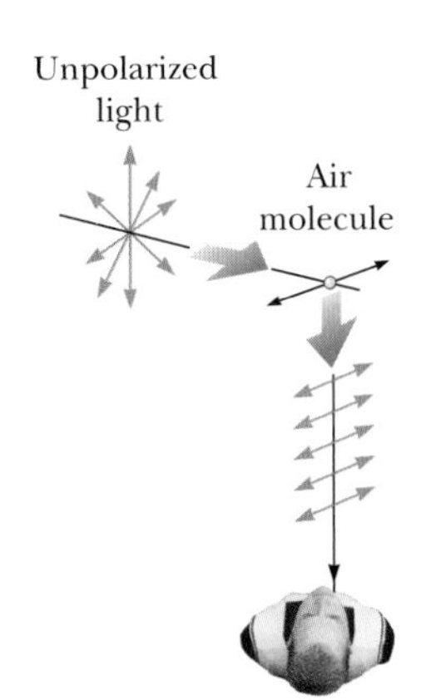

Figure 38.33 The scattering of unpolarized sunlight by air molecules. The scattered light traveling perpendicular to the incident light is plane-polarized because the vertical vibrations of the charges in the air molecule send no light in this direction.

Variations in the color of scattered light in the atmosphere can be understood as follows. When light of various wavelengths λ is incident on gas molecules of diameter d, where $d \ll \lambda$, the relative intensity of the scattered light varies as $1/\lambda^4$. The condition $d \ll \lambda$ is satisfied for scattering from oxygen (O_2) and nitrogen (N_2) molecules in the atmosphere, whose diameters are about 0.2 nm. Hence,

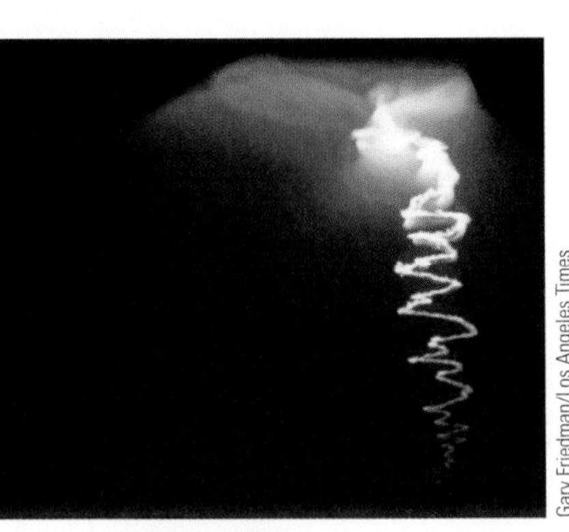
Gary Friedman/Los Angeles Times

This photograph is a view of a rocket launch from Vandenburg Air Force Base in California. The trail left by the rocket shows the effects of scattering of light by air molecules. The lower portion of the trail appears red due to the scattering of wavelengths at the violet end of the spectrum as the light from the Sun travels through a large portion of the atmosphere to light up the trail. The upper portion of the trail is illuminated by light that has traveled through much less atmosphere and appears white.

short wavelengths (violet light) are scattered more efficiently than long wavelengths (red light). Therefore, when sunlight is scattered by gas molecules in the air, the short-wavelength radiation (violet) is scattered more intensely than the long-wavelength radiation (red).

When you look up into the sky in a direction that is not toward the Sun, you see the scattered light, which is predominantly violet. Your eyes, however, are not very sensitive to violet light. Light of the next color in the spectrum, blue, is scattered with less intensity than violet, but your eyes are far more sensitive to blue light than to violet light. Hence, you see a blue sky. If you look toward the west at sunset (or toward the east at sunrise), you are looking in a direction toward the Sun and are seeing light that has passed through a large distance of air. Most of the blue light has been scattered by the air between you and the Sun. The light that survives this trip through the air to you has had much of its blue component scattered and is therefore heavily weighted toward the red end of the spectrum; as a result, you see the red and orange colors of sunset.

Optical Activity

Many important applications of polarized light involve materials that display **optical activity.** A material is said to be optically active if it rotates the plane of polarization of any light transmitted through the material. The angle through which the light is rotated by a specific material depends on the length of the path through the material and on concentration if the material is in solution. One optically active material is a solution of the common sugar dextrose. A standard method for determining the concentration of sugar solutions is to measure the rotation produced by a fixed length of the solution.

Molecular asymmetry determines whether a material is optically active. For example, some proteins are optically active because of their spiral shape.

The liquid crystal displays found in most calculators have their optical activity changed by the application of electric potential across different parts of the display. Try using a pair of polarizing sunglasses to investigate the polarization used in the display of your calculator.

Quick Quiz 38.6 A polarizer for microwaves can be made as a grid of parallel metal wires approximately 1 cm apart. Is the electric field vector for microwaves transmitted through this polarizer (a) parallel or (b) perpendicular to the metal wires?

Quick Quiz 38.7 You are walking down a long hallway that has many light fixtures in the ceiling and a very shiny, newly waxed floor. When looking at the floor, you see reflections of every light fixture. Now you put on sunglasses that are polarized. Some of the reflections of the light fixtures can no longer be seen. (Try it!) Are the reflections that disappear those (a) nearest to you, (b) farthest from you, or (c) at an intermediate distance from you?

Summary

ThomsonNOW™ Sign in at **www.thomsonedu.com** and go to ThomsonNOW to take a practice test for this chapter.

CONCEPTS AND PRINCIPLES

Diffraction is the deviation of light from a straight-line path when the light passes through an aperture or around an obstacle. Diffraction is due to the wave nature of light.

The **Fraunhofer diffraction pattern** produced by a single slit of width a on a distant screen consists of a central bright fringe and alternating bright and dark fringes of much lower intensities. The angles θ_{dark} at which the diffraction pattern has zero intensity, corresponding to destructive interference, are given by

$$\sin \theta_{\text{dark}} = m\frac{\lambda}{a} \qquad m = \pm 1, \pm 2, \pm 3, \ldots \qquad \textbf{(38.1)}$$

Rayleigh's criterion, which is a limiting condition of resolution, states that two images formed by an aperture are just distinguishable if the central maximum of the diffraction pattern for one image falls on the first minimum of the diffraction pattern for the other image. The limiting angle of resolution for a slit of width a is $\theta_{\text{min}} = \lambda/a$, and the limiting angle of resolution for a circular aperture of diameter D is given by $\theta_{\text{min}} = 1.22\lambda/D$.

A **diffraction grating** consists of a large number of equally spaced, identical slits. The condition for intensity maxima in the interference pattern of a diffraction grating for normal incidence is

$$d \sin \theta_{\text{bright}} = m\lambda \qquad m = 0, \pm 1, \pm 2, \pm 3, \ldots \qquad \textbf{(38.7)}$$

where d is the spacing between adjacent slits and m is the order number of the intensity maximum.

When polarized light of intensity I_{max} is emitted by a polarizer and then is incident on an analyzer, the light transmitted through the analyzer has an intensity equal to $I_{\text{max}} \cos^2 \theta$, where θ is the angle between the polarizer and analyzer transmission axes.

In general, reflected light is partially polarized. Reflected light, however, is completely polarized when the angle of incidence is such that the angle between the reflected and refracted beams is 90°. This angle of incidence, called the **polarizing angle** θ_p, satisfies **Brewster's law:**

$$\tan \theta_p = \frac{n_2}{n_1} \qquad \textbf{(38.10)}$$

where n_1 is the index of refraction of the medium in which the light initially travels and n_2 is the index of refraction of the reflecting medium.

Questions

☐ denotes answer available in *Student Solutions Manual/Study Guide;* **O** denotes objective question

☐**1.** Why can you hear around corners, but not see around corners?

2. Holding your hand at arm's length, you can readily block sunlight from reaching your eyes. Why can you not block sound from reaching your ears this way?

☐**3.** **O** Consider a wave passing through a single slit. What happens to the width of the central maximum of its diffraction pattern as the slit is made half as wide? (a) The central maximum becomes one-fourth as wide. (b) It becomes one-half as wide. (c) Its width does not change. (d) It becomes two times wider. (e) It becomes four times wider.

4. **O** Assume Figure 38.1 was photographed with red light of a single wavelength λ_0. The light passed through a single slit of width a and traveled distance L to the screen where the photograph was made. Consider the width of the central bright fringe, measured between the dark fringes on both sides of it. Rank from largest to smallest the widths of the central fringe in the following situations and note any cases of equality. (a) The experiment is performed as photographed. (b) The experiment is performed with light whose frequency is increased by 50%. (c) The experiment is performed with light whose wavelength is increased by 50%. (Its wavelength is $3\lambda_0/2$.) (d) The experiment is performed with the original light and with a slit of width $2a$. (e) The experiment is performed with the original light and slit, and with distance $2L$ to the screen. (f) The experiment is performed with light of twice the original intensity.

5. **O** In Active Figure 38.4, assume the slit is in a barrier that is opaque to x-rays as well as to visible light. The photograph in Active Figure 38.4b shows the diffraction pattern produced with visible light. What will happen if the experiment is repeated with x-rays as the incoming wave and with no other changes? (a) The diffraction pattern is similar. (b) There is no noticeable diffraction pattern but rather a projected shadow of high intensity on the screen, having the same width as the slit. (c) The central maximum is much wider and the minima occur at larger angles than with visible light. (d) No x-rays reach the screen.

6. **O** Off in the distance, you see the headlights of a car, but they are indistinguishable from the single headlight of a motorcycle. Assume the car's headlights are now switched from low beam to high beam so that the light intensity you receive becomes three times greater. What then happens to your ability to resolve the two light sources? (a) It increases by a factor of 9. (b) It increases by a factor of 3. (c) It remains the same. (d) It becomes one-third as good. (e) It becomes one-ninth as good.

7. A laser beam is incident at a shallow angle on a horizontal machinist's ruler that has a finely calibrated scale. The engraved rulings on the scale give rise to a diffraction pattern on a vertical screen. Discuss how you can use this technique to obtain a measure of the wavelength of the laser light.

8. **O** When you receive a chest x-ray at a hospital, the x-rays pass through a set of parallel ribs in your chest. Do your ribs act as a diffraction grating for x-rays? (a) Yes. They produce diffracted beams that can be observed separately. (b) Not to a measurable extent. The ribs are too far apart. (c) Essentially not. The ribs are too close together. (d) Essentially not. The ribs are too few in number. (e) Absolutely not. X-rays cannot diffract.

9. **O** Certain sunglasses use a polarizing material to reduce the intensity of light reflected as glare from water or automobiles. What orientation should the polarizing filters have to be most effective? (a) The polarizers should absorb light with its electric field horizontal. (b) The polarizers should absorb light with its electric field vertical. (c) The polarizers should absorb both horizontal and vertical electric fields. (d) The polarizers should not absorb either horizontal or vertical electric fields.

10. Is light from the sky polarized? Why is it that clouds seen through Polaroid glasses stand out in bold contrast to the sky?

11. **O** When unpolarized light passes straight through a diffraction grating, does it become polarized? (a) No, it does not. (b) Yes, it does, with the transmission axis parallel to the slits or grooves in the grating. (c) Yes, it does, with the transmission axis perpendicular to the slits or grooves in the grating. (d) It possibly does because an electric field above some threshold is blocked out by the grating if the field is perpendicular to the slits.

12. If a coin is glued to a glass sheet and this arrangement is held in front of a laser beam, the projected shadow has diffraction rings around its edge and a bright spot in the center. How are these effects possible?

13. How could the index of refraction of a flat piece of opaque volcanic glass be determined?

14. A laser produces a beam a few millimeters wide, with uniform intensity across its width. A hair is stretched vertically across the front of the laser to cross the beam. How is the diffraction pattern it produces on a distant screen related to that of a vertical slit equal in width to the hair? How could you determine the width of the hair from measurements of its diffraction pattern?

15. A radio station serves listeners in a city to the northeast of its broadcast site. It broadcasts from three adjacent towers on a mountain ridge, along a line running east and west. Show that by introducing time delays among the signals the individual towers radiate, the station can maximize net intensity in the direction toward the city (and in the opposite direction) and minimize the signal transmitted in other directions. The towers together are said to form a *phased array.*

16. John William Strutt, Lord Rayleigh (1842–1919), is known as the last person to understand all physics and all mathematics. He invented an improved foghorn. To warn ships of a coastline, a foghorn should radiate sound in a wide horizontal sheet over the ocean's surface. It should not waste energy by broadcasting sound upward. It should not emit sound downward because the water in front of the foghorn would reflect that sound upward. Rayleigh's foghorn trumpet is shown in Figure Q38.16. Is it installed in the correct orientation? Decide whether the long dimension of the rectangular opening should be horizontal or vertical, and argue for your decision.

Figure Q38.16

Problems

WebAssign The Problems from this chapter may be assigned online in WebAssign.

ThomsonNOW Sign in at **www.thomsonedu.com** and go to ThomsonNOW to assess your understanding of this chapter's topics with additional quizzing and conceptual questions.

1, 2, 3 denotes straightforward, intermediate, challenging; □ denotes full solution available in *Student Solutions Manual/Study Guide;* ▲ denotes coached solution with hints available at **www.thomsonedu.com;** ▭ denotes developing symbolic reasoning; ● denotes asking for qualitative reasoning; ▪ denotes computer useful in solving problem

Section 38.2 Diffraction Patterns from Narrow Slits

1. Helium–neon laser light ($\lambda = 632.8$ nm) is sent through a 0.300-mm-wide single slit. What is the width of the central maximum on a screen 1.00 m from the slit?

2. A beam of monochromatic green light is diffracted by a slit of width 0.550 mm. The diffraction pattern forms on a wall 2.06 m beyond the slit. The distance between the positions of zero intensity on both sides of the central bright fringe is 4.10 mm. Calculate the wavelength of the light.

3. ▲ A screen is placed 50.0 cm from a single slit, which is illuminated with 690-nm light. If the distance between the first and third minima in the diffraction pattern is 3.00 mm, what is the width of the slit?

4. Coherent microwaves of wavelength 5.00 cm enter a tall, narrow window in a building otherwise essentially opaque to the microwaves. If the window is 36.0 cm wide, what is the distance from the central maximum to the first-order minimum along a wall 6.50 m from the window?

5. Sound with a frequency 650 Hz from a distant source passes through a doorway 1.10 m wide in a sound-absorbing wall. Find the number and approximate directions of the diffraction-maximum beams radiated into the space beyond.

6. ● A horizontal laser beam of wavelength 632.8 nm has a circular cross section 2.00 mm in diameter. A rectangular aperture is to be placed in the center of the beam so that when the light falls perpendicularly on a wall 4.50 m away, the central maximum fills a rectangle 110 mm wide and 6.00 mm high. The dimensions are measured between the minima bracketing the central maximum. (a) Find the required width and height of the aperture. (b) Is the longer dimension of the central bright patch in the diffraction pattern horizontal or vertical? Is the longer dimension of the aperture horizontal or vertical? Explain the relationship between these two rectangles, using a diagram.

7. A diffraction pattern is formed on a screen 120 cm away from a 0.400-mm-wide slit. Monochromatic 546.1-nm light is used. Calculate the fractional intensity $I/I_{\max}$ at a point on the screen 4.10 mm from the center of the principal maximum.

8. **What If?** Assume the light in Figure 38.5 strikes the single slit at an angle β from the perpendicular direction. Show that Equation 38.1, the condition for destructive interference, must be modified to read

$$\sin \theta_{\text{dark}} = m\left(\frac{\lambda}{a}\right) - \sin \beta$$

9. Assume light with a wavelength of 650 nm passes through two slits 3.00 μm wide, with their centers 9.00 μm apart. Make a sketch of the combined diffraction and interference pattern in the form of a graph of intensity versus $\phi = (\pi a \sin \theta)/\lambda$. You may use Active Figure 38.7 as a starting point.

10. Coherent light of wavelength 501.5 nm is sent through two parallel slits in a large, flat wall. Each slit is 0.700 μm wide. Their centers are 2.80 μm apart. The light then falls on a semicylindrical screen, with its axis at the midline between the slits. (a) Predict the direction of each interference maximum on the screen as an angle away from the bisector of the line joining the slits. (b) Describe the pattern of light on the screen, specifying the number of bright fringes and the location of each. (c) Find the intensity of light on the screen at the center of each bright fringe, expressed as a fraction of the light intensity I_{max} at the center of the pattern.

Section 38.3 Resolution of Single-Slit and Circular Apertures

11. The pupil of a cat's eye narrows to a vertical slit of width 0.500 mm in daylight. What is the angular resolution for horizontally separated mice? Assume the average wavelength of the light is 500 nm.

12. ● Yellow light of wavelength 589 nm is used to view an object under a microscope. The objective diameter is 9.00 mm. (a) What is the limiting angle of resolution? (b) Suppose it is possible to use visible light of any wavelength. What color should you choose to give the smallest possible angle of resolution, and what is this angle? (c) Suppose water fills the space between the object and the objective. What effect does this change have on the resolving power when 589-nm light is used?

13. ▲ A helium–neon laser emits light that has a wavelength of 632.8 nm. The circular aperture through which the beam emerges has a diameter of 0.500 cm. Estimate the diameter of the beam 10.0 km from the laser.

14. ● Narrow, parallel, glowing gas-filled tubes in a variety of colors form block letters to spell out the name of a nightclub. Adjacent tubes are all 2.80 cm apart. The tubes forming one letter are filled with neon and radiate predominantly red light with a wavelength of 640 nm. For another letter, the tubes emit predominantly blue light at 440 nm. The pupil of a dark-adapted viewer's eye is 5.20 mm in diameter. If she is in a certain range of distances away, the viewer can resolve the separate tubes of one color but not the other. Which color is easier to resolve? State how you decide. The viewer's distance must be in what range for her to resolve the tubes of only one of these two colors?

15. Impressionist painter Georges Seurat created paintings with an enormous number of dots of pure pigment, each of which was approximately 2.00 mm in diameter. The idea was to have colors such as red and green next to each other to form a scintillating canvas (Fig. P38.15). Outside what distance would one be unable to discern individual dots on the canvas? Assume $\lambda = 500$ nm and a pupil diameter of 4.00 mm.

Figure P38.15

16. What are the approximate dimensions of the smallest object on the Earth that astronauts can resolve by eye when they are orbiting 250 km above the Earth? Assume $\lambda = 500$ nm and a pupil diameter of 5.00 mm.

17. A spy satellite can consist of a large-diameter concave mirror forming an image on a digital-camera detector and sending the picture to a ground receiver by radio waves. In effect, it is an astronomical telescope in orbit, looking down instead of up. Can a spy satellite read a license plate? Can it read the date on a dime? Argue for your answers by making an order-of-magnitude calculation, specifying the data you estimate.

18. A circular radar antenna on a Coast Guard ship has a diameter of 2.10 m and radiates at a frequency of 15.0 GHz. Two small boats are located 9.00 km away from the ship. How close together could the boats be and still be detected as two objects?

Section 38.4 The Diffraction Grating

Note: In the following problems, assume the light is incident normally on the gratings.

19. White light is spread out into its spectral components by a diffraction grating. If the grating has 2 000 grooves per centimeter, at what angle does red light of wavelength 640 nm appear in first order?

20. Light from an argon laser strikes a diffraction grating that has 5 310 grooves per centimeter. The central and first-order principal maxima are separated by 0.488 m on a wall 1.72 m from the grating. Determine the wavelength of the laser light.

21. ▲ The hydrogen spectrum includes a red line at 656 nm and a blue-violet line at 434 nm. What are the angular separations between these two spectral lines obtained with a diffraction grating that has 4 500 grooves/cm?

22. A helium–neon laser (λ = 632.8 nm) is used to calibrate a diffraction grating. If the first-order maximum occurs at 20.5°, what is the spacing between adjacent grooves in the grating?

23. Three discrete spectral lines occur at angles of 10.09°, 13.71°, and 14.77° in the first-order spectrum of a grating spectrometer. (a) If the grating has 3 660 slits/cm, what are the wavelengths of the light? (b) At what angles are these lines found in the second-order spectrum?

24. Show that whenever white light is passed through a diffraction grating of any spacing size, the violet end of the continuous visible spectrum in third order always overlaps with red light at the other end of the second-order spectrum.

25. A refrigerator shelf is an array of parallel wires with uniform spacing of 1.30 cm between centers. In air at 20°C, ultrasound with a frequency of 37.2 kHz from a distant source falls perpendicularly on the shelf. Find the number of diffracted beams leaving the other side of the shelf. Find the direction of each beam.

26. The laser in a CD player must precisely follow the spiral track, along which the distance between one loop of the spiral and the next is only about 1.25 μm. A feedback mechanism lets the player know if the laser drifts off the track so that the player can steer it back again. Figure P38.26 shows how a diffraction grating is used to provide information to keep the beam on track. The laser light passes through a diffraction grating before it reaches the disk. The strong central maximum of the diffraction pattern is used to read the information in the track of pits. The two first-order side maxima are used for steering. The grating is designed so that the first-order maxima fall on the flat surfaces on both sides of the information track. Both side beams are reflected into their own detectors. As long as both beams are reflecting from smooth nonpitted surfaces, they are detected with constant high intensity. If the main beam wanders off the track, however, one of the side beams begins to strike pits on the information track and the reflected light diminishes. This change is used with an electronic circuit to guide the beam back to the desired location. Assume the laser light has a wavelength of 780 nm and the diffraction grating is positioned 6.90 μm from the disk. Assume the first-order beams are to fall on the disk 0.400 μm on either side of the information track. What should be the number of grooves per millimeter in the grating?

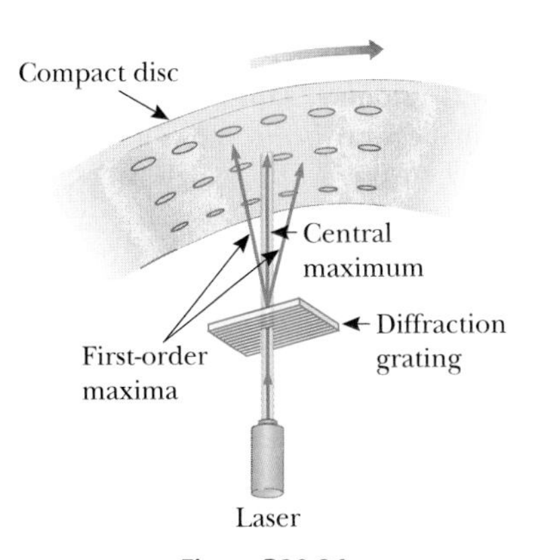

Figure P38.26

27. A grating with 250 grooves/mm is used with an incandescent light source. Assume the visible spectrum to range in

wavelength from 400 to 700 nm. In how many orders can one see (a) the entire visible spectrum and (b) the short-wavelength region?

28. ● A wide beam of laser light with a wavelength of 632.8 nm is directed through several narrow parallel slits, separated by 1.20 mm, and falls on a sheet of photographic film 1.40 m away. The exposure time is chosen so that the film stays unexposed everywhere except at the central region of each bright fringe. (a) Find the distance between these interference maxima. The film is printed as a transparency; it is opaque everywhere except at the exposed lines. Next, the same beam of laser light is directed through the transparency and allowed to fall on a screen 1.40 m beyond. (b) Argue that several narrow parallel bright regions, separated by 1.20 mm, appear on the screen as real images of the original slits. If the screen is removed, light diverges from the images of the original slits with the same reconstructed wave fronts as the original slits produced. *Suggestion:* You may find it useful to draw diagrams similar to Figure 38.12. A similar train of thought, at a soccer game, led Dennis Gabor to invent holography.

29. A diffraction grating has 4 200 rulings/cm. On a screen 2.00 m from the grating, it is found that for a particular order *m*, the maxima corresponding to two closely spaced wavelengths of sodium (589.0 nm and 589.6 nm) are separated by 1.59 mm. Determine the value of *m*.

Section 38.5 Diffraction of X-Rays by Crystals

30. Potassium iodide (KI) has the same crystalline structure as NaCl, with atomic planes separated by 0.353 nm. A monochromatic x-ray beam shows a first-order diffraction maximum when the grazing angle is 7.60°. Calculate the x-ray wavelength.

31. ▲ If the interplanar spacing of NaCl is 0.281 nm, what is the predicted angle at which 0.140-nm x-rays are diffracted in a first-order maximum?

32. In water of uniform depth, a wide pier is supported on pilings in several parallel rows 2.80 m apart. Ocean waves of uniform wavelength roll in, moving in a direction that makes an angle of 80.0° with the rows of posts. Find the three longest wavelengths of waves that are strongly reflected by the pilings.

33. ● The atoms in a crystal lie in planes separated by a few tenths of a nanometer. Can they produce a diffraction pattern for visible light as they do for x-rays? Explain your answer with reference to Bragg's law.

Section 38.6 Polarization of Light Waves

Problem 36 in Chapter 34 can be assigned with this section.

34. Unpolarized light passes through two ideal Polaroid sheets. The axis of the first is vertical and that of the second is at 30.0° to the vertical. What fraction of the incident light is transmitted?

35. Plane-polarized light is incident on a single polarizing disk with the direction of $\vec{\mathbf{E}}_0$ parallel to the direction of the transmission axis. Through what angle should the disk be rotated so that the intensity in the transmitted beam is reduced by a factor of (a) 3.00, (b) 5.00, and (c) 10.0?

36. The angle of incidence of a light beam onto a reflecting surface is continuously variable. The reflected ray in air is completely polarized when the angle of incidence is 48.0°. What is the index of refraction of the reflecting material?

37. The critical angle for total internal reflection for sapphire surrounded by air is 34.4°. Calculate the polarizing angle for sapphire.

38. For a particular transparent medium surrounded by air, show that the critical angle for total internal reflection and the polarizing angle are related by $\cot \theta_p = \sin \theta_c$.

39. ● **Review problem.** (a) A transparent plate with index of refraction n_2 is immersed in a medium with index n_1. Light traveling in the surrounding medium strikes the top surface of the plate at Brewster's angle. Show that if and only if the surfaces of the plate are parallel, the refracted light strikes the bottom surface of the plate at Brewster's angle for that interface. (b) **What If?** Instead of a plate, consider a prism of index of refraction n_2 separating

media of different refractive indices n_1 and n_3. The light propagates in a plane, containing also the apex angle of the prism. Is there one particular apex angle between the surfaces of the prism for which light can fall on both its surfaces at Brewster's angle as it passes through the prism? If so, determine it.

40. In Figure P38.40, suppose the transmission axes of the left and right polarizing disks are perpendicular to each other. Also, let the center disk be rotated on the common axis with an angular speed ω. Show that if unpolarized light is incident on the left disk with an intensity I_{max}, the intensity of the beam emerging from the right disk is

$$I = \frac{1}{16} I_{max}(1 - \cos 4\omega t)$$

This result means that the intensity of the emerging beam is modulated at a rate four times the rate of rotation of the center disk. *Suggestion:* Use the trigonometric identities $\cos^2 \theta = (1 + \cos 2\theta)/2$ and $\sin^2 \theta = (1 - \cos 2\theta)/2$, and recall that $\theta = \omega t$.

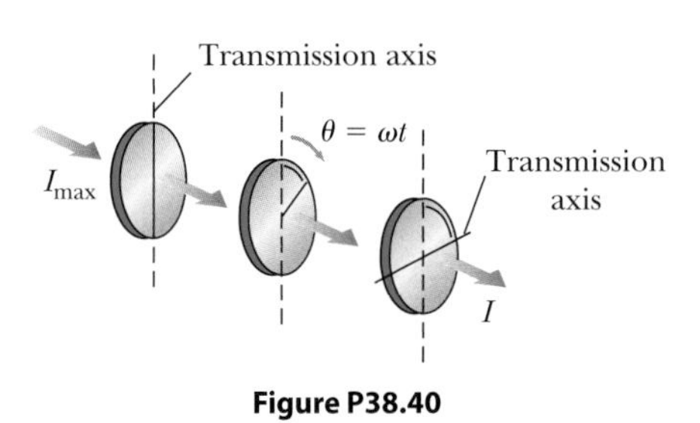

Figure P38.40

41. ● An unpolarized beam of light is incident on a stack of ideal polarizing filters. The axis of the first filter is perpendicular to the axis of the last filter in the stack. Find the fraction by which the transmitted beam's intensity is reduced in the following three cases. (a) Three filters are in the stack, each with its transmission axis at 45.0° relative to the preceding filter. (b) Four filters are in the stack, each with its transmission axis at 30.0° relative to the preceding filter. (c) Seven filters are in the stack, each with its axis at 15.0° relative to the preceding filter. (d) Comment on comparing the answers to parts (a), (b), and (c).

Additional Problems

42. ● Laser light with a wavelength of 632.8 nm is directed through one slit or two slits and allowed to fall on a screen 2.60 m beyond. Figure P38.42 shows the pattern on the screen, with a centimeter ruler below it. Did the light pass through one slit or two slits? Explain how you can tell. If one slit, find its width. If two slits, find the distance between their centers.

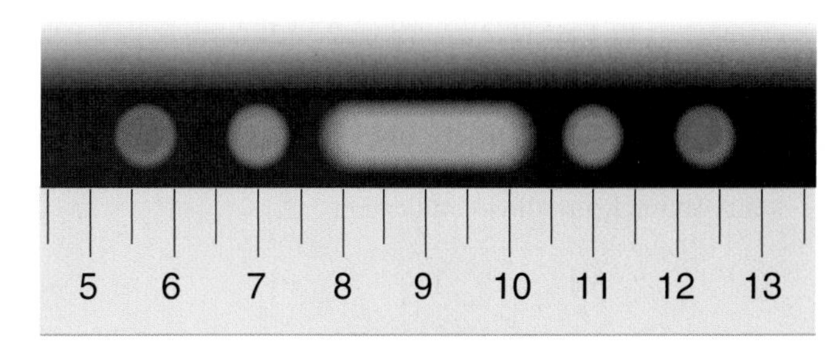

Figure P38.42

43. You use a sequence of ideal polarizing filters, each with its axis making the same angle with the axis of the previous filter, to rotate the plane of polarization of a polarized light beam by a total of 45.0°. You wish to have an intensity reduction no larger than 10.0%. (a) How many polarizers do you need to achieve your goal? (b) What is the angle between adjacent polarizers?

44. ● Figure P38.44 shows a megaphone in use. Construct a theoretical description of how a megaphone works. You may assume the sound of your voice radiates just through the opening of your mouth. Most of the information in speech is carried not in a signal at the fundamental frequency, but in noises and in harmonics, with frequencies of a few thousand hertz. Does your theory allow any prediction that is simple to test?

Figure P38.44

45. In a single-slit diffraction pattern, (a) find the ratio of the intensity of the first-order side maximum to the intensity of the central maximum. (b) Find the ratio of the intensity of the second-order side maximum to the intensity of the central maximum. You may assume each side maximum is halfway between the adjacent minima.

46. Consider a light wave passing through a slit. Give a mathematical argument that more than 90% of the transmitted energy is in the central maximum of the diffraction pattern. *Suggestions:* Think of the energy as represented by the shaded area in Figure 38.6a. Solve Problem 45 as preparation for this one. You are not expected to calculate the precise percentage, but explain the steps of your reasoning. You may use the identification

$$\frac{1}{1^2} + \frac{1}{3^2} + \frac{1}{5^2} + \cdots = \frac{\pi^2}{8}$$

47. Light from a helium–neon laser ($\lambda = 632.8$ nm) is incident on a single slit. What is the maximum width of the slit for which no diffraction minima are observed?

48. ● Two motorcycles separated laterally by 2.30 m are approaching an observer who is holding a "snooper scope" sensitive to infrared light of wavelength 885 nm. What aperture diameter is required if the motorcycles' headlights are to be resolved at a distance of 12.0 km? Assume the light propagates through perfectly steady and uniform air. Comment on how realistic this assumption is.

49. **Review problem.** A beam of 541-nm light is incident on a diffraction grating that has 400 grooves/mm. (a) Determine the angle of the second-order ray. (b) **What If?** If the entire apparatus is immersed in water, what is the new second-order angle of diffraction? (c) Show that the two diffracted rays of parts (a) and (b) are related through the law of refraction.

50. The *Very Large Array* (VLA) is a set of 27 radio telescope dishes in Catron and Socorro counties, New Mexico (Fig. P38.50). The antennas can be moved apart on railroad tracks, and their combined signals give the resolving power of a synthetic aperture 36.0 km in diameter. (a) If the detectors are tuned to a frequency of 1.40 GHz, what is the angular resolution of the VLA? (b) Clouds of hydrogen radiate at this frequency. What must be the separation distance of two clouds at the center of the galaxy, 26 000 light-years away, if they are to be resolved? (c) **What If?** As the telescope looks up, a circling hawk looks down. Find the angular resolution of the hawk's eye. Assume the hawk is most sensitive to green light having a wavelength of 500 nm and it has a pupil of diameter 12.0 mm. (d) A mouse is on the ground 30.0 m below. By what distance must the mouse's whiskers be separated if the hawk can resolve them?

Figure P38.50

51. A 750-nm light beam hits the flat surface of a certain liquid, and the beam is split into a reflected ray and a refracted ray. If the reflected ray is completely polarized at 36.0°, what is the wavelength of the refracted ray?

52. ● Iridescent peacock feathers are shown in Figure P38.52a. The surface of one microscopic barbule is composed of transparent keratin that supports rods of dark brown melanin in a regular lattice, represented in Figure P38.52b. (Your fingernails are made of keratin, and melanin is the dark pigment giving color to human skin.) In a portion of the feather that can appear turquoise

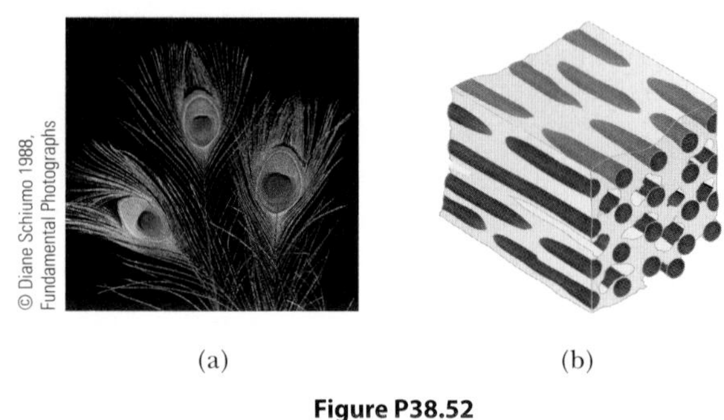

Figure P38.52

(blue-green), assume the melanin rods are uniformly separated by 0.25 μm, with air between them. (a) Explain how this structure can appear blue-green when it contains no blue or green pigment. (b) Explain how it can also appear violet if light falls on it in a different direction. (c) Explain how it can present different colors to your two eyes simultaneously, which is a characteristic of iridescence. (d) A compact disc can appear to be any color of the rainbow. Explain why this portion of the feather cannot appear yellow or red. (e) What could be different about the array of melanin rods in a portion of the feather that does appear to be red?

53. Light of wavelength 500 nm is incident normally on a diffraction grating. If the third-order maximum of the diffraction pattern is observed at 32.0°, (a) what is the number of rulings per centimeter for the grating? (b) Determine the total number of primary maxima that can be observed in this situation.

54. ● Light in air strikes a water surface at the polarizing angle. The part of the beam refracted into the water strikes a submerged slab of material with refractive index n as shown in Figure P38.54. The light reflected from the upper surface of the slab is completely polarized. (a) Find the angle θ between the water surface and the surface of the slab as a function of n. (b) Identify the maximum imaginable value of θ and describe the physical situation to which it corresponds. (c) Identify the minimum imaginable value of θ and describe the physical situation to which it corresponds.

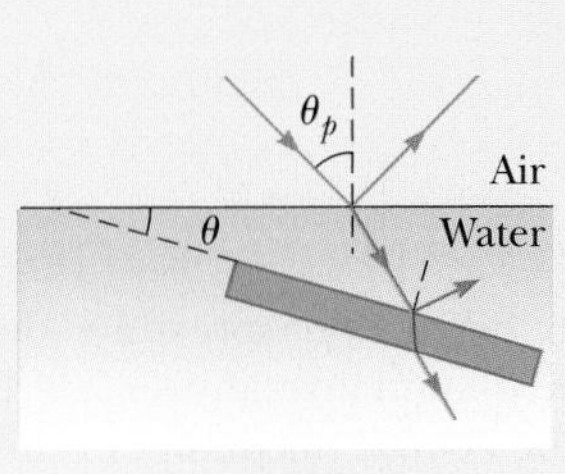

Figure P38.54

55. A beam of bright red light of wavelength 654 nm passes through a diffraction grating. Enclosing the space beyond the grating is a large screen forming one half of a cylinder centered on the grating, with its axis parallel to the slits in the grating. Fifteen bright spots appear on the screen. Find the maximum and minimum possible values for the slit separation in the diffraction grating.

56. A *pinhole camera* has a small circular aperture of diameter D. Light from distant objects passes through the aperture into an otherwise dark box, falling on a screen located a distance L away. If D is too large, the display on the screen will be fuzzy because a bright point in the field of view will send light onto a circle of diameter slightly larger than D. On the other hand, if D is too small, diffraction will blur the display on the screen. The screen shows a reasonably sharp image if the diameter of the central disk of the diffraction pattern, specified by Equation 38.6, is equal to D at the screen. (a) Show that for monochromatic light with plane wave fronts and $L \gg D$, the condition for a sharp view is fulfilled if $D^2 = 2.44\lambda L$. (b) Find the optimum pinhole diameter for 500-nm light projected onto a screen 15.0 cm away.

57. An American standard television picture is composed of approximately 485 horizontal lines of varying light intensity. Assume your ability to resolve the lines is limited only by the Rayleigh criterion and the pupils of your eyes are 5.00 mm in diameter. Calculate the ratio of minimum viewing distance to the vertical dimension of the picture such that you will not be able to resolve the lines. Assume the average wavelength of the light coming from the screen is 550 nm.

58. (a) Light traveling in a medium of index of refraction n_1 is incident at an angle θ on the surface of a medium of index n_2. The angle between reflected and refracted rays is β. Show that

$$\tan \theta = \frac{n_2 \sin \beta}{n_1 - n_2 \cos \beta}$$

Suggestion: Use the identity $\sin (A + B) = \sin A \cos B + \cos A \sin B$. (b) **What If?** Show that this expression for $\tan \theta$ reduces to Brewster's law when $\beta = 90°$, $n_1 = 1$, and $n_2 = n$.

59. Suppose the single slit in Active Figure 38.4 is 6.00 cm wide and in front of a microwave source operating at 7.50 GHz. (a) Calculate the angle subtended by the first minimum in the diffraction pattern. (b) What is the relative intensity I/I_{max} at $\theta = 15.0°$? (c) Assume two such sources, separated laterally by 20.0 cm, are behind the slit. What must the maximum distance between the plane of the sources and the slit be if the diffraction patterns are to be resolved? In this case, the approximation $\sin \theta \approx \tan \theta$ is not valid because of the relatively small value of a/λ.

60. ● (a) Two polarizing sheets are placed together with their transmission axes crossed so that no light is transmitted. A third sheet is inserted between them with its

transmission axis at an angle of 45.0° with respect to each of the other axes. Find the fraction of incident unpolarized light intensity transmitted by the three-sheet combination. Assume each polarizing sheet is ideal. (b) A parent is searching an Internet collection of recipes for easy main dishes. She uses a computer to eliminate all the recipes containing meat and then to eliminate all the remaining recipes containing cheese. No recipes from the original database remain after these two sorting processes. With the same database, she next tries a sequence of three selection rounds: eliminating all recipes containing meat, eliminating remaining recipes containing more than a little meat or cheese, and eliminating remaining recipes containing any cheese. Will any recipes remain in the list after these three sorting processes? Compare and contrast the results of the recipe-sorting experiment with the results of the polarization experiment in part (a).

61. The scale of a map is a number of kilometers per centimeter, specifying the distance on the ground that any distance on the map represents. The scale of a spectrum is its *dispersion*, a number of nanometers per centimeter, specifying the change in wavelength that a distance across the spectrum represents. You must know the dispersion if you want to compare one spectrum with another or to make a measurement of, for example, a Doppler shift. Let y represent the position relative to the center of a diffraction pattern projected onto a flat screen at distance L by a diffraction grating with slit spacing d. The dispersion is $d\lambda/dy$. (a) Prove that the dispersion is given by

$$\frac{d\lambda}{dy} = \frac{L^2 d}{m(L^2 + y^2)^{3/2}}$$

(b) Calculate the dispersion in first order for light with a mean wavelength of 550 nm, analyzed with a grating having 8 000 rulings/cm, and projected onto a screen 2.40 m away.

62. Two closely spaced wavelengths of light are incident on a diffraction grating. (a) Starting with Equation 38.7, show that the angular dispersion of the grating is given by

$$\frac{d\theta}{d\lambda} = \frac{m}{d \cos \theta}$$

(b) A square grating 2.00 cm on each side containing 8 000 equally spaced slits is used to analyze the spectrum of mercury. Two closely spaced lines emitted by this element have wavelengths of 579.065 nm and 576.959 nm. What is the angular separation of these two wavelengths in the second-order spectrum?

63. Figure P38.63a is a three-dimensional sketch of a birefringent crystal. The dotted lines illustrate how a thin, parallel-faced slab of material could be cut from the larger specimen with the crystal's optic axis parallel to the faces of the plate. A section cut from the crystal in this manner is known as a *retardation plate.* When a beam of light is incident on the plate perpendicular to the direction of the optic axis as shown in Figure P38.63b, the O ray and the E ray travel along a single straight line, but with different speeds. (a) Let the thickness of the plate be d. Show that the phase difference between the O ray and the E ray is

$$\theta = \frac{2\pi d}{\lambda} |n_O - n_E|$$

where λ is the wavelength in air. (b) In a particular case, the incident light has a wavelength of 550 nm. Find the minimum value of d for a quartz plate for which $\theta = \pi/2$. Such a plate is called a *quarter-wave plate.* Use values of n_O and n_E from Table 38.1.

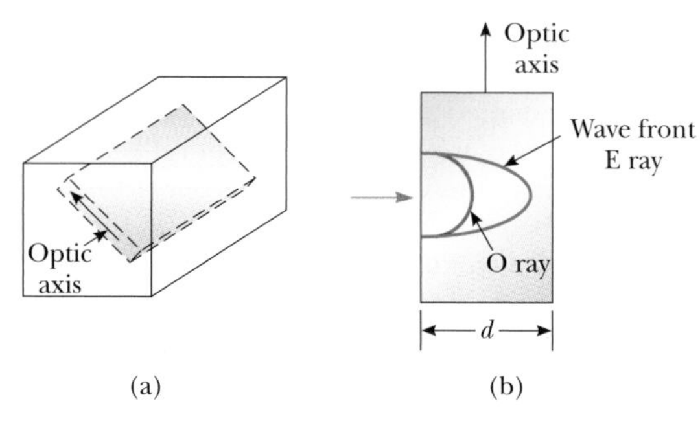

Figure P38.63

64. How much diffraction spreading does a light beam undergo? One quantitative answer is the *full width at half maximum* of the central maximum of the single-slit Fraunhofer diffraction pattern. You can evaluate this angle of spreading in this problem and the next. (a) In Equation 38.2, define $\pi a \sin \theta/\lambda = \phi$ and show that, at the point where $I = 0.5I_{max}$, we must have $\sin \phi = \phi/\sqrt{2}$. (b) Let $y_1 = \sin \phi$ and $y_2 = \phi/\sqrt{2}$. Plot y_1 and y_2 on the same set of axes over a range from $\phi = 1$ rad to $\phi = \pi/2$ rad. Determine ϕ from the point of intersection of the two curves. (c) Then show that if the fraction λ/a is not large, the angular full width at half maximum of the central diffraction maximum is $\Delta\theta = 0.886\lambda/a$.

65. Another method to solve the transcendental equation $\phi = \sqrt{2} \sin \phi$ in Problem 64 is to guess a first value of ϕ, use a computer or calculator to see how nearly it fits, and

continue to update your estimate until the equation balances. How many steps (iterations) does this process take?

66. The diffraction pattern of a single slit is described by the equation

$$I_\theta = I_{\max}\frac{\sin^2\phi}{\phi^2}$$

where $\phi = (\pi a \sin\theta)/\lambda$. The central maximum is at $\phi = 0$, and the side maxima are *approximately* at $\phi = (m + \frac{1}{2})\pi$ for $m = 1, 2, 3, \ldots$. Determine more precisely (a) the location of the first side maximum, where $m = 1$, and (b) the location of the second side maximum. Observe in Figure 38.6a that the graph of intensity versus ϕ has a horizontal tangent at maxima and also at minima. You will need to solve a transcendental equation.

67. Light of wavelength 632.8 nm illuminates a single slit, and a diffraction pattern is formed on a screen 1.00 m from the slit. Using the data in the following table, plot relative intensity versus position. Choose an appropriate value for the slit width a and, on the same graph used for the experimental data, plot the theoretical expression for the relative intensity

$$\frac{I_\theta}{I_{\max}} = \frac{\sin^2\phi}{\phi^2}$$

where $\phi = (\pi a \sin\theta)/\lambda$. What value of a gives the best fit of theory and experiment?

Relative Intensity	**Position Relative to Central Maximum (mm)**	**Relative Intensity**	**Position Relative to Central Maximum (mm)**
1.00	0	0.029	10.5
0.95	0.8	0.013	11.3
0.80	1.6	0.002	12.1
0.60	2.4	0.000 3	12.9
0.39	3.2	0.005	13.7
0.21	4.0	0.012	14.5
0.079	4.8	0.016	15.3
0.014	5.6	0.015	16.1
0.003	6.5	0.010	16.9
0.015	7.3	0.004 4	17.7
0.036	8.1	0.000 6	18.5
0.047	8.9	0.000 3	19.3
0.043	9.7	0.003	20.2

Answers to Quick Quizzes

38.1 (a). Equation 38.1 shows that a decrease in a results in an increase in the angles at which the dark fringes appear.

38.2 (i). In Equation 38.4, the ratio d/a is independent of wavelength, so the number of interference fringes in the central diffraction pattern peak remains the same. Equation 38.1 tells us that a decrease in wavelength causes a decrease in the width of the central peak if I is graphed against y as in Active Figure 38.4. If I is graphed against $(\pi/\lambda)\ a \sin\theta$ as in Active Figure 38.7, however, the peak width is independent of λ.

38.3 (b). The effective slit width in the vertical direction of the cat's eye is larger than that in the horizontal direction. Therefore, the cat's eye has more resolving power for lights separated in the vertical direction and would be more effective at resolving the mast lights on the boat.

38.4 (a). We would like to reduce the minimum angular separation for two objects below the angle subtended by the two stars in the binary system. That can be done by reducing the wavelength of the light, which in essence makes the aperture larger, relative to the light wavelength, increasing the resolving power. Therefore, we should choose a blue filter.

38.5 (c). Doubling the wavelength makes the pattern wider. Choices (a) and (d) make the pattern even wider. From Equation 38.10, we see that choice (b) causes $\sin\theta$ to be twice as large. Because the small angle approximation cannot be used, however, doubling $\sin\theta$ is not the same as doubling θ, which would translate to a doubling of the position of a maximum along the screen. If we only consider small-angle maxima, choice (b) would work, but it does not work in the large-angle case.

38.6 (b). Electric field vectors parallel to the metal wires cause electrons in the metal to oscillate parallel to the wires. Therefore, the energy from the waves with these electric field vectors is transferred to the metal by accelerating these electrons and is eventually transformed to internal energy through the resistance of the metal. Waves with electric field vectors perpendicular to the metal wires pass through because they are not able to accelerate electrons in the wires.

38.7 (c). At some intermediate distance, the light rays from the fixtures will strike the floor at Brewster's angle and reflect to your eyes. Because this light is polarized horizontally, it will not pass through your polarized sunglasses. Tilting your head to the side will cause the reflections to reappear.

PART 6

Modern Physics

At the end of the 19th century, many scientists believed they had learned most of what there was to know about physics. Newton's laws of motion and theory of universal gravitation, Maxwell's theoretical work in unifying electricity and magnetism, the laws of thermodynamics and kinetic theory, and the principles of optics were highly successful in explaining a variety of phenomena.

At the turn of the 20th century, however, a major revolution shook the world of physics. In 1900, Max Planck provided the basic ideas that led to the formulation of the quantum theory, and in 1905, Albert Einstein formulated his special theory of relativity. The excitement of the times is captured in Einstein's own words: "It was a marvelous time to be alive." Both theories were to have a profound effect on our understanding of nature. Within a few decades, they inspired new developments in the fields of atomic physics, nuclear physics, and condensed-matter physics.

In Chapter 39, we shall introduce the special theory of relativity. The theory provides us with a new and deeper view of physical laws. Although the predictions of this theory often violate our common sense, the theory correctly describes the results of experiments involving speeds near the speed of light. The extended version of this textbook, *Physics for Scientists and Engineers with Modern Physics,* covers the basic concepts of quantum mechanics and their application to atomic and molecular physics, and we introduce solid-state physics, nuclear physics, particle physics, and cosmology.

Even though the physics that was developed during the 20th century has led to a multitude of important technological achievements, the story is still incomplete. Discoveries will continue to evolve during our lifetimes, and many of these discoveries will deepen or refine our understanding of nature and the Universe around us. It is still a "marvelous time to be alive."

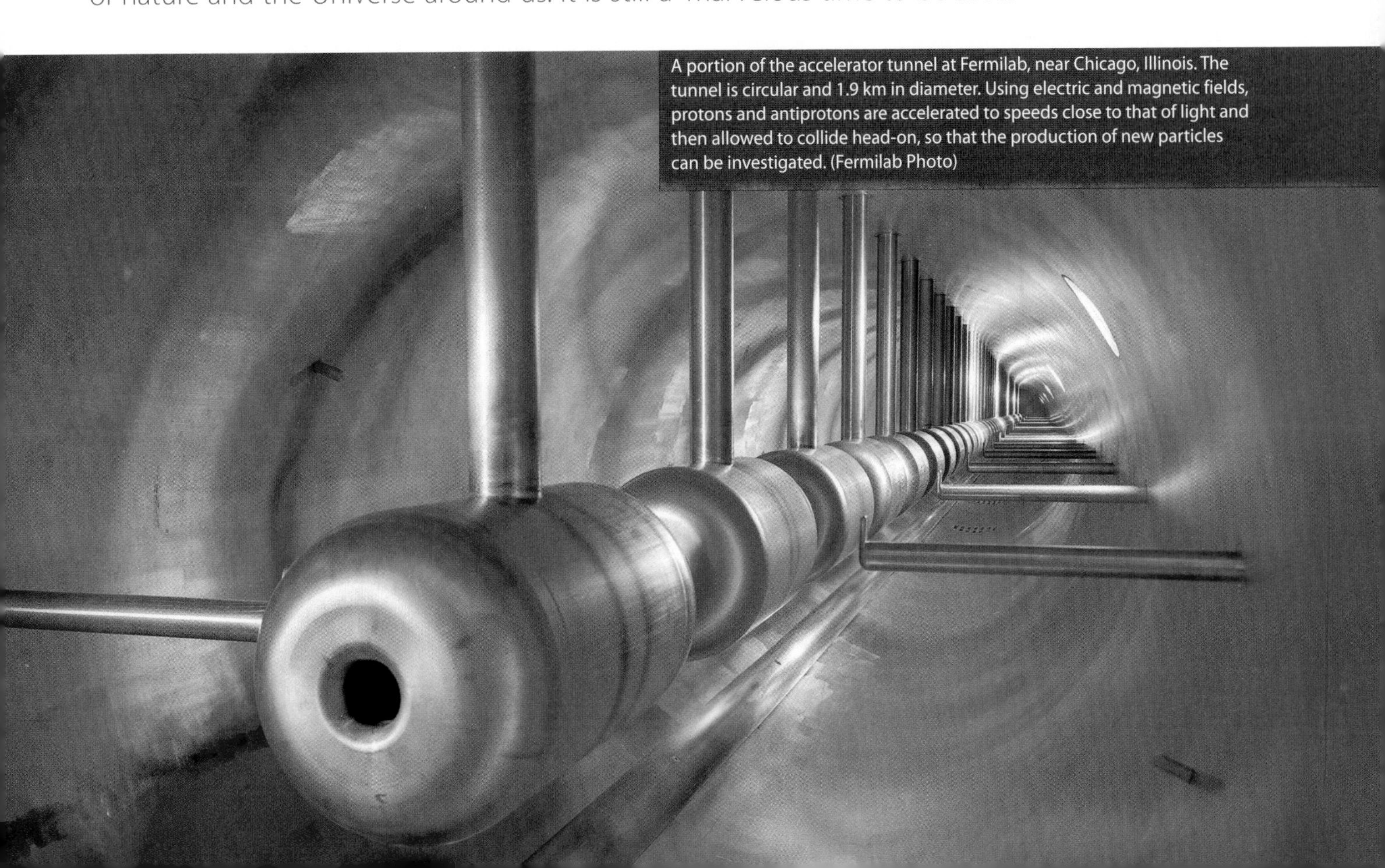

A portion of the accelerator tunnel at Fermilab, near Chicago, Illinois. The tunnel is circular and 1.9 km in diameter. Using electric and magnetic fields, protons and antiprotons are accelerated to speeds close to that of light and then allowed to collide head-on, so that the production of new particles can be investigated. (Fermilab Photo)

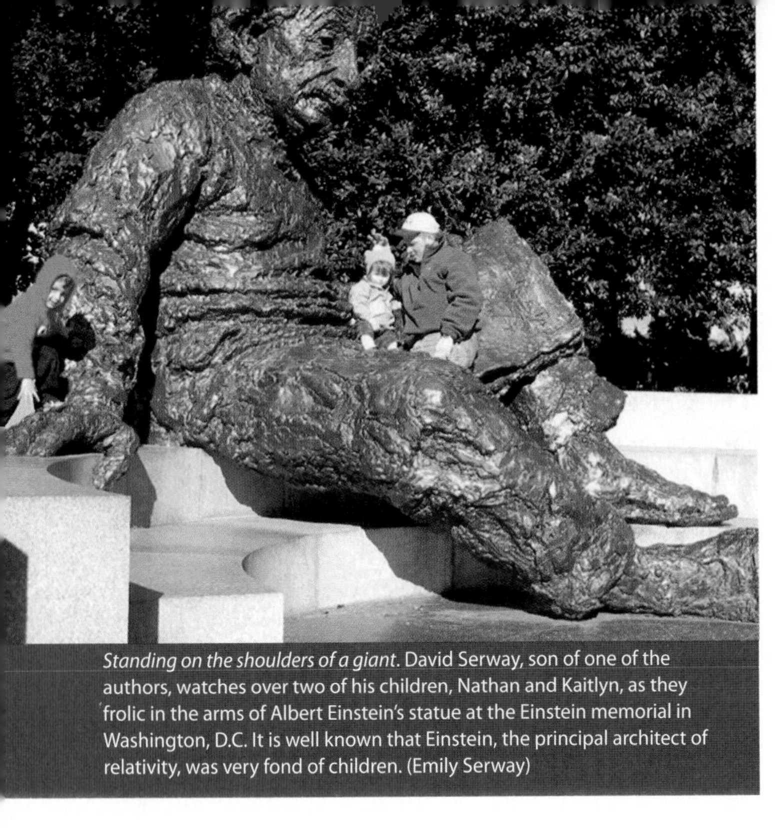

Standing on the shoulders of a giant. David Serway, son of one of the authors, watches over two of his children, Nathan and Kaitlyn, as they frolic in the arms of Albert Einstein's statue at the Einstein memorial in Washington, D.C. It is well known that Einstein, the principal architect of relativity, was very fond of children. (Emily Serway)

39 Relativity

Our everyday experiences and observations involve objects that move at speeds much less than the speed of light. Newtonian mechanics was formulated by observing and describing the motion of such objects, and this formalism is very successful in describing a wide range of phenomena that occur at low speeds. Nonetheless, it fails to describe properly the motion of objects whose speeds approach that of light.

Experimentally, the predictions of Newtonian theory can be tested at high speeds by accelerating electrons or other charged particles through a large electric potential difference. For example, it is possible to accelerate an electron to a speed of $0.99c$ (where c is the speed of light) by using a potential difference of several million volts. According to Newtonian mechanics, if the potential difference is increased by a factor of 4, the electron's kinetic energy is four times greater and its speed should double to $1.98c$. Experiments show, however, that the speed of the electron—as well as the speed of any other object in the Universe—always remains less than the speed of light, regardless of the size of the accelerating voltage. Because it places no upper limit on speed, Newtonian mechanics is contrary to modern experimental results and is clearly a limited theory.

In 1905, at the age of only 26, Einstein published his special theory of relativity. Regarding the theory, Einstein wrote:

> The relativity theory arose from necessity, from serious and deep contradictions in the old theory from which there seemed no escape. The strength of the new theory lies in the consistency and simplicity with which it solves all these difficulties.[1]

Although Einstein made many other important contributions to science, the special theory of relativity alone represents one of the greatest intellectual achievements of all time. With this theory, experimental observations can be correctly predicted over the range of speeds from $v = 0$ to speeds approaching the speed of light. At low speeds, Einstein's theory reduces to Newtonian mechanics as a limiting situation. It is important to recognize that Einstein was working on electromagnetism when he developed the special theory of relativity. He was convinced that Maxwell's equations were correct, and to reconcile them with one of his postulates, he was forced into the revolutionary notion of assuming that space and time are not absolute.

This chapter gives an introduction to the special theory of relativity, with emphasis on some of its predictions. In addition to its well-known and essential role in theoretical physics, the special theory of relativity has practical applications, including the design of nuclear power plants and modern global positioning system (GPS) units. These devices do not work if designed in accordance with nonrelativistic principles.

39.1 The Principle of Galilean Relativity

To describe a physical event, we must establish a frame of reference. You should recall from Chapter 5 that an inertial frame of reference is one in which an object is observed to have no acceleration when no forces act on it. Furthermore, any frame moving with constant velocity with respect to an inertial frame must also be an inertial frame.

There is no absolute inertial reference frame. Therefore, the results of an experiment performed in a vehicle moving with uniform velocity must be identical to the results of the same experiment performed in a stationary vehicle. The formal statement of this result is called the **principle of Galilean relativity:**

The laws of mechanics must be the same in all inertial frames of reference.

◀ Principle of Galilean relativity

Let's consider an observation that illustrates the equivalence of the laws of mechanics in different inertial frames. A pickup truck moves with a constant velocity as shown in Figure 39.1a. If a passenger in the truck throws a ball straight up

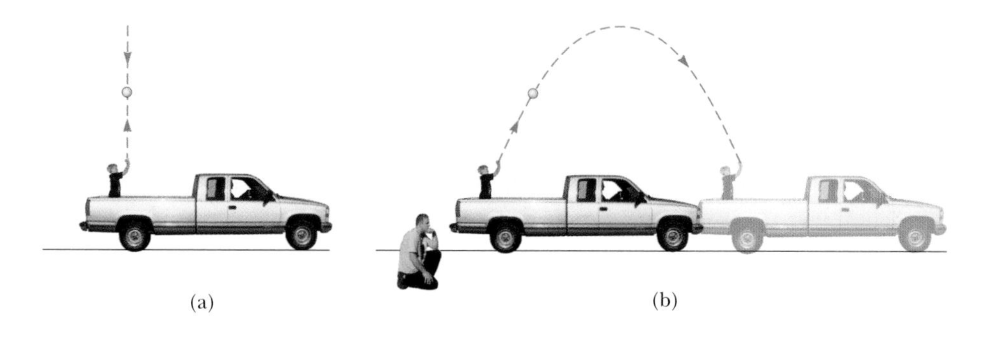

Figure 39.1 (a) The observer in the truck sees the ball move in a vertical path when thrown upward. (b) The Earth-based observer sees the ball's path as a parabola.

[1] A. Einstein and L. Infeld, *The Evolution of Physics* (New York: Simon and Schuster, 1961).

and if air effects are neglected, the passenger observes that the ball moves in a vertical path. The motion of the ball appears to be precisely the same as if the ball were thrown by a person at rest on the Earth. The law of universal gravitation and the equations of motion under constant acceleration are obeyed whether the truck is at rest or in uniform motion.

Both observers agree on the laws of physics: they each throw a ball straight up, and it rises and falls back into their own hand. Do the observers agree on the path of the ball thrown by the observer in the truck? The observer on the ground sees the path of the ball as a parabola as illustrated in Figure 39.1b, while, as mentioned earlier, the observer in the truck sees the ball move in a vertical path. Furthermore, according to the observer on the ground, the ball has a horizontal component of velocity equal to the velocity of the truck. Although the two observers disagree on certain aspects of the situation, they agree on the validity of Newton's laws and on such classical principles as conservation of energy and conservation of linear momentum. This agreement implies that no mechanical experiment can detect any difference between the two inertial frames. The only thing that can be detected is the relative motion of one frame with respect to the other.

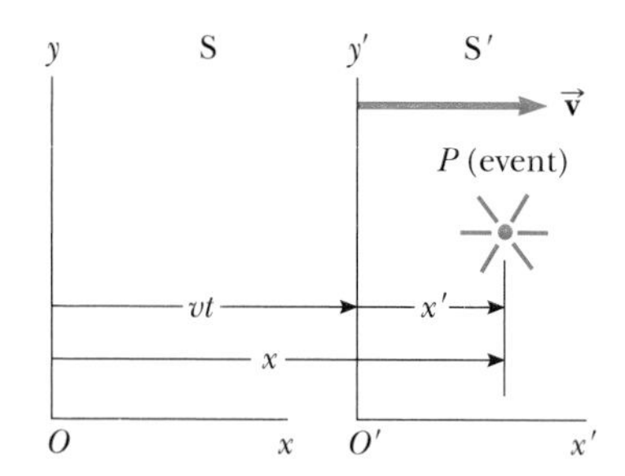

Figure 39.2 An event occurs at a point P. The event is seen by two observers in inertial frames S and S′, where S′ moves with a velocity $\vec{\mathbf{v}}$ relative to S.

Quick Quiz 39.1 Which observer in Figure 39.1 sees the ball's *correct* path? (a) the observer in the truck (b) the observer on the ground (c) both observers

---

Suppose some physical phenomenon, which we call an *event,* occurs and is observed by an observer at rest in an inertial reference frame. The wording "in a frame" means that the observer is at rest with respect to the origin of that frame. The event's location and time of occurrence can be specified by the four coordinates (x, y, z, t). We would like to be able to transform these coordinates from those of an observer in one inertial frame to those of another observer in a frame moving with uniform relative velocity compared with the first frame.

Consider two inertial frames S and S′ (Fig. 39.2). The S′ frame moves with a constant velocity $\vec{\mathbf{v}}$ along the common x and x' axes, where $\vec{\mathbf{v}}$ is measured relative to S. We assume the origins of S and S′ coincide at $t = 0$ and an event occurs at point P in space at some instant of time. An observer in S describes the event with space–time coordinates (x, y, z, t), whereas an observer in S′ uses the coordinates (x', y', z', t') to describe the same event. As we see from the geometry in Figure 39.2, the relationships among these various coordinates can be written

Galilean transformation equations ▶

$$x' = x - vt \qquad y' = y \qquad z' = z \qquad t' = t \tag{39.1}$$

These equations are the **Galilean space–time transformation equations.** Note that time is assumed to be the same in both inertial frames. That is, within the framework of classical mechanics, all clocks run at the same rate, regardless of their velocity, so the time at which an event occurs for an observer in S is the same as the time for the same event in S′. Consequently, the time interval between two successive events should be the same for both observers. Although this assumption may seem obvious, it turns out to be incorrect in situations where v is comparable to the speed of light.

Now suppose a particle moves through a displacement of magnitude dx along the x axis in a time interval dt as measured by an observer in S. It follows from Equations 39.1 that the corresponding displacement dx' measured by an observer in S′ is $dx' = dx - v\,dt$, where frame S′ is moving with speed v in the x direction relative to frame S. Because $dt = dt'$, we find that

$$\frac{dx'}{dt'} = \frac{dx}{dt} - v$$

or

$$u'_x = u_x - v \tag{39.2}$$

where u_x and u'_x are the x components of the velocity of the particle measured by observers in S and S′, respectively. (We use the symbol $\vec{\mathbf{u}}$ rather than $\vec{\mathbf{v}}$ for particle

PITFALL PREVENTION 39.1

The Relationship Between the S and S′ Frames

Many of the mathematical representations in this chapter are true *only* for the specified relationship between the S and S′ frames. The x and x' axes coincide, except their origins are different. The y and y' axes (and the z and z' axes) are parallel, but they do not coincide due to the displacement of the origin of S′ with respect to that of S. We choose the time $t = 0$ to be the instant at which the origins of the two coordinate systems coincide. If the S′ frame is moving in the positive x direction relative to S, then v is positive; otherwise, it is negative.

velocity because $\vec{\mathbf{v}}$ is already used for the relative velocity of two reference frames.) Equation 39.2 is the **Galilean velocity transformation equation.** It is consistent with our intuitive notion of time and space as well as with our discussions in Section 4.6. As we shall soon see, however, it leads to serious contradictions when applied to electromagnetic waves.

Quick Quiz 39.2 A baseball pitcher with a 90-mi/h fastball throws a ball while standing on a railroad flatcar moving at 110 mi/h. The ball is thrown in the same direction as that of the velocity of the train. If you apply the Galilean velocity transformation equation to this situation, is the speed of the ball relative to the Earth (a) 90 mi/h, (b) 110 mi/h, (c) 20 mi/h, (d) 200 mi/h, or (e) impossible to determine?

The Speed of Light

It is quite natural to ask whether the principle of Galilean relativity also applies to electricity, magnetism, and optics. Experiments indicate that the answer is no. Recall from Chapter 34 that Maxwell showed that the speed of light in free space is $c = 3.00 \times 10^8$ m/s. Physicists of the late 1800s thought light waves moved through a medium called the *ether* and the speed of light was c only in a special, absolute frame at rest with respect to the ether. The Galilean velocity transformation equation was expected to hold for observations of light made by an observer in any frame moving at speed v relative to the absolute ether frame. That is, if light travels along the x axis and an observer moves with velocity $\vec{\mathbf{v}}$ along the x axis, the observer measures the light to have speed $c \pm v$, depending on the directions of travel of the observer and the light.

Because the existence of a preferred, absolute ether frame would show that light is similar to other classical waves and that Newtonian ideas of an absolute frame are true, considerable importance was attached to establishing the existence of the ether frame. Prior to the late 1800s, experiments involving light traveling in media moving at the highest laboratory speeds attainable at that time were not capable of detecting differences as small as that between c and $c \pm v$. Starting in about 1880, scientists decided to use the Earth as the moving frame in an attempt to improve their chances of detecting these small changes in the speed of light.

Observers fixed on the Earth can take the view that they are stationary and that the absolute ether frame containing the medium for light propagation moves past them with speed v. Determining the speed of light under these circumstances is similar to determining the speed of an aircraft traveling in a moving air current, or wind; consequently, we speak of an "ether wind" blowing through our apparatus fixed to the Earth.

A direct method for detecting an ether wind would use an apparatus fixed to the Earth to measure the ether wind's influence on the speed of light. If v is the speed of the ether relative to the Earth, light should have its maximum speed $c + v$ when propagating downwind as in Figure 39.3a. Likewise, the speed of light should have its minimum value $c - v$ when the light is propagating upwind as in Figure 39.3b and an intermediate value $(c^2 - v^2)^{1/2}$ when the light is directed such that it travels perpendicular to the ether wind as in Figure 39.3c. If the Sun is assumed to be at rest in the ether, the velocity of the ether wind would be equal to the orbital velocity of the Earth around the Sun, which has a magnitude of approximately 30 km/s or 3×10^4 m/s. Because $c = 3 \times 10^8$ m/s, it is necessary to detect a change in speed of approximately 1 part in 10^4 for measurements in the upwind or downwind directions. Although such a change is experimentally measurable, all attempts to detect such changes and establish the existence of the ether wind (and hence the absolute frame) proved futile! We shall discuss the classic experimental search for the ether in Section 39.2.

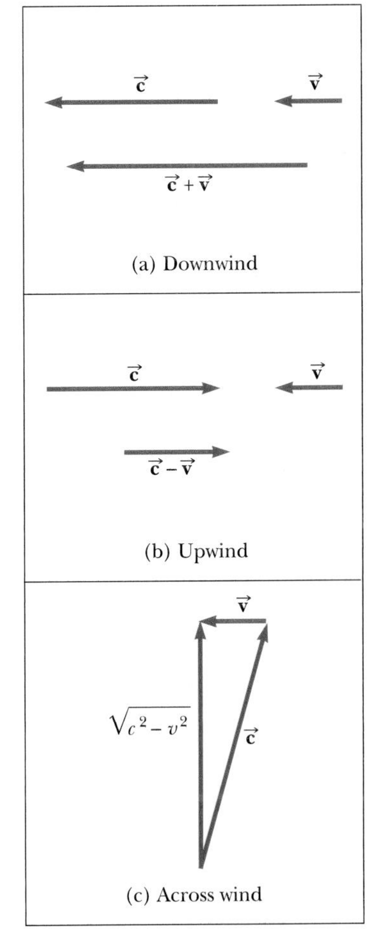

Figure 39.3 If the velocity of the ether wind relative to the Earth is $\vec{\mathbf{v}}$ and the velocity of light relative to the ether is $\vec{\mathbf{c}}$, the speed of light relative to the Earth is (a) $c + v$ in the downwind direction, (b) $c - v$ in the upwind direction, and (c) $(c^2 - v^2)^{1/2}$ in the direction perpendicular to the wind.

The principle of Galilean relativity refers only to the laws of mechanics. If it is assumed the laws of electricity and magnetism are the same in all inertial frames, a paradox concerning the speed of light immediately arises. That can be understood by recognizing that Maxwell's equations imply that the speed of light always has the fixed value 3.00×10^8 m/s in all inertial frames, a result in direct contradiction to what is expected based on the Galilean velocity transformation equation. According to Galilean relativity, the speed of light should *not* be the same in all inertial frames.

To resolve this contradiction in theories, we must conclude that either (1) the laws of electricity and magnetism are not the same in all inertial frames or (2) the Galilean velocity transformation equation is incorrect. If we assume the first alternative, a preferred reference frame in which the speed of light has the value c must exist and the measured speed must be greater or less than this value in any other reference frame, in accordance with the Galilean velocity transformation equation. If we assume the second alternative, we must abandon the notions of absolute time and absolute length that form the basis of the Galilean space–time transformation equations.

39.2 The Michelson–Morley Experiment

The most famous experiment designed to detect small changes in the speed of light was first performed in 1881 by Albert A. Michelson (see Section 37.7) and later repeated under various conditions by Michelson and Edward W. Morley (1838–1923). As we shall see, the outcome of the experiment contradicted the ether hypothesis.

The experiment was designed to determine the velocity of the Earth relative to that of the hypothetical ether. The experimental tool used was the Michelson interferometer, which was discussed in Section 37.7 and is shown again in Active Figure 39.4. Arm 2 is aligned along the direction of the Earth's motion through space. The Earth moving through the ether at speed v is equivalent to the ether flowing past the Earth in the opposite direction with speed v. This ether wind blowing in the direction opposite the direction of the Earth's motion should cause the speed of light measured in the Earth frame to be $c - v$ as the light approaches mirror M_2 and $c + v$ after reflection, where c is the speed of light in the ether frame.

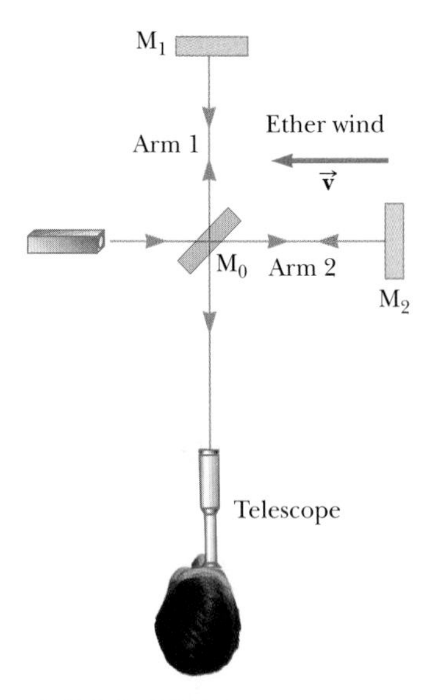

ACTIVE FIGURE 39.4

According to the ether wind theory, the speed of light should be $c - v$ as the beam approaches mirror M_2 and $c + v$ after reflection.

Sign in at www.thomsonedu.com and go to ThomsonNOW to adjust the speed of the ether wind and see the effect on the light beams if there were an ether.

The two light beams reflect from M_1 and M_2 and recombine, and an interference pattern is formed as discussed in Section 37.7. The interference pattern is observed while the interferometer is rotated through an angle of 90°. This rotation interchanges the speed of the ether wind between the arms of the interferometer. The rotation should cause the fringe pattern to shift slightly but measurably. Measurements failed, however, to show any change in the interference pattern! The Michelson–Morley experiment was repeated at different times of the year when the ether wind was expected to change direction and magnitude, but the results were always the same: **no fringe shift of the magnitude required was ever observed.**[2]

The negative results of the Michelson–Morley experiment not only contradicted the ether hypothesis, but also showed that it is impossible to measure the absolute velocity of the Earth with respect to the ether frame. Einstein, however, offered a postulate for his special theory of relativity that places quite a different interpretation on these null results. In later years, when more was known about the nature of light, the idea of an ether that permeates all of space was abandoned. **Light is now understood to be an electromagnetic wave, which requires no medium for its propagation.** As a result, the idea of an ether in which these waves travel became unnecessary.

[2] From an Earth-based observer's point of view, changes in the Earth's speed and direction of motion in the course of a year are viewed as ether wind shifts. Even if the speed of the Earth with respect to the ether were zero at some time, six months later the speed of the Earth would be 60 km/s with respect to the ether and as a result a fringe shift should be noticed. No shift has ever been observed, however.

Details of the Michelson–Morley Experiment

To understand the outcome of the Michelson–Morley experiment, let's assume the two arms of the interferometer in Active Figure 39.4 are of equal length L. We shall analyze the situation as if there were an ether wind because that is what Michelson and Morley expected to find. As noted above, the speed of the light beam along arm 2 should be $c - v$ as the beam approaches M_2 and $c + v$ after the beam is reflected. We model a pulse of light as a particle under constant speed. Therefore, the time interval for travel to the right for the pulse is $\Delta t = L/(c - v)$, and the time interval for travel to the left is $\Delta t = L/(c + v)$. The total time interval for the round trip along arm 2 is

$$\Delta t_{\text{arm 2}} = \frac{L}{c + v} + \frac{L}{c - v} = \frac{2Lc}{c^2 - v^2} = \frac{2L}{c}\left(1 - \frac{v^2}{c^2}\right)^{-1}$$

Now consider the light beam traveling along arm 1, perpendicular to the ether wind. Because the speed of the beam relative to the Earth is $(c^2 - v^2)^{1/2}$ in this case (see Fig. 39.3c), the time interval for travel for each half of the trip is $\Delta t = L/(c^2 - v^2)^{1/2}$ and the total time interval for the round trip is

$$\Delta t_{\text{arm 1}} = \frac{2L}{(c^2 - v^2)^{1/2}} = \frac{2L}{c}\left(1 - \frac{v^2}{c^2}\right)^{-1/2}$$

The time difference Δt between the horizontal round trip (arm 2) and the vertical round trip (arm 1) is

$$\Delta t = \Delta t_{\text{arm 2}} - \Delta t_{\text{arm 1}} = \frac{2L}{c}\left[\left(1 - \frac{v^2}{c^2}\right)^{-1} - \left(1 - \frac{v^2}{c^2}\right)^{-1/2}\right]$$

Because $v^2/c^2 \ll 1$, we can simplify this expression by using the following binomial expansion after dropping all terms higher than second order:

$$(1 - x)^n \approx 1 - nx \quad (\text{for } x \ll 1)$$

In our case, $x = v^2/c^2$, and we find that

$$\Delta t = \Delta t_{\text{arm 2}} - \Delta t_{\text{arm1}} \approx \frac{Lv^2}{c^3} \qquad \textbf{(39.3)}$$

This time difference between the two instants at which the reflected beams arrive at the viewing telescope gives rise to a phase difference between the beams, producing an interference pattern when they combine at the position of the telescope. A shift in the interference pattern should be detected when the interferometer is rotated through 90° in a horizontal plane so that the two beams exchange roles. This rotation results in a time difference twice that given by Equation 39.3. Therefore, the path difference that corresponds to this time difference is

$$\Delta d = c(2\,\Delta t) = \frac{2Lv^2}{c^2}$$

Because a change in path length of one wavelength corresponds to a shift of one fringe, the corresponding fringe shift is equal to this path difference divided by the wavelength of the light:

$$\text{Shift} = \frac{2Lv^2}{\lambda c^2} \qquad \textbf{(39.4)}$$

In the experiments by Michelson and Morley, each light beam was reflected by mirrors many times to give an effective path length L of approximately 11 m. Using this value, taking v to be equal to 3.0×10^4 m/s (the speed of the Earth around the Sun), and using 500 nm for the wavelength of the light, we expect a fringe shift of

$$\text{Shift} = \frac{2(11\text{ m})(3.0 \times 10^4\text{ m/s})^2}{(5.0 \times 10^{-7}\text{ m})(3.0 \times 10^8\text{ m/s})^2} = 0.44$$

The instrument used by Michelson and Morley could detect shifts as small as 0.01 fringe, but **it detected no shift whatsoever in the fringe pattern!** The experiment has been repeated many times since by different scientists under a wide variety of conditions, and no fringe shift has ever been detected. Therefore, it was concluded that the motion of the Earth with respect to the postulated ether cannot be detected.

Many efforts were made to explain the null results of the Michelson–Morley experiment and to save the ether frame concept and the Galilean velocity transformation equation for light. All proposals resulting from these efforts have been shown to be wrong. No experiment in the history of physics received such valiant efforts to explain the absence of an expected result as did the Michelson–Morley experiment. The stage was set for Einstein, who solved the problem in 1905 with his special theory of relativity.

39.3 Einstein's Principle of Relativity

AIP Niels Bohr Library

ALBERT EINSTEIN
German-American Physicist (1879–1955)
Einstein, one of the greatest physicists of all times, was born in Ulm, Germany. In 1905, at age 26, he published four scientific papers that revolutionized physics. Two of these papers were concerned with what is now considered his most important contribution: the special theory of relativity.

In 1916, Einstein published his work on the general theory of relativity. The most dramatic prediction of this theory is the degree to which light is deflected by a gravitational field. Measurements made by astronomers on bright stars in the vicinity of the eclipsed Sun in 1919 confirmed Einstein's prediction, and Einstein became a world celebrity as a result. Einstein was deeply disturbed by the development of quantum mechanics in the 1920s despite his own role as a scientific revolutionary. In particular, he could never accept the probabilistic view of events in nature that is a central feature of quantum theory. The last few decades of his life were devoted to an unsuccessful search for a unified theory that would combine gravitation and electromagnetism.

In the previous section, we noted the impossibility of measuring the speed of the ether with respect to the Earth and the failure of the Galilean velocity transformation equation in the case of light. Einstein proposed a theory that boldly removed these difficulties and at the same time completely altered our notion of space and time.[3] He based his special theory of relativity on two postulates:

1. **The principle of relativity:** The laws of physics must be the same in all inertial reference frames.
2. **The constancy of the speed of light:** The speed of light in vacuum has the same value, $c = 3.00 \times 10^8$ m/s, in all inertial frames, regardless of the velocity of the observer or the velocity of the source emitting the light.

The first postulate asserts that *all* the laws of physics—those dealing with mechanics, electricity and magnetism, optics, thermodynamics, and so on—are the same in all reference frames moving with constant velocity relative to one another. This postulate is a generalization of the principle of Galilean relativity, which refers only to the laws of mechanics. From an experimental point of view, Einstein's principle of relativity means that any kind of experiment (measuring the speed of light, for example) performed in a laboratory at rest must give the same result when performed in a laboratory moving at a constant velocity with respect to the first one. Hence, no preferred inertial reference frame exists, and it is impossible to detect absolute motion.

Note that postulate 2 is required by postulate 1: if the speed of light were not the same in all inertial frames, measurements of different speeds would make it possible to distinguish between inertial frames. As a result, a preferred, absolute frame could be identified, in contradiction to postulate 1.

Although the Michelson–Morley experiment was performed before Einstein published his work on relativity, it is not clear whether or not Einstein was aware of the details of the experiment. Nonetheless, the null result of the experiment can be readily understood within the framework of Einstein's theory. According to his principle of relativity, the premises of the Michelson–Morley experiment were incorrect. In the process of trying to explain the expected results, we stated that when light traveled against the ether wind, its speed was $c - v$, in accordance with the Galilean velocity transformation equation. If the state of motion of the observer or of the source has no influence on the value found for the speed of

[3] A. Einstein, "On the Electrodynamics of Moving Bodies," *Ann. Physik* **17**:891, 1905. For an English translation of this article and other publications by Einstein, see the book by H. Lorentz, A. Einstein, H. Minkowski, and H. Weyl, *The Principle of Relativity* (New York: Dover, 1958).

light, however, one always measures the value to be c. Likewise, the light makes the return trip after reflection from the mirror at speed c, not at speed $c + v$. Therefore, the motion of the Earth does not influence the fringe pattern observed in the Michelson–Morley experiment, and a null result should be expected.

If we accept Einstein's theory of relativity, we must conclude that relative motion is unimportant when measuring the speed of light. At the same time, we must alter our commonsense notion of space and time and be prepared for some surprising consequences. As you read the pages ahead, keep in mind that our commonsense ideas are based on a lifetime of everyday experiences and not on observations of objects moving at hundreds of thousands of kilometers per second. Therefore, these results may seem strange, but that is only because we have no experience with them.

39.4 Consequences of the Special Theory of Relativity

As we examine some of the consequences of relativity in this section, we restrict our discussion to the concepts of simultaneity, time intervals, and lengths, all three of which are quite different in relativistic mechanics from what they are in Newtonian mechanics. In relativistic mechanics, for example, the distance between two points and the time interval between two events depend on the frame of reference in which they are measured.

Simultaneity and the Relativity of Time

A basic premise of Newtonian mechanics is that a universal time scale exists that is the same for all observers. Newton and his followers took simultaneity for granted. In his special theory of relativity, Einstein abandoned this assumption.

Einstein devised the following thought experiment to illustrate this point. A boxcar moves with uniform velocity, and two bolts of lightning strike its ends as illustrated in Figure 39.5a, leaving marks on the boxcar and on the ground. The marks on the boxcar are labeled A' and B', and those on the ground are labeled A and B. An observer O' moving with the boxcar is midway between A' and B', and a ground observer O is midway between A and B. The events recorded by the observers are the striking of the boxcar by the two lightning bolts.

The light signals emitted from A and B at the instant at which the two bolts strike later reach observer O at the same time as indicated in Figure 39.5b. This observer realizes that the signals traveled at the same speed over equal distances and so concludes that the events at A and B occurred simultaneously. Now consider the same events as viewed by observer O'. By the time the signals have reached observer O, observer O' has moved as indicated in Figure 39.5b. Therefore, the signal from B' has already swept past O', but the signal from A' has not yet reached O'. In other words, O' sees the signal from B' before seeing the signal from A'. According to Einstein, *the two observers must find that light travels at the same*

PITFALL PREVENTION 39.2
Who's Right?

You might wonder which observer in Figure 39.5 is correct concerning the two lightning strikes. *Both are correct* because the principle of relativity states that *there is no preferred inertial frame of reference.* Although the two observers reach different conclusions, both are correct in their own reference frame because the concept of simultaneity is not absolute. That, in fact, is the central point of relativity: any uniformly moving frame of reference can be used to describe events and do physics.

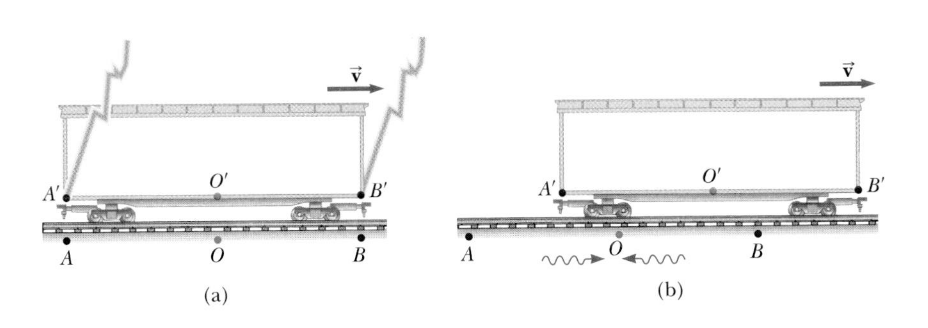

Figure 39.5 (a) Two lightning bolts strike the ends of a moving boxcar. (b) The events appear to be simultaneous to the stationary observer O who is standing midway between A and B. The events do not appear to be simultaneous to observer O', who claims that the front of the car is struck before the rear. Notice in (b) that the leftward-traveling light signal has already passed O', but the rightward-traveling signal has not yet reached O'.

speed. Therefore, observer O' concludes that one lightning bolt strikes the front of the boxcar *before* the other one strikes the back.

This thought experiment clearly demonstrates that the two events that appear to be simultaneous to observer O do *not* appear to be simultaneous to observer O'. In other words,

> two events that are simultaneous in one reference frame are in general not simultaneous in a second frame moving relative to the first.

Simultaneity is not an absolute concept but rather one that depends on the state of motion of the observer. Einstein's thought experiment demonstrates that two observers can disagree on the simultaneity of two events. **This disagreement, however, depends on the transit time of light to the observers and therefore does *not* demonstrate the deeper meaning of relativity.** In relativistic analyses of high-speed situations, simultaneity is relative even when the transit time is subtracted out. In fact, in all the relativistic effects that we discuss, we ignore differences caused by the transit time of light to the observers.

Time Dilation

To illustrate that observers in different inertial frames can measure different time intervals between a pair of events, consider a vehicle moving to the right with a speed v such as the boxcar shown in Active Figure 39.6a. A mirror is fixed to the ceiling of the vehicle, and observer O' at rest in the frame attached to the vehicle holds a flashlight a distance d below the mirror. At some instant, the flashlight emits a pulse of light directed toward the mirror (event 1), and at some later time after reflecting from the mirror, the pulse arrives back at the flashlight (event 2). Observer O' carries a clock and uses it to measure the time interval Δt_p between these two events. (The subscript p stands for *proper*, as we shall see in a moment.) We model the pulse of light as a particle under constant speed. Because the light pulse has a speed c, the time interval required for the pulse to travel from O' to the mirror and back is

$$\Delta t_p = \frac{\text{distance traveled}}{\text{speed}} = \frac{2d}{c} \quad \textbf{(39.5)}$$

Now consider the same pair of events as viewed by observer O in a second frame as shown in Active Figure 39.6b. According to this observer, the mirror and the flashlight are moving to the right with a speed v, and as a result, the sequence of

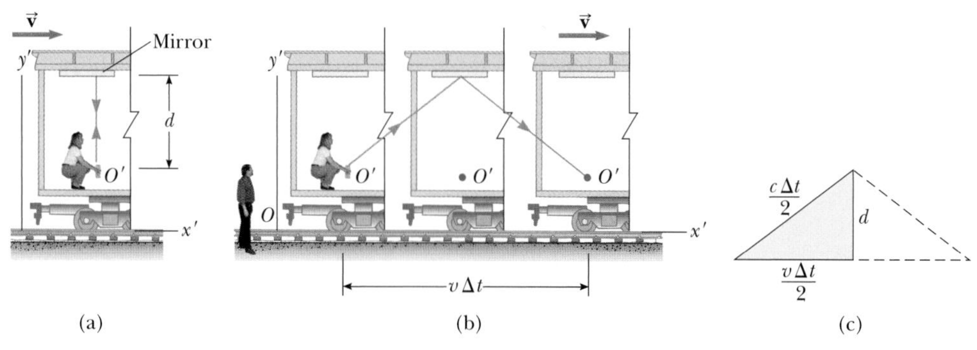

ACTIVE FIGURE 39.6

(a) A mirror is fixed to a moving vehicle, and a light pulse is sent out by observer O' at rest in the vehicle. (b) Relative to a stationary observer O standing alongside the vehicle, the mirror and O' move with a speed v. Notice that what observer O measures for the distance the pulse travels is greater than $2d$. (c) The right triangle for calculating the relationship between Δt and Δt_p.

Sign in at www.thomsonedu.com and go to ThomsonNOW to observe the bouncing of the light pulse for various speeds of the train.

events appears entirely different. By the time the light from the flashlight reaches the mirror, the mirror has moved to the right a distance $v\,\Delta t/2$, where Δt is the time interval required for the light to travel from O' to the mirror and back to O' as measured by O. Observer O concludes that because of the motion of the vehicle, if the light is to hit the mirror, it must leave the flashlight at an angle with respect to the vertical direction. Comparing Active Figure 39.6a with Active Figure 39.6b, we see that the light must travel farther in part (b) than in part (a). (Notice that neither observer "knows" that he or she is moving. Each is at rest in his or her own inertial frame.)

According to the second postulate of the special theory of relativity, both observers must measure c for the speed of light. Because the light travels farther according to O, the time interval Δt measured by O is longer than the time interval Δt_p measured by O'. To obtain a relationship between these two time intervals, let's use the right triangle shown in Active Figure 39.6c. The Pythagorean theorem gives

$$\left(\frac{c\,\Delta t}{2}\right)^2 = \left(\frac{v\,\Delta t}{2}\right)^2 + d^2$$

Solving for Δt gives

$$\Delta t = \frac{2d}{\sqrt{c^2 - v^2}} = \frac{2d}{c\sqrt{1 - \frac{v^2}{c^2}}} \qquad (39.6)$$

Because $\Delta t_p = 2d/c$, we can express this result as

$$\Delta t = \frac{\Delta t_p}{\sqrt{1 - \frac{v^2}{c^2}}} = \gamma \Delta t_p \qquad (39.7)$$

◀ Time dilation

where

$$\gamma = \frac{1}{\sqrt{1 - \frac{v^2}{c^2}}} \qquad (39.8)$$

Because γ is always greater than unity, Equation 39.7 shows that **the time interval Δt measured by an observer moving with respect to a clock is longer than the time interval Δt_p measured by an observer at rest with respect to the clock. This effect is known as time dilation.**

Time dilation is not observed in our everyday lives, which can be understood by considering the factor γ. This factor deviates significantly from a value of 1 only for very high speeds as shown in Figure 39.7 and Table 39.1. For example, for a speed of $0.1c$, the value of γ is 1.005. Therefore, there is a time dilation of only 0.5% at one-tenth the speed of light. Speeds encountered on an everyday basis are far slower than $0.1c$, so we do not experience time dilation in normal situations.

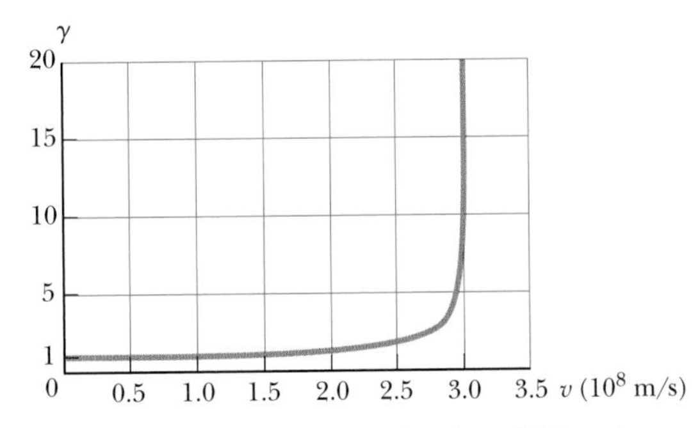

Figure 39.7 Graph of γ versus v. As the speed approaches that of light, γ increases rapidly.

TABLE 39.1

Approximate Values for γ at Various Speeds

v/c	γ
0.001 0	1.000 000 5
0.010	1.000 05
0.10	1.005
0.20	1.021
0.30	1.048
0.40	1.091
0.50	1.155
0.60	1.250
0.70	1.400
0.80	1.667
0.90	2.294
0.92	2.552
0.94	2.931
0.96	3.571
0.98	5.025
0.99	7.089
0.995	10.01
0.999	22.37

PITFALL PREVENTION 39.3

The Proper Time Interval

It is *very* important in relativistic calculations to correctly identify the observer who measures the proper time interval. The proper time interval between two events is always the time interval measured by an observer for whom the two events take place at the same position.

The time interval Δt_p in Equations 39.5 and 39.7 is called the **proper time interval.** (Einstein used the German term *Eigenzeit,* which means "own-time.") In general, **the proper time interval is the time interval between two events measured by an observer who sees the events occur at the same point in space.**

If a clock is moving with respect to you, the time interval between ticks of the moving clock is observed to be longer than the time interval between ticks of an identical clock in your reference frame. Therefore, it is often said that a moving clock is measured to run more slowly than a clock in your reference frame by a factor γ. We can generalize this result by stating that all physical processes, including mechanical, chemical, and biological ones, are measured to slow down when those processes occur in a frame moving with respect to the observer. For example, the heartbeat of an astronaut moving through space keeps time with a clock inside the spacecraft. Both the astronaut's clock and heartbeat are measured to slow down relative to a clock back on the Earth (although the astronaut would have no sensation of life slowing down in the spacecraft).

Quick Quiz 39.3 Suppose the observer O' on the train in Active Figure 39.6 aims her flashlight at the far wall of the boxcar and turns it on and off, sending a pulse of light toward the far wall. Both O' and O measure the time interval between when the pulse leaves the flashlight and when it hits the far wall. Which observer measures the proper time interval between these two events? (a) O' (b) O (c) both observers (d) neither observer

Quick Quiz 39.4 A crew on a spacecraft watches a movie that is two hours long. The spacecraft is moving at high speed through space. Does an Earth-based observer watching the movie screen on the spacecraft through a powerful telescope measure the duration of the movie to be (a) longer than, (b) shorter than, or (c) equal to two hours?

Muon is created

$\approx 6.6 \times 10^2$ m

Muon decays

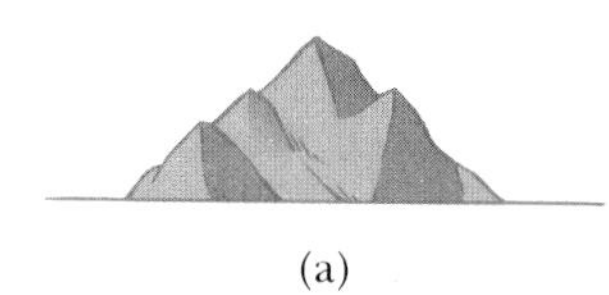

(a)

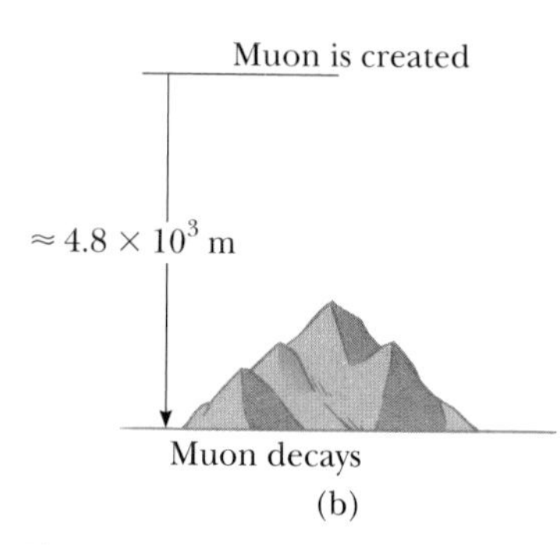

(b)

Figure 39.8 Travel of muons according to an Earth-based observer. (a) Without relativistic considerations, muons created in the atmosphere and traveling downward with a speed of $0.99c$ travel only about 6.6×10^2 m before decaying with an average lifetime of 2.2 μs. Therefore, very few muons reach the surface of the Earth. (b) With relativistic considerations, the muon's lifetime is dilated according to an observer on the Earth. Hence, according to this observer, the muon can travel about 4.8×10^3 m before decaying. The result is many of them arriving at the surface.

Time dilation is a very real phenomenon that has been verified by various experiments involving natural clocks. One experiment reported by J. C. Hafele and R. E. Keating provided direct evidence of time dilation.[4] Time intervals measured with four cesium atomic clocks in jet flight were compared with time intervals measured by Earth-based reference atomic clocks. To compare these results with theory, many factors had to be considered, including periods of speeding up and slowing down relative to the Earth, variations in direction of travel, and the weaker gravitational field experienced by the flying clocks than that experienced by the Earth-based clock. The results were in good agreement with the predictions of the special theory of relativity and were explained in terms of the relative motion between the Earth and the jet aircraft. In their paper, Hafele and Keating stated that "relative to the atomic time scale of the U.S. Naval Observatory, the flying clocks lost 59 ± 10 ns during the eastward trip and gained 273 ± 7 ns during the westward trip."

Another interesting example of time dilation involves the observation of *muons,* unstable elementary particles that have a charge equal to that of the electron and a mass 207 times that of the electron. Muons can be produced by the collision of cosmic radiation with atoms high in the atmosphere. Slow-moving muons in the laboratory have a lifetime that is measured to be the proper time interval $\Delta t_p = 2.2\ \mu$s. If we take 2.2 μs as the average lifetime of a muon and assume their speed is close to the speed of light, we find that these particles can travel a distance of approximately $(3.0 \times 10^8\ \text{m/s})(2.2 \times 10^{-6}\ \text{s}) \approx 6.6 \times 10^2$ m before they decay (Fig. 39.8a). Hence, they are unlikely to reach the surface of the Earth from high in the atmosphere where they are produced. Experiments show, however, that a large number of muons *do* reach the surface. The phenomenon of time dilation explains this effect. As measured by an observer on the Earth, the muons have a dilated lifetime

[4] J. C. Hafele and R. E. Keating, "Around the World Atomic Clocks: Relativistic Time Gains Observed," *Science* **177**:168, 1972.

equal to $\gamma\,\Delta t_p$. For example, for $v = 0.99c$, $\gamma \approx 7.1$, and $\gamma\,\Delta t_p \approx 16\ \mu$s. Hence, the average distance traveled by the muons in this time interval as measured by an observer on the Earth is approximately $(0.99)(3.0 \times 10^8\ \text{m/s})(16 \times 10^{-6}\ \text{s}) \approx 4.8 \times 10^3$ m as indicated in Figure 39.8b.

In 1976, at the laboratory of the European Council for Nuclear Research in Geneva, muons injected into a large storage ring reached speeds of approximately 0.999 4c. Electrons produced by the decaying muons were detected by counters around the ring, enabling scientists to measure the decay rate and hence the muon lifetime. The lifetime of the moving muons was measured to be approximately 30 times as long as that of the stationary muon, in agreement with the prediction of relativity to within two parts in a thousand.

EXAMPLE 39.1 What Is the Period of the Pendulum?

The period of a pendulum is measured to be 3.00 s in the reference frame of the pendulum. What is the period when measured by an observer moving at a speed of 0.960c relative to the pendulum?

SOLUTION

Conceptualize Let's change frames of reference. Instead of the observer moving at 0.960c, we can take the equivalent point of view that the observer is at rest and the pendulum is moving at 0.960c past the stationary observer. Hence, the pendulum is an example of a clock moving at high speed with respect to an observer.

Categorize Based on the Conceptualize step, we can categorize this problem as one involving time dilation.

Analyze The proper time interval, measured in the rest frame of the pendulum, is $\Delta t_p = 3.00$ s.

Use Equation 39.7 to find the dilated time interval:

$$\Delta t = \gamma\,\Delta t_p = \frac{1}{\sqrt{1 - \dfrac{(0.960c)^2}{c^2}}}\,\Delta t_p = \frac{1}{\sqrt{1 - 0.921\,6}}\,\Delta t_p$$

$$= 3.57(3.00\ \text{s}) = \boxed{10.7\ \text{s}}$$

Finalize This result shows that a moving pendulum is indeed measured to take longer to complete a period than a pendulum at rest does. The period increases by a factor of $\gamma = 3.57$.

What If? What if the speed of the observer increases by 4.00%? Does the dilated time interval increase by 4.00%?

Answer Based on the highly nonlinear behavior of γ as a function of v in Figure 39.7, we would guess that the increase in Δt would be different from 4.00%.

Find the new speed if it increases by 4.00%:

$$v_{\text{new}} = (1.040\,0)(0.960c) = 0.998\,4c$$

Perform the time dilation calculation again:

$$\Delta t = \gamma\,\Delta t_p = \frac{1}{\sqrt{1 - \dfrac{(0.998\,4c)^2}{c^2}}}\,\Delta t_p = \frac{1}{\sqrt{1 - 0.996\,8}}\,\Delta t_p$$

$$= 17.68(3.00\ \text{s}) = 53.1\ \text{s}$$

Therefore, the 4.00% increase in speed results in almost a 400% increase in the dilated time!

EXAMPLE 39.2 How Long Was Your Trip?

Suppose you are driving your car on a business trip and are traveling at 30 m/s. Your boss, who is waiting at your destination, expects the trip to take 5.0 h. When you arrive late, your excuse is that clock in your car registered the passage of 5.0 h but that you were driving fast and so your clock ran more slowly than the clock in your boss's office. If your car clock actually did indicate a 5.0-h trip, how much time passed on your boss's clock, which was at rest on the Earth?

SOLUTION

Conceptualize The observer is your boss standing stationary on the Earth. The clock is in your car, moving at 30 m/s with respect to your boss.

Categorize The speed of 30 m/s suggests we might categorize this problem as one in which we use classical concepts and equations. Based on the problem statement that the moving clock runs more slowly than a stationary clock however, we categorize this problem as one involving time dilation.

Analyze The proper time interval, measured in the rest frame of the car, is $\Delta t_p = 5.0$ h.

Use Equation 39.8 to evaluate γ:

$$\gamma = \frac{1}{\sqrt{1 - \frac{v^2}{c^2}}} = \frac{1}{\sqrt{1 - \frac{(3.0 \times 10^1 \text{ m/s})^2}{(3.0 \times 10^8 \text{ m/s})^2}}} = \frac{1}{\sqrt{1 - 10^{-14}}}$$

If you try to determine this value on your calculator, you will probably obtain $\gamma = 1$. Instead, perform a binomial expansion:

$$\gamma = (1 - 10^{-14})^{-1/2} \approx 1 + \tfrac{1}{2}(10^{-14}) = 1 + 5.0 \times 10^{-15}$$

Use Equation 39.7 to find the dilated time interval measured by your boss:

$$\Delta t = \gamma \, \Delta t_p = (1 + 5.0 \times 10^{-15})(5.0 \text{ h})$$

$$= 5.0 \text{ h} + 2.5 \times 10^{-14} \text{ h} = 5.0 \text{ h} + 0.090 \text{ ns}$$

Finalize Your boss's clock would be only 0.090 ns ahead of your car clock. You might want to think of another excuse!

The Twin Paradox

An intriguing consequence of time dilation is the *twin paradox* (Fig. 39.9). Consider an experiment involving a set of twins named Speedo and Goslo. When they are 20 years old, Speedo, the more adventuresome of the two, sets out on an epic journey from the Earth to Planet X, located 20 lightyears away. One lightyear (ly) is the distance light travels through free space in 1 year. Furthermore, Speedo's spacecraft is capable of reaching a speed of $0.95c$ relative to the inertial frame of his twin brother back home on the Earth. After reaching Planet X, Speedo becomes homesick and immediately returns to the Earth at the same speed $0.95c$.

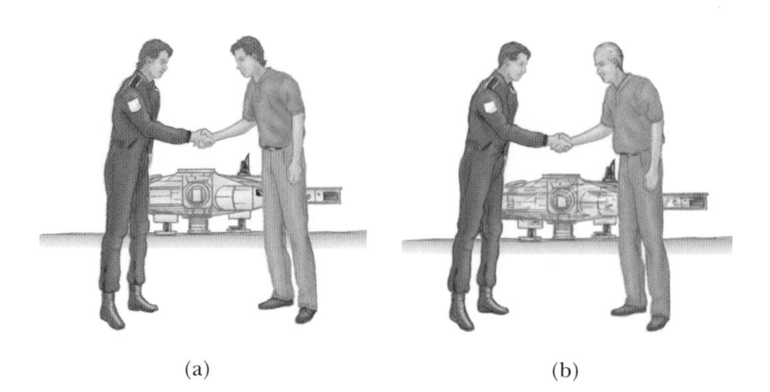

Figure 39.9 (a) As one twin leaves his brother on the Earth, both are the same age. (b) When Speedo returns from his journey to Planet X, he is younger than his twin Goslo.

Upon his return, Speedo is shocked to discover that Goslo has aged 42 years and is now 62 years old. Speedo, on the other hand, has aged only 13 years.

The paradox is *not* that the twins have aged at different rates. Here is the paradox. From Goslo's frame of reference, he was at rest while his brother traveled at a high speed away from him and then came back. According to Speedo, however, he himself remained stationary while Goslo and the Earth raced away from him and then headed back. Therefore, we might expect Speedo to claim that Goslo ages more slowly than himself. The situation appears to be symmetrical from either twin's point of view. Which twin *actually* ages more slowly?

The situation is actually not symmetrical. Consider a third observer moving at a constant speed relative to Goslo. According to the third observer, Goslo never changes inertial frames. Goslo's speed relative to the third observer is always the same. The third observer notes, however, that Speedo accelerates during his journey when he slows down and starts moving back toward the Earth, *changing reference frames in the process.* From the third observer's perspective, there is something very different about the motion of Goslo when compared to Speedo. Therefore, there is no paradox: only Goslo, who is always in a single inertial frame, can make correct predictions based on special relativity. Goslo finds that instead of aging 42 years, Speedo ages only $(1 - v^2/c^2)^{1/2}(42 \text{ years}) = 13$ years. Of these 13 years, Speedo spends 6.5 years traveling to Planet X and 6.5 years returning.

Quick Quiz 39.5 Suppose astronauts are paid according to the amount of time they spend traveling in space. After a long voyage traveling at a speed approaching c, would a crew rather be paid according to (a) an Earth-based clock, (b) their spacecraft's clock, or (c) either clock?

Length Contraction

The measured distance between two points in space also depends on the frame of reference of the observer. **The proper length L_p of an object is the length measured by someone at rest relative to the object.** The length of an object measured by someone in a reference frame that is moving with respect to the object is always less than the proper length. This effect is known as **length contraction.**

PITFALL PREVENTION 39.4

The Proper Length

As with the proper time interval, it is *very* important in relativistic calculations to correctly identify the observer who measures the proper length. The proper length between two points in space is always the length measured by an observer at rest with respect to the points. Often, the proper time interval and the proper length are *not* measured by the same observer.

To understand length contraction, consider a spacecraft traveling with a speed v from one star to another. There are two observers: one on the Earth and the other in the spacecraft. The observer at rest on the Earth (and also assumed to be at rest with respect to the two stars) measures the distance between the stars to be the proper length L_p. According to this observer, the time interval required for the spacecraft to complete the voyage is $\Delta t = L_p/v$. The passages of the two stars by the spacecraft occur at the same position for the space traveler. Therefore, the space traveler measures the proper time interval Δt_p. Because of time dilation, the proper time interval is related to the Earth-measured time interval by $\Delta t_p = \Delta t/\gamma$. Because the space traveler reaches the second star in the time Δt_p, he or she concludes that the distance L between the stars is

$$L = v\,\Delta t_p = v\frac{\Delta t}{\gamma}$$

Because the proper length is $L_p = v\,\Delta t$, we see that

$$L = \frac{L_p}{\gamma} = L_p\sqrt{1 - \frac{v^2}{c^2}} \qquad (39.9)$$

◀ Length contraction

where $\sqrt{1 - v^2/c^2}$ is a factor less than unity. **If an object has a proper length L_p when it is measured by an observer at rest with respect to the object, its length L when it moves with speed v in a direction parallel to its length is measured to be shorter according to $L = L_p\sqrt{1 - v^2/c^2} = L_p/\gamma$.**

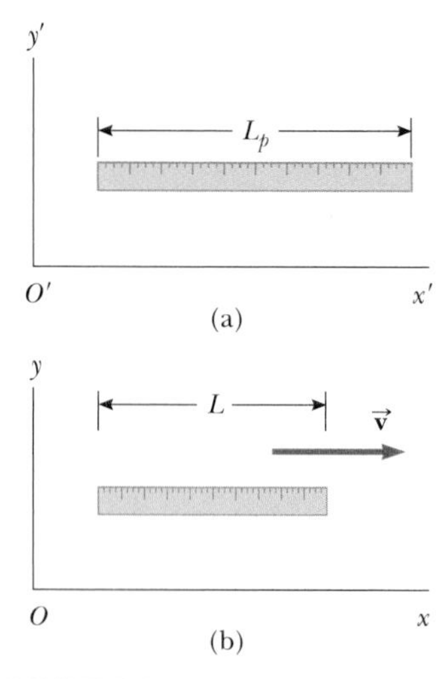

ACTIVE FIGURE 39.10

(a) A meterstick measured by an observer in a frame attached to the stick (that is, both have the same velocity) has its proper length L_p. (b) The meterstick measured by an observer in a frame in which the stick has a velocity $\vec{v}$ relative to the frame is measured to be shorter than its proper length L_p by a factor $(1 - v^2/c^2)^{1/2}$.

Sign in at www.thomsonedu.com and go to ThomsonNOW to view the meterstick from the points of view of two observers and compare the measured length of the stick.

For example, suppose a meterstick moves past a stationary Earth-based observer with speed v as in Active Figure 39.10. The length of the meterstick as measured by an observer in a frame attached to the stick is the proper length L_p shown in Active Figure 39.10a. The length of the stick L measured by the Earth observer is shorter than L_p by the factor $(1 - v^2/c^2)^{1/2}$ as suggested in Active Figure 39.10b. Notice that **length contraction takes place only along the direction of motion.**

The proper length and the proper time interval are defined differently. The proper length is measured by an observer for whom the end points of the length remain fixed in space. The proper time interval is measured by someone for whom the two events take place at the same position in space. As an example of this point, let's return to the decaying muons moving at speeds close to the speed of light. An observer in the muon's reference frame measures the proper lifetime, whereas an Earth-based observer measures the proper length (the distance between the creation point and the decay point in Fig. 39.8b). In the muon's reference frame, there is no time dilation, but the distance of travel to the surface is shorter when measured in this frame. Likewise, in the Earth observer's reference frame, there is time dilation, but the distance of travel is measured to be the proper length. Therefore, when calculations on the muon are performed in both frames, the outcome of the experiment in one frame is the same as the outcome in the other frame: more muons reach the surface than would be predicted without relativistic effects.

Quick Quiz 39.6 You are packing for a trip to another star. During the journey, you will be traveling at $0.99c$. You are trying to decide whether you should buy smaller sizes of your clothing, because you will be thinner on your trip due to length contraction. You also plan to save money by reserving a smaller cabin to sleep in because you will be shorter when you lie down. Should you (a) buy smaller sizes of clothing, (b) reserve a smaller cabin, (c) do neither of these things, or (d) do both of these things?

Quick Quiz 39.7 You are observing a spacecraft moving away from you. You measure it to be shorter than when it was at rest on the ground next to you. You also see a clock through the spacecraft window, and you observe that the passage of time on the clock is measured to be slower than that of the watch on your wrist. Compared with when the spacecraft was on the ground, what do you measure if the spacecraft turns around and comes *toward* you at the same speed? (a) The spacecraft is measured to be longer, and the clock runs faster. (b) The spacecraft is measured to be longer, and the clock runs slower. (c) The spacecraft is measured to be shorter, and the clock runs faster. (d) The spacecraft is measured to be shorter, and the clock runs slower.

Space–Time Graphs

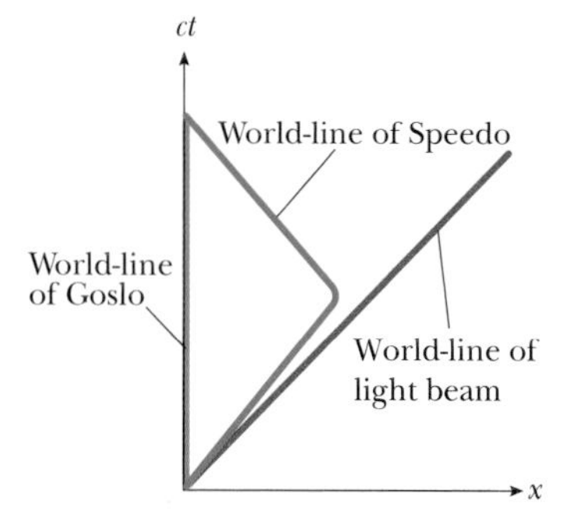

Figure 39.11 The twin paradox on a space–time graph. The twin who stays on the Earth has a world-line along the ct axis (green). The path of the traveling twin through space–time is represented by a world-line that changes direction (blue).

It is sometimes helpful to represent a physical situation with a *space–time graph,* in which ct is the ordinate and position x is the abscissa. The twin paradox is displayed in such a graph in Figure 39.11 from Goslo's point of view. A path through space–time is called a **world-line.** At the origin, the world-lines of Speedo (blue) and Goslo (green) coincide because the twins are in the same location at the same time. After Speedo leaves on his trip, his world-line diverges from that of his brother. Goslo's world-line is vertical because he remains fixed in location. At Goslo and Speedo's reunion, the two world-lines again come together. It would be impossible for Speedo to have a world-line that crossed the path of a light beam that left the Earth when he did. To do so would require him to have a speed greater than c (which, as shown in Sections 39.6 and 39.7, is not possible).

World-lines for light beams are diagonal lines on space–time graphs, typically drawn at 45° to the right or left of vertical (assuming that the x and ct axes have the same scales), depending on whether the light beam is traveling in the direction of increasing or decreasing x. These two world-lines mean that all possible future events for Goslo and Speedo lie within two 45° lines extending from the origin. Either twin's presence at an event outside this "light cone" would require that twin to move at a speed greater than c, which we have said is not possible. Also, the only past events that Goslo and Speedo could have experienced occur between two similar 45° world-lines that approach the origin from below the x axis.

EXAMPLE 39.3 A Voyage to Sirius

An astronaut takes a trip to Sirius, which is located a distance of 8 lightyears from the Earth. The astronaut measures the time of the one-way journey to be 6 years. If the spaceship moves at a constant speed of $0.8c$, how can the 8-ly distance be reconciled with the 6-year trip time measured by the astronaut?

SOLUTION

Conceptualize An observer on the Earth measures light to require 8 years to travel from Earth to Sirius. The astronaut measures a time interval of only 6 years. Is the astronaut traveling faster than light?

Categorize Because the astronaut is measuring a length of space between Earth and Sirius that is in motion with respect to her, we categorize this example as a length contraction problem.

Analyze The distance of 8 ly represents the proper length from the Earth to Sirius measured by an observer on the Earth seeing both objects nearly at rest.

Calculate the contracted length measured by the astronaut using Equation 39.9:

$$L = \frac{8 \text{ ly}}{\gamma} = (8 \text{ ly})\sqrt{1 - \frac{v^2}{c^2}} = (8 \text{ ly})\sqrt{1 - \frac{(0.8c)^2}{c^2}} = 5 \text{ ly}$$

Use the particle under constant speed model to find the travel time measured on the astronaut's clock:

$$\Delta t = \frac{L}{v} = \frac{5 \text{ ly}}{0.8c} = \frac{5 \text{ ly}}{0.8(1 \text{ ly/yr})} = 6 \text{ yr}$$

Finalize Note that we have used the value for the speed of light as $c = 1$ ly/yr. The trip takes a time interval shorter than 8 years for the astronaut because, to her, the distance between the Earth and Sirius is measured to be shorter.

What If? What if this trip is observed with a very powerful telescope by a technician in Mission Control on the Earth? At what time will this technician *see* that the astronaut has arrived at Sirius?

Answer The time interval the technician measures for the astronaut to arrive is

$$\Delta t = \frac{L_p}{v} = \frac{8 \text{ ly}}{0.8c} = 10 \text{ yr}$$

For the technician to *see* the arrival, the light from the scene of the arrival must travel back to the Earth and enter the telescope. This travel requires a time interval of

$$\Delta t = \frac{L_p}{v} = \frac{8 \text{ ly}}{c} = 8 \text{ yr}$$

Therefore, the technician sees the arrival after 10 yr + 8 yr = 18 yr. If the astronaut immediately turns around and comes back home, she arrives, according to the technician, 20 years after leaving, only 2 years *after the technician saw her arrive*! In addition, the astronaut would have aged by only 12 years.

EXAMPLE 39.4 The Pole-in-the-Barn Paradox

The twin paradox, discussed earlier, is a classic "paradox" in relativity. Another classic "paradox" is as follows. Suppose a runner moving at $0.75c$ carries a horizontal pole 15 m long toward a barn that is 10 m long. The barn has front and rear doors that are initially open. An observer on the ground can instantly and simultaneously close and open the two doors by remote control. When the runner and the pole are inside the barn, the ground observer closes and then opens both doors so that the runner and pole are momentarily captured inside the barn and then proceed to exit the barn from the back door. Do both the runner and the ground observer agree that the runner makes it safely through the barn?

SOLUTION

Conceptualize From your everyday experience, you would be surprised to see a 15-m pole fit inside a 10-m barn.

Categorize The pole is in motion with respect to the ground observer so that the observer measures its length to be contracted, whereas the stationary barn has a proper length of 10 m. We categorize this example as a length contraction problem.

Analyze Use Equation 39.9 to find the contracted length of the pole according to the ground observer:

$$L_{\text{pole}} = L_p\sqrt{1 - \frac{v^2}{c^2}} = (15\text{ m})\sqrt{1 - (0.75)^2} = 9.9\text{ m}$$

Therefore, the ground observer measures the pole to be slightly shorter than the barn and there is no problem with momentarily capturing the pole inside it. The "paradox" arises when we consider the runner's point of view.

Use Equation 39.9 to find the contracted length of the barn according to the running observer:

$$L_{\text{barn}} = L_p\sqrt{1 - \frac{v^2}{c^2}} = (10\text{ m})\sqrt{1 - (0.75)^2} = 6.6\text{ m}$$

Because the pole is in the rest frame of the runner, the runner measures it to have its proper length of 15 m. How can a 15-m pole fit inside a 6.6-m barn? Although this question is the classic one that is often asked, it is not the question we have asked because it is not the important one. We asked, *"Does the runner make it safely through the barn?"*

The resolution of the "paradox" lies in the relativity of simultaneity. The closing of the two doors is measured to be simultaneous by the ground observer. Because the doors are at different positions, however, they do not close simultaneously as measured by the runner. The rear door closes and then opens first, allowing the leading end of the pole to exit. The front door of the barn does not close until the trailing end of the pole passes by.

We can analyze this "paradox" using a space–time graph. Figure 39.12a is a space–time graph from the ground observer's point of view. We choose $x = 0$ as the position of the front door of the barn and $t = 0$ as the instant at which the leading end of the pole is located at the front door of the barn. The world-lines for the two doors of the barn are separated by 10 m and are vertical because the barn is not moving relative to this observer. For the pole, we follow two tilted world-lines, one for each end of the moving pole. These world-lines are 9.9 m apart horizontally, which is the con-

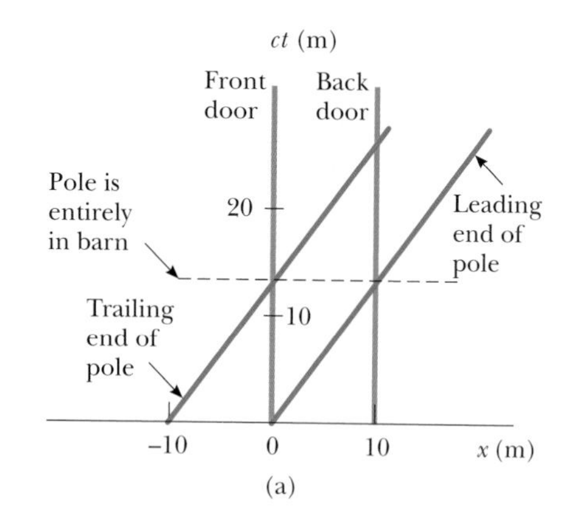

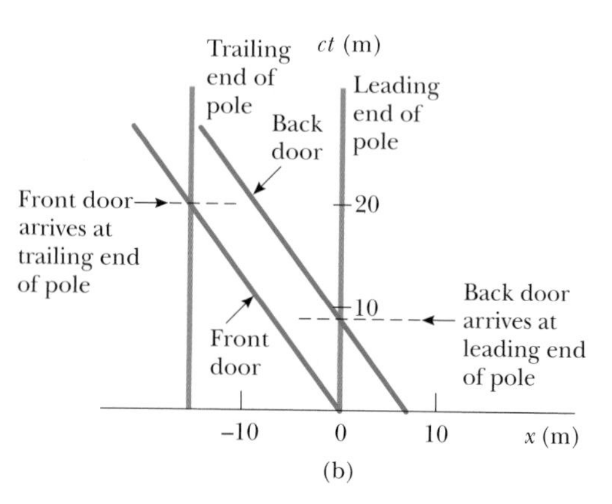

Figure 39.12 (Example 39.4) Space–time graphs for the pole-in-the-barn paradox. (a) From the ground observer's point of view, the world-lines for the front and back doors of the barn are vertical lines. The world-lines for the ends of the pole are tilted and are 9.9 m apart horizontally. The front door of the barn is at $x = 0$, and the leading end of the pole enters the front door at $t = 0$. The entire pole is inside the barn at the time indicated by the dashed line. (b) From the runner's point of view, the world-lines for the ends of the pole are vertical. The barn is moving in the negative direction, so the world-lines for the front and back doors are tilted to the left. The leading end of the pole exits the back door before the trailing end arrives at the front door.

tracted length seen by the ground observer. As seen in Figure 39.12a, the pole is entirely within the barn at one instant.

Figure 39.12b shows the space–time graph according to the runner. Here, the world-lines for the pole are separated by 15 m and are vertical because the pole is at rest in the runner's frame of reference. The barn is hurtling *toward* the runner, so the world-lines for the front and rear doors of the barn are tilted to the left. The world-lines for the barn are separated by 6.6 m, the contracted length as seen by the runner. The leading end of the pole leaves the rear door of the barn long before the trailing end of the pole enters the barn. Therefore, the opening of the rear door occurs before the closing of the front door.

From the ground observer's point of view, use the particle under constant velocity model to find the time after $t = 0$ at which the trailing end of the pole enters the barn:

$$(1)\quad t = \frac{\Delta x}{v} = \frac{9.9 \text{ m}}{0.75c} = \frac{13.2 \text{ m}}{c}$$

From the runner's point of view, use the particle under constant velocity model to find the time at which the leading end of the pole leaves the barn:

$$(2)\quad t = \frac{\Delta x}{v} = \frac{6.6 \text{ m}}{0.75c} = \frac{8.8 \text{ m}}{c}$$

Find the time at which the trailing end of the pole enters the front door of the barn:

$$(3)\quad t = \frac{\Delta x}{v} = \frac{15 \text{ m}}{0.75c} = \frac{20 \text{ m}}{c}$$

Finalize From Equation (1), the pole should be completely inside the barn at a time corresponding to $ct = 13.2$ m. This situation is consistent with the point on the ct axis in Figure 39.12a where the pole is inside the barn. From Equation (2), the leading end of the pole leaves the barn at $ct = 8.8$ m. This situation is consistent with the point on the ct axis in Figure 39.12b where the back door of the barn arrives at the leading end of the pole. Equation (3) gives $ct = 20$ m, which agrees with the instant shown in Figure 39.12b at which the front door of the barn arrives at the trailing end of the pole.

The Relativistic Doppler Effect

Another important consequence of time dilation is the shift in frequency observed for light emitted by atoms in motion as opposed to light emitted by atoms at rest. This phenomenon, known as the Doppler effect, was introduced in Chapter 17 as it pertains to sound waves. In the case of sound, the motion of the source with respect to the medium of propagation can be distinguished from the motion of the observer with respect to the medium. Light waves must be analyzed differently, however, because they require no medium of propagation and no method exists for distinguishing the motion of a light source from the motion of the observer.

If a light source and an observer approach each other with a relative speed v, the frequency f_{obs} measured by the observer is

$$f_{\text{obs}} = \frac{\sqrt{1 + v/c}}{\sqrt{1 - v/c}} f_{\text{source}} \qquad \textbf{(39.10)}$$

where f_{source} is the frequency of the source measured in its rest frame. This relativistic Doppler shift equation, unlike the Doppler shift equation for sound, depends only on the relative speed v of the source and observer and holds for relative speeds as great as c. As you might expect, the equation predicts that $f_{\text{obs}} > f_{\text{source}}$ when the source and observer approach each other. We obtain the expression for the case in which the source and observer recede from each other by substituting negative values for v in Equation 39.10.

The most spectacular and dramatic use of the relativistic Doppler effect is the measurement of shifts in the frequency of light emitted by a moving astronomical object such as a galaxy. Light emitted by atoms and normally found in the extreme violet region of the spectrum is shifted toward the red end of the spectrum for atoms in other galaxies, indicating that these galaxies are *receding* from us. American astronomer Edwin Hubble (1889–1953) performed extensive measurements of this *red shift* to confirm that most galaxies are moving away from us, indicating that the Universe is expanding.

39.5 The Lorentz Transformation Equations

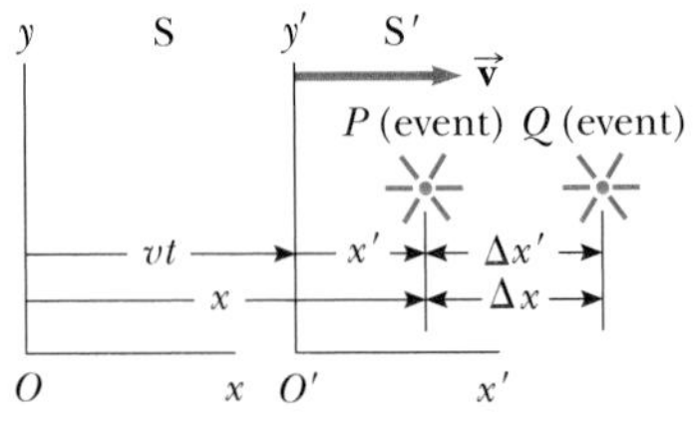

Figure 39.13 Events occur at points P and Q and are observed by an observer at rest in the S frame and another in the S′ frame, which is moving to the right with a speed v.

Suppose two events occur at points P and Q and are reported by two observers, one at rest in a frame S and another in a frame S′ that is moving to the right with speed v as in Figure 39.13. The observer in S reports the events with space–time coordinates (x, y, z, t) and the observer in S′ reports the same events using the coordinates (x', y', z', t'). Equation 39.1 predicts that the distance between the two points in space at which the events occur does not depend on motion of the observer: $\Delta x = \Delta x'$. Because this prediction is contradictory to the notion of length contraction, the Galilean transformation is not valid when v approaches the speed of light. In this section, we present the correct transformation equations that apply for all speeds in the range $0 < v < c$.

The equations that are valid for all speeds and that enable us to transform coordinates from S to S′ are the **Lorentz transformation equations:**

Lorentz transformation for S → S′

$$x' = \gamma(x - vt) \qquad y' = y \qquad z' = z \qquad t' = \gamma\left(t - \frac{v}{c^2}x\right) \tag{39.11}$$

These transformation equations were developed by Hendrik A. Lorentz (1853–1928) in 1890 in connection with electromagnetism. It was Einstein, however, who recognized their physical significance and took the bold step of interpreting them within the framework of the special theory of relativity.

Notice the difference between the Galilean and Lorentz time equations. In the Galilean case, $t = t'$. In the Lorentz case, however, the value for t' assigned to an event by an observer O' in the S′ frame in Figure 39.13 depends both on the time t and on the coordinate x as measured by an observer O in the S frame, which is consistent with the notion that an event is characterized by four space–time coordinates (x, y, z, t). In other words, in relativity, space and time are *not* separate concepts but rather are closely interwoven with each other.

If you wish to transform coordinates in the S′ frame to coordinates in the S frame, simply replace v by $-v$ and interchange the primed and unprimed coordinates in Equations 39.11:

Inverse Lorentz transformation for S′ → S

$$x = \gamma(x' + vt') \qquad y = y' \qquad z = z' \qquad t = \gamma\left(t' + \frac{v}{c^2}x'\right) \tag{39.12}$$

When $v \ll c$, the Lorentz transformation equations should reduce to the Galilean equations. As v approaches zero, $v/c \ll 1$; therefore, $\gamma \to 1$ and Equations 39.11 indeed reduce to the Galilean space–time transformation equations in Equation 39.1.

In many situations, we would like to know the difference in coordinates between two events or the time interval between two events as seen by observers O and O'. From Equations 39.11 and 39.12, we can express the differences between the four variables x, x', t, and t' in the form

$$\left.\begin{aligned} \Delta x' &= \gamma(\Delta x - v\,\Delta t) \\ \Delta t' &= \gamma\left(\Delta t - \frac{v}{c^2}\Delta x\right) \end{aligned}\right\} \text{S} \to \text{S}' \tag{39.13}$$

$$\left.\begin{aligned} \Delta x &= \gamma(\Delta x' + v\,\Delta t') \\ \Delta t &= \gamma\left(\Delta t' + \frac{v}{c^2}\Delta x'\right) \end{aligned}\right\} \text{S}' \to \text{S} \tag{39.14}$$

where $\Delta x' = x'_2 - x'_1$ and $\Delta t' = t'_2 - t'_1$ are the differences measured by observer O' and $\Delta x = x_2 - x_1$ and $\Delta t = t_2 - t_1$ are the differences measured by observer O. (We have not included the expressions for relating the y and z coordinates because they are unaffected by motion along the x direction.[5])

EXAMPLE 39.5 Simultaneity and Time Dilation Revisited

(A) Use the Lorentz transformation equations in difference form to show that simultaneity is not an absolute concept.

SOLUTION

Conceptualize Imagine two events that are simultaneous and separated in space such that $\Delta t' = 0$ and $\Delta x' \neq 0$ according to an observer O' who is moving with speed v relative to O.

Categorize The statement of the problem tells us to categorize this example as one involving the Lorentz transformation.

Analyze From the expression for Δt given in Equation 39.14, find the time interval Δt measured by observer O:

$$\Delta t = \gamma\left(\Delta t' + \frac{v}{c^2}\Delta x'\right) = \gamma\left(0 + \frac{v}{c^2}\Delta x'\right) = \gamma\frac{v}{c^2}\Delta x'$$

Finalize The time interval for the same two events as measured by O is nonzero, so the events do not appear to be simultaneous to O.

(B) Use the Lorentz transformation equations in difference form to show that a moving clock is measured to run more slowly than a clock that is at rest with respect to an observer.

SOLUTION

Conceptualize Imagine that observer O' carries a clock that he uses to measure a time interval $\Delta t'$. He finds that two events occur at the same place in his reference frame ($\Delta x' = 0$) but at different times ($\Delta t' \neq 0$). Observer O' is moving with speed v relative to O.

Categorize The statement of the problem tells us to categorize this example as one involving the Lorentz transformation.

Analyze From the expression for Δt given in Equation 39.14, find the time interval Δt measured by observer O:

$$\Delta t = \gamma\left(\Delta t' + \frac{v}{c^2}\Delta x'\right) = \gamma\left(\Delta t' + \frac{v}{c^2}(0)\right) = \gamma\Delta t'$$

Finalize This result is the equation for time dilation found earlier (Eq. 39.7), where $\Delta t' = \Delta t_p$ is the proper time interval measured by the clock carried by observer O'. Therefore, O measures the moving clock to run slow.

39.6 The Lorentz Velocity Transformation Equations

Suppose two observers in relative motion with respect to each other are both observing an object's motion. Previously, we defined an event as occurring at an instant of time. Now let's interpret the "event" as the object's motion. We know that the Galilean velocity transformation (Eq. 39.2) is valid for low speeds. How do the observers' measurements of the velocity of the object relate to each other if the speed of the object is close to that of light? Once again, S′ is our frame moving

[5] Although relative motion of the two frames along the x axis does not change the y and z coordinates of an object, it does change the y and z velocity components of an object moving in either frame as noted in Section 39.6.

at a speed v relative to S. Suppose an object has a velocity component u'_x measured in the S′ frame, where

$$u'_x = \frac{dx'}{dt'} \tag{39.15}$$

Using Equation 39.11, we have

$$dx' = \gamma(dx - v\,dt)$$

$$dt' = \gamma\left(dt - \frac{v}{c^2}\,dx\right)$$

Substituting these values into Equation 39.15 gives

$$u'_x = \frac{dx - v\,dt}{dt - \dfrac{v}{c^2}\,dx} = \frac{\dfrac{dx}{dt} - v}{1 - \dfrac{v}{c^2}\dfrac{dx}{dt}}$$

The term dx/dt, however, is simply the velocity component u_x of the object measured by an observer in S, so this expression becomes

Lorentz velocity transformation for S → S′

$$u'_x = \frac{u_x - v}{1 - \dfrac{u_x v}{c^2}} \tag{39.16}$$

If the object has velocity components along the y and z axes, the components as measured by an observer in S′ are

$$u'_y = \frac{u_y}{\gamma\left(1 - \dfrac{u_x v}{c^2}\right)} \quad \text{and} \quad u'_z = \frac{u_z}{\gamma\left(1 - \dfrac{u_x v}{c^2}\right)} \tag{39.17}$$

Notice that u'_y and u'_z do not contain the parameter v in the numerator because the relative velocity is along the x axis.

When v is much smaller than c (the nonrelativistic case), the denominator of Equation 39.16 approaches unity and so $u'_x \approx u_x - v$, which is the Galilean velocity transformation equation. In another extreme, when $u_x = c$, Equation 39.16 becomes

$$u'_x = \frac{c - v}{1 - \dfrac{cv}{c^2}} = \frac{c\left(1 - \dfrac{v}{c}\right)}{1 - \dfrac{v}{c}} = c$$

This result shows that a speed measured as c by an observer in S is also measured as c by an observer in S′, independent of the relative motion of S and S′. This conclusion is consistent with Einstein's second postulate: the speed of light must be c relative to all inertial reference frames. Furthermore, we find that the speed of an object can never be measured as larger than c. That is, the speed of light is the ultimate speed. We shall return to this point later.

To obtain u_x in terms of u'_x, we replace v by $-v$ in Equation 39.16 and interchange the roles of u_x and u'_x:

$$u_x = \frac{u'_x + v}{1 + \dfrac{u'_x v}{c^2}} \tag{39.18}$$

PITFALL PREVENTION 39.5
What Can the Observers Agree On?

We have seen several measurements that the two observers O and O' do *not* agree on: (1) the time interval between events that take place in the same position in one of the frames, (2) the distance between two points that remain fixed in one of their frames, (3) the velocity components of a moving particle, and (4) whether two events occurring at different locations in both frames are simultaneous or not. The two observers *can* agree on (1) their relative speed of motion v with respect to each other, (2) the speed c of any ray of light, and (3) the simultaneity of two events which take place at the same position *and* time in some frame.

Quick Quiz 39.8 You are driving on a freeway at a relativistic speed. **(i)** Straight ahead of you, a technician standing on the ground turns on a searchlight and a beam of light moves exactly vertically upward as seen by the technician. As you observe the beam of light, do you measure the magnitude of the vertical component of its velocity as (a) equal to c, (b) greater than c, or (c) less than c? **(ii)** If the technician aims the searchlight directly at you instead of upward, do you measure the magnitude of the horizontal component of its velocity as (a) equal to c, (b) greater than c, or (c) less than c?

EXAMPLE 39.6 Relative Velocity of Two Spacecraft

Two spacecraft A and B are moving in opposite directions as shown in Figure 39.14. An observer on the Earth measures the speed of spacecraft A to be $0.750c$ and the speed of spacecraft B to be $0.850c$. Find the velocity of spacecraft B as observed by the crew on spacecraft A.

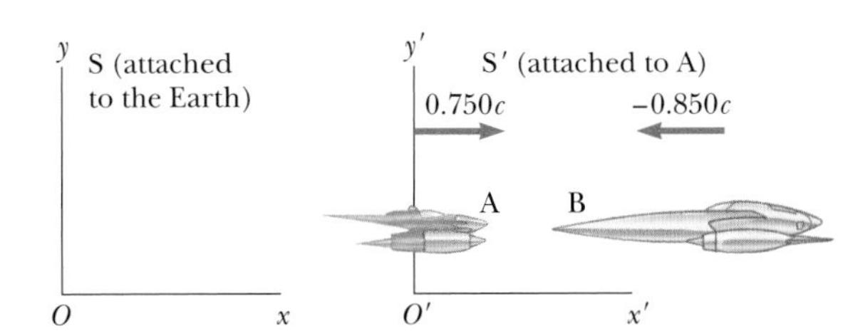

Figure 39.14 (Example 39.6) Two spacecraft A and B move in opposite directions. The speed of spacecraft B relative to spacecraft A is *less* than c and is obtained from the relativistic velocity transformation equation.

SOLUTION

Conceptualize There are two observers, one on the Earth and one on spacecraft A. The event is the motion of spacecraft B.

Categorize Because the problem asks to find an observed velocity, we categorize this example as one requiring the Lorentz velocity transformation.

Analyze The Earth-based observer at rest in the S frame makes two measurements, one of each spacecraft. We want to find the velocity of spacecraft B as measured by the crew on spacecraft A. Therefore, $u_x = -0.850c$. The velocity of spacecraft A is also the velocity of the observer at rest in spacecraft A (the S′ frame) relative to the observer at rest on the Earth. Therefore, $v = 0.750c$.

Obtain the velocity u'_x of spacecraft B relative to spacecraft A using Equation 39.16:

$$u'_x = \frac{u_x - v}{1 - \dfrac{u_x v}{c^2}} = \frac{-0.850c - 0.750c}{1 - \dfrac{(-0.850c)(0.750c)}{c^2}} = -0.977c$$

Finalize The negative sign indicates that spacecraft B is moving in the negative x direction as observed by the crew on spacecraft A. Is that consistent with your expectation from Figure 39.14? Notice that the speed is less than c. That is, an object whose speed is less than c in one frame of reference must have a speed less than c in any other frame. (Had you used the Galilean velocity transformation equation in this example, you would have found that $u'_x = u_x - v = -0.850c - 0.750c = -1.60c$, which is impossible. The Galilean transformation equation does not work in relativistic situations.)

What If? What if the two spacecraft pass each other? What is their relative speed now?

Answer The calculation using Equation 39.16 involves only the velocities of the two spacecraft and does not depend on their locations. After they pass each other, they have the same velocities, so the velocity of spacecraft B as observed by the crew on spacecraft A is the same, $-0.977c$. The only difference after they pass is that spacecraft B is receding from spacecraft A, whereas it was approaching spacecraft A before it passed.

EXAMPLE 39.7 Relativistic Leaders of the Pack

Two motorcycle pack leaders named David and Emily are racing at relativistic speeds along perpendicular paths as shown in Figure 39.15. How fast does Emily recede as seen by David over his right shoulder?

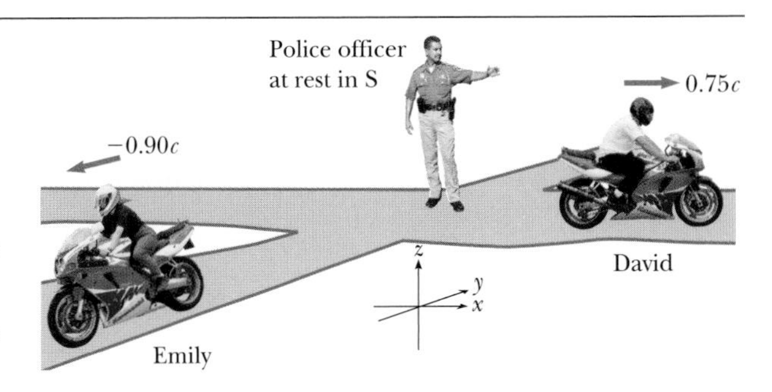

Figure 39.15 (Example 39.7) David moves east with a speed $0.75c$ relative to the police officer, and Emily travels south at a speed $0.90c$ relative to the officer.

SOLUTION

Conceptualize The two observers are David and the police officer in Figure 39.15. The event is the motion of Emily. Figure 39.15 represents the situation as seen by the police officer at rest in frame S. Frame S′ moves along with David.

Categorize Because the problem asks to find an observed velocity, we categorize this problem as one requiring the Lorentz velocity transformation. The motion takes place in two dimensions.

Analyze Identify the velocity components for David and Emily according to the police officer:

$$\text{David: } v_x = v = 0.75c \qquad v_y = 0$$

$$\text{Emily: } u_x = 0 \qquad u_y = -0.90c$$

Using Equations 39.16 and 39.17, calculate u'_x and u'_y for Emily as measured by David:

$$u'_x = \frac{u_x - v}{1 - \dfrac{u_x v}{c^2}} = \frac{0 - 0.75c}{1 - \dfrac{(0)(0.75c)}{c^2}} = -0.75c$$

$$u'_y = \frac{u_y}{\gamma\left(1 - \dfrac{u_x v}{c^2}\right)} = \frac{\sqrt{1 - \dfrac{(0.75c)^2}{c^2}}\,(-0.90c)}{\left(1 - \dfrac{(0)(0.75c)}{c^2}\right)} = -0.60c$$

Using the Pythagorean theorem, find the speed of Emily as measured by David:

$$u' = \sqrt{(u'_x)^2 + (u'_y)^2} = \sqrt{(-0.75c)^2 + (-0.60c)^2} = 0.96c$$

Finalize This speed is less than c, as required by the special theory of relativity.

PITFALL PREVENTION 39.6
Watch Out for "Relativistic Mass"

Some older treatments of relativity maintained the conservation of momentum principle at high speeds by using a model in which a particle's mass increases with speed. You might still encounter this notion of "relativistic mass" in your outside reading, especially in older books. Be aware that this notion is no longer widely accepted; today, mass is considered as *invariant*, independent of speed. The mass of an object in all frames is considered to be the mass as measured by an observer at rest with respect to the object.

39.7 Relativistic Linear Momentum

To describe the motion of particles within the framework of the special theory of relativity properly, you must replace the Galilean transformation equations by the Lorentz transformation equations. Because the laws of physics must remain unchanged under the Lorentz transformation, we must generalize Newton's laws and the definitions of linear momentum and energy to conform to the Lorentz transformation equations and the principle of relativity. These generalized definitions should reduce to the classical (nonrelativistic) definitions for $v \ll c$.

First, recall from the isolated system model that when two particles (or objects that can be modeled as particles) collide, the total momentum of the isolated system of the two particles remains constant. Suppose we observe this collision in a reference frame S and confirm that the momentum of the system is conserved. Now imagine that the momenta of the particles are measured by an observer in a second reference frame S′ moving with velocity $\vec{\mathbf{v}}$ relative to the first frame. Using the Lorentz velocity transformation equation and the classical definition of linear momentum, $\vec{\mathbf{p}} = m\vec{\mathbf{u}}$ (where $\vec{\mathbf{u}}$ is the velocity of a particle), we find that linear momentum is *not* measured to be conserved by the observer in S′. Because the laws of physics are the same in all inertial frames, however, linear momentum of the system must be conserved in all frames. We have a contradiction. In view of this contradiction and assuming the Lorentz velocity transformation equation is correct, we must modify the definition of linear momentum so that the momentum of an isolated system is conserved for all observers. For any particle, the correct relativistic equation for linear momentum that satisfies this condition is

Definition of relativistic linear momentum ▶

$$\vec{\mathbf{p}} \equiv \frac{m\vec{\mathbf{u}}}{\sqrt{1 - \dfrac{u^2}{c^2}}} = \gamma m\vec{\mathbf{u}} \qquad (39.19)$$

where m is the mass of the particle and $\vec{\mathbf{u}}$ is the velocity of the particle. When u is much less than c, $\gamma = (1 - u^2/c^2)^{-1/2}$ approaches unity and $\vec{\mathbf{p}}$ approaches $m\vec{\mathbf{u}}$. Therefore, the relativistic equation for $\vec{\mathbf{p}}$ reduces to the classical expression when u is much smaller than c, as it should.

The relativistic force $\vec{\mathbf{F}}$ acting on a particle whose linear momentum is $\vec{\mathbf{p}}$ is defined as

$$\vec{\mathbf{F}} \equiv \frac{d\vec{\mathbf{p}}}{dt} \qquad (39.20)$$

where $\vec{\mathbf{p}}$ is given by Equation 39.19. This expression, which is the relativistic form of Newton's second law, is reasonable because it preserves classical mechanics in the limit of low velocities and is consistent with conservation of linear momentum for an isolated system ($\vec{\mathbf{F}}_{\text{ext}} = 0$) both relativistically and classically.

It is left as an end-of-chapter problem (Problem 61) to show that under relativistic conditions, the acceleration $\vec{\mathbf{a}}$ of a particle decreases under the action of a constant force, in which case $a \propto (1 - u^2/c^2)^{3/2}$. This proportionality shows that as the particle's speed approaches c, the acceleration caused by any finite force approaches zero. Hence, it is impossible to accelerate a particle from rest to a speed $u \geq c$. This argument reinforces that the speed of light is the ultimate speed, the speed limit of the Universe. It is the maximum possible speed for energy transfer and for information transfer. Any object with mass must move at a lower speed.

EXAMPLE 39.8 Linear Momentum of an Electron

An electron, which has a mass of 9.11×10^{-31} kg, moves with a speed of $0.750c$. Find the magnitude of its relativistic momentum and compare this value with the momentum calculated from the classical expression.

SOLUTION

Conceptualize Imagine an electron moving with high speed. The electron carries momentum, but the magnitude of its momentum is not given by $p = mu$ because the speed is relativistic.

Categorize We categorize this example as a substitution problem involving a relativistic equation.

Use Equation 39.19 with $u = 0.750c$ to find the momentum:

$$p = \frac{m_e u}{\sqrt{1 - \dfrac{u^2}{c^2}}}$$

$$p = \frac{(9.11 \times 10^{-31}\text{ kg})(0.750)(3.00 \times 10^8\text{ m/s})}{\sqrt{1 - \dfrac{(0.750c)^2}{c^2}}}$$

$$= 3.10 \times 10^{-22}\text{ kg} \cdot \text{m/s}$$

The classical expression (used incorrectly here) gives $p_{\text{classical}} = m_e u = 2.05 \times 10^{-22}$ kg · m/s. Hence, the correct relativistic result is 50% greater than the classical result!

39.8 Relativistic Energy

We have seen that the definition of linear momentum requires generalization to make it compatible with Einstein's postulates. This conclusion implies that the definition of kinetic energy must most likely be modified also.

To derive the relativistic form of the work–kinetic energy theorem, imagine a particle moving in one dimension along the x axis. A force in the x direction causes the momentum of the particle to change according to Equation 39.20. In what follows, we assume the particle is accelerated from rest to some final speed u. The work done by the force F on the particle is

$$W = \int_{x_1}^{x_2} F\,dx = \int_{x_1}^{x_2} \frac{dp}{dt}\,dx \tag{39.21}$$

To perform this integration and find the work done on the particle and the relativistic kinetic energy as a function of u, we first evaluate dp/dt:

$$\frac{dp}{dt} = \frac{d}{dt}\frac{mu}{\sqrt{1-\dfrac{u^2}{c^2}}} = \frac{m}{\left(1-\dfrac{u^2}{c^2}\right)^{3/2}}\frac{du}{dt}$$

Substituting this expression for dp/dt and $dx = u\,dt$ into Equation 39.21 gives

$$W = \int_0^t \frac{m}{\left(1-\dfrac{u^2}{c^2}\right)^{3/2}}\frac{du}{dt}(u\,dt) = m\int_0^u \frac{u}{\left(1-\dfrac{u^2}{c^2}\right)^{3/2}}\,du$$

where we use the limits 0 and u in the integral because the integration variable has been changed from t to u. Evaluating the integral gives

$$W = \frac{mc^2}{\sqrt{1-\dfrac{u^2}{c^2}}} - mc^2 \tag{39.22}$$

Recall from Chapter 7 that the work done by a force acting on a system consisting of a single particle equals the change in kinetic energy of the particle. Because we assumed the initial speed of the particle is zero, its initial kinetic energy is zero. Therefore, the work W in Equation 39.22 is equivalent to the relativistic kinetic energy K:

Relativistic kinetic energy ▶

$$K = \frac{mc^2}{\sqrt{1-\dfrac{u^2}{c^2}}} - mc^2 = \gamma mc^2 - mc^2 = (\gamma - 1)mc^2 \tag{39.23}$$

This equation is routinely confirmed by experiments using high-energy particle accelerators.

At low speeds, where $u/c \ll 1$, Equation 39.23 should reduce to the classical expression $K = \frac{1}{2}mu^2$. We can check that by using the binomial expansion $(1-\beta^2)^{-1/2} \approx 1 + \frac{1}{2}\beta^2 + \cdots$ for $\beta \ll 1$, where the higher-order powers of β are neglected in the expansion. (In treatments of relativity, β is a common symbol used to represent u/c or v/c.) In our case, $\beta = u/c$, so

$$\gamma = \frac{1}{\sqrt{1-\dfrac{u^2}{c^2}}} = \left(1-\frac{u^2}{c^2}\right)^{-1/2} \approx 1 + \frac{1}{2}\frac{u^2}{c^2}$$

Substituting this result into Equation 39.23 gives

$$K \approx \left[\left(1 + \frac{1}{2}\frac{u^2}{c^2}\right) - 1\right]mc^2 = \frac{1}{2}mu^2 \quad (\text{for } u/c \ll 1)$$

which is the classical expression for kinetic energy. A graph comparing the relativistic and nonrelativistic expressions is given in Figure 39.16. In the relativistic case, the particle speed never exceeds c, regardless of the kinetic energy. The two curves are in good agreement when $u \ll c$.

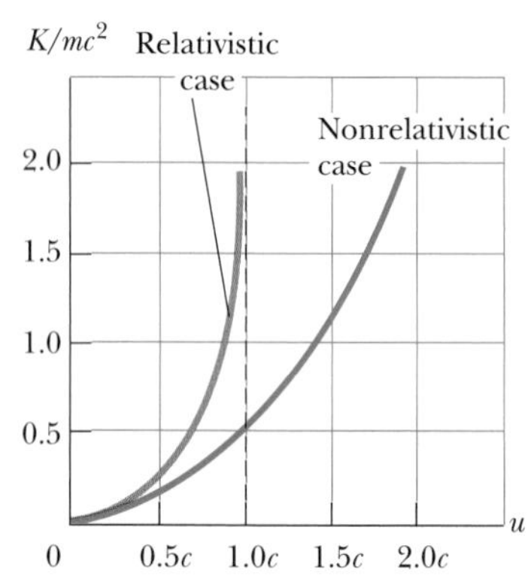

Figure 39.16 A graph comparing relativistic and nonrelativistic kinetic energy of a moving particle. The energies are plotted as a function of particle speed u. In the relativistic case, u is always less than c.

The constant term mc^2 in Equation 39.23, which is independent of the speed of the particle, is called the **rest energy** E_R of the particle:

$$E_R = mc^2 \qquad (39.24)$$

◀ Rest energy

Equation 39.24 shows that **mass is a form of energy,** where c^2 is simply a constant conversion factor. This expression also shows that a small mass corresponds to an enormous amount of energy, a concept fundamental to nuclear and elementary-particle physics.

The term γmc^2 in Equation 39.23, which depends on the particle speed, is the sum of the kinetic and rest energies. It is called the **total energy** E:

$$\text{Total energy} = \text{kinetic energy} + \text{rest energy}$$

$$E = K + mc^2 \qquad (39.25)$$

or

$$E = \frac{mc^2}{\sqrt{1 - \dfrac{u^2}{c^2}}} = \gamma mc^2 \qquad (39.26)$$

◀ Total energy of a relativistic particle

In many situations, the linear momentum or energy of a particle rather than its speed is measured. It is therefore useful to have an expression relating the total energy E to the relativistic linear momentum p, which is accomplished by using the expressions $E = \gamma mc^2$ and $p = \gamma mu$. By squaring these equations and subtracting, we can eliminate u (Problem 37). The result, after some algebra, is[6]

$$E^2 = p^2c^2 + (mc^2)^2 \qquad (39.27)$$

◀ Energy–momentum relationship for a relativistic particle

When the particle is at rest, $p = 0$, so $E = E_R = mc^2$.

In Section 35.1, we introduced the concept of a particle of light, called a **photon.** For particles that have zero mass, such as photons, we set $m = 0$ in Equation 39.27 and find that

$$E = pc \qquad (39.28)$$

This equation is an exact expression relating total energy and linear momentum for photons, which always travel at the speed of light (in vacuum).

Finally, because the mass m of a particle is independent of its motion, m must have the same value in all reference frames. For this reason, m is often called the **invariant mass.** On the other hand, because the total energy and linear momentum of a particle both depend on velocity, these quantities depend on the reference frame in which they are measured.

When dealing with subatomic particles, it is convenient to express their energy in electron volts (Section 25.1) because the particles are usually given this energy by acceleration through a potential difference. The conversion factor, as you recall from Equation 25.5, is

$$1 \text{ eV} = 1.60 \times 10^{-19} \text{ J}$$

For example, the mass of an electron is 9.11×10^{-31} kg. Hence, the rest energy of the electron is

$$m_ec^2 = (9.109 \times 10^{-31} \text{ kg})(2.998 \times 10^8 \text{ m/s})^2 = 8.187 \times 10^{-14} \text{ J}$$

$$= (8.187 \times 10^{-14} \text{ J})(1 \text{ eV}/1.602 \times 10^{-19} \text{ J}) = 0.511 \text{ MeV}$$

Quick Quiz 39.9 The following *pairs* of energies—particle 1: E, $2E$; particle 2: E, $3E$; particle 3: $2E$, $4E$—represent the rest energy and total energy of three different particles. Rank the particles from greatest to least according to their (a) mass, (b) kinetic energy, and (c) speed.

[6] One way to remember this relationship is to draw a right triangle having a hypotenuse of length E and legs of lengths pc and mc^2.

EXAMPLE 39.9 The Energy of a Speedy Proton

(A) Find the rest energy of a proton in units of electron volts.

SOLUTION

Conceptualize Even if the proton is not moving, it has energy associated with its mass. If it moves, the proton possesses more energy, with the total energy being the sum of its rest energy and its kinetic energy.

Categorize The phrase "rest energy" suggests we must take a relativistic rather than a classical approach to this problem.

Analyze Use Equation 39.24 to find the rest energy:

$$E_R = m_p c^2 = (1.673 \times 10^{-27}\ \text{kg})(2.998 \times 10^8\ \text{m/s})^2$$

$$= (1.504 \times 10^{-10}\ \text{J})\left(\frac{1.00\ \text{eV}}{1.602 \times 10^{-19}\ \text{J}}\right) = 938\ \text{MeV}$$

(B) If the total energy of a proton is three times its rest energy, what is the speed of the proton?

SOLUTION

Use Equation 39.26 to relate the total energy of the proton to the rest energy:

$$E = 3m_p c^2 = \frac{m_p c^2}{\sqrt{1 - \frac{u^2}{c^2}}} \rightarrow 3 = \frac{1}{\sqrt{1 - \frac{u^2}{c^2}}}$$

Solve for u:

$$\left(1 - \frac{u^2}{c^2}\right) = \frac{1}{9} \rightarrow \frac{u^2}{c^2} = \frac{8}{9}$$

$$u = \frac{\sqrt{8}}{3}c = 0.943c = 2.83 \times 10^8\ \text{m/s}$$

(C) Determine the kinetic energy of the proton in units of electron volts.

SOLUTION

Use Equation 39.25 to find the kinetic energy of the proton:

$$K = E - m_p c^2 = 3m_p c^2 - m_p c^2 = 2m_p c^2$$

$$= 2(938\ \text{MeV}) = 1.88 \times 10^3\ \text{MeV}$$

(D) What is the proton's momentum?

SOLUTION

Use Equation 39.27 to calculate the momentum:

$$E^2 = p^2c^2 + (m_p c^2)^2 = (3m_p c^2)^2$$

$$p^2c^2 = 9(m_p c^2)^2 - (m_p c^2)^2 = 8(m_p c^2)^2$$

$$p = \sqrt{8}\,\frac{m_p c^2}{c} = \sqrt{8}\,\frac{(938\ \text{MeV})}{c} = 2.65 \times 10^3\ \text{MeV}/c$$

Finalize The unit of momentum in part (D) is written MeV/c, which is a common unit in particle physics. For comparison, you might want to solve this example using classical equations.

What If? In classical physics, if the momentum of a particle doubles, the kinetic energy increases by a factor of 4. What happens to the kinetic energy of the proton in this example if its momentum doubles?

Answer Based on what we have seen so far in relativity, it is likely you would predict that its kinetic energy does not increase by a factor of 4.

Find the new doubled momentum:

$$p_{\text{new}} = 2\left(\sqrt{8}\,\frac{m_pc^2}{c}\right) = 4\sqrt{2}\,\frac{m_pc^2}{c}$$

Use this result in Equation 39.27 to find the new total energy:

$$E_{\text{new}}^2 = p_{\text{new}}^2c^2 + (m_pc^2)^2$$

$$E_{\text{new}}^2 = \left(4\sqrt{2}\,\frac{m_pc^2}{c}\right)^2 c^2 + (m_pc^2)^2 = 33(m_pc^2)^2$$

$$E_{\text{new}} = \sqrt{33}(m_pc^2) = 5.7m_pc^2$$

Use Equation 39.25 to find the new kinetic energy:

$$K_{\text{new}} = E_{\text{new}} - m_pc^2 = 5.7m_pc^2 - m_pc^2 = 4.7m_pc^2$$

This value is a little more than twice the kinetic energy found in part (C), not four times. In general, the factor by which the kinetic energy increases if the momentum doubles depends on the initial momentum, but it approaches 4 as the momentum approaches zero. In this latter situation, classical physics correctly describes the situation.

39.9 Mass and Energy

Equation 39.26, $E = \gamma mc^2$, represents the total energy of a particle. This important equation suggests that even when a particle is at rest ($\gamma = 1$), it still possesses enormous energy through its mass. The clearest experimental proof of the equivalence of mass and energy occurs in nuclear and elementary-particle interactions in which the conversion of mass into kinetic energy takes place. Consequently, we cannot use the principle of conservation of energy in relativistic situations as it was outlined in Chapter 8. We must modify the principle by including rest energy as another form of energy storage.

This concept is important in atomic and nuclear processes, in which the change in mass is a relatively large fraction of the initial mass. In a conventional nuclear reactor, for example, the uranium nucleus undergoes *fission*, a reaction that results in several lighter fragments having considerable kinetic energy. In the case of ^{235}U, which is used as fuel in nuclear power plants, the fragments are two lighter nuclei and a few neutrons. The total mass of the fragments is less than that of the ^{235}U by an amount Δm. The corresponding energy Δmc^2 associated with this mass difference is exactly equal to the total kinetic energy of the fragments. The kinetic energy is absorbed as the fragments move through water, raising the internal energy of the water. This internal energy is used to produce steam for the generation of electricity.

Next, consider a basic *fusion* reaction in which two deuterium atoms combine to form one helium atom. The decrease in mass that results from the creation of one helium atom from two deuterium atoms is $\Delta m = 4.25 \times 10^{-29}$ kg. Hence, the corresponding energy that results from one fusion reaction is $\Delta mc^2 = 3.83 \times 10^{-12}$ J = 23.9 MeV. To appreciate the magnitude of this result, consider that if only 1 g of deuterium were converted to helium, the energy released would be on the order of 10^{12} J! In 2007's cost of electrical energy, this energy would be worth approximately \$30 000. We shall present more details of these nuclear processes in Chapter 45 of the extended version of this textbook.

EXAMPLE 39.10 Mass Change in a Radioactive Decay

The ^{216}Po nucleus is unstable and exhibits radioactivity (Chapter 44). It decays to ^{212}Pb by emitting an alpha particle, which is a helium nucleus, ^{4}He. The relevant masses are $m_i = m(^{216}\text{Po}) = 216.001\ 905$ u, and $m_f = m(^{212}\text{Pb}) + m(^4\text{He}) = 211.991\ 888\ \text{u} + 4.002\ 603$ u.

(A) Find the mass change of the system in this decay.

SOLUTION

Conceptualize The initial system is the ^{216}Po nucleus. Imagine the mass of the system decreasing during the decay and transforming to kinetic energy of the alpha particle and the ^{212}Pb nucleus after the decay.

Categorize We use concepts discussed in this section, so we categorize this example as a substitution problem.

Calculate the mass change:

$$\Delta m = 216.001\,905\ \text{u} - (211.991\,888\ \text{u} + 4.002\,603\ \text{u})$$
$$= 0.007\,414\ \text{u} = \boxed{1.23 \times 10^{-29}\ \text{kg}}$$

(B) Find the energy this mass change represents.

SOLUTION

Use Equation 39.24 to find the energy associated with this mass change:

$$E = \Delta mc^2 = (1.23 \times 10^{-29}\ \text{kg})(3.00 \times 10^8\ \text{m/s})^2$$
$$= 1.11 \times 10^{-12}\ \text{J} = \boxed{6.92\ \text{MeV}}$$

39.10 The General Theory of Relativity

Up to this point, we have sidestepped a curious puzzle. Mass has two seemingly different properties: a *gravitational attraction* for other masses and an *inertial* property that represents a resistance to acceleration. To designate these two attributes, we use the subscripts g and i and write

$$\text{Gravitational property:} \quad F_g = m_g g$$

$$\text{Inertial property:} \quad \sum F = m_i a$$

The value for the gravitational constant G was chosen to make the magnitudes of m_g and m_i numerically equal. Regardless of how G is chosen, however, the strict proportionality of m_g and m_i has been established experimentally to an extremely high degree: a few parts in 10^{12}. Therefore, it appears that gravitational mass and inertial mass may indeed be exactly proportional.

Why, though? They seem to involve two entirely different concepts: a force of mutual gravitational attraction between two masses and the resistance of a single mass to being accelerated. This question, which puzzled Newton and many other physicists over the years, was answered by Einstein in 1916 when he published his theory of gravitation, known as the *general theory of relativity*. Because it is a mathematically complex theory, we offer merely a hint of its elegance and insight.

In Einstein's view, the dual behavior of mass was evidence for a very intimate and basic connection between the two behaviors. He pointed out that no mechanical experiment (such as dropping an object) could distinguish between the two situations illustrated in Figures 39.17a and 39.17b. In Figure 39.17a, a person standing in an elevator on the surface of a planet feels pressed into the floor due to the gravitational force. If he releases his briefcase, he observes it moving toward the floor with acceleration $\vec{\mathbf{g}} = -g\hat{\mathbf{j}}$. In Figure 39.17b, the person is in an elevator in empty space accelerating upward with $\vec{\mathbf{a}}_{el} = +g\hat{\mathbf{j}}$. The person feels pressed into the floor with the same force as in Figure 39.17a. If he releases his briefcase, he observes it moving toward the floor with acceleration g, exactly as in the previous situation. In each situation, an object released by the observer undergoes a downward acceleration of magnitude g relative to the floor. In Figure 39.17a, the person is at rest in an inertial frame in a gravitational field due to the planet. In Figure 39.17b, the person is in a noninertial frame accelerating in gravity-free space. Einstein's claim is that these two situations are completely equivalent.

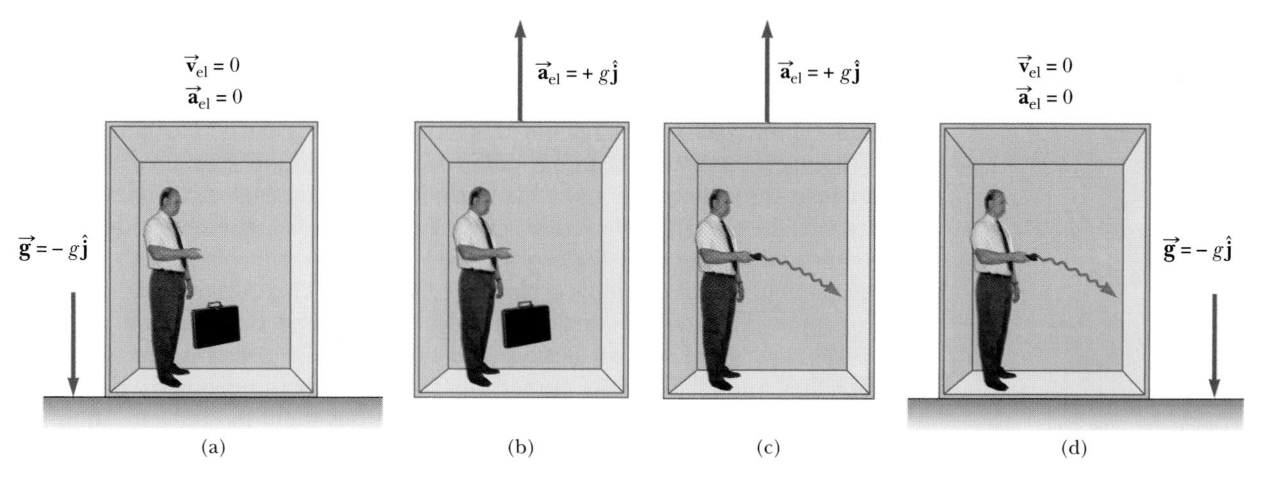

Figure 39.17 (a) The observer is at rest in an elevator in a uniform gravitational field $\vec{g} = -g\hat{j}$, directed downward. The observer drops his briefcase, which moves downward with acceleration g. (b) The observer is in a region where gravity is negligible, but the elevator moves upward with an acceleration $\vec{a}_{el} = +g\hat{j}$. The observer releases his briefcase, which moves downward (according to the observer) with acceleration g relative to the floor of the elevator. According to Einstein, the frames of reference in (a) and (b) are equivalent in every way. No local experiment can distinguish any difference between the two frames. (c) In the accelerating frame, a ray of light would appear to bend downward due to the acceleration. (d) If (a) and (b) are truly equivalent, as Einstein proposed, (c) suggests that a ray of light would bend downward in a gravitational field.

Einstein carried this idea further and proposed that *no* experiment, mechanical or otherwise, could distinguish between the two situations. This extension to include all phenomena (not just mechanical ones) has interesting consequences. For example, suppose a light pulse is sent horizontally across the elevator as in Figure 39.17c, in which the elevator is accelerating upward in empty space. From the point of view of an observer in an inertial frame outside the elevator, the light travels in a straight line while the floor of the elevator accelerates upward. According to the observer on the elevator, however, the trajectory of the light pulse bends downward as the floor of the elevator (and the observer) accelerates upward. Therefore, based on the equality of parts (a) and (b) of the figure, Einstein proposed that **a beam of light should also be bent downward by a gravitational field** as in Figure 39.17d. Experiments have verified the effect, although the bending is small. A laser aimed at the horizon falls less than 1 cm after traveling 6 000 km. (No such bending is predicted in Newton's theory of gravitation.)

Einstein's **general theory of relativity** has two postulates:

◀ Postulates of the general theory of relativity

- All the laws of nature have the same form for observers in any frame of reference, whether accelerated or not.
- In the vicinity of any point, a gravitational field is equivalent to an accelerated frame of reference in gravity-free space (the **principle of equivalence**).

One interesting effect predicted by the general theory is that time is altered by gravity. A clock in the presence of gravity runs slower than one located where gravity is negligible. Consequently, the frequencies of radiation emitted by atoms in the presence of a strong gravitational field are *redshifted* to lower frequencies when compared with the same emissions in the presence of a weak field. This gravitational redshift has been detected in spectral lines emitted by atoms in massive stars. It has also been verified on the Earth by comparing the frequencies of gamma rays emitted from nuclei separated vertically by about 20 m.

The second postulate suggests a gravitational field may be "transformed away" at any point if we choose an appropriate accelerated frame of reference, a freely falling one. Einstein developed an ingenious method of describing the acceleration necessary to make the gravitational field "disappear." He specified a concept, the *curvature of space–time,* that describes the gravitational effect at every point. In fact, the curvature of space–time completely replaces Newton's gravitational theory. According to Einstein, there is no such thing as a gravitational force. Rather, the presence of a mass causes a curvature of space–time in the vicinity of the mass,

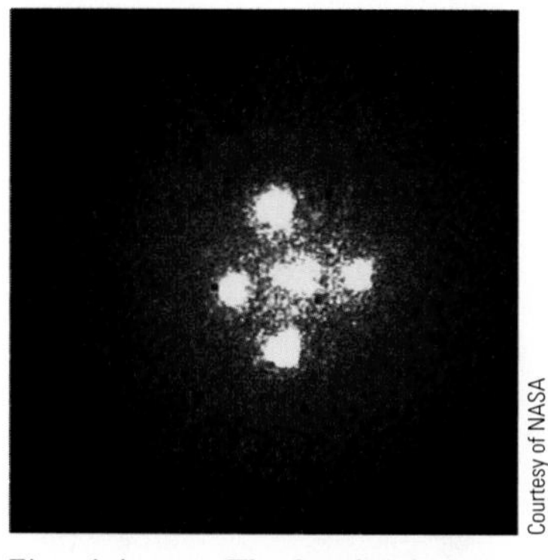

Einstein's cross. The four bright spots are images of the same galaxy that have been bent around a massive object located between the galaxy and the Earth. The massive object acts like a lens, causing the rays of light that were diverging from the distant galaxy to converge on the Earth. (If the intervening massive object had a uniform mass distribution, we would see a bright ring instead of four spots.)

and this curvature dictates the space–time path that all freely moving objects must follow.

As an example of the effects of curved space–time, imagine two travelers moving on parallel paths a few meters apart on the surface of the Earth and maintaining an exact northward heading along two longitude lines. As they observe each other near the equator, they will claim that their paths are exactly parallel. As they approach the North Pole, however, they notice that they are moving closer together and will meet at the North Pole. Therefore, they claim that they moved along parallel paths, but moved toward each other, *as if there were an attractive force between them.* The travelers make this conclusion based on their everyday experience of moving on flat surfaces. From our mental representation, however, we realize they are walking on a curved surface, and it is the geometry of the curved surface, rather than an attractive force, that causes them to converge. In a similar way, general relativity replaces the notion of forces with the movement of objects through curved space–time.

One prediction of the general theory of relativity is that a light ray passing near the Sun should be deflected in the curved space–time created by the Sun's mass. This prediction was confirmed when astronomers detected the bending of starlight near the Sun during a total solar eclipse that occurred shortly after World War I (Fig. 39.18). When this discovery was announced, Einstein became an international celebrity.

If the concentration of mass becomes very great as is believed to occur when a large star exhausts its nuclear fuel and collapses to a very small volume, a **black hole** may form. Here, the curvature of space–time is so extreme that within a certain distance from the center of the black hole all matter and light become trapped as discussed in Section 13.6.

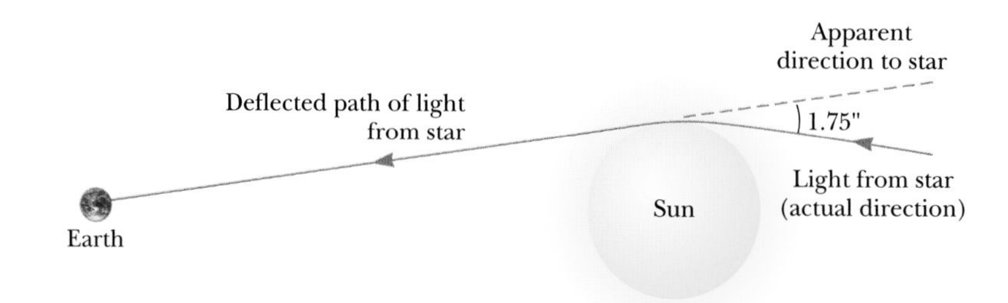

Figure 39.18 Deflection of starlight passing near the Sun. Because of this effect, the Sun or some other remote object can act as a *gravitational lens.* In his general theory of relativity, Einstein calculated that starlight just grazing the Sun's surface should be deflected by an angle of 1.75 s of arc.

Summary

ThomsonNOW™ Sign in at **www.thomsonedu.com** and go to ThomsonNOW to take a practice test for this chapter.

DEFINITIONS

The relativistic expression for the **linear momentum** of a particle moving with a velocity $\vec{\mathbf{u}}$ is

$$\vec{\mathbf{p}} \equiv \frac{m\vec{\mathbf{u}}}{\sqrt{1 - \dfrac{u^2}{c^2}}} = \gamma m\vec{\mathbf{u}} \quad \textbf{(39.19)}$$

The relativistic force $\vec{\mathbf{F}}$ acting on a particle whose linear momentum is $\vec{\mathbf{p}}$ is defined as

$$\vec{\mathbf{F}} \equiv \frac{d\vec{\mathbf{p}}}{dt} \quad \textbf{(39.20)}$$

(continued)

CONCEPTS AND PRINCIPLES

The two basic postulates of the special theory of relativity are as follows:

- The laws of physics must be the same in all inertial reference frames.
- The speed of light in vacuum has the same value, $c = 3.00 \times 10^8$ m/s, in all inertial frames, regardless of the velocity of the observer or the velocity of the source emitting the light.

Three consequences of the special theory of relativity are as follows:

- Events that are measured to be simultaneous for one observer are not necessarily measured to be simultaneous for another observer who is in motion relative to the first.
- Clocks in motion relative to an observer are measured to run slower by a factor $\gamma = (1 - v^2/c^2)^{-1/2}$. This phenomenon is known as **time dilation.**
- The length of objects in motion are measured to be contracted in the direction of motion by a factor $1/\gamma = (1 - v^2/c^2)^{1/2}$. This phenomenon is known as **length contraction.**

To satisfy the postulates of special relativity, the Galilean transformation equations must be replaced by the **Lorentz transformation equations:**

$$x' = \gamma(x - vt) \qquad y' = y \qquad z' = z \qquad t' = \gamma\left(t - \frac{v}{c^2}x\right) \qquad \textbf{(39.11)}$$

where $\gamma = (1 - v^2/c^2)^{-1/2}$ and the S′ frame moves in the x direction relative to the S frame.

The relativistic form of the **Lorentz velocity transformation equation** is

$$u'_x = \frac{u_x - v}{1 - \dfrac{u_x v}{c^2}} \qquad \textbf{(39.16)}$$

where u'_x is the x component of the velocity of an object as measured in the S′ frame and u_x is its component as measured in the S frame.

The relativistic expression for the **kinetic energy** of a particle is

$$K = \frac{mc^2}{\sqrt{1 - \dfrac{u^2}{c^2}}} - mc^2 = (\gamma - 1)mc^2 \qquad \textbf{(39.23)}$$

The constant term mc^2 in Equation 39.23 is called the **rest energy** E_R of the particle:

$$E_R = mc^2 \qquad \textbf{(39.24)}$$

The total energy E of a particle is given by

$$E = \frac{mc^2}{\sqrt{1 - \dfrac{u^2}{c^2}}} = \gamma mc^2 \qquad \textbf{(39.26)}$$

The relativistic linear momentum of a particle is related to its total energy through the equation

$$E^2 = p^2c^2 + (mc^2)^2 \qquad \textbf{(39.27)}$$

Questions

☐ denotes answer available in *Student Solutions Manual/Study Guide;* **O** denotes objective question

1. The speed of light in water is 230 Mm/s. Suppose an electron is moving through water at 250 Mm/s. Does that motion violate the principle of relativity?

2. **O** You measure the volume of a cube at rest to be V_0. You then measure the volume of the same cube as it passes you in a direction parallel to one side of the cube. The speed of the cube is $0.98c$, so $\gamma \approx 5$. Is the volume you measure close to (a) $V_0/125$, (b) $V_0/25$, (c) $V_0/5$, (d) V_0, (e) $5V_0$, (f) $25V_0$, or (g) $125V_0$?

3. **O** A spacecraft built in the shape of a sphere moves past an observer on the Earth with a speed of $0.5c$. What shape does the observer measure for the spacecraft as it goes by? (a) a sphere (b) a cigar shape, elongated along the direction of motion (c) a round pillow shape, flattened along the direction of motion (d) a conical shape, pointing in the direction of motion

4. **O** A spacecraft zooms past the Earth with a constant velocity. An observer on the Earth measures that an undamaged clock on the spacecraft is ticking at one-third the rate of an identical clock on the Earth. What does an observer on the spacecraft measure about the Earth clock's ticking rate? (a) It runs more than three times faster than his own clock. (b) It runs three times faster than his own. (c) It runs at the same rate as his own. (d) It runs at approximately half the rate of his own. (e) It runs at one-third the rate of his own. (f) It runs at less than one-third the rate of his own.

5. Explain why, when defining the length of a rod, it is necessary to specify that the positions of the ends of the rod are to be measured simultaneously.

6. **O** Two identical clocks are set side by side and synchronized. One remains on the Earth. The other is put into orbit around the Earth moving toward the east. **(i)** As measured by an observer on the Earth, while in rapid motion does the orbiting clock (a) run faster than the Earth-based clock, (b) run at the same rate, or (c) run slower? **(ii)** The orbiting clock is returned to its original location and brought to rest relative to the Earth. Thereafter, (a) its reading lags farther and farther behind the Earth-based clock, (b) it lags behind the Earth-based clock by a constant amount, (c) it is synchronized with the Earth-based clock, (d) it is ahead of the Earth-based clock by a constant amount, or (e) it gets farther and farther ahead of the Earth-based clock.

7. A train is approaching you at very high speed as you stand next to the tracks. Just as an observer on the train passes you, you both begin to play the same Beethoven symphony on portable CD players. (a) According to you, whose CD player finishes the symphony first? (b) **What If?** According to the observer on the train, whose CD player finishes the symphony first? (c) Whose CD player actually finishes the symphony first?

8. List some ways our day-to-day lives would change if the speed of light were only 50 m/s.

9. How is acceleration indicated on a space–time graph?

10. Explain how the Doppler effect with microwaves is used to determine the speed of an automobile.

11. In several cases, a nearby star has been found to have a large planet orbiting about it, although light from the planet could not be seen separately from the starlight. Using the ideas of a system rotating about its center of mass and of the Doppler shift for light, explain how an astronomer could determine the presence of the invisible planet.

12. A particle is moving at a speed less than $c/2$. If the speed of the particle is doubled, what happens to its momentum?

13. **O** Rank the following particles according to the magnitudes of their momentum from the largest to the smallest. If any have equal amounts of momentum, or zero momentum, display that fact in your ranking. (a) a 1-MeV photon (b) a proton with kinetic energy $K = 1$ MeV (c) an electron with $K = 1$ MeV (d) a grain of dust with $K = 1$ MeV $= 160$ fJ

14. Give a physical argument that shows it is impossible to accelerate an object of mass m to the speed of light, even with a continuous force acting on it.

15. **O** **(i)** Does the speed of an electron have an upper limit? (a) yes, the speed of light c (b) yes, with another value (c) no **(ii)** Does the magnitude of an electron's momentum have an upper limit? (a) yes, $m_e c$ (b) yes, with another value (c) no **(iii)** Does the electron's kinetic energy have an upper limit? (a) yes, $m_e c^2$ (b) yes, $\frac{1}{2} m_e c^2$ (c) yes, with another value (d) no

16. **O** A distant astronomical object (a quasar) is moving away from us at half the speed of light. What is the speed of the light we receive from this quasar? (a) greater than c (b) c (c) between $c/2$ and c (d) $c/2$ (e) between 0 and $c/2$ (f) 0

17. "Newtonian mechanics correctly describes objects moving at ordinary speeds and relativistic mechanics correctly describes objects moving very fast." "Relativistic mechanics must make a smooth transition as it reduces to Newtonian mechanics in a case in which the speed of an object becomes small compared with the speed of light." Argue for or against each of these two statements.

18. Two cards have straight edges. Suppose the top edge of one card crosses the bottom edge of another card at a small angle as shown in Figure Q39.18a. A person slides the cards together at a moderately high speed. In what direction does the intersection point of the edges move? Show that the intersection point can move at a speed greater than the speed of light.

A small flashlight is suspended in a horizontal plane and set into rapid rotation. Show that the spot of light it produces on a distant screen can move across the screen at a speed greater than the speed of light. (If you use a laser pointer as shown in Figure Q39.18b, make sure the direct laser light cannot enter a person's eyes.) Argue that these experiments do not invalidate the principle that no material, no energy, and no information can move faster than light moves in a vacuum.

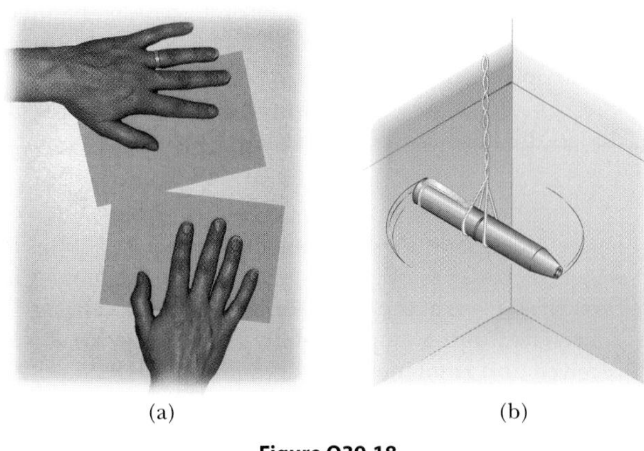

Figure Q39.18

19. With regard to reference frames, how does general relativity differ from special relativity?

20. Two identical clocks are in the same house, one upstairs in a bedroom and the other downstairs in the kitchen. Which clock runs slower? Explain.

Problems

WebAssign The Problems from this chapter may be assigned online in WebAssign.

ThomsonNOW Sign in at **www.thomsonedu.com** and go to ThomsonNOW to assess your understanding of this chapter's topics with additional quizzing and conceptual questions.

1, 2, 3 denotes straightforward, intermediate, challenging; □ denotes full solution available in *Student Solutions Manual/Study Guide;* ▲ denotes coached solution with hints available at **www.thomsonedu.com;** denotes developing symbolic reasoning; ● denotes asking for qualitative reasoning; denotes computer useful in solving problem

Section 39.1 The Principle of Galilean Relativity

1. In a laboratory frame of reference, an observer notes that Newton's second law is valid. Show that it is also valid for an observer moving at a constant speed, small compared with the speed of light, relative to the laboratory frame.

2. Show that Newton's second law is *not* valid in a reference frame moving past the laboratory frame of Problem 1 with a constant acceleration.

3. A 2 000-kg car moving at 20.0 m/s collides and locks together with a 1 500-kg car at rest at a stop sign. Show that momentum is conserved in a reference frame moving at 10.0 m/s in the direction of the moving car.

Section 39.2 The Michelson–Morley Experiment

Section 39.3 Einstein's Principle of Relativity

Section 39.4 Consequences of the Special Theory of Relativity

Problem 37 in Chapter 4 can be assigned with this section.

4. How fast must a meterstick be moving if its length is measured to shrink to 0.500 m?

5. At what speed does a clock move if it is measured to run at a rate one-half the rate of a clock at rest with respect to an observer?

6. An astronaut is traveling in a space vehicle moving at $0.500c$ relative to the Earth. The astronaut measures her pulse rate at 75.0 beats per minute. Signals generated by the astronaut's pulse are radioed to the Earth when the vehicle is moving in a direction perpendicular to the line that connects the vehicle with an observer on the Earth. (a) What pulse rate does the Earth-based observer measure? (b) **What If?** What would be the pulse rate if the speed of the space vehicle were increased to $0.990c$?

7. An atomic clock moves at 1 000 km/h for 1.00 h as measured by an identical clock on the Earth. At the end of the 1.00-h interval, how many nanoseconds slow will the moving clock be compared with the Earth clock?

8. A muon formed high in the Earth's atmosphere travels at speed $v = 0.990c$ for a distance of 4.60 km before it decays into an electron, a neutrino, and an antineutrino ($\mu^- \rightarrow e^- + \nu + \bar{\nu}$). (a) For what time interval does the muon live as measured in its reference frame? (b) How far does the Earth travel as measured in the frame of the muon?

9. ▲ A spacecraft with a proper length of 300 m takes 0.750 μs to pass an Earth-based observer. Determine the speed of the spacecraft as measured by the Earth observer.

10. (a) An object of proper length L_p takes a time interval Δt to pass an Earth-based observer. Determine the speed of the object as measured by the Earth observer. (b) A column of tanks, 300 m long, takes 75.0 s to pass a child waiting at a street corner on her way to school. Determine the speed of the armored vehicles. (c) Show that the answer to part (a) includes the answer to Problem 9 as a special case and includes the answer to part (b) as another special case.

11. ● **Review problem.** In 1963, astronaut Gordon Cooper orbited the Earth 22 times. The press stated that for each orbit, he aged 2 millionths of a second less than he would have had he remained on the Earth. (a) Assuming that he was 160 km above the Earth in a circular orbit, determine the difference in elapsed time between someone on the Earth and the orbiting astronaut for the 22 orbits. You may use the approximation

$$\frac{1}{\sqrt{1-x}} \approx 1 + \frac{x}{2}$$

for small x. (b) Did the press report accurate information? Explain.

12. For what value of v does $\gamma = 1.010\,0$? Observe that for speeds lower than this value, time dilation and length contraction are effects amounting to less than 1%.

13. A friend passes by you in a spacecraft traveling at a high speed. He tells you that his spacecraft is 20.0 m long and that the identically constructed spacecraft you are sitting in is 19.0 m long. According to your observations, (a) how long is your spacecraft, (b) how long is your friend's spacecraft, and (c) what is the speed of your friend's spacecraft?

14. The identical twins Speedo and Goslo join a migration from the Earth to Planet X. It is 20.0 ly away in a reference frame in which both planets are at rest. The twins, of the same age, depart at the same moment on different spacecraft. Speedo's spacecraft travels steadily at $0.950c$ and Goslo's at $0.750c$. Calculate the age difference between the twins after Goslo's spacecraft lands on Planet X. Which twin is older?

15. **Review problem.** An alien civilization occupies a brown dwarf, nearly stationary relative to the Sun, several lightyears away. The extraterrestrials have come to love original broadcasts of *I Love Lucy,* on television channel 2, at carrier frequency 57.0 MHz. Their line of sight to us is in the plane of the Earth's orbit. Find the difference between the highest and lowest frequencies they receive due to the Earth's orbital motion around the Sun.

16. Police radar detects the speed of a car (Fig. P39.16) as follows. Microwaves of a precisely known frequency are broadcast toward the car. The moving car reflects the microwaves with a Doppler shift. The reflected waves are received and combined with an attenuated version of the transmitted wave. Beats occur between the two microwave signals. The beat frequency is measured. (a) For an electromagnetic wave reflected back to its source from a mirror approaching at speed v, show that the reflected wave has frequency

$$f = f_{\text{source}}\frac{c+v}{c-v}$$

where f_{source} is the source frequency. (b) When v is much less than c, the beat frequency is much smaller than the transmitted frequency. In this case, use the approximation $f + f_{\text{source}} \approx 2f_{\text{source}}$ and show that the beat frequency can be written as $f_{\text{beat}} = 2v/\lambda$. (c) What beat frequency is measured for a car speed of 30.0 m/s if the microwaves have frequency 10.0 GHz? (d) If the beat frequency measurement is accurate to ± 5 Hz, how accurate is the speed measurement?

Figure P39.16

17. *The redshift.* A light source recedes from an observer with a speed v_{source} that is small compared with c. (a) Show that the fractional shift in the measured wavelength is given by the approximate expression

$$\frac{\Delta\lambda}{\lambda} \approx \frac{v_{\text{source}}}{c}$$

This phenomenon is known as the redshift because the visible light is shifted toward the red. (b) Spectroscopic measurements of light at $\lambda = 397$ nm coming from a galaxy in Ursa Major reveal a redshift of 20.0 nm. What is the recessional speed of the galaxy?

18. A physicist drives through a stop light. When he is pulled over, he tells the police officer that the Doppler shift made the red light of wavelength 650 nm appear green to him, with a wavelength of 520 nm. The police officer writes out a traffic citation for speeding. How fast was the physicist traveling, according to his own testimony?

Section 39.5 The Lorentz Transformation Equations

19. Suzanne observes two light pulses to be emitted from the same location, but separated in time by 3.00 μs. Mark observes the emission of the same two pulses to be separated in time by 9.00 μs. (a) How fast is Mark moving relative to Suzanne? (b) According to Mark, what is the separation in space of the two pulses?

20. A moving rod is observed to have a length of 2.00 m and to be oriented at an angle of 30.0° with respect to the direction of motion as shown in Figure P39.20. The rod has a speed of $0.995c$. (a) What is the proper length of the rod? (b) What is the orientation angle in the proper frame?

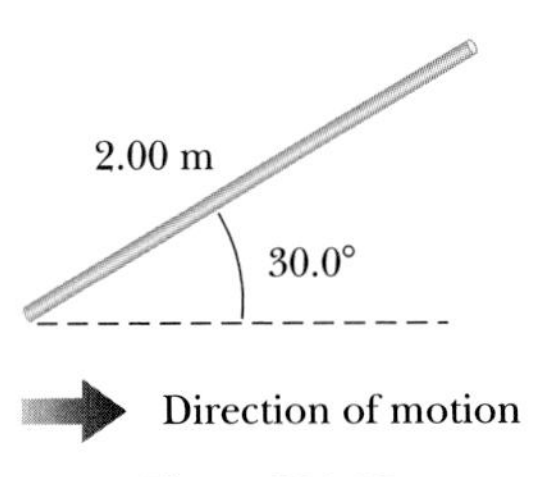

Figure P39.20

21. An observer in reference frame S measures two events to be simultaneous. Event A occurs at the point (50.0 m, 0, 0) at the instant 9:00:00 Universal time on January 15, 2008. Event B occurs at the point (150 m, 0, 0) at the same moment. A second observer, moving past with a velocity of $0.800c\hat{\mathbf{i}}$, also observes the two events. In her reference frame S′, which event occurred first and what time interval elapsed between the events?

22. A red light flashes at position $x_R = 3.00$ m and time $t_R = 1.00 \times 10^{-9}$ s, and a blue light flashes at $x_B = 5.00$ m and $t_B = 9.00 \times 10^{-9}$ s, all measured in the S reference frame. Reference frame S′ moves uniformly to the right and has its origin at the same point as S at $t = t' = 0$. Both flashes are observed to occur at the same place in S′. (a) Find the relative speed between S and S′. (b) Find the location of the two flashes in frame S′. (c) At what time does the red flash occur in the S′ frame?

Section 39.6 The Lorentz Velocity Transformation Equations

23. ▲ Two jets of material from the center of a radio galaxy are ejected in opposite directions. Both jets move at $0.750c$ relative to the galaxy. Determine the speed of one jet relative to the other.

24. A Klingon spacecraft moves away from the Earth at a speed of $0.800c$ (Fig. P39.24). The starship *Enterprise* pursues at a speed of $0.900c$ relative to the Earth. Observers on the Earth measure the *Enterprise* to be overtaking the Klingon craft at a relative speed of $0.100c$. With what speed is the *Enterprise* overtaking the Klingon craft as measured by the crew of the *Enterprise*?

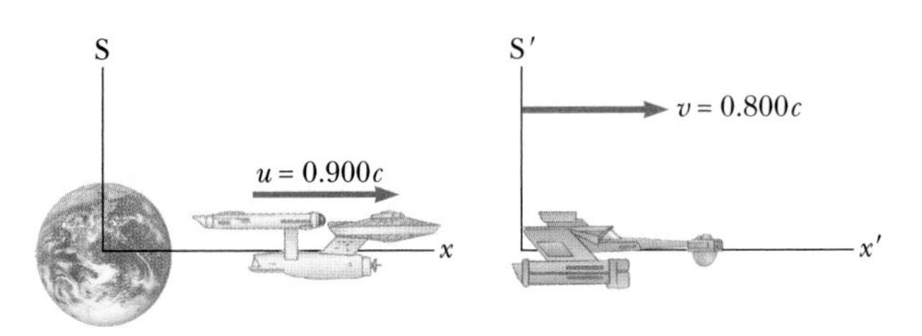

Figure P39.24

Section 39.7 Relativistic Linear Momentum

25. Calculate the momentum of an electron moving with a speed of (a) $0.010\,0c$, (b) $0.500c$, and (c) $0.900c$.

26. The nonrelativistic expression for the momentum of a particle, $p = mu$, agrees with experiment if $u \ll c$. For what speed does the use of this equation give an error in the momentum of (a) 1.00% and (b) 10.0%?

27. A golf ball travels with a speed of 90.0 m/s. By what fraction does its relativistic momentum magnitude p differ from its classical value mu? That is, calculate the ratio $(p - mu)/mu$.

28. The speed limit on a certain roadway is 90.0 km/h. Suppose speeding fines are made proportional to the amount by which a vehicle's momentum exceeds the momentum it would have when traveling at the speed limit. The fine for driving at 190 km/h (that is, 100 km/h over the speed limit) is \$80.0. What then will be the fine for traveling (a) at 1 090 km/h? (b) At 1 000 000 090 km/h?

29. ▲ An unstable particle at rest spontaneously breaks into two fragments of unequal mass. The mass of the first fragment is 2.50×10^{-28} kg, and that of the other is 1.67×10^{-27} kg. If the lighter fragment has a speed of $0.893c$ after the breakup, what is the speed of the heavier fragment?

Section 39.8 Relativistic Energy

30. An electron has a kinetic energy five times greater than its rest energy. Find its (a) total energy and (b) speed.

31. A proton in a high-energy accelerator moves with a speed of $c/2$. Use the work–kinetic energy theorem to find the work required to increase its speed to (a) $0.750c$ and (b) $0.995c$.

32. Show that for any object moving at less than one-tenth the speed of light, the relativistic kinetic energy agrees with the result of the classical equation $K = \frac{1}{2}mu^2$ to within less than 1%. Therefore, for most purposes, the classical equation is good enough to describe these objects.

33. Find the momentum of a proton in MeV/c units assuming its total energy is twice its rest energy.

34. ● (a) Find the kinetic energy of a 78.0-kg spacecraft launched out of the solar system with speed 106 km/s by using the classical equation $K = \frac{1}{2}mu^2$. (b) **What If?** Calculate its kinetic energy using the relativistic equation. (c) Explain the result of comparing the results of parts (a) and (b).

35. ▲ A proton moves at $0.950c$. Calculate its (a) rest energy, (b) total energy, and (c) kinetic energy.

36. An unstable particle with a mass of 3.34×10^{-27} kg is initially at rest. The particle decays into two fragments that fly off along the x axis with velocity components $0.987c$ and $-0.868c$. Find the masses of the fragments. *Suggestion:* Use conservation of both energy and momentum.

37. Show that the energy–momentum relationship $E^2 = p^2c^2 + (mc^2)^2$ follows from the expressions $E = \gamma mc^2$ and $p = \gamma mu$.

38. In a typical color television picture tube, the electrons are accelerated from rest through a potential difference of 25 000 V. (a) What speed do the electrons have when they strike the screen? (b) What is their kinetic energy in joules?

39. The rest energy of an electron is 0.511 MeV. The rest energy of a proton is 938 MeV. Assume both particles have kinetic energies of 2.00 MeV. Find the speed of (a) the electron and (b) the proton. (c) By how much does the speed of the electron exceed that of the proton? (d) Repeat the calculations assuming both particles have kinetic energies of 2 000 MeV.

40. Consider electrons accelerated to an energy of 20.0 GeV in the 3.00-km-long Stanford Linear Accelerator. (a) What is the γ factor for the electrons? (b) What is the electrons' speed? (c) How long does the accelerator appear to the electrons?

41. A pion at rest ($m_\pi = 273m_e$) decays to a muon ($m_\mu = 207m_e$) and an antineutrino ($m_{\bar{\nu}} \approx 0$). The reaction is written $\pi^- \rightarrow \mu^- + \bar{\nu}$. Find the kinetic energy of the muon and the energy of the antineutrino in electron volts. *Suggestion:* Use conservation of both energy and momentum for the decay process.

42. Consider a car moving at highway speed u. Is its actual kinetic energy larger or smaller than $\frac{1}{2}mu^2$? Make an order-of-magnitude estimate of the amount by which its actual kinetic energy differs from $\frac{1}{2}mu^2$. In your solution, state the quantities you take as data and the values you measure or estimate for them. You may find Appendix B.5 useful.

Section 39.9 Mass and Energy

43. ● When 1.00 g of hydrogen combines with 8.00 g of oxygen, 9.00 g of water is formed. During this chemical reaction, 2.86×10^5 J of energy is released. Is the mass of the water larger or smaller than the mass of the reactants? What is the difference in mass? Explain whether the change in mass is likely to be detectable.

44. In a nuclear power plant, the fuel rods last 3 yr before they are replaced. If a plant with rated thermal power 1.00 GW operates at 80.0% capacity for 3.00 yr, what is the loss of mass of the fuel?

45. The power output of the Sun is 3.85×10^{26} W. How much mass is converted to energy in the Sun each second?

46. A gamma ray (a high-energy photon) can produce an electron (e^-) and a positron (e^+) when it enters the electric field of a heavy nucleus: $\gamma \rightarrow e^+ + e^-$. What minimum gamma-ray energy is required to accomplish this task? *Note:* The masses of the electron and the positron are equal.

Section 39.10 The General Theory of Relativity

47. An Earth satellite used in the global positioning system (GPS) moves in a circular orbit with period 11 h 58 min. (a) Determine the radius of its orbit. (b) Determine its speed. (c) The satellite contains an oscillator producing the principal nonmilitary GPS signal. Its frequency is 1 575.42 MHz in the reference frame of the satellite. When it is received on the Earth's surface, what is the fractional change in this frequency due to time dilation as described by special relativity? (d) The gravitational "blueshift" of the frequency according to general relativity is a separate effect. It is called a blueshift to indicate a change to a higher frequency. The magnitude of that fractional change is given by

$$\frac{\Delta f}{f} = \frac{\Delta U_g}{mc^2}$$

where ΔU_g is the change in gravitational potential energy of an object–Earth system when the object of mass m is moved between the two points where the signal is observed. Calculate this fractional change in frequency. (e) What is the overall fractional change in frequency? Superposed on both of these relativistic effects is a Doppler shift that is generally much larger. It can be a redshift or a blueshift, depending on the motion of a particular satellite relative to a GPS receiver (Fig. P39.47).

Figure P39.47

Additional Problems

48. *Houston, we've got a problem.* An astronaut wishes to visit the Andromeda galaxy, making a one-way trip that will take 30.0 yr in the spacecraft's frame of reference. Assume the galaxy is 2.00×10^6 ly away and the astronaut's speed is constant. (a) How fast must he travel relative to the Earth? (b) What will be the kinetic energy of his 1 000-metric-ton spacecraft? (c) What is the cost of this energy if it is purchased at a typical consumer price for electric energy of \$0.130/kWh?

49. ▲ The cosmic rays of highest energy are protons that have kinetic energy on the order of 10^{13} MeV. (a) How long would it take a proton of this energy to travel across the Milky Way galaxy, having a diameter $\sim 10^5$ ly, as measured in the proton's frame? (b) From the point of view of the proton, how many kilometers across is the galaxy?

50. An electron has a speed of $0.750c$. (a) Find the speed of a proton that has the same kinetic energy as the electron. (b) **What If?** Find the speed of a proton that has the same momentum as the electron.

51. ● The equation

$$K = \left(\frac{1}{\sqrt{1 - u^2/c^2}} - 1\right)mc^2$$

gives the kinetic energy of a particle moving at speed u. (a) Solve the equation for u. (b) From the equation for u, identify the minimum possible value of speed and the corresponding kinetic energy. (c) Identify the maximum possible speed and the corresponding kinetic energy. (d) Differentiate the equation for u with respect to time to obtain an equation describing the acceleration of a particle as a function of its kinetic energy and the power input to the particle. (e) Observe that for a nonrelativistic particle we have $u = (2K/m)^{1/2}$ and that differentiating this equation with respect to time gives $a = \mathcal{P}/(2mK)^{1/2}$. State the limiting form of the expression in part (d) at low energy. State how it compares with the nonrelativistic expression. (f) State the limiting form of the expression in part (d) at high energy. (g) Consider a particle with constant input power. Explain how the answer to part (f) helps account for the answer to part (c).

52. Ted and Mary are playing a game of catch in frame S′, which is moving at $0.600c$ with respect to frame S, while Jim, at rest in frame S, watches the action (Fig. P39.52). Ted throws the ball to Mary at $0.800c$ (according to Ted), and their separation (measured in S′) is 1.80×10^{12} m. (a) According to Mary, how fast is the ball moving? (b) According to Mary, what time interval is required for the ball to reach her? (c) According to Jim, how far apart are Ted and Mary and how fast is the ball moving? (d) According to Jim, what time interval is required for the ball to reach Mary?

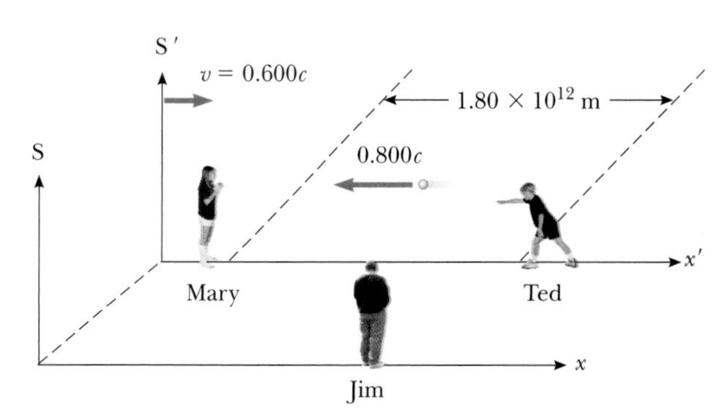

Figure P39.52

53. The net nuclear fusion reaction inside the Sun can be written as $4^1\text{H} \rightarrow {}^4\text{He} + E$. The rest energy of each hydrogen atom is 938.78 MeV, and the rest energy of the helium-4 atom is 3 728.4 MeV. Calculate the percentage of the starting mass that is transformed to other forms of energy.

54. An object disintegrates into two fragments. One fragment has mass $1.00 \text{ MeV}/c^2$ and momentum $1.75 \text{ MeV}/c$ in the positive x direction. The other fragment has mass $1.50 \text{ MeV}/c^2$ and momentum $2.00 \text{ MeV}/c$ in the positive y direction. Find the (a) mass and (b) speed of the original object.

55. Spacecraft I, containing students taking a physics exam, approaches the Earth with a speed of $0.600c$ (relative to the Earth), while spacecraft II, containing professors proctoring the exam, moves at $0.280c$ (relative to the Earth) directly toward the students. If the professors stop the exam after 50.0 min have passed on their clock, for what time interval does the exam last as measured by (a) the students and (b) an observer on the Earth?

56. **Review problem.** An electron is traveling through water at a speed 10.0% faster than the speed of light in water. Determine the electron's (a) total energy, (b) kinetic energy, and (c) momentum. The electron gives off Cerenkov radiation, the electromagnetic equivalent of a bow wave or a sonic boom. (d) Find the angle between the shock wave and the electron's direction of motion. Around the core of a nuclear reactor shielded by a large pool of water, Cerenkov radiation appears as a blue glow.

57. An alien spaceship traveling at $0.600c$ toward the Earth launches a landing craft with an advance guard of purchasing agents and environmental educators. The landing craft travels in the same direction with a speed of $0.800c$ relative to the mother ship. As observed on the Earth, the spaceship is 0.200 ly from the Earth when the landing craft is launched. (a) What speed do the Earth-based observers measure for the approaching landing craft? (b) What is the distance to the Earth at the moment of the landing craft's launch as observed by the aliens? (c) What travel time is required for the landing craft to reach the Earth as observed by the aliens on the mother ship? (d) If the landing craft has a mass of 4.00×10^5 kg, what is its kinetic energy as observed in the Earth reference frame?

58. ● *Speed of light in a moving medium.* The motion of a transparent medium influences the speed of light. This effect was first observed by Fizeau in 1851. Consider a light beam in water that moves with speed v in a horizontal pipe. Assume the light travels in the same direction as the water. The speed of light with respect to the water is c/n, where $n = 1.33$ is the index of refraction of water. (a) Use the velocity transformation equation to show that the speed of the light measured in the laboratory frame is

$$u = \frac{c}{n}\left(\frac{1 + nv/c}{1 + v/nc}\right)$$

(b) Show that for $v \ll c$, the expression from part (a) becomes, to a good approximation,

$$u \approx \frac{c}{n} + v - \frac{v}{n^2}$$

Argue for or against the view that we should expect the result to be $u = (c/n) + v$ according to the Galilean transformation and that the presence of the term $-v/n^2$ represents a relativistic effect appearing even at "nonrelativistic" speeds. (c) Evaluate u in the limit as the speed of the water approaches c.

59. A supertrain (proper length 100 m) travels at a speed of $0.950c$ as it passes through a tunnel (proper length 50.0 m). As seen by a trackside observer, is the train ever completely within the tunnel? If so, how much space is there to spare?

60. Imagine that the entire Sun collapses to a sphere of radius R_g such that the work required to remove a small mass m from the surface would be equal to its rest energy mc^2. This radius is called the *gravitational radius* for the Sun. Find R_g. The ultimate fate of very massive stars is thought to be collapsing beyond their gravitational radii into black holes.

61. ● A particle with electric charge q moves along a straight line in a uniform electric field $\vec{\mathbf{E}}$ with a speed of u. The electric force exerted on the charge is $q\vec{\mathbf{E}}$. The motion and the electric field are both in the x direction. (a) Show that the acceleration of the particle in the x direction is given by

$$a = \frac{du}{dt} = \frac{qE}{m}\left(1 - \frac{u^2}{c^2}\right)^{3/2}$$

(b) Discuss the significance of the dependence of the acceleration on the speed. (c) **What If?** If the particle starts from rest at $x = 0$ at $t = 0$, how would you proceed to find the speed of the particle and its position at time t?

62. An observer in a coasting spacecraft moves toward a mirror at speed v relative to the reference frame labeled by S in Figure P39.62. The mirror is stationary with respect to S. A light pulse emitted by the spacecraft travels toward the mirror and is reflected back to the spacecraft. The front of the spacecraft is a distance d from the mirror (as measured by observers in S) at the moment the light pulse leaves the spacecraft. What is the total travel time of the pulse as measured by observers in (a) the S frame and (b) the front of the spacecraft?

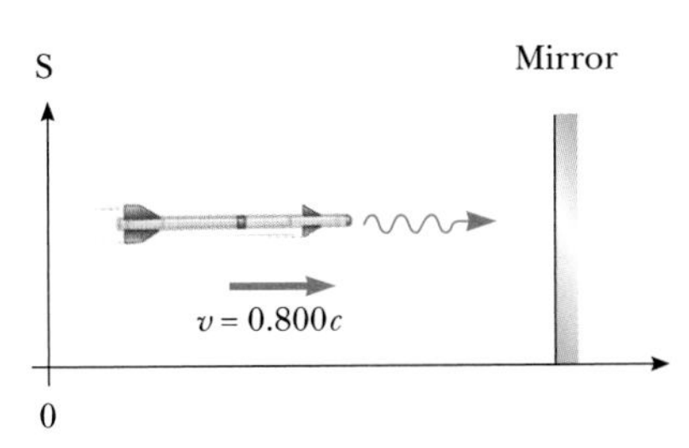

Figure P39.62

63. ● Massive stars ending their lives in supernova explosions produce the nuclei of all the atoms in the bottom half of the periodic table, by fusion of smaller nuclei. This problem roughly models that process. A particle of mass m moving along the x axis with a velocity component $+u$ collides head-on and sticks to a particle of mass $m/3$ moving along the x axis with the velocity component $-u$. (a) What is the mass M of the resulting particle? (b) Evaluate the expression from part (a) in the limit $u \to 0$. Explain whether the result agrees with what you should expect from nonrelativistic physics.

64. The creation and study of new elementary particles is an important part of contemporary physics. Especially interesting is the discovery of a very massive particle. To create a particle of mass M requires an energy Mc^2. With enough energy, an exotic particle can be created by allowing a fast-moving particle of ordinary matter, such as a proton, to collide with a similar target particle. Consider a perfectly inelastic collision between two protons: an incident proton with mass m_p, kinetic energy K, and momentum magnitude p joins with an originally stationary target proton to form a single product particle of mass M. You might think that the creation of a new product particle, nine times more massive than in a previous experiment, would require only nine times more energy for the incident proton. Unfortunately, not all the kinetic energy of the incoming proton is available to create the product particle because conservation of momentum requires that the system as a whole still must have some kinetic energy after the collision. Only a fraction of the energy of the incident particle is therefore available to create a new particle. In this problem, you must determine how the energy available for particle creation depends on the energy of the moving proton. Show that the energy available to create a product particle is given by

$$Mc^2 = 2m_pc^2\sqrt{1 + \frac{K}{2m_pc^2}}$$

This result shows that when the kinetic energy K of the incident proton is large compared with its rest energy m_pc^2, then M approaches $(2m_pK)^{1/2}/c$. Therefore, if the energy of the incoming proton is increased by a factor of 9, the mass you can create increases only by a factor of 3. This disappointing result is the main reason that most modern accelerators such as those at CERN (in Europe), at Fermilab (near Chicago), at SLAC (at Stanford), and at DESY (in Germany) use *colliding beams.* Here the total momentum of a pair of interacting particles can be zero. The center of mass can be at rest after the collision, so, in principle, all the initial kinetic energy can be used for particle creation, according to

$$Mc^2 = 2mc^2 + K = 2mc^2\left(1 + \frac{K}{2mc^2}\right)$$

where K is the total kinetic energy of two identical colliding particles. Here if $K \gg mc^2$, we have M directly proportional to K as we would desire. These machines are difficult to build and to operate, but they open new vistas in physics.

65. ● Suppose our Sun is about to explode. In an effort to escape, we depart in a spacecraft at $v = 0.800c$ and head toward the star Tau Ceti, 12.0 ly away. When we reach the midpoint of our journey from the Earth, we see our Sun explode, and, unfortunately, at the same instant we see Tau Ceti explode as well. (a) In the spacecraft's frame of reference, should we conclude that the two explosions occurred simultaneously? If not, which occurred first? (b) **What If?** In a frame of reference in which the Sun and Tau Ceti are at rest, did they explode simultaneously? If not, which exploded first?

66. Prepare a graph of the relativistic kinetic energy and the classical kinetic energy, both as a function of speed, for an object with a mass of your choice. At what speed does the classical kinetic energy underestimate the experimental value by 1%? By 5%? By 50%?

67. A ^{57}Fe nucleus at rest emits a 14.0-keV photon. Use conservation of energy and momentum to deduce the kinetic energy of the recoiling nucleus in electron volts. Use $Mc^2 = 8.60 \times 10^{-9}$ J for the final state of the ^{57}Fe nucleus.

Answers to Quick Quizzes

39.1 (c). Although the observers' measurements differ, both are correct.

39.2 (d). The Galilean velocity transformation gives us $u_x = u_x' + v = 90$ mi/h $+ 110$ mi/h $= 200$ mi/h.

39.3 (d). The two events (the pulse leaving the flashlight and the pulse hitting the far wall) take place at different locations for both observers, so neither measures the proper time interval.

39.4 (a). The two events are the beginning and the end of the movie, both of which take place at rest with respect to the spacecraft crew. Therefore, the crew measures the proper time interval of 2 h. Any observer in motion with respect to the spacecraft, which includes the observer on Earth, will measure a longer time interval due to time dilation.

39.5 (a). If their on-duty time is based on clocks that remain on the Earth, the astronauts will have larger paychecks. A shorter time interval will have passed for the astronauts in their frame of reference than for their employer back on the Earth.

39.6 (c). Both your body and your sleeping cabin are at rest in your reference frame; therefore, they will have their proper length according to you. There will be no change in measured lengths of objects, including yourself, within your spacecraft.

39.7 (d). Time dilation and length contraction depend only on the relative speed of one observer relative to another, not on whether the observers are receding or approaching each other.

39.8 **(i),** (c). Because of your motion toward the source of the light, the light beam has a horizontal component of velocity as measured by you. The magnitude of the vector sum of the horizontal and vertical component vectors must be equal to c, so the magnitude of the vertical component must be smaller than c. **(ii),** (a). In this case, there is only a horizontal component of the velocity of the light and you must measure a speed of c.

39.9 (a) $m_3 > m_2 = m_1$; the rest energy of particle 3 is $2E$, whereas it is E for particles 1 and 2. (b) $K_3 = K_2 > K_1$; the kinetic energy is the difference between the total energy and the rest energy. The kinetic energy is $4E - 2E = 2E$ for particle 3, $3E - E = 2E$ for particle 2, and $2E - E = E$ for particle 1. (c) $u_2 > u_3 = u_1$; from Equation 39.26, $E = \gamma E_R$. Solving for the square of the particle speed u, we find that $u^2 = c^2(1 - (E_R/E)^2)$. Therefore, the particle with the smallest ratio of rest energy to total energy will have the largest speed. Particles 1 and 3 have the same ratio as each other, and the ratio of particle 2 is smaller.

TABLE A.1

Conversion Factors

Length

	m	cm	km	in.	ft	mi
1 meter	1	10^2	10^{-3}	39.37	3.281	6.214×10^{-4}
1 centimeter	10^{-2}	1	10^{-5}	0.393 7	3.281×10^{-2}	6.214×10^{-6}
1 kilometer	10^3	10^5	1	3.937×10^4	3.281×10^3	0.621 4
1 inch	2.540×10^{-2}	2.540	2.540×10^{-5}	1	8.333×10^{-2}	1.578×10^{-5}
1 foot	0.304 8	30.48	3.048×10^{-4}	12	1	1.894×10^{-4}
1 mile	1 609	1.609×10^5	1.609	6.336×10^4	5 280	1

Mass

	kg	g	slug	u
1 kilogram	1	10^3	6.852×10^{-2}	6.024×10^{26}
1 gram	10^{-3}	1	6.852×10^{-5}	6.024×10^{23}
1 slug	14.59	1.459×10^4	1	8.789×10^{27}
1 atomic mass unit	1.660×10^{-27}	1.660×10^{-24}	1.137×10^{-28}	1

Note: 1 metric ton = 1 000 kg.

Time

	s	min	h	day	yr
1 second	1	1.667×10^{-2}	2.778×10^{-4}	1.157×10^{-5}	3.169×10^{-8}
1 minute	60	1	1.667×10^{-2}	6.994×10^{-4}	1.901×10^{-6}
1 hour	3 600	60	1	4.167×10^{-2}	1.141×10^{-4}
1 day	8.640×10^4	1 440	24	1	2.738×10^{-5}
1 year	3.156×10^7	5.259×10^5	8.766×10^3	365.2	1

Speed

	m/s	cm/s	ft/s	mi/h
1 meter per second	1	10^2	3.281	2.237
1 centimeter per second	10^{-2}	1	3.281×10^{-2}	2.237×10^{-2}
1 foot per second	0.304 8	30.48	1	0.681 8
1 mile per hour	0.447 0	44.70	1.467	1

Note: 1 mi/min = 60 mi/h = 88 ft/s.

Force

	N	lb
1 newton	1	0.224 8
1 pound	4.448	1

(*Continued*)

TABLE A.1

Conversion Factors *(Continued)*

Energy, Energy Transfer

	J	ft · lb	eV
1 joule	1	0.737 6	6.242×10^{18}
1 foot-pound	1.356	1	8.464×10^{18}
1 electron volt	1.602×10^{-19}	1.182×10^{-19}	1
1 calorie	4.186	3.087	2.613×10^{19}
1 British thermal unit	1.055×10^{3}	7.779×10^{2}	6.585×10^{21}
1 kilowatt-hour	3.600×10^{6}	2.655×10^{6}	2.247×10^{25}

	cal	Btu	kWh
1 joule	0.238 9	9.481×10^{-4}	2.778×10^{-7}
1 foot-pound	0.323 9	1.285×10^{-3}	3.766×10^{-7}
1 electron volt	3.827×10^{-20}	1.519×10^{-22}	4.450×10^{-26}
1 calorie	1	3.968×10^{-3}	1.163×10^{-6}
1 British thermal unit	2.520×10^{2}	1	2.930×10^{-4}
1 kilowatt-hour	8.601×10^{5}	3.413×10^{2}	1

Pressure

	Pa	atm
1 pascal	1	9.869×10^{-6}
1 atmosphere	1.013×10^{5}	1
1 centimeter mercury[a]	1.333×10^{3}	1.316×10^{-2}
1 pound per square inch	6.895×10^{3}	6.805×10^{-2}
1 pound per square foot	47.88	4.725×10^{-4}

	cm Hg	lb/in.^{2}	lb/ft^2
1 pascal	7.501×10^{-4}	1.450×10^{-4}	2.089×10^{-2}
1 atmosphere	76	14.70	2.116×10^{3}
1 centimeter mercury[a]	1	0.194 3	27.85
1 pound per square inch	5.171	1	144
1 pound per square foot	3.591×10^{-2}	6.944×10^{-3}	1

[a]At 0°C and at a location where the free-fall acceleration has its "standard" value, 9.806 65 m/s^2.

TABLE A.2

Symbols, Dimensions, and Units of Physical Quantities

Quantity	Common Symbol	Unit[a]	Dimensions[b]	Unit in Terms of Base SI Units
Acceleration	$\vec{\mathbf{a}}$	m/s^2	L/T^2	m/s^2
Amount of substance	n	MOLE		mol
Angle	θ, ϕ	radian (rad)	1	
Angular acceleration	$\vec{\alpha}$	rad/s^2	T^{-2}	s^{-2}
Angular frequency	ω	rad/s	T^{-1}	s^{-1}
Angular momentum	$\vec{\mathbf{L}}$	kg · m^2/s	ML^2/T	kg · m^2/s
Angular velocity	$\vec{\omega}$	rad/s	T^{-1}	s^{-1}
Area	A	m^2	L^2	m^2
Atomic number	Z			
Capacitance	C	farad (F)	Q^{2}T^2/ML^2	A^2 · s^4/kg · m^2
Charge	q, Q, e	coulomb (C)	Q	A · s

(Continued)

TABLE A.2

Symbols, Dimensions, and Units of Physical Quantities *(Continued)*

Quantity	Common Symbol	Unit[a]	Dimensions[b]	Unit in Terms of Base SI Units
Charge density				
Line	λ	C/m	Q/L	A · s/m
Surface	σ	C/m^2	Q/L^2	A · s/m^2
Volume	ρ	C/m^3	Q/L^3	A · s/m^3
Conductivity	σ	1/Ω · m	Q^{2}T/ML^3	A^2 · s^3/kg · m^3
Current	I	AMPERE	Q/T	A
Current density	J	A/m^2	Q/TL^2	A/m^2
Density	ρ	kg/m^3	M/L^3	kg/m^3
Dielectric constant	κ			
Electric dipole moment	$\vec{\mathbf{p}}$	C · m	QL	A · s · m
Electric field	$\vec{\mathbf{E}}$	V/m	ML/QT^2	kg · m/A · s^3
Electric flux	Φ_E	V · m	ML^3/QT^2	kg · m^3/A · s^3
Electromotive force	$\mathcal{E}$	volt (V)	ML^2/QT^2	kg · m^2/A · s^3
Energy	E, U, K	joule (J)	ML^2/T^2	kg · m^2/s^2
Entropy	S	J/K	ML^2/T^{2}K	kg · m^2/s^2 · K
Force	$\vec{\mathbf{F}}$	newton (N)	ML/T^2	kg · m/s^2
Frequency	f	hertz (Hz)	T^{-1}	s^{-1}
Heat	Q	joule (J)	ML^2/T^2	kg · m^2/s^2
Inductance	L	henry (H)	ML^2/Q^2	kg · m^2/A^2 · s^2
Length	ℓ, L	METER	L	m
Displacement	$\Delta x, \Delta\vec{\mathbf{r}}$			
Distance	d, h			
Position	$x, y, z, \vec{\mathbf{r}}$			
Magnetic dipole moment	$\vec{\boldsymbol{\mu}}$	N · m/T	QL^2/T	A · m^2
Magnetic field	$\vec{\mathbf{B}}$	tesla (T) (= Wb/m^2)	M/QT	kg/A · s^2
Magnetic flux	Φ_B	weber (Wb)	ML^2/QT	kg · m^2/A · s^2
Mass	m, M	KILOGRAM	M	kg
Molar specific heat	C	J/mol · K		kg · m^2/s^2 · mol · K
Moment of inertia	I	kg · m^2	ML^2	kg · m^2
Momentum	$\vec{\mathbf{p}}$	kg · m/s	ML/T	kg · m/s
Period	T	s	T	s
Permeability of free space	μ_0	N/A^2 (= H/m)	ML/Q^2	kg · m/A^2 · s^2
Permittivity of free space	ϵ_0	C^2/N · m^2 (= F/m)	Q^{2}T^2/ML^3	A^2 · s^4/kg · m^3
Potential	V	volt (V) (= J/C)	ML^2/QT^2	kg · m^2/A · s^3
Power	$\mathcal{P}$	watt (W) (= J/s)	ML^2/T^3	kg · m^2/s^3
Pressure	P	pascal (Pa) (= N/m^2)	M/LT^2	kg/m · s^2
Resistance	R	ohm (Ω) (= V/A)	ML^2/Q^{2}T	kg · m^2/A^2 · s^3
Specific heat	c	J/kg · K	L^2/T^{2}K	m^2/s^2 · K
Speed	v	m/s	L/T	m/s
Temperature	T	KELVIN	K	K
Time	t	SECOND	T	s
Torque	$\vec{\boldsymbol{\tau}}$	N · m	ML^2/T^2	kg · m^2/s^2
Velocity	$\vec{\mathbf{v}}$	m/s	L/T	m/s
Volume	V	m^3	L^3	m^3
Wavelength	λ	m	L	m
Work	W	joule (J) (= N · m)	ML^2/T^2	kg · m^2/s^2

[a]The base SI units are given in uppercase letters.

[b]The symbols M, L, T, K, and Q denote mass, length, time, temperature, and charge, respectively.

This appendix in mathematics is intended as a brief review of operations and methods. Early in this course, you should be totally familiar with basic algebraic techniques, analytic geometry, and trigonometry. The sections on differential and integral calculus are more detailed and are intended for students who have difficulty applying calculus concepts to physical situations.

B.1 Scientific Notation

Many quantities used by scientists often have very large or very small values. The speed of light, for example, is about 300 000 000 m/s, and the ink required to make the dot over an *i* in this textbook has a mass of about 0.000 000 001 kg. Obviously, it is very cumbersome to read, write, and keep track of such numbers. We avoid this problem by using a method incorporating powers of the number 10:

$$10^0 = 1$$

$$10^1 = 10$$

$$10^2 = 10 \times 10 = 100$$

$$10^3 = 10 \times 10 \times 10 = 1\,000$$

$$10^4 = 10 \times 10 \times 10 \times 10 = 10\,000$$

$$10^5 = 10 \times 10 \times 10 \times 10 \times 10 = 100\,000$$

and so on. The number of zeros corresponds to the power to which ten is raised, called the **exponent** of ten. For example, the speed of light, 300 000 000 m/s, can be expressed as 3.00×10^8 m/s.

In this method, some representative numbers smaller than unity are the following:

$$10^{-1} = \frac{1}{10} = 0.1$$

$$10^{-2} = \frac{1}{10 \times 10} = 0.01$$

$$10^{-3} = \frac{1}{10 \times 10 \times 10} = 0.001$$

$$10^{-4} = \frac{1}{10 \times 10 \times 10 \times 10} = 0.000\,1$$

$$10^{-5} = \frac{1}{10 \times 10 \times 10 \times 10 \times 10} = 0.000\,01$$

In these cases, the number of places the decimal point is to the left of the digit 1 equals the value of the (negative) exponent. Numbers expressed as some power of ten multiplied by another number between one and ten are said to be in **scientific notation.** For example, the scientific notation for 5 943 000 000 is 5.943×10^9 and that for 0.000 083 2 is 8.32×10^{-5}.

When numbers expressed in scientific notation are being multiplied, the following general rule is very useful:

$$10^n \times 10^m = 10^{n+m} \qquad \textbf{(B.1)}$$

where n and m can be *any* numbers (not necessarily integers). For example, $10^2 \times 10^5 = 10^7$. The rule also applies if one of the exponents is negative: $10^3 \times 10^{-8} = 10^{-5}$.

When dividing numbers expressed in scientific notation, note that

$$\frac{10^n}{10^m} = 10^n \times 10^{-m} = 10^{n-m} \qquad \textbf{(B.2)}$$

Exercises

With help from the preceding rules, verify the answers to the following equations:

1. $86\,400 = 8.64 \times 10^4$
2. $9\,816\,762.5 = 9.816\,762\,5 \times 10^6$
3. $0.000\,000\,039\,8 = 3.98 \times 10^{-8}$
4. $(4.0 \times 10^8)(9.0 \times 10^9) = 3.6 \times 10^{18}$
5. $(3.0 \times 10^7)(6.0 \times 10^{-12}) = 1.8 \times 10^{-4}$
6. $\dfrac{75 \times 10^{-11}}{5.0 \times 10^{-3}} = 1.5 \times 10^{-7}$
7. $\dfrac{(3 \times 10^6)(8 \times 10^{-2})}{(2 \times 10^{17})(6 \times 10^5)} = 2 \times 10^{-18}$

B.2 Algebra

Some Basic Rules

When algebraic operations are performed, the laws of arithmetic apply. Symbols such as x, y, and z are usually used to represent unspecified quantities, called the **unknowns.**

First, consider the equation

$$8x = 32$$

If we wish to solve for x, we can divide (or multiply) each side of the equation by the same factor without destroying the equality. In this case, if we divide both sides by 8, we have

$$\frac{8x}{8} = \frac{32}{8}$$

$$x = 4$$

Next consider the equation

$$x + 2 = 8$$

In this type of expression, we can add or subtract the same quantity from each side. If we subtract 2 from each side, we have

$$x + 2 - 2 = 8 - 2$$

$$x = 6$$

In general, if $x + a = b$, then $x = b - a$.

Now consider the equation

$$\frac{x}{5} = 9$$

If we multiply each side by 5, we are left with x on the left by itself and 45 on the right:

$$\left(\frac{x}{5}\right)(5) = 9 \times 5$$

$$x = 45$$

In all cases, *whatever operation is performed on the left side of the equality must also be performed on the right side.*

The following rules for multiplying, dividing, adding, and subtracting fractions should be recalled, where a, b, c, and d are four numbers:

	Rule	Example
Multiplying	$\left(\frac{a}{b}\right)\left(\frac{c}{d}\right) = \frac{ac}{bd}$	$\left(\frac{2}{3}\right)\left(\frac{4}{5}\right) = \frac{8}{15}$
Dividing	$\frac{(a/b)}{(c/d)} = \frac{ad}{bc}$	$\frac{2/3}{4/5} = \frac{(2)(5)}{(4)(3)} = \frac{10}{12}$
Adding	$\frac{a}{b} \pm \frac{c}{d} = \frac{ad \pm bc}{bd}$	$\frac{2}{3} - \frac{4}{5} = \frac{(2)(5) - (4)(3)}{(3)(5)} = -\frac{2}{15}$

Exercises

In the following exercises, solve for x.

	Answers
1. $a = \frac{1}{1+x}$	$x = \frac{1-a}{a}$
2. $3x - 5 = 13$	$x = 6$
3. $ax - 5 = bx + 2$	$x = \frac{7}{a-b}$
4. $\frac{5}{2x+6} = \frac{3}{4x+8}$	$x = -\frac{11}{7}$

Powers

When powers of a given quantity x are multiplied, the following rule applies:

$$x^n x^m = x^{n+m} \quad \textbf{(B.3)}$$

For example, $x^2x^4 = x^{2+4} = x^6$.

When dividing the powers of a given quantity, the rule is

$$\frac{x^n}{x^m} = x^{n-m} \quad \textbf{(B.4)}$$

For example, $x^8/x^2 = x^{8-2} = x^6$.

A power that is a fraction, such as $\frac{1}{3}$, corresponds to a root as follows:

$$x^{1/n} = \sqrt[n]{x} \quad \textbf{(B.5)}$$

For example, $4^{1/3} = \sqrt[3]{4} = 1.587\,4$. (A scientific calculator is useful for such calculations.)

Finally, any quantity x^n raised to the mth power is

$$(x^n)^m = x^{nm} \quad \textbf{(B.6)}$$

Table B.1 summarizes the rules of exponents.

TABLE B.1

Rules of Exponents
$x^0 = 1$
$x^1 = x$
$x^n x^m = x^{n+m}$
$x^n/x^m = x^{n-m}$
$x^{1/n} = \sqrt[n]{x}$
$(x^n)^m = x^{nm}$

Exercises

Verify the following equations:

1. $3^2 \times 3^3 = 243$
2. $x^5x^{-8} = x^{-3}$
3. $x^{10}/x^{-5} = x^{15}$
4. $5^{1/3} = 1.709\,976$ (Use your calculator.)
5. $60^{1/4} = 2.783\,158$ (Use your calculator.)
6. $(x^4)^3 = x^{12}$

Factoring

Some useful formulas for factoring an equation are the following:

$ax + ay + az = a(x + y + z)$ common factor

$a^2 + 2ab + b^2 = (a + b)^2$ perfect square

$a^2 - b^2 = (a + b)(a - b)$ differences of squares

Quadratic Equations

The general form of a quadratic equation is

$$ax^2 + bx + c = 0 \quad \textbf{(B.7)}$$

where x is the unknown quantity and a, b, and c are numerical factors referred to as **coefficients** of the equation. This equation has two roots, given by

$$x = \frac{-b \pm \sqrt{b^2 - 4ac}}{2a} \quad \textbf{(B.8)}$$

If $b^2 \geq 4ac$, the roots are real.

EXAMPLE B.1

The equation $x^2 + 5x + 4 = 0$ has the following roots corresponding to the two signs of the square-root term:

$$x = \frac{-5 \pm \sqrt{5^2 - (4)(1)(4)}}{2(1)} = \frac{-5 \pm \sqrt{9}}{2} = \frac{-5 \pm 3}{2}$$

$$x_+ = \frac{-5 + 3}{2} = -1 \qquad x_- = \frac{-5 - 3}{2} = -4$$

where x_+ refers to the root corresponding to the positive sign and x_- refers to the root corresponding to the negative sign.

Exercises

Solve the following quadratic equations:

		Answers	
1.	$x^2 + 2x - 3 = 0$	$x_+ = 1$	$x_- = -3$
2.	$2x^2 - 5x + 2 = 0$	$x_+ = 2$	$x_- = \frac{1}{2}$
3.	$2x^2 - 4x - 9 = 0$	$x_+ = 1 + \sqrt{22}/2$	$x_- = 1 - \sqrt{22}/2$

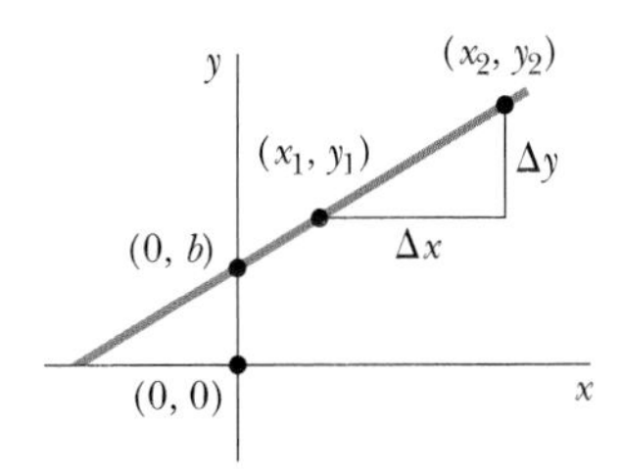

Figure B.1 A straight line graphed on an xy coordinate system. The slope of the line is the ratio of Δy to Δx.

Linear Equations

A linear equation has the general form

$$y = mx + b \quad \textbf{(B.9)}$$

where m and b are constants. This equation is referred to as linear because the graph of y versus x is a straight line as shown in Figure B.1. The constant b, called the ***y*-intercept,** represents the value of y at which the straight line intersects the y axis. The constant m is equal to the **slope** of the straight line. If any two points on the straight line are specified by the coordinates (x_1, y_1) and (x_2, y_2) as in Figure B.1, the slope of the straight line can be expressed as

$$\text{Slope} = \frac{y_2 - y_1}{x_2 - x_1} = \frac{\Delta y}{\Delta x} \quad \textbf{(B.10)}$$

Note that m and b can have either positive or negative values. If $m > 0$, the straight line has a *positive* slope as in Figure B.1. If $m < 0$, the straight line has a *negative* slope. In Figure B.1, both m and b are positive. Three other possible situations are shown in Figure B.2.

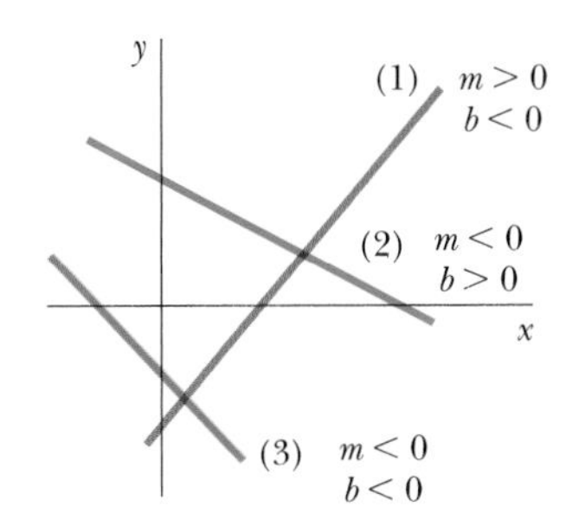

Figure B.2 The brown line has a positive slope and a negative y-intercept. The blue line has a negative slope and a positive y-intercept. The green line has a negative slope and a negative y-intercept.

Exercises

1. Draw graphs of the following straight lines: (a) $y = 5x + 3$ (b) $y = -2x + 4$ (c) $y = -3x - 6$
2. Find the slopes of the straight lines described in Exercise 1.

Answers (a) 5 (b) -2 (c) -3

3. Find the slopes of the straight lines that pass through the following sets of points: (a) $(0, -4)$ and $(4, 2)$ (b) $(0, 0)$ and $(2, -5)$ (c) $(-5, 2)$ and $(4, -2)$

Answers (a) $\frac{3}{2}$ (b) $-\frac{5}{2}$ (c) $-\frac{4}{9}$

Solving Simultaneous Linear Equations

Consider the equation $3x + 5y = 15$, which has two unknowns, x and y. Such an equation does not have a unique solution. For example, $(x = 0, y = 3)$, $(x = 5, y = 0)$, and $(x = 2, y = \frac{9}{5})$ are all solutions to this equation.

If a problem has two unknowns, a unique solution is possible only if we have *two* equations. In general, if a problem has n unknowns, its solution requires n equations. To solve two simultaneous equations involving two unknowns, x and y, we solve one of the equations for x in terms of y and substitute this expression into the other equation.

EXAMPLE B.2

Solve the two simultaneous equations

$$(1) \qquad 5x + y = -8$$

$$(2) \qquad 2x - 2y = 4$$

Solution From Equation (2), $x = y + 2$. Substitution of this equation into Equation (1) gives

$$5(y + 2) + y = -8$$

$$6y = -18$$

$$y = -3$$

$$x = y + 2 = -1$$

Alternative Solution Multiply each term in Equation (1) by the factor 2 and add the result to Equation (2):

$$10x + 2y = -16$$

$$2x - 2y = 4$$

$$12x = -12$$

$$x = -1$$

$$y = x - 2 = -3$$

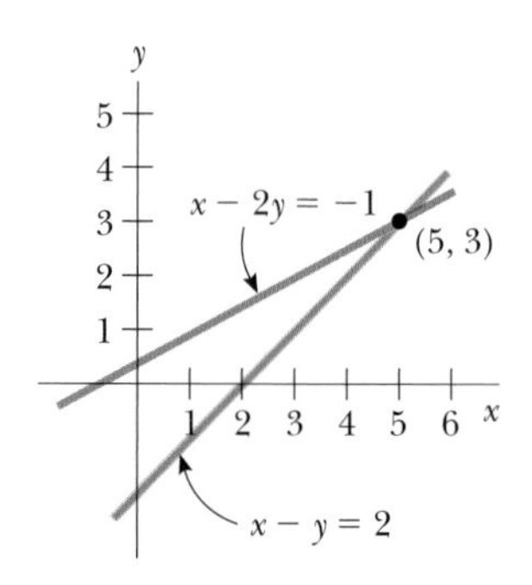

Figure B.3 A graphical solution for two linear equations.

Two linear equations containing two unknowns can also be solved by a graphical method. If the straight lines corresponding to the two equations are plotted in a conventional coordinate system, the intersection of the two lines represents the solution. For example, consider the two equations

$$x - y = 2$$

$$x - 2y = -1$$

These equations are plotted in Figure B.3. The intersection of the two lines has the coordinates $x = 5$ and $y = 3$, which represents the solution to the equations. You should check this solution by the analytical technique discussed earlier.

Exercises

Solve the following pairs of simultaneous equations involving two unknowns:

	Answers
1. $x + y = 8$ $x - y = 2$	$x = 5,\ y = 3$
2. $98 - T = 10a$ $T - 49 = 5a$	$T = 65,\ a = 3.27$
3. $6x + 2y = 6$ $8x - 4y = 28$	$x = 2,\ y = -3$

Logarithms

Suppose a quantity x is expressed as a power of some quantity a:

$$x = a^y \tag{B.11}$$

The number a is called the **base** number. The **logarithm** of x with respect to the base a is equal to the exponent to which the base must be raised to satisfy the expression $x = a^y$:

$$y = \log_a x \tag{B.12}$$

Conversely, the **antilogarithm** of y is the number x:

$$x = \text{antilog}_a\ y \tag{B.13}$$

In practice, the two bases most often used are base 10, called the *common* logarithm base, and base $e = 2.718\,282$, called Euler's constant or the *natural* logarithm base. When common logarithms are used,

$$y = \log_{10} x \quad (\text{or } x = 10^y) \tag{B.14}$$

When natural logarithms are used,

$$y = \ln x \quad (\text{or } x = e^y) \tag{B.15}$$

For example, $\log_{10} 52 = 1.716$, so $\text{antilog}_{10} 1.716 = 10^{1.716} = 52$. Likewise, $\ln 52 = 3.951$, so $\text{antiln } 3.951 = e^{3.951} = 52$.

In general, note you can convert between base 10 and base e with the equality

$$\ln x = (2.302\,585) \log_{10} x \tag{B.16}$$

Finally, some useful properties of logarithms are the following:

$$\left.\begin{aligned} \log(ab) &= \log a + \log b \\ \log(a/b) &= \log a - \log b \\ \log(a^n) &= n \log a \end{aligned}\right\} \text{any base}$$

$$\ln e = 1$$

$$\ln e^a = a$$

$$\ln\left(\frac{1}{a}\right) = -\ln a$$

B.3 Geometry

The **distance** d between two points having coordinates (x_1, y_1) and (x_2, y_2) is

$$d = \sqrt{(x_2 - x_1)^2 + (y_2 - y_1)^2} \tag{B.17}$$

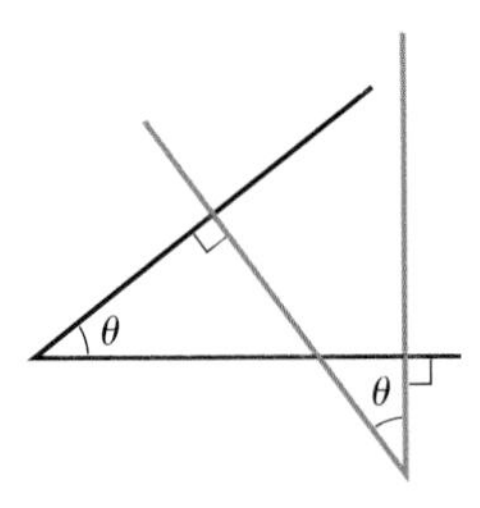

Figure B.4 The angles are equal because their sides are perpendicular.

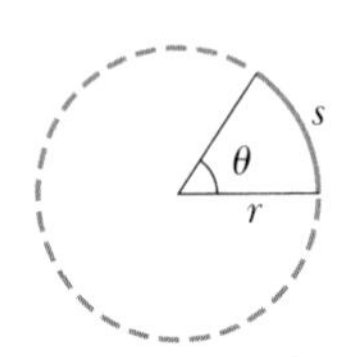

Figure B.5 The angle θ in radians is the ratio of the arc length s to the radius r of the circle.

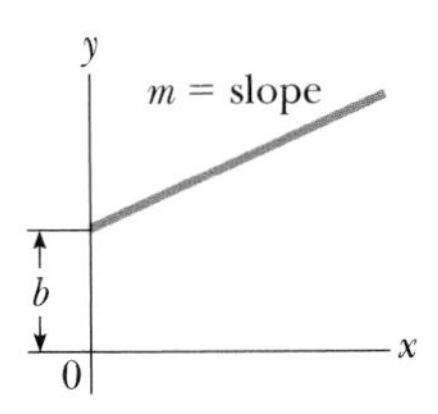

Figure B.6 A straight line with a slope of m and a y-intercept of b.

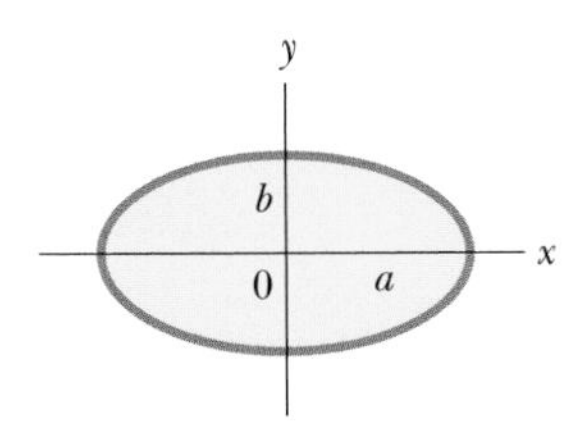

Figure B.7 An ellipse with semimajor axis a and semiminor axis b.

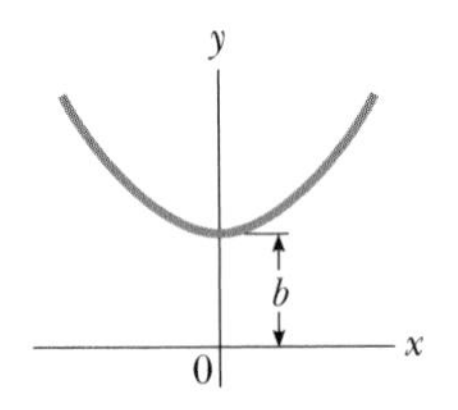

Figure B.8 A parabola with its vertex at $y = b$.

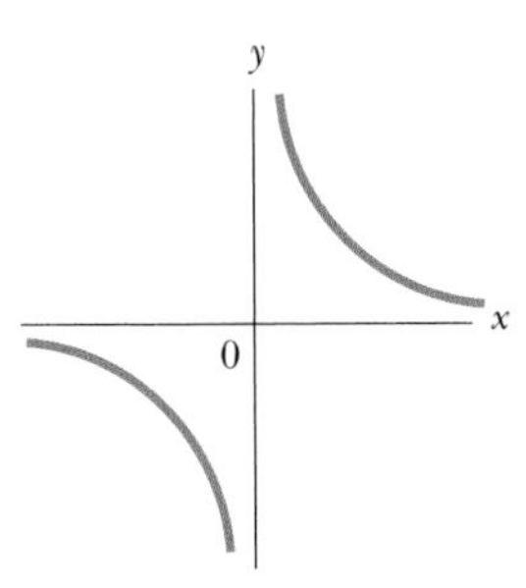

Figure B.9 A hyperbola.

TABLE B.2

Useful Information for Geometry

Shape	Area or Volume	Shape	Area or Volume
Rectangle (ℓ, w)	Area $= \ell w$	Sphere (r)	Surface area $= 4\pi r^2$ Volume $= \dfrac{4\pi r^3}{3}$
Circle (r)	Area $= \pi r^2$ Circumference $= 2\pi r$	Cylinder (r, ℓ)	Lateral surface area $= 2\pi r\ell$ Volume $= \pi r^2\ell$
Triangle (b, h)	Area $= \frac{1}{2}bh$	Rectangular box (ℓ, w, h)	Surface area $= 2(\ell h + \ell w + hw)$ Volume $= \ell wh$

Two angles are equal if their sides are perpendicular, right side to right side and left side to left side. For example, the two angles marked θ in Figure B.4 are the same because of the perpendicularity of the sides of the angles. To distinguish the left and right sides of an angle, imagine standing at the angle's apex and facing into the angle.

Radian measure: The arc length s of a circular arc (Fig. B.5) is proportional to the radius r for a fixed value of θ (in radians):

$$s = r\theta \qquad \theta = \frac{s}{r} \tag{B.18}$$

Table B.2 gives the **areas** and **volumes** for several geometric shapes used throughout this text.

The equation of a **straight line** (Fig. B.6) is

$$y = mx + b \tag{B.19}$$

where b is the y-intercept and m is the slope of the line.

The equation of a **circle** of radius R centered at the origin is

$$x^2 + y^2 = R^2 \tag{B.20}$$

The equation of an **ellipse** having the origin at its center (Fig. B.7) is

$$\frac{x^2}{a^2} + \frac{y^2}{b^2} = 1 \tag{B.21}$$

where a is the length of the semimajor axis (the longer one) and b is the length of the semiminor axis (the shorter one).

The equation of a **parabola** the vertex of which is at $y = b$ (Fig. B.8) is

$$y = ax^2 + b \tag{B.22}$$

The equation of a **rectangular hyperbola** (Fig. B.9) is

$$xy = \text{constant} \tag{B.23}$$

B.4 Trigonometry

That portion of mathematics based on the special properties of the right triangle is called trigonometry. By definition, a right triangle is a triangle containing a 90° angle. Consider the right triangle shown in Figure B.10, where side a is opposite the angle θ, side b is adjacent to the angle θ, and side c is the hypotenuse of the triangle. The three basic trigonometric functions defined by such a triangle are the sine (sin), cosine (cos), and tangent (tan). In terms of the angle θ, these functions are defined as follows:

$$\sin\theta = \frac{\text{side opposite } \theta}{\text{hypotenuse}} = \frac{a}{c} \quad \textbf{(B.24)}$$

$$\cos\theta = \frac{\text{side adjacent to } \theta}{\text{hypotenuse}} = \frac{b}{c} \quad \textbf{(B.25)}$$

$$\tan\theta = \frac{\text{side opposite } \theta}{\text{side adjacent to } \theta} = \frac{a}{b} \quad \textbf{(B.26)}$$

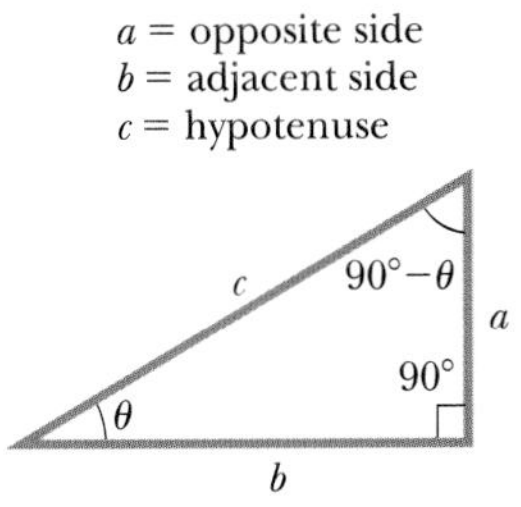

a = opposite side
b = adjacent side
c = hypotenuse

Figure B.10 A right triangle, used to define the basic functions of trigonometry.

The Pythagorean theorem provides the following relationship among the sides of a right triangle:

$$c^2 = a^2 + b^2 \quad \textbf{(B.27)}$$

From the preceding definitions and the Pythagorean theorem, it follows that

$$\sin^2\theta + \cos^2\theta = 1$$

$$\tan\theta = \frac{\sin\theta}{\cos\theta}$$

The cosecant, secant, and cotangent functions are defined by

$$\csc\theta = \frac{1}{\sin\theta} \qquad \sec\theta = \frac{1}{\cos\theta} \qquad \cot\theta = \frac{1}{\tan\theta}$$

The following relationships are derived directly from the right triangle shown in Figure B.10:

$$\sin\theta = \cos(90^\circ - \theta)$$

$$\cos\theta = \sin(90^\circ - \theta)$$

$$\cot\theta = \tan(90^\circ - \theta)$$

Some properties of trigonometric functions are the following:

$$\sin(-\theta) = -\sin\theta$$

$$\cos(-\theta) = \cos\theta$$

$$\tan(-\theta) = -\tan\theta$$

The following relationships apply to *any* triangle as shown in Figure B.11:

$$\alpha + \beta + \gamma = 180^\circ$$

$$\text{Law of cosines} \begin{cases} a^2 = b^2 + c^2 - 2bc\cos\alpha \\ b^2 = a^2 + c^2 - 2ac\cos\beta \\ c^2 = a^2 + b^2 - 2ab\cos\gamma \end{cases}$$

$$\text{Law of sines} \qquad \frac{a}{\sin\alpha} = \frac{b}{\sin\beta} = \frac{c}{\sin\gamma}$$

Table B.3 (page A-12) lists a number of useful trigonometric identities.

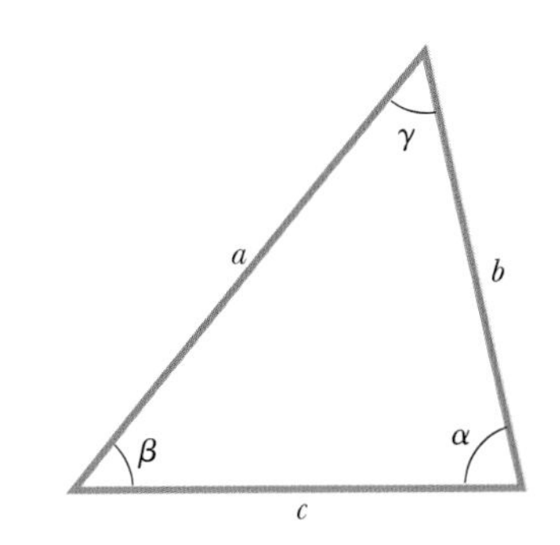

Figure B.11 An arbitrary, nonright triangle.

EXAMPLE B.3

Consider the right triangle in Figure B.12 in which $a = 2.00$, $b = 5.00$, and c is unknown. From the Pythagorean theorem, we have

$$c^2 = a^2 + b^2 = 2.00^2 + 5.00^2 = 4.00 + 25.0 = 29.0$$

$$c = \sqrt{29.0} = 5.39$$

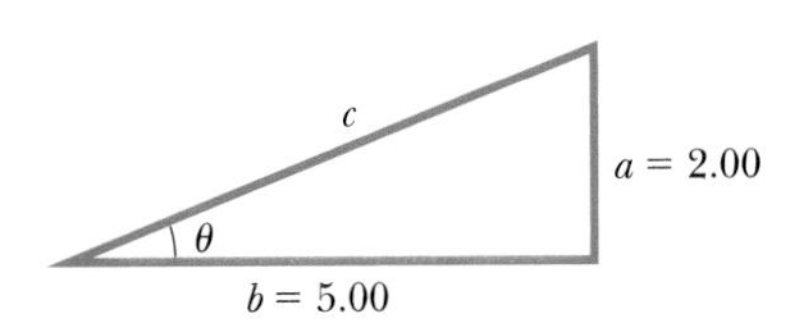

Figure B.12 (Example B.3)

To find the angle θ, note that

$$\tan \theta = \frac{a}{b} = \frac{2.00}{5.00} = 0.400$$

Using a calculator, we find that

$$\theta = \tan^{-1}(0.400) = 21.8°$$

where $\tan^{-1}(0.400)$ is the notation for "angle whose tangent is 0.400," sometimes written as arctan (0.400).

TABLE B.3

Some Trigonometric Identities

$\sin^2\theta + \cos^2\theta = 1$	$\csc^2\theta = 1 + \cot^2\theta$
$\sec^2\theta = 1 + \tan^2\theta$	$\sin^2\frac{\theta}{2} = \frac{1}{2}(1 - \cos\theta)$
$\sin 2\theta = 2\sin\theta\cos\theta$	$\cos^2\frac{\theta}{2} = \frac{1}{2}(1 + \cos\theta)$
$\cos 2\theta = \cos^2\theta - \sin^2\theta$	$1 - \cos\theta = 2\sin^2\frac{\theta}{2}$
$\tan 2\theta = \frac{2\tan\theta}{1 - \tan^2\theta}$	$\tan\frac{\theta}{2} = \sqrt{\frac{1 - \cos\theta}{1 + \cos\theta}}$

$\sin(A \pm B) = \sin A\cos B \pm \cos A\sin B$

$\cos(A \pm B) = \cos A\cos B \mp \sin A\sin B$

$\sin A \pm \sin B = 2\sin\left[\frac{1}{2}(A \pm B)\right]\cos\left[\frac{1}{2}(A \mp B)\right]$

$\cos A + \cos B = 2\cos\left[\frac{1}{2}(A + B)\right]\cos\left[\frac{1}{2}(A - B)\right]$

$\cos A - \cos B = 2\sin\left[\frac{1}{2}(A + B)\right]\sin\left[\frac{1}{2}(B - A)\right]$

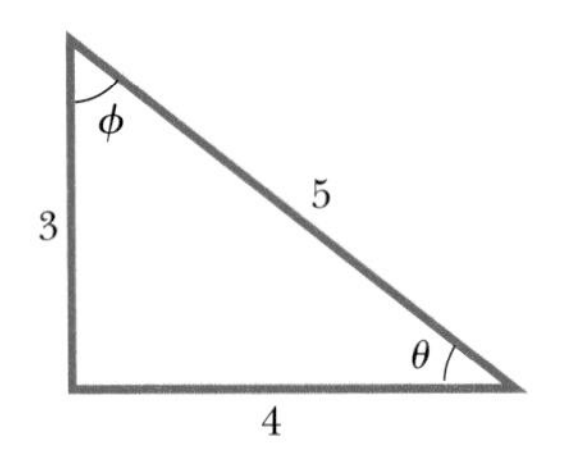

Figure B.13 (Exercise 1)

Exercises

1. In Figure B.13, identify (a) the side opposite θ (b) the side adjacent to ϕ and then find (c) $\cos\theta$, (d) $\sin\phi$, and (e) $\tan\phi$.

Answers (a) 3 (b) 3 (c) $\frac{4}{5}$ (d) $\frac{4}{5}$ (e) $\frac{4}{3}$

2. In a certain right triangle, the two sides that are perpendicular to each other are 5.00 m and 7.00 m long. What is the length of the third side?

Answer 8.60 m

3. A right triangle has a hypotenuse of length 3.0 m, and one of its angles is 30°. (a) What is the length of the side opposite the 30° angle? (b) What is the side adjacent to the 30° angle?

Answers (a) 1.5 m (b) 2.6 m

B.5 Series Expansions

$$(a + b)^n = a^n + \frac{n}{1!}a^{n-1}b + \frac{n(n-1)}{2!}a^{n-2}b^2 + \cdots$$

$$(1 + x)^n = 1 + nx + \frac{n(n-1)}{2!}x^2 + \cdots$$

$$e^x = 1 + x + \frac{x^2}{2!} + \frac{x^3}{3!} + \cdots$$

$$\ln(1 \pm x) = \pm x - \tfrac{1}{2}x^2 \pm \tfrac{1}{3}x^3 - \cdots$$

$$\left.\begin{aligned} \sin x &= x - \frac{x^3}{3!} + \frac{x^5}{5!} - \cdots \\ \cos x &= 1 - \frac{x^2}{2!} + \frac{x^4}{4!} - \cdots \\ \tan x &= x + \frac{x^3}{3} + \frac{2x^5}{15} + \cdots \quad |x| < \frac{\pi}{2} \end{aligned}\right\} x \text{ in radians}$$

For $x \ll 1$, the following approximations can be used:[1]

$$(1 + x)^n \approx 1 + nx \qquad \sin x \approx x$$

$$e^x \approx 1 + x \qquad \cos x \approx 1$$

$$\ln(1 \pm x) \approx \pm x \qquad \tan x \approx x$$

B.6 Differential Calculus

In various branches of science, it is sometimes necessary to use the basic tools of calculus, invented by Newton, to describe physical phenomena. The use of calculus is fundamental in the treatment of various problems in Newtonian mechanics, electricity, and magnetism. In this section, we simply state some basic properties and "rules of thumb" that should be a useful review to the student.

First, a **function** must be specified that relates one variable to another (e.g., a coordinate as a function of time). Suppose one of the variables is called y (the dependent variable), and the other x (the independent variable). We might have a function relationship such as

$$y(x) = ax^3 + bx^2 + cx + d$$

If a, b, c, and d are specified constants, y can be calculated for any value of x. We usually deal with continuous functions, that is, those for which y varies "smoothly" with x.

The **derivative** of y with respect to x is defined as the limit as Δx approaches zero of the slopes of chords drawn between two points on the y versus x curve. Mathematically, we write this definition as

$$\frac{dy}{dx} = \lim_{\Delta x \to 0} \frac{\Delta y}{\Delta x} = \lim_{\Delta x \to 0} \frac{y(x + \Delta x) - y(x)}{\Delta x} \tag{B.28}$$

where Δy and Δx are defined as $\Delta x = x_2 - x_1$ and $\Delta y = y_2 - y_1$ (Fig. B.14). Note that dy/dx *does not* mean dy divided by dx, but rather is simply a notation of the limiting process of the derivative as defined by Equation B.28.

A useful expression to remember when $y(x) = ax^n$, where a is a *constant* and n is *any* positive or negative number (integer or fraction), is

$$\frac{dy}{dx} = nax^{n-1} \tag{B.29}$$

If $y(x)$ is a polynomial or algebraic function of x, we apply Equation B.29 to *each* term in the polynomial and take $d[\text{constant}]/dx = 0$. In Examples B.4 through B.7, we evaluate the derivatives of several functions.

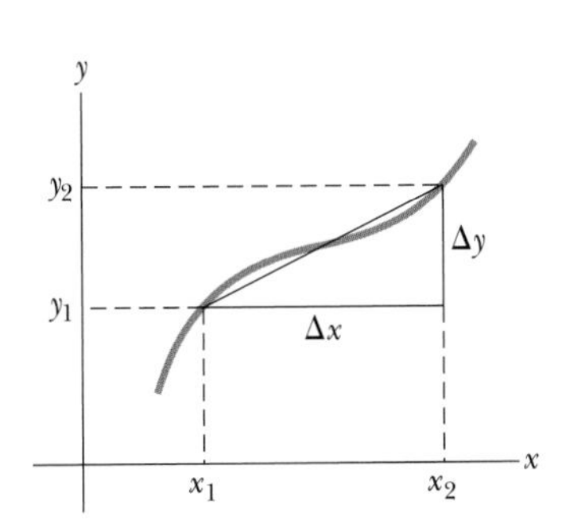

Figure B.14 The lengths Δx and Δy are used to define the derivative of this function at a point.

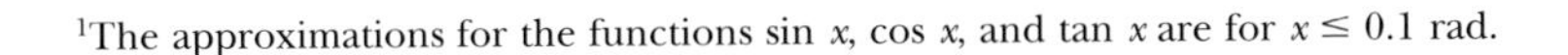

[1]The approximations for the functions sin x, cos x, and tan x are for $x \leq 0.1$ rad.

TABLE B.4

Derivative for Several Functions

$$\frac{d}{dx}(a) = 0$$

$$\frac{d}{dx}(ax^n) = nax^{n-1}$$

$$\frac{d}{dx}(e^{ax}) = ae^{ax}$$

$$\frac{d}{dx}(\sin ax) = a\cos ax$$

$$\frac{d}{dx}(\cos ax) = -a\sin ax$$

$$\frac{d}{dx}(\tan ax) = a\sec^2 ax$$

$$\frac{d}{dx}(\cot ax) = -a\csc^2 ax$$

$$\frac{d}{dx}(\sec x) = \tan x \sec x$$

$$\frac{d}{dx}(\csc x) = -\cot x \csc x$$

$$\frac{d}{dx}(\ln ax) = \frac{1}{x}$$

$$\frac{d}{dx}(\sin^{-1} ax) = \frac{a}{\sqrt{1 - a^2x^2}}$$

$$\frac{d}{dx}(\cos^{-1} ax) = \frac{-a}{\sqrt{1 - a^2x^2}}$$

$$\frac{d}{dx}(\tan^{-1} ax) = \frac{a}{1 + a^2x^2}$$

Note: The symbols a and n represent constants.

Special Properties of the Derivative

A. Derivative of the product of two functions If a function $f(x)$ is given by the product of two functions—say, $g(x)$ and $h(x)$—the derivative of $f(x)$ is defined as

$$\frac{d}{dx} f(x) = \frac{d}{dx}[g(x)h(x)] = g\frac{dh}{dx} + h\frac{dg}{dx} \quad \textbf{(B.30)}$$

B. Derivative of the sum of two functions If a function $f(x)$ is equal to the sum of two functions, the derivative of the sum is equal to the sum of the derivatives:

$$\frac{d}{dx} f(x) = \frac{d}{dx}[g(x) + h(x)] = \frac{dg}{dx} + \frac{dh}{dx} \quad \textbf{(B.31)}$$

C. Chain rule of differential calculus If $y = f(x)$ and $x = g(z)$, then dy/dz can be written as the product of two derivatives:

$$\frac{dy}{dz} = \frac{dy}{dx}\frac{dx}{dz} \quad \textbf{(B.32)}$$

D. The second derivative The second derivative of y with respect to x is defined as the derivative of the function dy/dx (the derivative of the derivative). It is usually written as

$$\frac{d^2y}{dx^2} = \frac{d}{dx}\left(\frac{dy}{dx}\right) \quad \textbf{(B.33)}$$

Some of the more commonly used derivatives of functions are listed in Table B.4.

EXAMPLE B.4

Suppose $y(x)$ (that is, y as a function of x) is given by

$$y(x) = ax^3 + bx + c$$

where a and b are constants. It follows that

$$y(x + \Delta x) = a(x + \Delta x)^3 + b(x + \Delta x) + c$$

$$= a(x^3 + 3x^2\,\Delta x + 3x\,\Delta x^2 + \Delta x^3) + b(x + \Delta x) + c$$

so

$$\Delta y = y(x + \Delta x) - y(x) = a(3x^2\,\Delta x + 3x\,\Delta x^2 + \Delta x^3) + b\,\Delta x$$

Substituting this into Equation B.28 gives

$$\frac{dy}{dx} = \lim_{\Delta x \to 0} \frac{\Delta y}{\Delta x} = \lim_{\Delta x \to 0} [3ax^2 + 3ax\,\Delta x + a\,\Delta x^2] + b$$

$$\frac{dy}{dx} = 3ax^2 + b$$

EXAMPLE B.5

Find the derivative of

$$y(x) = 8x^5 + 4x^3 + 2x + 7$$

Solution Applying Equation B.29 to each term independently and remembering that d/dx (constant) $= 0$, we have

$$\frac{dy}{dx} = 8(5)x^4 + 4(3)x^2 + 2(1)x^0 + 0$$

$$\frac{dy}{dx} = 40x^4 + 12x^2 + 2$$

EXAMPLE B.6

Find the derivative of $y(x) = x^3/(x+1)^2$ with respect to x.

Solution We can rewrite this function as $y(x) = x^3(x+1)^{-2}$ and apply Equation B.30:

$$\frac{dy}{dx} = (x+1)^{-2}\frac{d}{dx}(x^3) + x^3\frac{d}{dx}(x+1)^{-2}$$

$$= (x+1)^{-2}3x^2 + x^3(-2)(x+1)^{-3}$$

$$\frac{dy}{dx} = \frac{3x^2}{(x+1)^2} - \frac{2x^3}{(x+1)^3}$$

EXAMPLE B.7

A useful formula that follows from Equation B.30 is the derivative of the quotient of two functions. Show that

$$\frac{d}{dx}\left[\frac{g(x)}{h(x)}\right] = \frac{h\frac{dg}{dx} - g\frac{dh}{dx}}{h^2}$$

Solution We can write the quotient as gh^{-1} and then apply Equations B.29 and B.30:

$$\frac{d}{dx}\left(\frac{g}{h}\right) = \frac{d}{dx}(gh^{-1}) = g\frac{d}{dx}(h^{-1}) + h^{-1}\frac{d}{dx}(g)$$

$$= -gh^{-2}\frac{dh}{dx} + h^{-1}\frac{dg}{dx}$$

$$= \frac{h\frac{dg}{dx} - g\frac{dh}{dx}}{h^2}$$

B.7 Integral Calculus

We think of integration as the inverse of differentiation. As an example, consider the expression

$$f(x) = \frac{dy}{dx} = 3ax^2 + b \tag{B.34}$$

which was the result of differentiating the function

$$y(x) = ax^3 + bx + c$$

in Example B.4. We can write Equation B.34 as $dy = f(x)\ dx = (3ax^2 + b)\ dx$ and obtain $y(x)$ by "summing" over all values of x. Mathematically, we write this inverse operation as

$$y(x) = \int f(x)\ dx$$

For the function $f(x)$ given by Equation B.34, we have

$$y(x) = \int (3ax^2 + b)\ dx = ax^3 + bx + c$$

where c is a constant of the integration. This type of integral is called an *indefinite integral* because its value depends on the choice of c.

A general **indefinite integral** $I(x)$ is defined as

$$I(x) = \int f(x)\ dx \tag{B.35}$$

where $f(x)$ is called the *integrand* and $f(x) = dI(x)/dx$.

For a *general continuous* function $f(x)$, the integral can be described as the area under the curve bounded by $f(x)$ and the x axis, between two specified values of x, say, x_1 and x_2, as in Figure B.15.

The area of the blue element in Figure B.15 is approximately $f(x_i)\ \Delta x_i$. If we sum all these area elements between x_1 and x_2 and take the limit of this sum as $\Delta x_i \rightarrow 0$, we obtain the *true* area under the curve bounded by $f(x)$ and the x axis, between the limits x_1 and x_2:

$$\text{Area} = \lim_{\Delta x_i \rightarrow 0} \sum_i f(x_i)\Delta x_i = \int_{x_1}^{x_2} f(x)\ dx \tag{B.36}$$

Integrals of the type defined by Equation B.36 are called **definite integrals.**

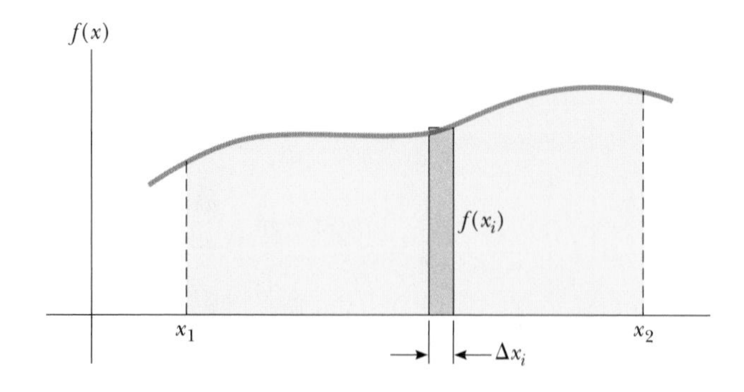

Figure B.15 The definite integral of a function is the area under the curve of the function between the limits x_1 and x_2.

One common integral that arises in practical situations has the form

$$\int x^n \, dx = \frac{x^{n+1}}{n+1} + c \quad (n \neq -1) \tag{B.37}$$

This result is obvious, being that differentiation of the right-hand side with respect to x gives $f(x) = x^n$ directly. If the limits of the integration are known, this integral becomes a *definite integral* and is written

$$\int_{x_1}^{x_2} x^n \, dx = \frac{x^{n+1}}{n+1}\bigg|_{x_1}^{x_2} = \frac{x_2^{\,n+1} - x_1^{\,n+1}}{n+1} \quad (n \neq -1) \tag{B.38}$$

EXAMPLES

1. $\displaystyle\int_0^a x^2 \, dx = \frac{x^3}{3}\bigg]_0^a = \frac{a^3}{3}$

2. $\displaystyle\int_0^b x^{3/2} dx = \frac{x^{5/2}}{5/2}\bigg]_0^b = \tfrac{2}{5}b^{5/2}$

3. $\displaystyle\int_3^5 x \, dx = \frac{x^2}{2}\bigg]_3^5 = \frac{5^2 - 3^2}{2} = 8$

Partial Integration

Sometimes it is useful to apply the method of *partial integration* (also called "integrating by parts") to evaluate certain integrals. This method uses the property

$$\int u \, dv = uv - \int v \, du \tag{B.39}$$

where u and v are *carefully* chosen so as to reduce a complex integral to a simpler one. In many cases, several reductions have to be made. Consider the function

$$I(x) = \int x^2 e^x \, dx$$

which can be evaluated by integrating by parts twice. First, if we choose $u = x^2$, $v = e^x$, we obtain

$$\int x^2 e^x \, dx = \int x^2 \, d(e^x) = x^2 e^x - 2\int e^x x \, dx + c_1$$

Now, in the second term, choose $u = x$, $v = e^x$, which gives

$$\int x^2 e^x \, dx = x^2 e^x - 2x\,e^x + 2\int e^x \, dx + c_1$$

or

$$\int x^2 e^x \, dx = x^2 e^x - 2xe^x + 2e^x + c_2$$

TABLE B.5

Some Indefinite Integrals (An arbitrary constant should be added to each of these integrals.)

$$\int x^n\,dx = \frac{x^{n+1}}{n+1} \quad \text{(provided } n \neq 1\text{)}$$

$$\int \frac{dx}{x} = \int x^{-1}\,dx = \ln x$$

$$\int \frac{dx}{a+bx} = \frac{1}{b}\ln(a+bx)$$

$$\int \frac{x\,dx}{a+bx} = \frac{x}{b} - \frac{a}{b^2}\ln(a+bx)$$

$$\int \frac{dx}{x(x+a)} = -\frac{1}{a}\ln\frac{x+a}{x}$$

$$\int \frac{dx}{(a+bx)^2} = -\frac{1}{b(a+bx)}$$

$$\int \frac{dx}{a^2+x^2} = \frac{1}{a}\tan^{-1}\frac{x}{a}$$

$$\int \frac{dx}{a^2-x^2} = \frac{1}{2a}\ln\frac{a+x}{a-x} \quad (a^2 - x^2 > 0)$$

$$\int \frac{dx}{x^2-a^2} = \frac{1}{2a}\ln\frac{x-a}{x+a} \quad (x^2 - a^2 > 0)$$

$$\int \frac{x\,dx}{a^2 \pm x^2} = \pm\tfrac{1}{2}\ln(a^2 \pm x^2)$$

$$\int \frac{dx}{\sqrt{a^2-x^2}} = \sin^{-1}\frac{x}{a} = -\cos^{-1}\frac{x}{a} \quad (a^2 - x^2 > 0)$$

$$\int \frac{dx}{\sqrt{x^2+a^2}} = \ln(x + \sqrt{x^2 \pm a^2})$$

$$\int \frac{x\,dx}{\sqrt{a^2-x^2}} = -\sqrt{a^2-x^2}$$

$$\int \frac{x\,dx}{\sqrt{x^2 \pm a^2}} = \sqrt{x^2 \pm a^2}$$

$$\int \sqrt{a^2-x^2}\,dx = \tfrac{1}{2}\left(x\sqrt{a^2-x^2} + a^2\sin^{-1}\frac{x}{a}\right)$$

$$\int x\sqrt{a^2-x^2}\,dx = -\tfrac{1}{3}(a^2-x^2)^{3/2}$$

$$\int \sqrt{x^2 \pm a^2}\,dx = \tfrac{1}{2}\left[x\sqrt{x^2 \pm a^2} \pm a^2\ln(x + \sqrt{x^2 \pm a^2})\right]$$

$$\int x(\sqrt{x^2 \pm a^2})\,dx = \tfrac{1}{3}(x^2 \pm a^2)^{3/2}$$

$$\int e^{ax}\,dx = \frac{1}{a}e^{ax}$$

$$\int \ln ax\,dx = (x\ln ax) - x$$

$$\int xe^{ax}\,dx = \frac{e^{ax}}{a^2}(ax-1)$$

$$\int \frac{dx}{a+be^{cx}} = \frac{x}{a} - \frac{1}{ac}\ln(a+be^{cx})$$

$$\int \sin ax\,dx = \frac{1}{a}\cos ax$$

$$\int \cos ax\,dx = \frac{1}{a}\sin ax$$

$$\int \tan ax\,dx = -\frac{1}{a}\ln(\cos ax) = \frac{1}{a}\ln(\sec ax)$$

$$\int \cot ax\,dx = \frac{1}{a}\ln(\sin ax)$$

$$\int \sec ax\,dx = \frac{1}{a}\ln(\sec ax + \tan ax) = \frac{1}{a}\ln\left[\tan\left(\frac{ax}{2} + \frac{\pi}{4}\right)\right]$$

$$\int \csc ax\,dx = \frac{1}{a}\ln(\csc ax - \cot ax) = \frac{1}{a}\ln\left(\tan\frac{ax}{2}\right)$$

$$\int \sin^2 ax\,dx = \frac{x}{2} + \frac{\sin 2ax}{4a}$$

$$\int \cos^2 ax\,dx = \frac{x}{2} + \frac{\sin 2ax}{4a}$$

$$\int \frac{dx}{\sin^2 ax} = -\frac{1}{a}\cot ax$$

$$\int \frac{dx}{\cos^2 ax} = \frac{1}{a}\tan ax$$

$$\int \tan^2 ax\,dx = \frac{1}{a}(\tan ax) - x$$

$$\int \cot^2 ax\,dx = -\frac{1}{a}(\cot ax) - x$$

$$\int \sin^{-1} ax\,dx = x(\sin^{-1} ax) + \frac{\sqrt{1-a^2x^2}}{a}$$

$$\int \cos^{-1} ax\,dx = x(\cos^{-1} ax) - \frac{\sqrt{1-a^2x^2}}{a}$$

$$\int \frac{dx}{(x^2+a^2)^{3/2}} = \frac{x}{a^2\sqrt{x^2+a^2}}$$

$$\int \frac{x\,dx}{(x^2+a^2)^{3/2}} = -\frac{1}{\sqrt{x^2+a^2}}$$

TABLE B.6

Gauss's Probability Integral and Other Definite Integrals

$$\int_0^\infty x^n e^{-ax}\, dx = \frac{n!}{a^{n+1}}$$

$$I_0 = \int_0^\infty e^{-ax^2} dx = \frac{1}{2}\sqrt{\frac{\pi}{a}} \quad \text{(Gauss's probability integral)}$$

$$I_1 = \int_0^\infty x e^{-ax^2}\, dx = \frac{1}{2a}$$

$$I_2 = \int_0^\infty x^2 e^{-ax^2} dx = -\frac{dI_0}{da} = \frac{1}{4}\sqrt{\frac{\pi}{a^3}}$$

$$I_3 = \int_0^\infty x^3 e^{-ax^2}\, dx = -\frac{dI_1}{da} = \frac{1}{2a^2}$$

$$I_4 = \int_0^\infty x^4 e^{-ax^2} dx = \frac{d^2 I_0}{da^2} = \frac{3}{8}\sqrt{\frac{\pi}{a^5}}$$

$$I_5 = \int_0^\infty x^5 e^{-ax^2}\, dx = \frac{d^2 I_1}{da^2} = \frac{1}{a^3}$$

$$\vdots$$

$$I_{2n} = (-1)^n \frac{d^n}{da^n} I_0$$

$$I_{2n+1} = (-1)^n \frac{d^n}{da^n} I_1$$

The Perfect Differential

Another useful method to remember is that of the *perfect differential,* in which we look for a change of variable such that the differential of the function is the differential of the independent variable appearing in the integrand. For example, consider the integral

$$I(x) = \int \cos^2 x \sin x \, dx$$

This integral becomes easy to evaluate if we rewrite the differential as $d(\cos x) = -\sin x\, dx$. The integral then becomes

$$\int \cos^2 x \sin x \, dx = -\int \cos^2 x \, d(\cos x)$$

If we now change variables, letting $y = \cos x$, we obtain

$$\int \cos^2 x \sin x \, dx = -\int y^2\, dy = -\frac{y^3}{3} + c = -\frac{\cos^3 x}{3} + c$$

Table B.5 (page A-18) lists some useful indefinite integrals. Table B.6 gives Gauss's probability integral and other definite integrals. A more complete list can be found in various handbooks, such as *The Handbook of Chemistry and Physics* (Boca Raton, FL: CRC Press, published annually).

B.8 Propagation of Uncertainty

In laboratory experiments, a common activity is to take measurements that act as raw data. These measurements are of several types—length, time interval, temperature, voltage, and so on—and are taken by a variety of instruments. Regardless of the measurement and the quality of the instrumentation, **there is always uncertainty associated with a physical measurement.** This uncertainty is a combination of that associated with the instrument and that related to the system being measured. An example of the former is the inability to exactly determine the position of a length measurement between the lines on a meterstick. An example of uncertainty related to the system being measured is the variation of temperature within a sample of water so that a single temperature for the sample is difficult to determine.

Uncertainties can be expressed in two ways. **Absolute uncertainty** refers to an uncertainty expressed in the same units as the measurement. Therefore, the length of a computer disk label might be expressed as (5.5 ± 0.1) cm. The uncertainty of ±0.1 cm by itself is not descriptive enough for some purposes, however. This uncertainty is large if the measurement is 1.0 cm, but it is small if the measurement is 100 m. To give a more descriptive account of the uncertainty, **fractional uncertainty** or **percent uncertainty** is used. In this type of description, the uncertainty is divided by the actual measurement. Therefore, the length of the computer disk label could be expressed as

$$\ell = 5.5 \text{ cm} \pm \frac{0.1 \text{ cm}}{5.5 \text{ cm}} = 5.5 \text{ cm} \pm 0.018 \quad \text{(fractional uncertainty)}$$

or as

$$\ell = 5.5 \text{ cm} \pm 1.8\% \quad \text{(percent uncertainty)}$$

When combining measurements in a calculation, the percent uncertainty in the final result is generally larger than the uncertainty in the individual measurements. This is called **propagation of uncertainty** and is one of the challenges of experimental physics.

Some simple rules can provide a reasonable estimate of the uncertainty in a calculated result:

Multiplication and division: When measurements with uncertainties are multiplied or divided, add the *percent uncertainties* to obtain the percent uncertainty in the result.

Example: The Area of a Rectangular Plate

$$A = \ell w = (5.5 \text{ cm} \pm 1.8\%) \times (6.4 \text{ cm} \pm 1.6\%) = 35 \text{ cm}^2 \pm 3.4\%$$
$$= (35 \pm 1) \text{ cm}^2$$

Addition and subtraction: When measurements with uncertainties are added or subtracted, add the *absolute uncertainties* to obtain the absolute uncertainty in the result.

Example: A Change in Temperature

$$\Delta T = T_2 - T_1 = (99.2 \pm 1.5)^\circ\text{C} - (27.6 \pm 1.5)^\circ\text{C} = (71.6 \pm 3.0)^\circ\text{C}$$
$$= 71.6^\circ\text{C} \pm 4.2\%$$

Powers: If a measurement is taken to a power, the percent uncertainty is multiplied by that power to obtain the percent uncertainty in the result.

Example: The Volume of a Sphere

$$V = \tfrac{4}{3}\pi r^3 = \tfrac{4}{3}\pi(6.20 \text{ cm} \pm 2.0\%)^3 = 998 \text{ cm}^3 \pm 6.0\%$$
$$= (998 \pm 60) \text{ cm}^3$$

For complicated calculations, many uncertainties are added together, which can cause the uncertainty in the final result to be undesirably large. Experiments should be designed such that calculations are as simple as possible.

Notice that uncertainties in a calculation always add. As a result, an experiment involving a subtraction should be avoided if possible, especially if the measurements being subtracted are close together. The result of such a calculation is a small difference in the measurements and uncertainties that add together. It is possible that the uncertainty in the result could be larger than the result itself!

Group I	Group II	Transition elements						
H 1 1.007 9 $1s$								
Li 3 6.941 $2s^1$	Be 4 9.0122 $2s^2$							
Na 11 22.990 $3s^1$	Mg 12 24.305 $3s^2$							
K 19 39.098 $4s^1$	Ca 20 40.078 $4s^2$	Sc 21 44.956 $3d^14s^2$	Ti 22 47.867 $3d^24s^2$	V 23 50.942 $3d^34s^2$	Cr 24 51.996 $3d^54s^1$	Mn 25 54.938 $3d^54s^2$	Fe 26 55.845 $3d^64s^2$	Co 27 58.933 $3d^74s^2$
Rb 37 85.468 $5s^1$	Sr 38 87.62 $5s^2$	Y 39 88.906 $4d^15s^2$	Zr 40 91.224 $4d^25s^2$	Nb 41 92.906 $4d^45s^1$	Mo 42 95.94 $4d^55s^1$	Tc 43 (98) $4d^55s^2$	Ru 44 101.07 $4d^75s^1$	Rh 45 102.91 $4d^85s^1$
Cs 55 132.91 $6s^1$	Ba 56 137.33 $6s^2$	57–71*	Hf 72 178.49 $5d^26s^2$	Ta 73 180.95 $5d^36s^2$	W 74 183.84 $5d^46s^2$	Re 75 186.21 $5d^56s^2$	Os 76 190.23 $5d^66s^2$	Ir 77 192.2 $5d^76s^2$
Fr 87 (223) $7s^1$	Ra 88 (226) $7s^2$	89–103**	Rf 104 (261) $6d^27s^2$	Db 105 (262) $6d^37s^2$	Sg 106 (266)	Bh 107 (264)	Hs 108 (277)	Mt 109 (268)

Symbol — Ca 20 — Atomic number
Atomic mass† — 40.078
$4s^2$ — Electron configuration

*Lanthanide series	La 57 138.91 $5d^16s^2$	Ce 58 140.12 $5d^14f^16s^2$	Pr 59 140.91 $4f^36s^2$	Nd 60 144.24 $4f^46s^2$	Pm 61 (145) $4f^56s^2$	Sm 62 150.36 $4f^66s^2$
**Actinide series	Ac 89 (227) $6d^17s^2$	Th 90 232.04 $6d^27s^2$	Pa 91 231.04 $5f^26d^17s^2$	U 92 238.03 $5f^36d^17s^2$	Np 93 (237) $5f^46d^17s^2$	Pu 94 (244) $5f^66d^07s^2$

Note: Atomic mass values given are averaged over isotopes in the percentages in which they exist in nature.
† For an unstable element, mass number of the most stable known isotope is given in parentheses.
†† Elements 112 and 114 have not yet been named.
††† For a description of the atomic data, visit *physics.nist.gov/PhysRefData/Elements/per_text.html*

			Group III	Group IV	Group V	Group VI	Group VII	Group 0
							H 1 1.007 9 $1s^1$	**He** 2 4.002 6 $1s^2$
			B 5 10.811 $2p^1$	**C** 6 12.011 $2p^2$	**N** 7 14.007 $2p^3$	**O** 8 15.999 $2p^4$	**F** 9 18.998 $2p^5$	**Ne** 10 20.180 $2p^6$
			Al 13 26.982 $3p^1$	**Si** 14 28.086 $3p^2$	**P** 15 30.974 $3p^3$	**S** 16 32.066 $3p^4$	**Cl** 17 35.453 $3p^5$	**Ar** 18 39.948 $3p^6$
Ni 28 58.693 $3d^84s^2$	**Cu** 29 63.546 $3d^{10}4s^1$	**Zn** 30 65.41 $3d^{10}4s^2$	**Ga** 31 69.723 $4p^1$	**Ge** 32 72.64 $4p^2$	**As** 33 74.922 $4p^3$	**Se** 34 78.96 $4p^4$	**Br** 35 79.904 $4p^5$	**Kr** 36 83.80 $4p^6$
Pd 46 106.42 $4d^{10}$	**Ag** 47 107.87 $4d^{10}5s^1$	**Cd** 48 112.41 $4d^{10}5s^2$	**In** 49 114.82 $5p^1$	**Sn** 50 118.71 $5p^2$	**Sb** 51 121.76 $5p^3$	**Te** 52 127.60 $5p^4$	**I** 53 126.90 $5p^5$	**Xe** 54 131.29 $5p^6$
Pt 78 195.08 $5d^96s^1$	**Au** 79 196.97 $5d^{10}6s^1$	**Hg** 80 200.59 $5d^{10}6s^2$	**Tl** 81 204.38 $6p^1$	**Pb** 82 207.2 $6p^2$	**Bi** 83 208.98 $6p^3$	**Po** 84 (209) $6p^4$	**At** 85 (210) $6p^5$	**Rn** 86 (222) $6p^6$
Ds 110 (271)	**Rg** 111 (272)	112†† (285)		114†† (289)				

Eu 63 151.96 $4f^76s^2$	**Gd** 64 157.25 $4f^75d^16s^2$	**Tb** 65 158.93 $4f^85d^16s^2$	**Dy** 66 162.50 $4f^{10}6s^2$	**Ho** 67 164.93 $4f^{11}6s^2$	**Er** 68 167.26 $4f^{12}6s^2$	**Tm** 69 168.93 $4f^{13}6s^2$	**Yb** 70 173.04 $4f^{14}6s^2$	**Lu** 71 174.97 $4f^{14}5d^16s^2$
Am 95 (243) $5f^77s^2$	**Cm** 96 (247) $5f^76d^17s^2$	**Bk** 97 (247) $5f^86d^17s^2$	**Cf** 98 (251) $5f^{10}7s^2$	**Es** 99 (252) $5f^{11}7s^2$	**Fm** 100 (257) $5f^{12}7s^2$	**Md** 101 (258) $5f^{13}7s^2$	**No** 102 (259) $5f^{14}7s^2$	**Lr** 103 (262) $6d^15f^{14}7s^2$

TABLE D.1

SI Units

Base Quantity	SI Base Unit	
	Name	**Symbol**
Length	meter	m
Mass	kilogram	kg
Time	second	s
Electric current	ampere	A
Temperature	kelvin	K
Amount of substance	mole	mol
Luminous intensity	candela	cd

TABLE D.2

Some Derived SI Units

Quantity	Name	Symbol	Expression in Terms of Base Units	Expression in Terms of Other SI Units
Plane angle	radian	rad	m/m	
Frequency	hertz	Hz	s^{-1}	
Force	newton	N	$kg \cdot m/s^2$	J/m
Pressure	pascal	Pa	$kg/m \cdot s^2$	N/m^2
Energy	joule	J	$kg \cdot m^2/s^2$	$N \cdot m$
Power	watt	W	$kg \cdot m^2/s^3$	J/s
Electric charge	coulomb	C	$A \cdot s$	
Electric potential	volt	V	$kg \cdot m^2/A \cdot s^3$	W/A
Capacitance	farad	F	$A^2 \cdot s^4/kg \cdot m^2$	C/V
Electric resistance	ohm	Ω	$kg \cdot m^2/A^2 \cdot s^3$	V/A
Magnetic flux	weber	Wb	$kg \cdot m^2/A \cdot s^2$	$V \cdot s$
Magnetic field	tesla	T	$kg/A \cdot s^2$	
Inductance	henry	H	$kg \cdot m^2/A^2 \cdot s^2$	$T \cdot m^2/A$

CHAPTER 1

1. 5.52×10^3 kg/m^3, between the density of aluminum and iron and greater than the densities of typical surface rocks
3. 23.0 kg
5. 7.69 cm
7. (b) only
9. The units of G are m^3/kg · s^2.
11. 1.39×10^3 m^2
13. Not with the pages from Volume 1, but yes with the pages from the full version. Each page has area 0.059 m^2. The room has wall area 37 m^2, requiring 630 sheets, which would be counted as 1 260 pages.
15. 11.4×10^3 kg/m^3
17. (a) 250 yr (b) 3.09×10^4 times
19. 1.00×10^{10} lb
21. 151 μm
23. 2.86 cm
25. $\sim 10^6$ balls
27. $\sim 10^2$ kg; $\sim 10^3$ kg
29. $\sim 10^2$ tuners
31. (a) 3 (b) 4 (c) 3 (d) 2
33. (a) 797 (b) 1.1 (c) 17.66
35. 8.80%
37. 9
39. 63
41. 108° and 288°
43. 48.6 kg
45. (a) smaller by nine times (b) Δt is inversely proportional to d^2. (c) Plot Δt on the vertical axis and $1/d^2$ on the horizontal axis. (d) $4QL/[k\pi(T_h - T_c)]$
47. (a) $m = 346$ g $- (14.5$ g/cm$^3)a^3$ (b) $a = 0$ (c) 346 g (d) yes (e) $a = 2.60$ cm (f) 90.6 g (g) yes (h) 218 g (i) No; 218 g is not equal to 314 g. (j) Parts (b), (c), and (d) describe a uniform solid sphere with $\rho = 4.70$ g/cm^3 as a approaches zero. Parts (e), (f), and (g) describe a uniform liquid drop with $\rho = 1.23$ g/cm^3 as a approaches 2.60 cm. The function $m(a)$ is not a linear function, so a halfway between 0 and 2.60 cm does not give a value for m halfway between the minimum and maximum values. The graph of m versus a starts at $a = 0$ with a horizontal tangent. Then it curves down more and more steeply as a increases. The liquid drop of radius 1.30 cm has only one eighth the volume of the whole sphere, so its presence brings down the mass by only a small amount, from 346 g to 314 g. (k) The answer would not change as long as the wall of the shell is unbroken.
49. 5.0 m
51. $0.579t$ ft^3/s $+ (1.19 \times 10^{-9})t^2$ ft^3/s^2
53. 3.41 m
55. 0.449%
57. (a) 0.529 cm/s (b) 11.5 cm/s
59. 1×10^{10} gal/yr

CHAPTER 2

1. (a) 5 m/s (b) 1.2 m/s (c) −2.5 m/s (d) −3.3 m/s (e) 0
3. (a) 3.75 m/s (b) 0
5. (a) −2.4 m/s (b) −3.8 m/s (c) 4.0 s
7. (a) and (c)

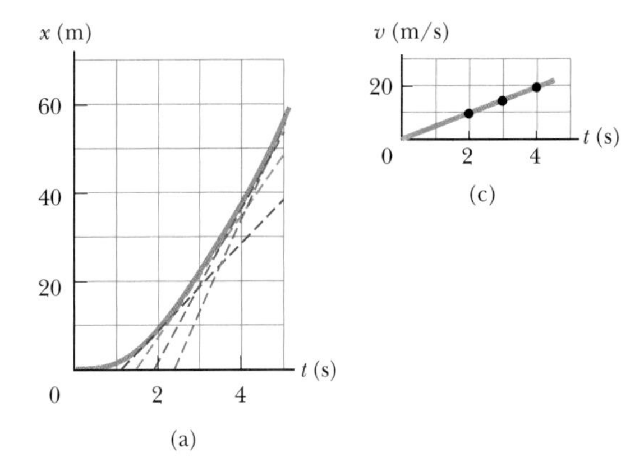

(b) $v_{t=5.0\text{ s}} = 23$ m/s, $v_{t=4.0\text{ s}} = 18$ m/s, $v_{t=3.0\text{ s}} = 14$ m/s, $v_{t=2.0\text{ s}} = 9.0$ m/s (c) 4.6 m/s^2 (d) 0
9. 5.00 m
11. (a) 20.0 m/s, 5.00 m/s (b) 262 m
13. (a) 2.00 m (b) −3.00 m/s (c) −2.00 m/s^2
15. (a) 13.0 m/s (b) 10.0 m/s, 16.0 m/s (c) 6.00 m/s^2 (d) 6.00 m/s^2
17.

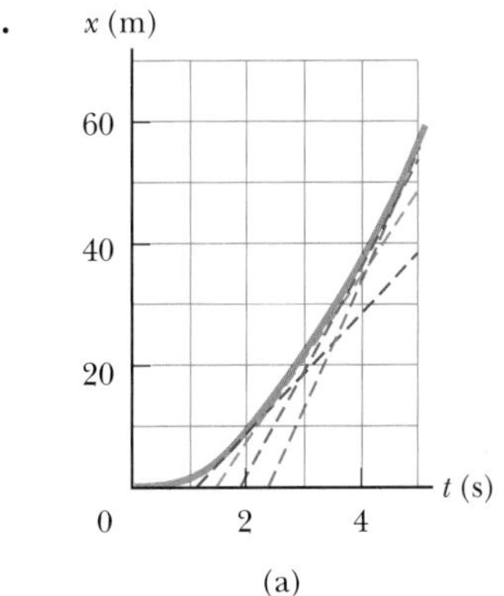

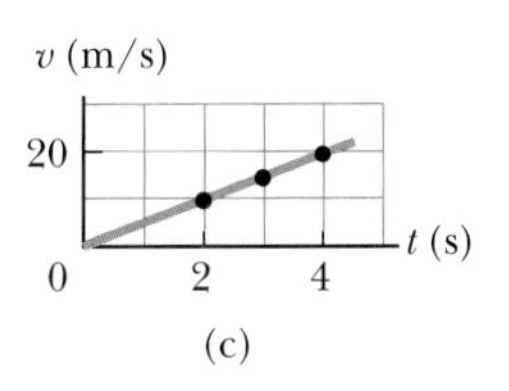

19. (a) 9.00 m/s (b) 5.00 m/s (c) 3.00 m/s (d) −3.00 m/s (e) 17.0 m/s (f) The graph of velocity versus time is a straight line passing through 13 m/s at 10:05 a.m. and sloping downward, decreasing by 4 m/s for each second thereafter. (g) If and only if we know the object's velocity at one instant of time, knowing its acceleration tells us its velocity at every other moment, as long as the acceleration is constant.
21. −16.0 cm/s^2
23. (a) 20.0 s (b) It cannot; it would need a longer runway.
25. 3.10 m/s
27. (a) −202 m/s^2 (b) 198 m
29. (a) 4.98×10^{-9} s (b) 1.20×10^{15} m/s^2
31. (a) False unless the acceleration is zero. We define constant acceleration to mean that the velocity is changing steadily in time. Then the velocity cannot be changing steadily in space. (b) True. Because the velocity is changing steadily in time, the velocity halfway through an interval is equal to the average of its initial and final values.
33. (a) 3.45 s (b) 10.0 ft
35. (a) 19.7 cm/s (b) 4.70 cm/s^2 (c) The time interval required for the speed to change between Ⓐ and Ⓑ is

sufficient to find the acceleration, more directly than we could find it from the distance between the points.

37. We ignore air resistance. We assume the worker's flight time, "a mile," and "a dollar" were measured to three-digit precision. We have interpreted "up in the sky" as referring to free-fall time, not to the launch and landing times. Therefore, the wage was \$99.3/h.

39. (a) 10.0 m/s up (b) 4.68 m/s down

41. (a) 29.4 m/s (b) 44.1 m

43. (a) 7.82 m (b) 0.782 s

45. 38.2 m

47. (a) $a_x(t) = a_{xi} + Jt$, $v_x(t) = v_{xi} + a_{xi}t + \frac{1}{2}Jt^2$, $x(t) = x_i + v_{xi}t + \frac{1}{2}a_{xi}t^2 + \frac{1}{6}Jt^3$

49. (a) 0 (b) 6.0 m/s² (c) −3.6 m/s² (d) 6 s and 18 s (e) 18 s (f) 84 m (g) 204 m

51. (a) 41.0 s (b) 1.73 km (c) −184 m/s

53. (a) 5.43 m/s² and 3.83 m/s² (b) 10.9 m/s and 11.5 m/s (c) Maggie by 2.62 m

55. 155 s, 129 s

57. (a) 3.00 s (b) −15.3 m/s (c) 31.4 m/s down and 34.8 m/s down

59. (a) 5.46 s (b) 73.0 m (c) $v_{\text{Stan}} = 22.6$ m/s, $v_{\text{Kathy}} = 26.7$ m/s

61. (a) yes, to two significant digits (b) 0.742 s (c) Yes; the braking distance is proportional to the square of the original speed. (d) −19.7 ft/s² = −6.01 m/s²

63. $0.577v$

CHAPTER 3

1. (−2.75, −4.76) m

3. (a) 2.24 m (b) 2.24 m at 26.6°

5. (a) r, 180° − θ (b) $2r$, 180° + θ (c) $3r$, $-\theta$

7. 70.0 m

9. (a) 10.0 m (b) 15.7 m (c) 0

11. (a) 5.2 m at 60° (b) 3.0 m at 330° (c) 3.0 m at 150° (d) 5.2 m at 300°

13. approximately 420 ft at −3°

15. 47.2 units at 122°

17. Yes. The speed of the camper should be 28.3 m/s or greater.

19. (a) $(-11.1\hat{\mathbf{i}} + 6.40\hat{\mathbf{j}})$ m (b) $(1.65\hat{\mathbf{i}} + 2.86\hat{\mathbf{j}})$ cm (c) $(-18.0\hat{\mathbf{i}} - 12.6\hat{\mathbf{j}})$ in.

21. 358 m at 2.00° S of E

23. 196 cm at 345°

25. (a) $2.00\hat{\mathbf{i}} - 6.00\hat{\mathbf{j}}$ (b) $4.00\hat{\mathbf{i}} + 2.00\hat{\mathbf{j}}$ (c) 6.32 (d) 4.47 (e) 288°, 26.6°

27. 9.48 m at 166°

29. 4.64 m at 78.6° N of E

31. (a) 185 N at 77.8° from the $+x$ axis (b) $(-39.3\hat{\mathbf{i}} - 181\hat{\mathbf{j}})$ N

33. $|\vec{\mathbf{B}}| = 7.81$, $\theta_x = 59.2°$, $\theta_y = 39.8°$, $\theta_z = 67.4°$

35. (a) 5.92 m is the magnitude of $(5.00\hat{\mathbf{i}} - 1.00\hat{\mathbf{j}} - 3.00\hat{\mathbf{k}})$ m. (b) 19.0 m is the magnitude of $(4.00\hat{\mathbf{i}} - 11.0\hat{\mathbf{j}} - 15.0\hat{\mathbf{k}})$ m.

37. (a) $8.00\hat{\mathbf{i}} + 12.0\hat{\mathbf{j}} - 4.00\hat{\mathbf{k}}$ (b) $2.00\hat{\mathbf{i}} + 3.00\hat{\mathbf{j}} - 1.00\hat{\mathbf{k}}$ (c) $-24.0\hat{\mathbf{i}} - 36.0\hat{\mathbf{j}} + 12.0\hat{\mathbf{k}}$

39. (a) $(3.12\hat{\mathbf{i}} + 5.02\hat{\mathbf{j}} - 2.20\hat{\mathbf{k}})$ km (b) 6.31 km

41. (a) $-3.00\hat{\mathbf{i}} + 2.00\hat{\mathbf{j}}$ (b) 3.61 at 146° (c) $3.00\hat{\mathbf{i}} - 6.00\hat{\mathbf{j}}$

43. (a) $49.5\hat{\mathbf{i}} + 27.1\hat{\mathbf{j}}$ (b) 56.4 units at 28.7°

45. (a) $[(5 + 11f)\hat{\mathbf{i}} + (3 + 9f)\hat{\mathbf{j}}]$ m (b) $(5\hat{\mathbf{i}} + 3\hat{\mathbf{j}})$ m is reasonable because it is the starting point. (c) $(16\hat{\mathbf{i}} + 12\hat{\mathbf{j}})$ m is reasonable because it is the endpoint.

47. 1.15°

49. 2.29 km

51. (a) 7.17 km (b) 6.15 km

53. 390 mi/h at 7.37° N of E

55. $(0.456\hat{\mathbf{i}} - 0.708\hat{\mathbf{j}})$ m

57. 240 m at 237°

59. (a) (10.0 m, 16.0 m) (b) You will arrive at the treasure if you take the trees in any order. The directions take you to the average position of the trees.

61. 106°

CHAPTER 4

1. (a) 4.87 km at 209° from E (b) 23.3 m/s (c) 13.5 m/s at 209°

3. 2.50 m/s

5. (a) $(0.800\hat{\mathbf{i}} - 0.300\hat{\mathbf{j}})$ m/s² (b) 339° (c) $(360\hat{\mathbf{i}} - 72.7\hat{\mathbf{j}})$ m, −15.2°

7. (a) $\vec{\mathbf{v}} = 5\hat{\mathbf{i}} + 4t^{3/2}\hat{\mathbf{j}}$ (b) $\vec{\mathbf{r}} = 5t\hat{\mathbf{i}} + 1.6t^{5/2}\hat{\mathbf{j}}$

9. (a) $3.34\hat{\mathbf{i}}$ m/s (b) −50.9°

11. $(7.23 \times 10^3$ m, 1.68×10^3 m)

13. 53.1°

15. (a) 22.6 m (b) 52.3 m (c) 1.18 s

17. (a) The ball clears by 0.889 m. (b) while descending

19. (a) 18.1 m/s (b) 1.13 m (c) 2.79 m

21. 9.91 m/s

23. $\tan^{-1}[(2gh)^{1/2}/v]$

25. 377 m/s²

27. (a) 6.00 rev/s (b) 1.52 km/s² (c) 1.28 km/s²

29. 1.48 m/s² inward and 29.9° backward

31. (a) 13.0 m/s² (b) 5.70 m/s (c) 7.50 m/s²

33. (a) 57.7 km/h at 60.0° W of vertical (b) 28.9 km/h downward

35. 2.02×10^3 s; 21.0% longer

37. $t_{\text{Alan}} = \dfrac{2L/c}{1 - v^2/c^2}$, $t_{\text{Beth}} = \dfrac{2L/c}{\sqrt{1 - v^2/c^2}}$. Beth returns first.

39. 15.3 m

41. 27.7° E of N

43. (a) 9.80 m/s² down (b) 3.72 m

45. (a) 41.7 m/s (b) 3.81 s (c) $(34.1\hat{\mathbf{i}} - 13.4\hat{\mathbf{j}})$ m/s; 36.7 m/s

47. (a) 25.0 m/s²; 9.80 m/s² (b)

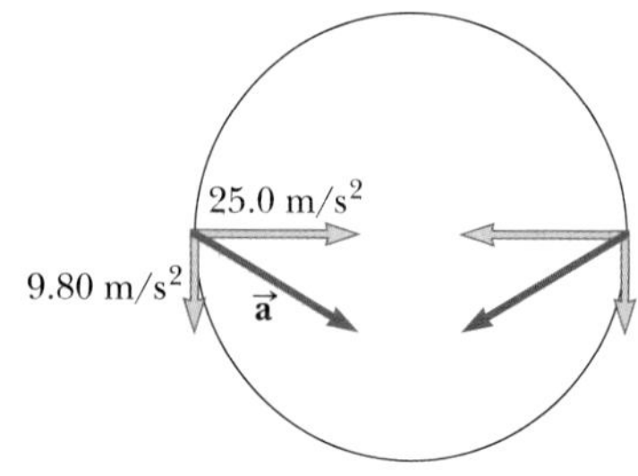

(c) 26.8 m/s² inward at 21.4° below the horizontal

49. (a)

t (s)	0	1	2	3	4	5
r (m)	0	45.7	82.0	109	127	136

t (s)	6	7	8	9	10
r (m)	138	133	124	117	120

(b) The vector $\vec{v}$ tells how $\vec{r}$ is changing. If $\vec{v}$ at a particular point has a component along $\vec{r}$, then $\vec{r}$ will be increasing in magnitude (if $\vec{v}$ is at an angle less than 90° from $\vec{r}$) or decreasing (if the angle between $\vec{v}$ and $\vec{r}$ is more than 90°). To be at a maximum, the distance from the origin must be momentarily staying constant, and the only way that can happen is if the angle between velocity and position is a right angle. Then $\vec{r}$ will be changing in direction at that point, but not in magnitude. (c) The requirement for perpendicularity can be defined as equality between the tangent of the angle between $\vec{v}$ and the x direction and the tangent of the angle between $\vec{r}$ and the y direction. In symbols, this equality can be written $(9.8t - 49)/12 = 12t/(49t - 4.9t^2)$, which has the solution $t = 5.70$ s, giving, in turn, $r = 138$ m. Alternatively, we can require $dr^2/dt = 0 = (d/dt)[(12t)^2 + (49t - 4.9t^2)^2]$, which results in the same equation with the same solution.

51. (a) 26.6° (b) 0.949

53. (a) 6.80 km (b) 3.00 km vertically above the impact point (c) 66.2°

55. (a) 46.5 m/s (b) −77.6° (c) 6.34 s

57. (a) 20.0 m/s, 5.00 s (b) $(16.0\hat{i} - 27.1\hat{j})$ m/s (c) 6.53 s (d) $24.5\hat{i}$ m

59. (a) 43.2 m (b) $(9.66\hat{i} - 25.5\hat{j})$ m/s. Air resistance would ordinarily make the jump distance smaller and the final horizontal and vertical velocity components both somewhat smaller. When the skilled jumper makes his body into an airfoil, he deflects downward the air through which he passes so that it deflects him upward, giving him more time in the air and a longer jump.

61. Safe distances are less than 270 m or greater than 3.48×10^3 m from the western shore.

CHAPTER 5

1. $(6.00\hat{i} + 15.0\hat{j})$ N; 16.2 N

3. (a) $(2.50\hat{i} + 5.00\hat{j})$ N (b) 5.59 N

5. (a) 3.64×10^{-18} N (b) 8.93×10^{-30} N is 408 billion times smaller

7. 2.55 N for an 88.7-kg person

9. (a) 5.00 m/s² at 36.9° (b) 6.08 m/s² at 25.3°

11. (a) $\sim 10^{-22}$ m/s² (b) $\sim 10^{-23}$ m

13. (a) 15.0 lb up (b) 5.00 lb up (c) 0

15. (a) 3.43 kN (b) 0.967 m/s horizontally forward

17.

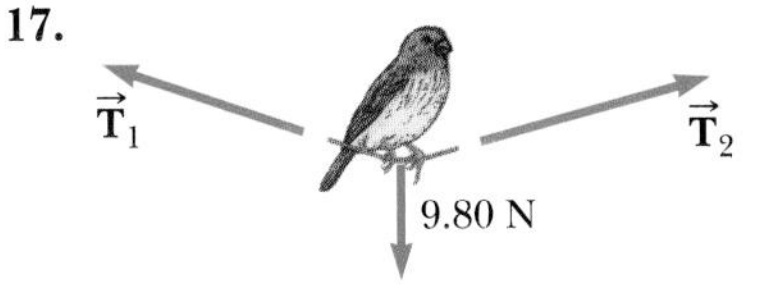

613 N

19. (a) $P\cos 40° - n = 0$ and $P\sin 40° - 220\text{ N} = 0$; $P = 342$ N and $n = 262$ N (b) $P - n\cos 40° - (220\text{ N})\sin 40° = 0$ and $n\sin 40 - (220\text{ N})\cos 40° = 0$; $n = 262$ N and $P = 342$ N (c) The results agree. The methods have a similar level of difficulty. Each involves one equation in one unknown and one equation in two unknowns. If we are interested in finding n without finding P, method (b) is simpler.

23. (a) 49.0 N (b) 49.0 N (c) 98.0 N (d) 24.5 N

25. 8.66 N east

27. (a) 646 N up (b) 646 N up (c) 627 N up (d) 589 N up

29. 3.73 m

31. (a) $F_x > 19.6$ N (b) $F_x \leq -78.4$ N (c)

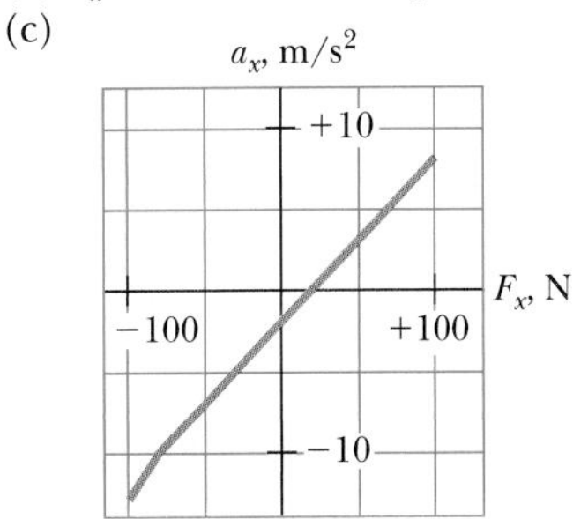

33. (a) 706 N (b) 814 N (c) 706 N (d) 648 N

35. (a) 256 m (b) 42.7 m

37. (a) no (b) 16.9 N backwards + 37.2 N upward = 40.9 N upward and backward at 65.6° with the horizontal

39. (a) 1.78 m/s² (b) 0.368 (c) 9.37 N (d) 2.67 m/s

41. 37.8 N

43. (a)

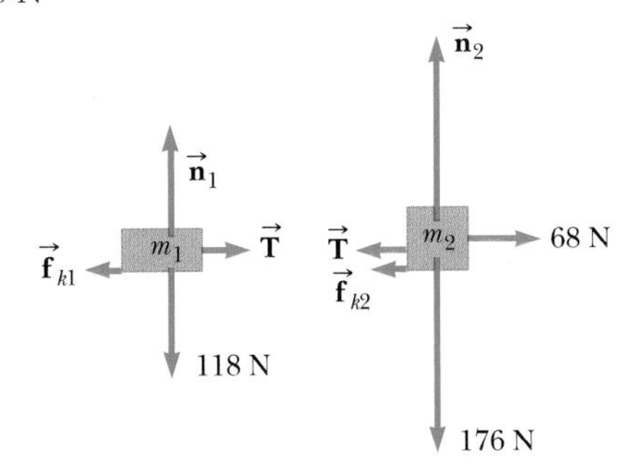

(b) 27.2 N, 1.29 m/s²

45. (a) $a = 0$ if $P < 8.11$ N; $a = -3.33$ m/s² + (1.41/kg) P to the right if $P > 8.11$ N (b) $a = 0$; 3.99 N horizontally backward (c) 10.8 m/s² to the right; 3.45 N to the left (d) The acceleration is zero for all values of P less than 8.11 N. When P passes this threshold, the acceleration jumps to its minimum nonzero value of 8.14 m/s². From there it increases linearly with P toward arbitrarily high values.

47. 72.0 N

49. (a) 2.94 m/s² forward (b) 2.45 m/s² forward (c) 1.19 m/s² up the incline (d) 0.711 m/s² up the incline (e) 16.7° (f) The mass makes no difference. Mathematically, the mass divides out in determinations of acceleration. If several packages of dishes were placed in the truck, they would all slide together, whether they were tied to one another or not.

51. (a)

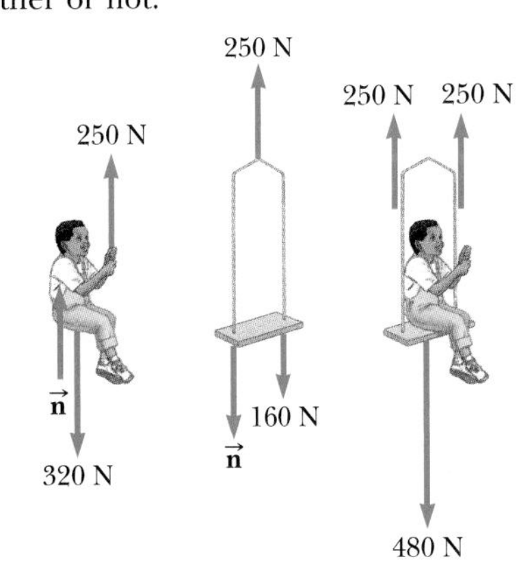

(b) 0.408 m/s² (c) 83.3 N

53. (a) 3.00 s (b) 20.1 m (c) $(18.0\hat{i} - 9.00\hat{j})$ m

55. (a) $a = 12\text{ N}/(4\text{ kg} + m_1)$ forward (b) $12\text{ N}/(1 + m_1/4\text{ kg})$ forward (c) 2.50 m/s^2 forward and 10.0 N forward (d) The force approaches zero (e) The force approaches 12.0 N (f) The tension in a cord of negligible mass is constant along its length.
57. (a) $Mg/2$, $Mg/2$, $Mg/2$, $3Mg/2$, Mg (b) $Mg/2$
59. (a) Both are equal respectively. (b) 1.61×10^4 N (c) 2.95×10^4 N (d) 0 N; 3.51 m/s upward. The first 3.50 m/s of the speed of 3.51 m/s needs no dynamic cause; the motion of the cable continues on its own, as described by the law of "inertia" or "pigheadedness." The increase from 3.50 m/s to 3.51 m/s must be caused by some total upward force on the section of cable. Because its mass is very small compared to a thousand kilograms, however, the force is very small compared to 1.61×10^4 N, the nearly uniform tension of this section of cable.
61. (b)

$\boldsymbol{\theta}$	0	15°	30°	45°	60°
P (N)	40.0	46.4	60.1	94.3	260

63. (a) The net force on the cushion is in a fixed direction, downward and forward making angle $\tan^{-1}(F/mg)$ with the vertical. Starting from rest, it will move along this line with (b) increasing speed. Its velocity changes in magnitude. (c) 1.63 m (d) It will move along a parabola. The axis of the parabola is parallel to the dashed line in the problem figure. If the cushion is thrown in a direction above the dashed line, its path will be concave downward, making its velocity become more and more nearly parallel to the dashed line over time. If the cushion is thrown down more steeply, its path will be concave upward, again making its velocity turn toward the fixed direction of its acceleration.
65. (a) 19.3° (b) 4.21 N
67. $(M + m_1 + m_2)(m_2 g/m_1)$
69. (a) 30.7° (b) 0.843 N
71. (a) $T_1 = \dfrac{2mg}{\sin\theta_1}$, $T_2 = \dfrac{mg}{\sin\theta_2} = \dfrac{mg}{\sin\left[\tan^{-1}\left(\frac{1}{2}\tan\theta_1\right)\right]}$,

$$T_3 = \frac{2\,mg}{\tan\theta_1}$$

(b) $\theta_2 = \tan^{-1}\left(\dfrac{\tan\theta_1}{2}\right)$

CHAPTER 6

1. Any speed up to 8.08 m/s
3. (a) 8.32×10^{-8} N toward the nucleus (b) 9.13×10^{22} m/s^2 inward
5. (a) static friction (b) 0.085 0
7. 2.14 rev/min
9. $v \leq 14.3$ m/s
11. (a) 108 N (b) 56.2 N
13. (a) 4.81 m/s (b) 700 N up
15. No. Tarzan needs a vine of tensile strength 1.38 kN.
17. 3.13 m/s
19. (a) 3.60 m/s^2 (b) zero (c) An observer in the car (a noninertial frame) claims an 18.0-N force toward the left and an 18.0-N force toward the right. An inertial observer (outside the car) claims only an 18.0-N force toward the right.
21. (a) 17.0° (b) 5.12 N
23. (a) 491 N (b) 50.1 kg (c) 2.00 m/s
25. 0.092 8°
27. (a) 32.7 s^{-1} (b) 9.80 m/s^2 down (c) 4.90 m/s^2 down
29. 3.01 N up
31. (a) 1.47 N·s/m (b) 2.04×10^{-3} s (c) 2.94×10^{-2} N
33. (a) 78.3 m/s (b) 11.1 s (c) 121 m
35. (a) $x = k^{-1}\ln(1 + kv_0 t)$ (b) $v = v_0 e^{-kx}$
37. (a) 0.034 7 s^{-1} (b) 2.50 m/s (c) $a = -cv$
39. $v = v_0 e^{-bt/m}$

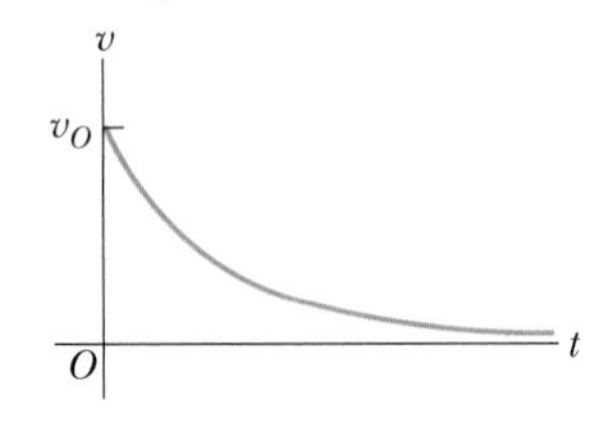

In this model, the object keeps moving forever. It travels a finite distance in an infinite time interval.
41. (a) 106 N up the incline (b) 0.396
43. (a) 11.5 kN (b) 14.1 m/s
45. (a) 0.016 2 kg/m (b) $\frac{1}{2}D\rho A$ (c) 0.778 (d) 1.5% (e) For stacked coffee filters falling in air at terminal speed, the graph of air resistance force as a function of the square of speed demonstrates that the force is proportional to the speed squared, within the experimental uncertainty estimated as 2%. This proportionality agrees with the theoretical model of air resistance at high speeds. The drag coefficient of a coffee filter is $D = 0.78 \pm 2\%$.
47. $g(\cos\phi\tan\theta - \sin\phi)$
49. (b) 732 N down at the equator and 735 N down at the poles
51. (a) The only horizontal force on the car is the force of friction, with a maximum value determined by the surface roughness (described by the coefficient of static friction) and the normal force (here equal to the gravitational force on the car). (b) 34.3 m (c) 68.6 m (d) Braking is better. You should not turn the wheel. If you used any of the available friction force to change the direction of the car, it would be unavailable to slow the car and the stopping distance would be longer. (e) The conclusion is true in general. The radius of the curve you can barely make is twice your minimum stopping distance.
53. (a) 5.19 m/s (b) $T = 555$ N

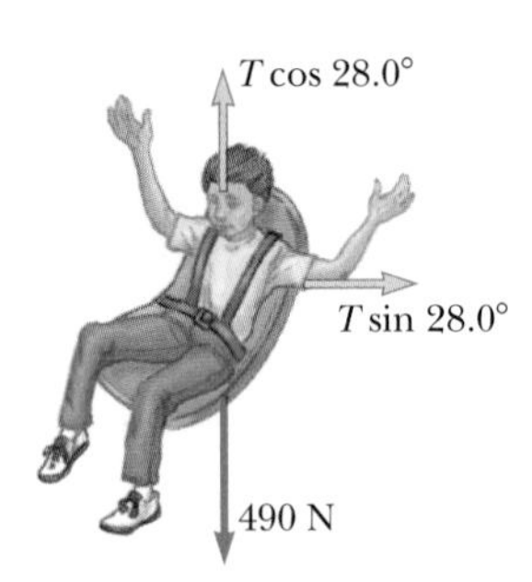

55. (b) 2.54 s; 23.6 rev/min (c) The gravitational and friction forces remain constant. The normal force increases. The person remains in motion with the wall. (d) The gravitational force remains constant. The normal and friction forces decrease. The person slides relative to the wall and downward into the pit.
57. (a) $v_{\min} = \sqrt{\dfrac{Rg(\tan\theta - \mu_s)}{1 + \mu_s\tan\theta}}$, $v_{\max} = \sqrt{\dfrac{Rg(\tan\theta + \mu_s)}{1 - \mu_s\tan\theta}}$

(b) $\mu_s = \tan\theta$ (c) 8.57 m/s $\leq v \leq$ 16.6 m/s
59. (a) 0.013 2 m/s (b) 1.03 m/s (c) 6.87 m/s
61. 12.8 N

CHAPTER 7

1. (a) 31.9 J (b) 0 (c) 0 (d) 31.9 J
3. −4.70 kJ
7. (a) 16.0 J (b) 36.9°
9. (a) 11.3° (b) 156° (c) 82.3°
11. $\vec{\mathbf{A}}$ = 7.05 m at 28.4°
13. (a) 24.0 J (b) −3.00 J (c) 21.0 J
15. (a) 7.50 J (b) 15.0 J (c) 7.50 J (d) 30.0 J
17. (a) 0.938 cm (b) 1.25 J
19. 7.37 N/m
21. 0.299 m/s
23. (a) 0.020 4 m (b) 720 N/m
25. (b) mgR
27. (a) 0.600 J (b) −0.600 J (c) 1.50 J
29. (a) 1.20 J (b) 5.00 m/s (c) 6.30 J
31. (a) 60.0 J (b) 60.0 J
33. 878 kN up
35. (a) 4.56 kJ (b) 6.34 kN (c) 422 km/s^2 (d) 6.34 kN (e) The forces are the same. The two theories agree.
37. (a) 259 kJ, 0, −259 kJ (b) 0, −259 kJ, −259 kJ
39. (a) −196 J (b) −196 J (c) −196 J. The force is conservative.
41. (a) 125 J (b) 50.0 J (c) 66.7 J (d) The force is nonconservative. The results differ.
43. (a) 40.0 J (b) −40.0 J (c) 62.5 J
45. (A/r^2) away from the other particle
47. (a) + at Ⓑ, − at Ⓓ, 0 at Ⓐ, Ⓒ, and Ⓔ
(b) Ⓒ stable; Ⓐ and Ⓔ unstable
(c)

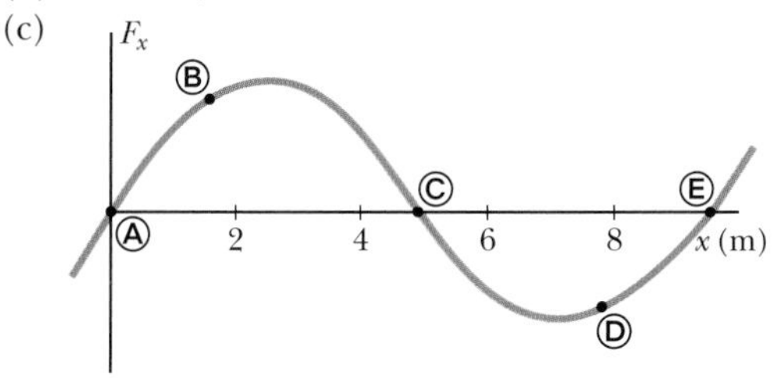

49. (c)

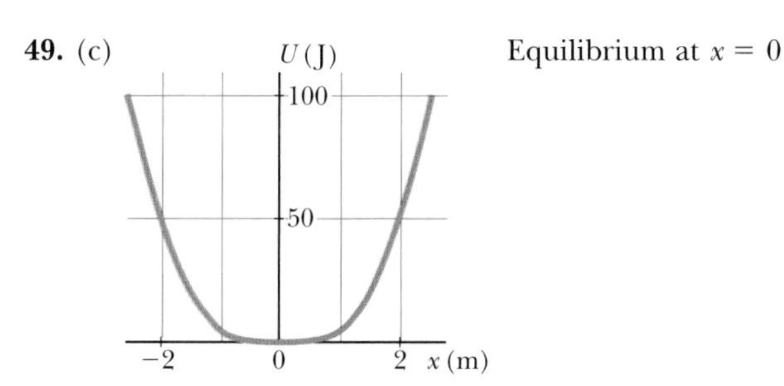

Equilibrium at $x = 0$

(d) 0.823 m/s
51. 90.0 J
53. (a) $x = (3.62\ m)/(4.30 - 23.4m)$ where x is in meters and m is in kilograms (b) 0.095 1 m (c) 0.492 m (d) 6.85 m (e) The situation is impossible. (f) The extension is directly proportional to m when m is only a few grams. Then it grows faster and faster, diverging to infinity for $m = 0.184$ kg.
55. $U(x) = 1 + 4e^{-2x}$. The force must be conservative because the work the force does on the object on which it acts depends only on the original and final positions of the object, not on the path between them.
57. 1.68 m/s
59. 0.799 J

CHAPTER 8

1. (a) $\Delta E_{\text{int}} = Q + T_{\text{ET}} + T_{\text{ER}}$ (b) $\Delta K + \Delta U + \Delta E_{\text{int}} = W + Q + T_{\text{MW}} + T_{\text{MT}}$ (c) $\Delta U = Q + T_{\text{MT}}$
(d) $0 = Q + T_{\text{MT}} + T_{\text{ET}} + T_{\text{ER}}$
3. (a) $v = (3gR)^{1/2}$ (b) 0.098 0 N down
5. 10.2 m
7. (a) 4.43 m/s (b) 5.00 m
9. 5.49 m/s
11. (a) 25.8 m (b) 27.1 m/s^2
13. (a) 650 J (b) 588 J (c) 0 (d) 0 (e) 62.0 J (f) 1.76 m/s
15. (a) −168 J (b) 184 J (c) 500 J (d) 148 J (e) 5.65 m/s
17. 2.04 m
19. 3.74 m/s
21. (a) −160 J (b) 73.5 J (c) 28.8 N (d) 0.679
23. (a) 1.40 m/s (b) 4.60 cm after release (c) 1.79 m/s
25. (a) 0.381 m (b) 0.143 m (c) 0.371 m
27. (a) $a_x = -\mu_k gx/L$ (b) $v = (\mu_k gL)^{1/2}$
29. 875 W
31. ~ 10^4 W
33. $46.2
35. (a) 10.2 kW (b) 10.6 kW (c) 5.82 MJ
37. (a) 11.1 m/s (b) 19.6 m/s^2 upward (c) 2.23×10^3 N upward (d) 1.01×10^3 J (e) 5.14 m/s (f) 1.35 m (g) 1.39 s
39. (a) $(2 + 24t^2 + 72t^4)$ J (b) $12t$ m/s^2; $48t$ N
(c) $(48t + 288t^3)$ W (d) 1 250 J
41. (a) 1.38×10^4 J (b) 3.02×10^4 W
43. (a) 4.12 m (b) 3.35 m
45. (a) 2.17 kW (b) 58.6 kW
47. (a) $x = -4.0$ mm (b) −1.0 cm
49. 33.4 kW
51. (a) 0.225 J (b) $\Delta E_{\text{mech}} = -0.363$ J (c) No. The normal force changes in a complicated way.
53. (a) 100 J (b) 0.410 m (c) 2.84 m/s (d) −9.80 mm (e) 2.85 m/s
55. 0.328
57. 1.24 m/s
59. (a) 0.400 m (b) 4.10 m/s (c) The block stays on the track.
61. $2m$
65. (a) 14.1 m/s (b) −7.90 kJ (c) 800 N (d) 771 N (e) 1.57 kN up

CHAPTER 9

1. (a) $(9.00\hat{\mathbf{i}} - 12.0\hat{\mathbf{j}})$ kg·m/s (b) 15.0 kg·m/s at 307°
3. ~ 10^{-23} m/s
5. (b) $p = \sqrt{2mK}$
7. (a) 13.5 N·s (b) 9.00 kN (c) 18.0 kN
9. 260 N normal to the wall
11. (a) $12.0\hat{\mathbf{i}}$ N·s (b) $4.80\hat{\mathbf{i}}$ m/s (c) $2.80\hat{\mathbf{i}}$ m/s (d) $2.40\hat{\mathbf{i}}$ N
13. (b) small (d) large (e) no difference
15. 301 m/s
17. (a) 2.50 m/s (b) 37.5 kJ (c) Each process is the time-reversal of the other. The same momentum conservation equation describes both.
19. 0.556 m
21. (a) $\vec{\mathbf{v}}_g = 1.15\hat{\mathbf{i}}$ m/s (b) $\vec{\mathbf{v}}_p = -0.346\hat{\mathbf{i}}$ m/s
23. (a) 0.284 (b) 115 fJ and 45.4 fJ

25. 91.2 m/s
27. 2.50 m/s at $-60.0°$
29. $v_{\text{orange}} = 3.99$ m/s, $v_{\text{yellow}} = 3.01$ m/s
31. $(3.00\hat{\mathbf{i}} - 1.20\hat{\mathbf{j}})$ m/s
33. (a) $(-9.33\hat{\mathbf{i}} - 8.33\hat{\mathbf{j}})$ Mm/s (b) 439 fJ
35. $\vec{\mathbf{r}}_{CM} = (0\hat{\mathbf{i}} + 1.00\hat{\mathbf{j}})$ m
37. $\vec{\mathbf{r}}_{CM} = (11.7\hat{\mathbf{i}} + 13.3\hat{\mathbf{j}})$ cm
39. (a) 15.9 g (b) 0.153 m
41. (a) $(1.40\hat{\mathbf{i}} + 2.40\hat{\mathbf{j}})$ m/s (b) $(7.00\hat{\mathbf{i}} + 12.0\hat{\mathbf{j}})$ kg · m/s
43. 0.700 m
45. (a) Yes. $18.0\hat{\mathbf{i}}$ kg · m/s. (b) No. The floor does zero work. (c) Yes. We could say that the final momentum of the cart came from the floor or from the Earth through the floor. (d) No. The kinetic energy came from the original gravitational energy of the elevated load, in amount 27.0 J. (e) Yes. The acceleration is caused by the static friction force exerted by the floor that prevents the caterpillar tracks from slipping backward.
47. (b) 2.06 m/s (c) Yes. The bumper continues to exert a force to the left until the particle has swung down to its lowest point.
49. (a) 3.75 kg · m/s² to the right (b) 3.75 N to the right (c) 3.75 N (d) 2.81 J (e) 1.41 J (f) Friction between sand and belt converts half of the input work into extra internal energy.
51. (a) 39.0 MN (b) 3.20 m/s² up
53. (a) 442 metric tons (b) 19.2 metric tons. This amount is much less than the value suggested. Mathematically, the logarithm in the rocket propulsion equation is not a linear function. Physically, a higher exhaust speed has an extra-large cumulative effect on the rocket frame's final speed, by counting again and again in the speed the frame attains second after second during its burn.
55. 240 s
57. $\left(\dfrac{M + m}{m}\right)\sqrt{\dfrac{gd^2}{2h}}$
59. (a) 0; inelastic
(b) $(-0.250\hat{\mathbf{i}} + 0.750\hat{\mathbf{j}} - 2.00\hat{\mathbf{k}})$ m/s; perfectly inelastic
(c) either $a = -6.74$ with $\vec{\mathbf{v}} = -0.419\,\hat{\mathbf{k}}$ m/s or $a = 2.74$ with $\vec{\mathbf{v}} = -3.58\,\hat{\mathbf{k}}$ m/s
61. (a) $m/M = 0.403$ (b) no changes; no difference
63. (b) 0.042 9 (c) 1.00 (d) Energy is an entirely different thing from momentum. A comparison: When children eat their soup, they do not eat the tablecloth. Another comparison: When a photographer's single-use flashbulb flashes, a magnesium filament oxidizes. Chemical energy disappears. (Internal energy appears and light carries some energy away.) The measured mass of the flashbulb is the same before and after. It can be the same despite the 100% energy conversion because energy and mass are totally different things in classical physics. In the ballistic pendulum, conversion of energy from mechanical into internal does not upset conservation of mass or conservation of momentum.
65. (a) $-0.256\hat{\mathbf{i}}$ m/s and $0.128\hat{\mathbf{i}}$ m/s
(b) $-0.064\,2\hat{\mathbf{i}}$ m/s and 0 (c) 0 and 0
67. (a) 100 m/s (b) 374 J
69. $(3Mgx/L)\hat{\mathbf{j}}$

CHAPTER 10

1. (a) 5.00 rad, 10.0 rad/s, 4.00 rad/s² (b) 53.0 rad, 22.0 rad/s, 4.00 rad/s²
3. (a) 4.00 rad/s² (b) 18.0 rad
5. (a) 5.24 s (b) 27.4 rad
7. (a) 7.27×10^{-5} rad/s (b) 2.57×10^4 s = 428 min
9. 50.0 rev
11. $\sim 10^7$ rev
13. (a) 8.00 rad/s (b) 8.00 m/s, $a_r = -64.0$ m/s², $a_t = 4.00$ m/s² (c) 9.00 rad
15. (a) $(-2.73\hat{\mathbf{i}} + 1.24\hat{\mathbf{j}})$ m (b) in the second quadrant, at 156° (c) $(-1.85\hat{\mathbf{i}} - 4.10\hat{\mathbf{j}})$ m/s (d) toward the third quadrant, at 246°

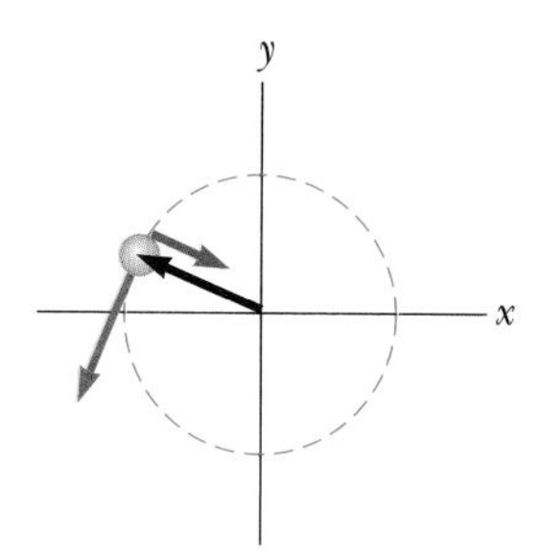

(e) $(6.15\hat{\mathbf{i}} - 2.78\hat{\mathbf{j}})$ m/s² (f) $(24.6\hat{\mathbf{i}} - 11.1\hat{\mathbf{j}})$ N
17. (a) 126 rad/s (b) 3.77 m/s (c) 1.26 km/s² (d) 20.1 m
19. 0.572
21. (a) 143 kg · m² (b) 2.57 kJ
25. (a) 24.5 m/s (b) no; no; no; no; yes
27. 1.28 kg · m²
29. $\sim 10^0$ kg · m²
33. -3.55 N · m
35. (a) 24.0 N · m (b) 0.035 6 rad/s² (c) 1.07 m/s²
37. (a) 0.309 m/s² (b) 7.67 N and 9.22 N
39. 21.5 N
41. 24.5 km
43. 149 rad/s
45. (a) 1.59 m/s (b) 53.1 rad/s
47. (a) 11.4 N, 7.57 m/s², 9.53 m/s down (b) 9.53 m/s
51. (a) $2(Rg/3)^{1/2}$ (b) $4(Rg/3)^{1/2}$ (c) $(Rg)^{1/2}$
53. (a) 500 J (b) 250 J (c) 750 J
55. (a) $\frac{2}{3}g\sin\theta$ for the disk, larger than $\frac{1}{2}g\sin\theta$ for the hoop (b) $\frac{1}{3}\tan\theta$
57. 1.21×10^{-4} kg · m²; height is unnecessary
59. $\frac{1}{3}\ell$
61. (a) 4.00 J (b) 1.60 s (c) yes
63. (a) $\omega = 3F\ell/b$ (b) $\alpha = 3F\ell/mL^2$ (c) and (d) Both larger. A component of the thrust force, exerted by the water about to spray from the ends of the arms, causes a forward torque on the rotor. Notice also that the rotor with bent arms has a slightly smaller moment of inertia than it would if the same metal tubes were straight.
65. (a) $(3g/L)^{1/2}$ (b) $3g/2L$ (c) $-\frac{3}{2}g\hat{\mathbf{i}} - \frac{3}{4}g\hat{\mathbf{j}}$
(d) $-\frac{3}{2}Mg\hat{\mathbf{i}} + \frac{1}{4}Mg\hat{\mathbf{j}}$
67. -0.322 rad/s²
71. (a) 118 N and 156 N (b) 1.17 kg · m²
73. (a) $\alpha = -0.176$ rad/s² (b) 1.29 rev (c) 9.26 rev
75. (a) $\omega(2h^3/g)^{1/2}$ (b) 0.011 6 m (c) Yes; the deflection is only 0.02% of the original height.
79. (a) $2.70R$ (b) $\Sigma F_x = -20mg/7$, $\Sigma F_y = -5mg/7$
81. (a) $(3gh/4)^{1/2}$ (b) $(3gh/4)^{1/2}$
83. (c) $(8Fd/3M)^{1/2}$
85. to the left

CHAPTER 11

1. $-7.00\hat{\mathbf{i}} + 16.0\hat{\mathbf{j}} - 10.0\hat{\mathbf{k}}$
3. (a) $-17.0\hat{\mathbf{k}}$ (b) 70.6°
5. 0.343 N · m horizontally north
7. 45.0°
9. $F_3 = F_1 + F_2$; no
11. $17.5\hat{\mathbf{k}}$ kg · m²/s
13. $(60.0\hat{\mathbf{k}})$ kg · m²/s
15. $mvR[\cos(vt/R) + 1]\hat{\mathbf{k}}$
17. (a) zero (b) $(-mv_i^3 \sin^2\theta \cos\theta/2g)\hat{\mathbf{k}}$ (c) $(-2mv_i^3 \sin^2\theta \cos\theta/g)\hat{\mathbf{k}}$ (d) The downward gravitational force exerts a torque in the $-z$ direction.
19. (a) $-m\ell gt \cos\theta\,\hat{\mathbf{k}}$ (b) The planet exerts a gravitational torque on the ball. (c) $-mg\ell \cos\theta\,\hat{\mathbf{k}}$
23. (a) 0.360 kg · m²/s (b) 0.540 kg · m²/s
25. (a) 0.433 kg · m²/s (b) 1.73 kg · m²/s
27. (a) 1.57×10^8 kg · m²/s (b) 6.26×10^3 s = 1.74 h
29. (a) $\omega_f = \omega_i I_1/(I_1 + I_2)$ (b) $I_1/(I_1 + I_2)$
31. (a) 11.1 rad/s counterclockwise (b) No. 507 J is transformed into internal energy. (c) No. The turntable bearing promptly imparts impulse 44.9 kg · m/s north into the turntable-clay system and thereafter keeps changing the system momentum.
33. 7.14 rev/min
35. (a) Mechanical energy is not conserved; some chemical energy is converted into mechanical energy. Momentum is not conserved. The turntable bearing exerts an external northward force on the axle. Angular momentum is conserved. (b) 0.360 rad/s counterclockwise (c) 99.9 J
37. (a) $mv\ell$ down (b) $M/(M + m)$
39. (a) $\omega = 2mv_i d/[M + 2m]R^2$ (b) No; some mechanical energy changes into internal energy. (c) Momentum is not conserved. The axle exerts a backward force on the cylinder.
41. ~ 10^{-13} rad/s
43. 5.45×10^{22} N · m
45. (a) $1.67\hat{\mathbf{i}}$ m/s (b) 0.033 5 = 3.35% (c) $1.67\hat{\mathbf{i}}$ m/s (d) 15.8 rad/s (e) 1.00 = 100%
47. (a) $7md^2/3$ (b) $mgd\hat{\mathbf{k}}$ (c) $3g/7d$ counterclockwise (d) $2g/7$ upward (e) mgd (f) $\sqrt{6g/7d}$ (g) $m\sqrt{14gd^3/3}$ (h) $\sqrt{2gd/21}$
49. 0.910 km/s
51. (a) $v_i r_i/r$ (b) $T = (mv_i^2 r_i^2)r^{-3}$ (c) $\frac{1}{2}mv_i^2(r_i^2/r^2 - 1)$ (d) 4.50 m/s, 10.1 N, 0.450 J
53. (a) 3 750 kg · m²/s (b) 1.88 kJ (c) 3 750 kg · m²/s (d) 10.0 m/s (e) 7.50 kJ (f) 5.62 kJ
55. (a) $2mv_0$ (b) $2v_0/3$ (c) $4m\ell v_0/3$ (d) $4v_0/9\ell$ (e) mv_0^2 (f) $26mv_0^2/27$ (g) No horizontal forces act on the bola from outside after release, so the horizontal momentum stays constant. Its center of mass moves steadily with the horizontal velocity it had at release. No torques about its axis of rotation act on the bola, so its spin angular momentum stays constant. Internal forces cannot affect momentum conservation and angular momentum conservation, but they can affect mechanical energy. Energy $mv_0^2/27$ changes from mechanical energy into internal energy as the bola takes its stable configuration.
57. An increase of 0.550 s. It is not a significant change.

CHAPTER 12

1. $[(m_1 + m_b)d + m_1\ell/2]/m_2$
3. (3.85 cm, 6.85 cm)
5. (−1.50 m, −1.50 m)
7. (2.54 m, 4.75 m)
9. 177 kg
11. (a) $f_s = 268$ N, $n = 1\,300$ N (b) 0.324
13. 2.94 kN on each rear wheel and 4.41 kN on each front wheel
15. (a) 29.9 N (b) 22.2 N
17. (a) 1.73 rad/s² (b) 1.56 rad/s (c) $(-4.72\hat{\mathbf{i}} + 6.62\hat{\mathbf{j}})$ kN (d) $38.9\hat{\mathbf{j}}$ kN
19. 2.82 m
21. 88.2 N and 58.8 N
23. 4.90 mm
25. 23.8 μm
27. (a) 3.14×10^4 N (b) 6.28×10^4 N
29. 1.65×10^8 N/m²
31. 0.860 mm
33. $n_A = 5.98 \times 10^5$ N, $n_B = 4.80 \times 10^5$ N
35. 9.00 ft
37. (a)

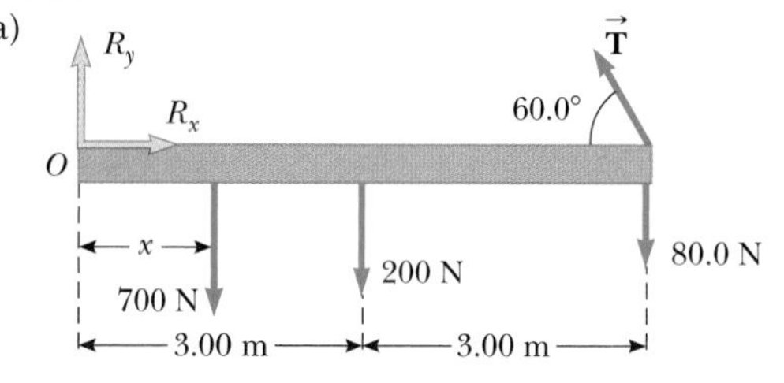

(b) $T = 343$ N, $R_x = 171$ N to the right, $R_y = 683$ N up (c) 5.13 m
39. (a) $T = F_g(L + d)/[\sin\theta\,(2L + d)]$ (b) $R_x = F_g(L + d)\cot\theta/(2L + d)$, $R_y = F_gL/(2L + d)$
41. $\vec{\mathbf{F}}_A = (-6.47 \times 10^5\hat{\mathbf{i}} + 1.27 \times 10^5\hat{\mathbf{j}})$ N, $\vec{\mathbf{F}}_B = 6.47 \times 10^5\hat{\mathbf{i}}$ N
43. 5.08 kN, $R_x = 4.77$ kN, $R_y = 8.26$ kN
45. (a) 20.1 cm to the left of the front edge; $\mu_k = 0.571$ (b) 0.501 m
47. (a) $M = (m/2)(2\mu_s \sin\theta - \cos\theta)(\cos\theta - \mu_s \sin\theta)^{-1}$ (b) $R = (m + M)g(1 + \mu_s^2)^{1/2}$ $F = g[M^2 + \mu_s^2(m + M)^2]^{1/2}$
49. (b) AB compression 732 N, AC tension 634 N, BC compression 897 N
51. (a) 133 N (b) $n_A = 429$ N and $n_B = 257$ N (c) $R_x = 133$ N and $R_y = -257$ N
55. 1.09 m
57. (a) 4 500 N (b) 4.50×10^6 N/m² (c) The board will break.
59. (a) $P_y = (F_g/L)(d - ah/g)$ (b) 0.306 m (c) $(-306\hat{\mathbf{i}} + 553\hat{\mathbf{j}})$ N

CHAPTER 13

1. ~ 10^{-7} N toward you
3. (a) 2.50×10^{-5} N toward the 500-kg object (b) between the objects and 0.245 m from the 500-kg object
5. $(-100\hat{\mathbf{i}} + 59.3\hat{\mathbf{j}})$ pN
7. 7.41×10^{-10} N
9. 0.613 m/s² toward the Earth
11. $\rho_{\text{Moon}}/\rho_{\text{Earth}} = \frac{2}{3}$
13. 1.26×10^{32} kg
15. 1.90×10^{27} kg
17. 8.92×10^7 m
19. After 3.93 yr, Mercury would be farther from the Sun than Pluto.

21. $\vec{\mathbf{g}} = \frac{Gm}{\ell^2}\left(\frac{1}{2} + \sqrt{2}\right)$ toward the opposite corner

23. (a) $\vec{\mathbf{g}} = 2MGr(r^2 + a^2)^{-3/2}$ toward the center of mass (b) At $r = 0$, the fields of the two objects are equal in magnitude and opposite in direction, to add to zero. (d) When r is much greater than a, the fact that the two masses are separate is unimportant. They create a total field like that of a single object of mass $2M$.

25. (a) 1.84×10^9 kg/m^3 (b) 3.27×10^6 m/s^2 (c) -2.08×10^{13} J

27. (a) -1.67×10^{-14} J (b) Each object will slowly accelerate toward the center of the triangle, where the three will simultaneously collide.

29. (b) 340 s

31. 1.66×10^4 m/s

35. (a) 5.30×10^3 s (b) 7.79 km/s (c) 6.43×10^9 J

37. (b) 1.00×10^7 m (c) 1.00×10^4 m/s

39. (a) 0.980 (b) 127 yr (c) -2.13×10^{17} J

43. (b) $2[Gm^3(1/2r - 1/R)]^{1/2}$

45. (a) -7.04×10^4 J (b) -1.57×10^5 J (c) 13.2 m/s

47. 7.79×10^{14} kg

49. $\omega = 0.057\,2$ rad/s or 1 rev in 110 s

51. (a) $m_2(2G/d)^{1/2}(m_1 + m_2)^{-1/2}$ and $m_1(2G/d)^{1/2}(m_1 + m_2)^{-1/2}$; relative speed $(2G/d)^{1/2}(m_1 + m_2)^{1/2}$ (b) 1.07×10^{32} J and 2.67×10^{31} J

53. (a) 200 Myr (b) $\sim 10^{41}$ kg; $\sim 10^{11}$ stars

55. $(GM_E/4R_E)^{1/2}$

59. $(800 + 1.73 \times 10^{-4})\hat{\mathbf{i}}$ m/s and $(800 - 1.73 \times 10^{-4})\hat{\mathbf{i}}$ m/s

61. 18.2 ms

CHAPTER 14

1. 0.111 kg

3. 6.24 MPa

5. 1.62 m

7. 7.74×10^{-3} m^2

9. 271 kN horizontally backward

11. 5.88×10^6 N down; 196 kN outward; 588 kN outward

13. 0.722 mm

15. 10.5 m; no because some alcohol and water evaporate

17. 98.6 kPa

19. (a) 1.57 Pa, 1.55×10^{-2} atm, 11.8 mm Hg (b) The fluid level in the tap should rise. (c) blockage of flow of the cerebrospinal fluid

21. 0.258 N down

23. (a) $1.017\,9 \times 10^3$ N down, $1.029\,7 \times 10^3$ N up (b) 86.2 N (c) By either method of evaluation, the buoyant force is 11.8 N up.

25. (a) 1.20×10^3 N/s (b) 0

27. (a) 7.00 cm (b) 2.80 kg

31. 1 430 m^3

33. 1 250 kg/m^3 and 500 kg/m^3

35. (a) 17.7 m/s (b) 1.73 mm

37. 31.6 m/s

39. 0.247 cm

41. (a) 2.28 N toward Holland (b) 1.74×10^6 s

43. (a) 1 atm + 15.0 MPa (b) 2.95 m/s (c) 4.34 kPa

45. 2.51×10^{-3} m^3/s

47. (a) 4.43 m/s (b) The siphon can be no higher than 10.3 m.

49. 12.6 m/s

51. 1.91 m

55. 0.604 m

57. If the helicopter could create the air it expels downward, the mass flow rate of the air would have to be at least 233 kg/s. In reality, the rotor takes in air from above, which is moving over a larger area with lower speed, and blows it downward at higher speed. The amount of this air has to be at least a few times larger than 233 kg every second.

61. 17.3 N and 31.7 N

63. 90.04%

65. 758 Pa

67. 4.43 m/s

69. (a) 1.25 cm (b) 13.8 m/s

71. (c) 1.70 m^2

CHAPTER 15

1. (a) The motion repeats precisely. (b) 1.81 s (c) No, the force is not in the form of Hooke's law

3. (a) 1.50 Hz, 0.667 s (b) 4.00 m (c) π rad (d) 2.83 m

5. (b) 18.8 cm/s, 0.333 s (c) 178 cm/s^2, 0.500 s (d) 12.0 cm

7. 40.9 N/m

9. 18.8 m/s, 7.11 km/s^2

11. (a) 40.0 cm/s, 160 cm/s^2 (b) 32.0 cm/s, -96.0 cm/s^2 (c) 0.232 s

13. 0.628 m/s

15. 2.23 m/s

17. (a) 28.0 mJ (b) 1.02 m/s (c) 12.2 mJ (d) 15.8 mJ

19. 2.60 cm and -2.60 cm

21. (a) at 0.218 s and at 1.09 s (b) 0.014 6 W

23. (b) 0.628 s

25. Assuming simple harmonic motion, (a) 0.820 m/s, (b) 2.57 rad/s^2, and (c) 0.641 N. More precisely, (a) 0.817 m/s, (b) 2.54 rad/s^2, and (c) 0.634 N. The answers agree to two digits. The answers computed from conservation of energy and from Newton's second law are more precisely correct. With this amplitude, the motion of the pendulum is approximately simple harmonic.

29. 0.944 kg · m^2

33. (a) 5.00×10^{-7} kg · m^2 (b) 3.16×10^{-4} N · m/rad

35. 1.00×10^{-3} s^{-1}

37. (a) 7.00 Hz (b) 2.00% (c) 10.6 s

39. (a) 1.00 s (b) 5.09 cm

41. 318 N

43. 1.74 Hz

45. (a) 2.09 s (b) 0.477 Hz (c) 36.0 cm/s (d) $(0.064\,8\ \text{m}^2/\text{s}^2)\,m$ (e) $(9.00/\text{s}^2)\,m$ (f) Period, frequency, and maximum speed are all independent of mass in this situation. The energy and the force constant are directly proportional to mass.

47. (a) $2Mg$, $Mg(1 + y/L)$ (b) $T = (4\pi/3)(2L/g)^{1/2}$, 2.68 s

49. 6.62 cm

51. 9.19×10^{13} Hz

53. (a)

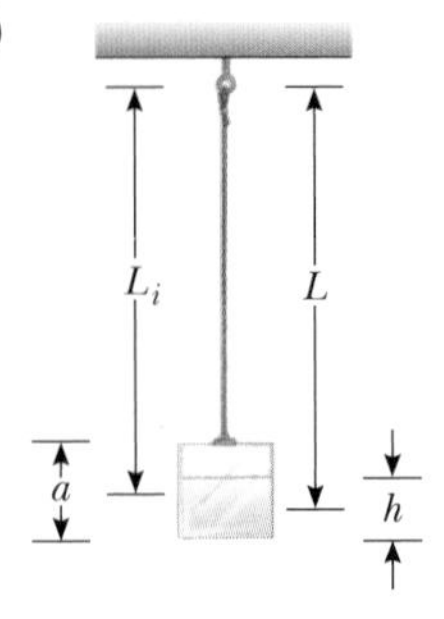

(b) $\dfrac{dT}{dt} = \dfrac{\pi\, dM/dt}{2\rho a^2 g^{1/2}[L_i + (dM/dt)t/2\rho a^2]^{1/2}}$

(c) $T = 2\pi g^{-1/2}\left[L_i + \left(\dfrac{dM}{dt}\right)\left(\dfrac{t}{2\rho a^2}\right)\right]^{1/2}$

55. $f = (2\pi L)^{-1}\left(gL + \dfrac{kh^2}{M}\right)^{1/2}$

57. (b) 1.23 Hz

59. (a) 3.00 s (b) 14.3 J (c) 25.5°

61. If the cyclist goes over washboard bumps at one certain speed, they can excite a resonance vibration of the bike, so large in amplitude as to make the rider lose control. $\sim 10^1$ m

69. (b) after 42.2 minutes

CHAPTER 16

1. $y = 6\,[(x - 4.5t)^2 + 3]^{-1}$

3. (a) the P wave (b) 665 s

5. (a) $(3.33\hat{\mathbf{i}})$ m/s (b) −5.48 cm (c) 0.667 m, 5.00 Hz (d) 11.0 m/s

7. 0.319 m

9. 2.00 cm, 2.98 m, 0.576 Hz, 1.72 m/s

11. (a) 31.4 rad/s (b) 1.57 rad/m (c) $y = (0.120 \text{ m}) \sin(1.57x - 31.4t)$ where x is in meters and t is in seconds (d) 3.77 m/s (e) 118 m/s²

13. (a) 0.250 m (b) 40.0 rad/s (c) 0.300 rad/m (d) 20.9 m (e) 133 m/s (f) $+x$

15. (a) $y = (8.00 \text{ cm}) \sin(7.85x + 6\pi t)$ (b) $y = (8.00 \text{ cm}) \sin(7.85x + 6\pi t - 0.785)$

17. (a) −1.51 m/s, 0 (b) 16.0 m, 0.500 s, 32.0 m/s

19. (a) 0.500 Hz, 3.14 rad/s (b) 3.14 rad/m (c) $(0.100 \text{ m}) \sin(3.14\, x/\text{m} - 3.14\, t/\text{s})$ (d) $(0.100 \text{ m}) \sin(-3.14\, t/\text{s})$ (e) $(0.100 \text{ m}) \sin(4.71 \text{ rad} - 3.14\, t/\text{s})$ (f) 0.314 m/s

21. 80.0 N

23. 520 m/s

25. 1.64 m/s²

27. 13.5 N

29. 185 m/s

31. 0.329 s

35. 55.1 Hz

37. (a) 62.5 m/s (b) 7.85 m (c) 7.96 Hz (d) 21.1 W

39. $\sqrt{2}\,\mathcal{P}_0$

41. (a) $A = 40$ (b) $A = 7.00$, $B = 0$, $C = 3.00$. One can take the dot product of the given equation with each one of $\hat{\mathbf{i}}, \hat{\mathbf{j}}$, and $\hat{\mathbf{k}}$. (c) $A = 0$, $B = 7.00$ mm, $C = 3.00$/m, $D = 4.00$/s, $E = 2.00$. Consider the average value of both sides of the given equation to find A. Then consider the maximum value of both sides to find B. You can evaluate the partial derivative of both sides of the given equation with respect to x and separately with respect to t to obtain equations yielding C and D upon chosen substitutions for x and t. Then substitute $x = 0$ and $t = 0$ to obtain E.

45. ~ 1 min

47. 0.456 m/s

49. (a) 39.2 N (b) 0.892 m (c) 83.6 m/s

51. (a) The energy a wave crest carries is constant in the absence of absorption. Then the rate at which energy moves beyond a fixed distance from the source, which is the power of the wave, is constant. The power is proportional to the square of the amplitude and to the wave speed. The speed decreases as the wave moves into shallower water near shore, so the amplitude must increase. (b) 8.31 m (c) As the water depth goes to zero, our model would predict zero speed and infinite amplitude. The amplitude must be finite as the wave comes ashore. As the speed decreases, the wavelength also decreases. When it becomes comparable to the water depth, or smaller, the expression $v = \sqrt{gd}$ no longer applies.

53. (a) $\mathcal{P} = (0.050\,0 \text{ kg/s})v_{y,\max}^2$ (b) The power is proportional to the square of the maximum element speed. (c) $(7.5 \times 10^{-4} \text{ kg})\, v_{y,\max}^2 = \frac{1}{2}m_3 v_{y,\max}^2$ (d) $(0.300 \text{ kg})\, v_{y,\max}^2$

55. 0.084 3 rad

59. (a) $(0.707)2(L/g)^{1/2}$ (b) $L/4$

61. 3.86×10^{-4}

63. (a) $\dfrac{\mu\omega^3}{2k}A_0^2 e^{-2bx}$ (b) $\dfrac{\mu\omega^3}{2k}A_0^2$ (c) e^{-2bx}

65. (a) $\mu_0 + (\mu_L - \mu_0)x/L$

CHAPTER 17

1. 5.56 km. As long as the speed of light is much greater than the speed of sound, its actual value does not matter.

3. 0.196 s

5. 7.82 m

7. (a) 826 m (b) 1.47 s

9. (a) 0.625 mm (b) 1.50 mm to 75.0 μm

11. (a) 2.00 μm, 40.0 cm, 54.6 m/s (b) −0.433 μm (c) 1.72 mm/s

13. $\Delta P = (0.200 \text{ N/m}^2) \sin(62.8x/\text{m} - 2.16 \times 10^4 t/\text{s})$

15. 5.81 m

17. 66.0 dB

19. (a) 3.75 W/m² (b) 0.600 W/m²

21. (a) 2.34 m and 0.390 m (b) 0.161 N/m² for both notes (c) 4.25×10^{-7} m and 7.09×10^{-8} m (d) The wavelengths and displacement amplitudes would be larger by a factor of 1.09. The answer to part (b) would be unchanged.

23. (a) 1.32×10^{-4} W/m² (b) 81.2 dB

25. (a) 0.691 m (b) 691 km

27. 65.6 dB

29. (a) 30.0 m (b) 9.49×10^5 m

31. (a) 332 J (b) 46.4 dB

33. (a) 3.04 kHz (b) 2.08 kHz (c) 2.62 kHz, 2.40 kHz

35. 26.4 m/s

37. 19.3 m

39. (a) 56.3 s (b) 56.6 km farther along

41. 2.82×10^8 m/s

43. It is unreasonable, implying a sound level of 123 dB. Nearly all the missing mechanical energy becomes internal energy in the latch.

45. (a) f is a few hundred hertz. $\lambda \sim 1$ m, duration ~ 0.1 s. (b) Yes. The frequency can be close to 1 000 Hz. If the person clapping his or her hands is at the base of the pyramid, the echo can drop somewhat in frequency and in loudness as sound returns, with the later cycles coming from the smaller and more distant upper risers. The sound could imitate some particular bird and could in fact be a recording of the call.

49. (a) 0.515/min (b) 0.614/min

51. (a) 55.8 m/s (b) 2 500 Hz

53. 1 204.2 Hz

55. (a) 0.642 W (b) 0.004 28 = 0.428%

57. (a) The sound through the metal arrives first. (b) (365 m/s) Δt (c) 46.3 m (d) The answer becomes

$$\ell = \frac{\Delta t}{\dfrac{1}{331\text{ m/s}} - \dfrac{1}{v_r}}$$

where v_r is the speed of sound in the rod. As v_r goes to infinity, the travel time in the rod becomes negligible. The answer approaches (331 m/s) Δt, which is the distance the sound travels in air during the delay time.

59. (a) 0.948° (b) 4.40°
61. 1.34×10^4 N
63. (a) 6.45 (b) 0

CHAPTER 18

1. (a) −1.65 cm (b) −6.02 cm (c) 1.15 cm
3. (a) $+x$, $-x$ (b) 0.750 s (c) 1.00 m
5. (a) 9.24 m (b) 600 Hz
7. (a) 2 (b) 9.28 m and 1.99 m
9. (a) 156° (b) 0.058 4 cm
11. 15.7 m, 31.8 Hz, 500 m/s
13. At 0.089 1 m, 0.303 m, 0.518 m, 0.732 m, 0.947 m, 1.16 m from one speaker
15. (a) 4.24 cm (b) 6.00 cm (c) 6.00 cm (d) 0.500 cm, 1.50 cm, 2.50 cm
17. 0.786 Hz, 1.57 Hz, 2.36 Hz, 3.14 Hz
19. (a) 350 Hz (b) 400 kg
21. (a) 163 N (b) 660 Hz
23. $\dfrac{Mg}{4Lf^2 \tan\theta}$
25. (a) 3 loops (b) 16.7 Hz (c) 1 loop
27. (a) 3.66 m/s (b) 0.200 Hz
29. (a) 0.357 m (b) 0.715 m
31. 0.656 m and 1.64 m
33. n(206 Hz) for $n = 1$ to 9 and n(84.5 Hz) for $n = 2$ to 23
35. 50.0 Hz, 1.70 m
37. (a) 350 m/s (b) 1.14 m
39. (21.5 ± 0.1) m. The data suggest 0.6-Hz uncertainty in the frequency measurements, which is only a little more than 1%.
41. (a) 1.59 kHz (b) odd-numbered harmonics (c) 1.11 kHz
43. 5.64 beats/s
45. (a) 1.99 beats/s (b) 3.38 m/s
47. The second harmonic of E is close to the third harmonic of A, and the fourth harmonic of C# is close to the fifth harmonic of A.
49. (a) The yo-yo's downward speed is $dL/dt = (0.8\text{ m/s}^2)(1.2\text{ s}) = 0.960$ m/s. The instantaneous wavelength of the fundamental string wave is given by $d_{NN} = \lambda/2 = L$, so $\lambda = 2L$ and $d\lambda/dt = 2\,dL/dt = 2(0.96\text{ m/s}) = 1.92$ m/s. (b) For the second harmonic, the wavelength is equal to the length of the string. Then the rate of change of wavelength is equal to $dL/dt = 0.960$ m/s, half as much as for the first harmonic. (c) A yo-yo of different mass will hold the string under different tension to make each string wave vibrate with a different frequency, but the geometrical argument given in parts (a) and (b) still applies to the wavelength. The answers are unchanged: $d\lambda_1/dt = 1.92$ m/s and $d\lambda_2/dt = 0.960$ m/s.
51. (a) 34.8 m/s (b) 0.977 m
53. 3.85 m/s away from the station or 3.77 m/s toward the station
55. (a) 59.9 Hz (b) 20.0 cm
57. (a) $\frac{1}{2}$ (b) $[n/(n+1)]^2 T$ (c) $\frac{9}{16}$
59. $y_1 + y_2 = 11.2 \sin(2.00x - 10.0t + 63.4°)$
61. (a) 78.9 N (b) 211 Hz

CHAPTER 19

1. (a) −274°C (b) 1.27 atm (c) 1.74 atm
3. (a) −320°F (b) 77.3 K
5. 3.27 cm
7. (a) 0.176 mm (b) 8.78 μm (c) 0.093 0 cm³
9. (a) −179°C is attainable. (b) −376°C is below 0 K and unattainable.
11. (a) 99.8 mL (b) about 6% of the volume change of the acetone
13. (a) 99.4 cm³ (b) 0.943 cm
15. 5 336 images
17. (a) 400 kPa (b) 449 kPa
19. 1.50×10^{29} molecules
21. 472 K
23. (a) 41.6 mol (b) 1.20 kg, nearly in agreement with the tabulated density
25. (a) 1.17 g (b) 11.5 mN (c) 1.01 kN (d) The molecules must be moving very fast.
27. 4.39 kg
29. (a) 7.13 m (b) The open end of the tube should be at the bottom after the bird surfaces so that the water can drain out. There is no other requirement. Air does not tend to bubble out of a narrow tube.
31. (a) 94.97 cm (b) 95.03 cm
33. 3.55 cm
35. It falls by 0.094 3 Hz.
37. (a) Expansion makes density drop. (b) $5 \times 10^{-5}(°\text{C})^{-1}$
39. (a) $h = nRT/(mg + P_0A)$ (b) 0.661 m
41. We assume $\alpha\,\Delta T$ is much less than 1.
43. Yes, as long as the coefficients of expansion remain constant. The lengths L_C and L_S at 0°C need to satisfy $17L_C = 11L_S$. Then the steel rod must be longer. With $L_S - L_C = 5.00$ cm, the only possibility is $L_S = 14.2$ cm and $L_C = 9.17$ cm.
45. (a) 0.340% (b) 0.480%
47. 2.74 m
49. (b) 1.33 kg/m³
53. No. Steel would need to be 2.30 times stronger.
55. (a) $L_f = L_i e^{\alpha\Delta T}$ (b) 2.00×10^{-4}%; 59.4%
57. (a) 6.17×10^{-3} kg/m (b) 632 N (c) 580 N; 192 Hz
59. 4.54 m

CHAPTER 20

1. (10.0 + 0.117)°C
3. 0.234 kJ/kg · °C
5. 1.78×10^4 kg
7. 29.6°C
9. (a) 0.435 cal/g · °C (b) We cannot make a definite identification. The material might be an unknown alloy or a material not listed in the table. It might be beryllium.
11. 23.6°C
13. 1.22×10^5 J
15. 0.294 g
17. 0.414 kg
19. (a) 0°C (b) 114 g
21. −1.18 MJ

23. -466 J

25. (a) $-4P_iV_i$ (b) It is proportional to the square of the volume, according to $T = (P_i/nRV_i)V^2$.

27. $Q = -720$ J

29.

	Q	W	ΔE_{int}
BC	$-$	0	$-$
CA	$-$	$+$	$-$
AB	$+$	$-$	$+$

31. (a) 7.50 kJ (b) 900 K

33. -3.10 kJ, 37.6 kJ

35. (a) 0.041 0 m^3 (b) $+5.48$ kJ (c) -5.48 kJ

37. 10.0 kW

39. 51.2°C

41. 74.8 kJ

43. (a) 0.964 kg or more (b) The test samples and the inner surface of the insulation can be prewarmed to 37.0°C as the box is assembled. Then nothing changes in temperature during the test period, and the masses of the test samples and insulation make no difference.

45. 3.49×10^3 K

47. Intensity is defined as power per area perpendicular to the direction of energy flow. The direction of sunlight is along the line from the Sun to the object. The perpendicular area is the projected flat, circular area enclosed by the *terminator*, the line that separates day and night on the object. The object radiates infrared light outward in all directions. The area perpendicular to this energy flow is its spherical surface area. The steady-state surface temperature is 279 K = 6°C. We find this temperature to be chilly, well below comfortable room temperatures.

49. 2.27 km

51. (a) 16.8 L (b) 0.351 L/s

53. $c = \mathcal{P}/\rho R\,\Delta T$

55. 5.87×10^{4}°C

57. 5.31 h

59. 1.44 kg

61. 38.6 m^3/d

63. 9.32 kW

65. (a) The equation $dT/dr = \mathcal{P}/4\pi kr^2$ represents the law of thermal conduction, incorporating the definition of thermal conductivity, applied to a spherical surface within the shell. The rate of energy transfer $\mathcal{P}$ must be the same for all radii so that each bit of material stays at a temperature that is constant in time. (b) We separate the variables T and r in the thermal conduction equation and integrate the equation between points on the interior and exterior surfaces. (c) 18.5 W (d) With $\mathcal{P}$ now known, we separate the variables again and integrate between a point on the interior surface and any point within the shell. (e) $T = 5°\text{C} + 184\ \text{cm}\cdot°\text{C}\,[1/(3\ \text{cm}) - 1/r]$ (f) 29.5°C

CHAPTER 21

1. (a) 4.00 u $= 6.64 \times 10^{-24}$ g (b) 55.9 u $= 9.28 \times 10^{-23}$ g (c) 207 u $= 3.44 \times 10^{-22}$ g

3. 0.943 N, 1.57 Pa

5. 3.21×10^{12} molecules

7. 3.32 mol

9. (a) 3.54×10^{23} atoms (b) 6.07×10^{-21} J (c) 1.35 km/s

11. (a) 8.76×10^{-21} J for both (b) 1.62 km/s for helium and 514 m/s for argon

13. (a) 3.46 kJ (b) 2.45 kJ (c) -1.01 kJ

15. Between 10^{-2}°C and 10^{-3}°C

17. $13.5PV$

19. (a) 1.39 atm (b) 366 K, 253 K (c) 0, -4.66 kJ, -4.66 kJ

21. 227 K

23. (a)

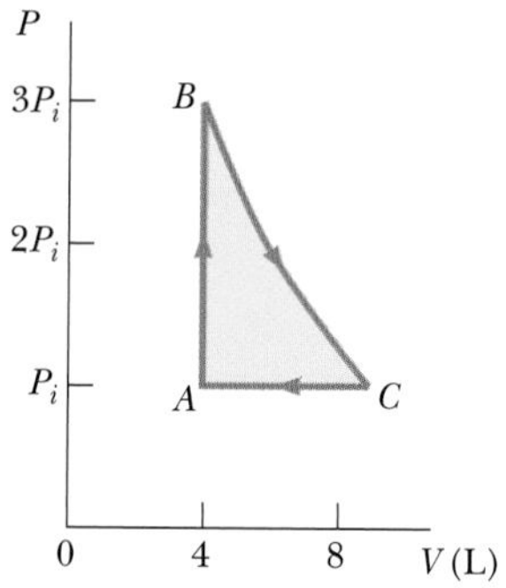

(b) 8.77 L (c) 900 K (d) 300 K (e) -336 J

25. (a) 28.0 kJ (b) 46.0 kJ (c) isothermal process: $P_f = 10.0$ atm; adiabatic process: $P_f = 25.1$ atm

27. (a) 9.95 cal/K, 13.9 cal/K (b) 13.9 cal/K, 17.9 cal/K

29. Sulfur dioxide is the gas in Table 21.2 with the greatest molecular mass. If the effective spring constants for various chemical bonds are comparable, SO_2 can then be expected to have low frequencies of atomic vibration. Vibration can be excited at lower temperature for sulfur dioxide than for the other gases. Some vibration may be going on at 300 K.

31. (a) 6.80 m/s (b) 7.41 m/s (c) 7.00 m/s

35. (a) 2.37×10^4 K (b) 1.06×10^3 K

37. (b) 0.278

39. (a) 100 kPa, 66.5 L, 400 K, 5.82 kJ, 7.48 kJ, -1.66 kJ
(b) 133 kPa, 49.9 L, 400 K, 5.82 kJ, 5.82 kJ, 0
(c) 120 kPa, 41.6 L, 300 K, 0, -909 J, $+909$ J
(d) 120 kPa, 43.3 L, 312 K, 722 J, 0, $+722$ J

41. (b) 447 J/kg·°C agrees with the tabulated value within 0.3%. (c) 127 J/kg·°C agrees with the tabulated value within 2%.

43. (b) The expressions are equal because $PV = nRT$ and $\gamma = (C_V + R)/C_V = 1 + R/C_V$ give $R = (\gamma - 1)C_V$, so $PV = n(\gamma - 1)C_VT$ and $PV/(\gamma - 1) = nC_VT$

45. 510 K and 290 K

47. 0.623

49. (a) Pressure increases as volume decreases. (d) 0.500 atm^{-1}, 0.300 atm^{-1}

51. (a) 7.27×10^{-20} J (b) 2.20 km/s (c) 3 510 K. The evaporating molecules are exceptional, at the high-speed tail of the distribution of molecular speeds. The average speed of molecules in the liquid and in the vapor is appropriate only to room temperature.

53. (a) 0.514 m^3 (b) 2.06 m^3 (c) 2.38×10^3 K (d) -480 kJ (e) 2.28 MJ

55. 1.09×10^{-3}, 2.69×10^{-2}, 0.529, 1.00, 0.199, 1.01×10^{-41}, $1.25 \times 10^{-1\,082}$

59. (a) 0.203 mol (b) $T_B = T_C = 900$ K, $V_C = 15.0$ L

(c, d)	P, atm	V, L	T, K	E_{int}, kJ
A	1.00	5.00	300	0.760
B	3.00	5.00	900	2.28
C	1.00	15.0	900	2.28
A	1.00	5.00	300	0.760

(e) Lock the piston in place and put the cylinder into an oven at 900 K. Keep the gas in the oven while gradually letting the gas expand to lift a load on the piston as far as it can. Move the cylinder from the oven back to the 300-K room and let the gas cool and contract.

(f, g)	Q, kJ	W, kJ	ΔE_{int}, kJ
AB	1.52	0	1.52
BC	1.67	−1.67	0
CA	−2.53	+1.01	−1.52
$ABCA$	0.656	−0.656	0

61. (b) 1.60×10^4 K

CHAPTER 22

1. (a) 6.94% (b) 335 J
3. (a) 10.7 kJ (b) 0.533 s
5. 55.4%
7. 77.8 W
9. (a) 67.2% (b) 58.8 kW
11. The actual efficiency of 0.069 8 is less than four-tenths of the Carnot efficiency of 0.177.
13. (a) 741 J (b) 459 J
15. (a) 564 K (b) 212 kW (c) 47.5%
17. (b) $1 - T_c/T_h$, the same as for a single reversible engine (c) $(T_c + T_h)/2$ (d) $(T_h T_c)^{1/2}$
19. 9.00
23. 72.2 J
25. 23.1 mW
27. (a) 244 kPa (b) 192 J
29. (a) 51.2% (b) 36.2%
33. 195 J/K
35. 1.02 kJ/K
37. ~ 10^0 W/K from metabolism; much more if you are using high-power electric appliances or an automobile
39. 5.76 J/K; the temperature is constant if the gas is ideal.
41. (a) 1 (b) 6
43. (a)

Result	Number of ways to draw
All R	1
2 R, 1 G	3
1 R, 2 G	3
All G	1

(b)

Result	Number of ways to draw
All R	1
4R, 1G	5
3R, 2G	10
2R, 3G	10
1R, 4G	5
All G	1

45. (a) 214 J, 64.3 J (b) −35.7 J, −35.7 J. The net effect would be the transport of energy by heat from the cold to the hot reservoir without expenditure of external work. (c) 333 J, 233 J (d) 83.3 J, 83.3 J, 0. The net effect would be converting energy, taken in by heat, entirely into energy output by work in a cyclic process. (e) −0.111 J/K. The entropy of the Universe would have decreased.
47. (a) 5.00 kW (b) 763 W
49. (a) $2nRT_i \ln 2$ (b) 0.273
51. 5.97×10^4 kg/s
53. (a) 8.48 kW (b) 1.52 kW (c) 1.09×10^4 J/K (d) The COP drops by 20.0%.
55. (a) $10.5nRT_i$ (b) $8.50nRT_i$ (c) 0.190 (d) This efficiency is much less than the 0.833 for a Carnot engine operating between the temperatures used here.
57. (a) $nC_P \ln 3$ (b) Both ask for the change in entropy between the same two states of the same system. Entropy is a state variable. The change in entropy does not depend on path, but only on original and final states.
61. (a) 20.0°C (c) $\Delta S = +4.88$ J/K (d) The mixing is irreversible. It is clear that warm water and cool water do not come unmixed, and the entropy change is positive.

CHAPTER 23

1. (a) +160 zC, 1.01 u (b) +160 zC, 23.0 u (c) −160 zC, 35.5 u (d) +320 zC, 40.1 u (e) −480 zC, 14.0 u (f) +640 zC, 14.0 u (g) +1.12 aC, 14.0 u (h) −160 zC, 18.0 u
3. The force is ~ 10^{26} N.
5. (a) 1.59 nN away from the other (b) 1.24×10^{36} times larger (c) 8.61×10^{-11} C/kg
7. 0.872 N at 330°
9. (a) 2.16×10^{-5} N toward the other (b) 8.99×10^{-7} N away from the other
11. (a) 82.2 nN toward the other particle (b) 2.19 Mm/s
13. (a) 55.8 pN/C down (b) 102 nN/C up
15. The field at the origin can be to the right if the unknown charge is $-9Q$, or the field can be to the left if and only if the unknown charge is $+27Q$.
17. (a) $5.91k_e q/a^2$ at 58.8° (b) $5.91k_e q^2/a^2$ at 58.8°
19. (a) $k_e Qx\hat{\mathbf{i}}/(R^2 + x^2)^{3/2}$ (b) As long as the charge is symmetrically placed, the number of charges does not matter. A continuous ring corresponds to n becoming larger without limit.
21. 1.59×10^6 N/C toward the rod
23. (a) $6.64\hat{\mathbf{i}}$ MN/C (b) $24.1\hat{\mathbf{i}}$ MN/C (c) $6.40\hat{\mathbf{i}}$ MN/C (d) $0.664\hat{\mathbf{i}}$ MN/C, taking the axis of the ring as the x axis
25. (a) 93.6 MN/C; the near-field approximation is 104 MN/C, about 11% high. (b) 0.516 MN/C; the charged-particle approximation is 0.519 MN/C, about 0.6% high.
27. $-21.6\hat{\mathbf{i}}$ MN/C
31. (a) 86.4 pC for each (b) 324 pC, 459 pC, 459 pC, 432 pC (c) 57.6 pC, 106 pC, 154 pC, 96.0 pC
33.

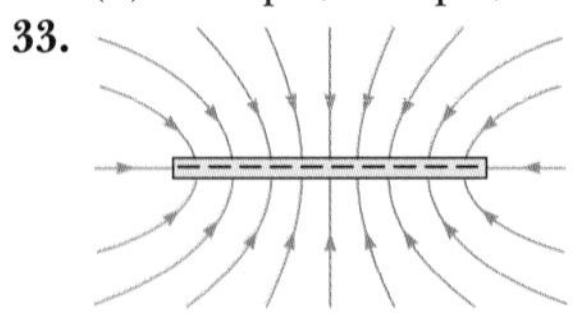

35. (a)

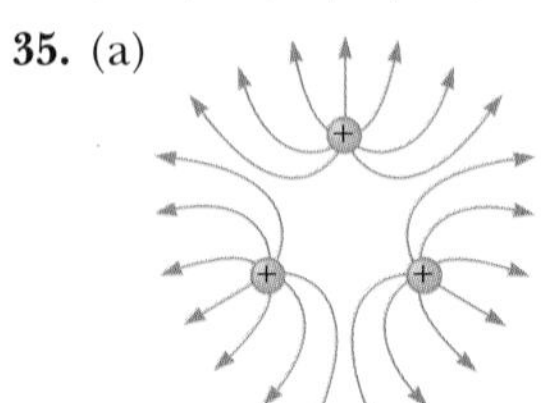

The field is zero at the center of the triangle. (b) $1.73\, k_e q\hat{\mathbf{j}}/a^2$
37. (a) 61.3 Gm/s² (b) 19.5 μs (c) 11.7 m (d) 1.20 fJ
39. K/ed in the direction of motion
41. (a) 111 ns (b) 5.68 mm (c) $(450\hat{\mathbf{i}} + 102\hat{\mathbf{j}})$ km/s

43. (a) 21.8 μm (b) 2.43 cm
45. (a) 10.9 nC (b) 5.44 mN
47. 40.9 N at 263°
49. $Q = 2L\sqrt{\dfrac{k(L - L_i)}{k_e}}$
53. $-707\hat{\mathbf{j}}$ mN
55. (a) $\theta_1 = \theta_2$
57. (a) 0.307 s (b) Yes. Ignoring gravity makes a difference of 2.28%.
59. (a) $\vec{\mathbf{F}} = 1.90(k_e q^2/s^2)(\hat{\mathbf{i}} + \hat{\mathbf{j}} + \hat{\mathbf{k}})$ (b) $\vec{\mathbf{F}} = 3.29(k_e q^2/s^2)$ in the direction away from the diagonally opposite vertex
65. $\dfrac{k_e \lambda_0}{2x_0}(-\hat{\mathbf{i}})$

CHAPTER 24

1. 4.14 MN/C
3. (a) aA (b) bA (c) 0
5. 1.87 kN $\cdot$ m²/C
7. (a) -6.89 MN $\cdot$ m²/C (b) The number of lines entering exceeds the number leaving by 2.91 times or more.
9. $-Q/\epsilon_0$ for S_1; 0 for S_2; $-2Q/\epsilon_0$ for S_3; 0 for S_4
11. (a) $+Q/2\epsilon_0$ (b) $-Q/2\epsilon_0$
13. -18.8 kN $\cdot$ m²/C
15. 0 if $R \le d$; $(2\lambda/\epsilon_0)\sqrt{R^2 - d^2}$ if $R > d$
17. (a) 3.20 MN $\cdot$ m²/C (b) 19.2 MN $\cdot$ m²/C (c) The answer to part (a) could change, but the answer to part (b) would stay the same.
19. 2.33×10^{21} N/C
21. 508 kN/C up
23. -2.48 μC/m²
25. 5.94×10^5 m/s
27. $\vec{\mathbf{E}} = \rho r/2\epsilon_0$ away from the axis
29. (a) 0 (b) 7.19 MN/C away from the center
31. (a) 51.4 kN/C outward (b) 646 N $\cdot$ m²/C
33. (a) 0 (b) 5 400 N/C outward (c) 540 N/C outward
35. (a) +708 nC/m² and −708 nC/m² (b) +177 nC and −177 nC
37. 2.00 N
39. (a) $-\lambda, +3\lambda$ (b) $3\lambda/2\pi\epsilon_0 r$ radially outward
41. (a) 80.0 nC/m² on each face (b) $9.04\hat{\mathbf{k}}$ kN/C (c) $-9.04\hat{\mathbf{k}}$ kN/C
43. (b) $Q/2\epsilon_0$ (c) Q/ϵ_0
45. (a) The charge on the exterior surface is −55.7 nC distributed uniformly. (b) The charge on the interior surface is +55.7 nC. It might have any distribution. (c) The charge within the shell is −55.7 nC. It might have any distribution.
47. (a) $\rho r/3\epsilon_0$, $Q/4\pi\epsilon_0 r^2$, 0, $Q/4\pi\epsilon_0 r^2$, all radially outward (b) $-Q/4\pi b^2$ and $+Q/4\pi c^2$
49. $\theta = \tan^{-1}[qQ/(2\pi\epsilon_0 dmv^2)]$
51. (a) σ/ϵ_0 away from both plates (b) 0 (c) σ/ϵ_0 away from both plates
53. $\sigma/2\epsilon_0$ radially outward
57. $\vec{\mathbf{E}} = a/2\epsilon_0$ radially outward
61. (b) $\vec{\mathbf{g}} = GM_E r/R_E{}^3$ radially inward
63. (a) −4.00 nC (b) +9.56 nC (c) +4.00 nC and +5.56 nC
65. (a) If the volume charge density is nonzero, the field cannot be uniform in magnitude. (b) The field must be uniform in magnitude along any line in the direction of the field. The field magnitude can vary between points in a plane perpendicular to the field lines.

CHAPTER 25

1. (a) 152 km/s (b) 6.49 Mm/s
3. 1.67 MN/C
5. 38.9 V; the origin
7. (a) $2QE/k$ (b) QE/k (c) $2\pi\sqrt{m/k}$ (d) $2(QE - \mu_k mg)/k$
9. (a) 0.400 m/s (b) It is the same. Each bit of the rod feels a force of the same size as before.
11. (a) 1.44×10^{-7} V (b) -7.19×10^{-8} V (c) -1.44×10^{-7} V, $+7.19 \times 10^{-8}$ V
13. (a) 6.00 m (b) −2.00 μC
15. −11.0 MV
17. 8.95 J
21. (a) no point at a finite distance from the particles (b) $2k_e q/a$
23. (a) 10.8 m/s and 1.55 m/s (b) Greater. The conducting spheres will polarize each other, with most of the positive charge of one and of the negative charge of the other on their inside faces. Immediately before they collide, their centers of charge will be closer than their geometric centers, so they will have less electric potential energy and more kinetic energy.
25. $5k_e q^2/9d$
27. $\left[\left(1 + \sqrt{\tfrac{1}{8}}\right)\dfrac{k_e q^2}{mL}\right]^{1/2}$
29. (a) 10.0 V, −11.0 V, −32.0 V (b) 7.00 N/C in the $+x$ direction
31. $\vec{\mathbf{E}} = (-5 + 6xy)\hat{\mathbf{i}} + (3x^2 - 2z^2)\hat{\mathbf{j}} - 4yz\hat{\mathbf{k}}$; 7.07 N/C
33. $E_y = \dfrac{k_e Q}{y\sqrt{\ell^2 + y^2}}$
35. (a) C/m² (b) $k_e\alpha[L - d\ln(1 + L/d)]$
37. −1.51 MV
39. (a) 0, 1.67 MV (b) 5.84 MN/C away, 1.17 MV (c) 11.9 MN/C away, 1.67 MV
41. (a) 248 nC/m² (b) 496 nC/m²
43. (a) 450 kV (b) 7.51 μC
45. (a) 1.42 mm (b) 9.20 kV/m
47. 253 MeV
49. (a) −27.2 eV (b) −6.80 eV (c) 0
51. (a) Yes. The inverse proportionality of potential to radius is sufficient to show that $200R = 150(R + 10\text{ cm})$, so $R = 30.0$ cm. Then $Q = 6.67$ nC. (b) Almost but not quite. Two possibilities exist: $R = 29.1$ cm with $Q = 6.79$ nC and $R = 3.44$ cm with $Q = 804$ pC.
53. 4.00 nC at (−1.00 m, 0) and −5.01 nC at (0, 2.00 m)
55. $k_e Q^2/2R$
57. $V_2 - V_1 = (-\lambda/2\pi\epsilon_0)\ln(r_2/r_1)$
61. (b) $E_r = 2k_e p\cos\theta/r^3$; $E_\theta = k_e p\sin\theta/r^3$; yes; no (c) $V = k_e py(x^2 + y^2)^{-3/2}$; $\vec{\mathbf{E}} = 3k_e pxy(x^2 + y^2)^{-5/2}\hat{\mathbf{i}} + k_e p(2y^2 - x^2)(x^2 + y^2)^{-5/2}\hat{\mathbf{j}}$
63. $V = \pi k_e C\left[R\sqrt{x^2 + R^2} + x^2\ln\left(\dfrac{x}{R + \sqrt{x^2 + R^2}}\right)\right]$
65. (a) 488 V (b) 78.1 aJ (c) 306 km/s (d) 390 Gm/s² toward the negative plate (e) 651 aN toward the negative plate (f) 4.07 kN/C
67. Outside the sphere, $E_x = 3E_0a^3xz(x^2 + y^2 + z^2)^{-5/2}$, $E_y = 3E_0a^3yz(x^2 + y^2 + z^2)^{-5/2}$, and $E_z = E_0 + E_0a^3(2z^2 - x^2 - y^2)(x^2 + y^2 + z^2)^{-5/2}$. Inside the sphere, $E_x = E_y = E_z = 0$.

CHAPTER 26

1. (a) 48.0 μC (b) 6.00 μC
3. (a) 1.33 $\mu C/m^2$ (b) 13.3 pF
5. (a) 11.1 kV/m toward the negative plate (b) 98.3 nC/m^2 (c) 3.74 pF (d) 74.7 pC
7. 4.42 μm
9. (a) 2.68 nF (b) 3.02 kV
11. (a) 15.6 pF (b) 256 kV
13. (a) 3.53 μF (b) 6.35 V and 2.65 V (c) 31.8 μC on each
15. 6.00 pF and 3.00 pF
17. (a) 5.96 μF (b) 89.5 μC on 20 μF, 63.2 μC on 6 μF, 26.3 μC on 15 μF and on 3 μF
19. 120 μC; 80.0 μC and 40.0 μC
21. ten
23. 6.04 μF
25. 12.9 μF
27. (a) 216 μJ (b) 54.0 μJ
31. (a) 1.50 μC (b) 1.83 kV
35. 9.79 kg
37. (a) 81.3 pF (b) 2.40 kV
39. 1.04 m
41. 22.5 V
43. (b) -8.78×10^6 N/C·m; $-5.53 \times 10^{-2}\hat{\mathbf{i}}$ N
45. 19.0 kV
47. (a) 11.2 pF (b) 134 pC (c) 16.7 pF (d) 66.9 pC
49. (a) 40.0 μJ (b) 500 V
51. 0.188 m^2
55. Gasoline has 194 times the specific energy content of the battery and 727 000 times that of the capacitor.
57. (a) $Q_0^2 d(\ell - x)/(2\ell^3\epsilon_0)$ (b) $Q_0^2 d/(2\ell^3\epsilon_0)$ to the right (c) $Q_0^2/(2\ell^4\epsilon_0)$ (d) $Q_0^2/(2\ell^4\epsilon_0)$; they are precisely the same.
59. 4.29 μF
61. (a) The additional energy comes from work done by the electric field in the wires as it forces more charge onto the already-charged plates. (b) The charge increases according to $Q/Q_0 = \kappa$.
63. 750 μC on C_1 and 250 μC on C_2
65. $\frac{4}{3}C$

CHAPTER 27

1. 7.50×10^{15} electrons
3. (a) $0.632 I_0\tau$ (b) $0.999\,95 I_0\tau$ (c) $I_0\tau$
5. (a) 17.0 A (b) 85.0 kA/m^2
7. (a) 2.55 A/m^2 (b) $5.31 \times 10^{10}\ m^{-3}$ (c) 1.20×10^{10} s
9. (a) 221 nm (b) No. The deuterons are so far apart that one does not produce a significant potential at the location of the next.
11. 6.43 A
13. (a) 1.82 m (b) 280 μm
15. $6.00 \times 10^{-15}/\Omega \cdot m$
17. 0.180 V/m
19. (a) 31.5 n$\Omega \cdot$m (b) 6.35 MA/m^2 (c) 49.9 mA (d) 659 μm/s (e) 0.400 V
21. 0.125
23. 5.00 A, 24.0 Ω
25. 5.49 Ω
27. 36.1%
29. (a) 3.17 m (b) 340 W
31. (a) 0.660 kWh (b) $0.039 6
33. $0.232
35. $0.269/day
37. (a) 184 W (b) 461°C
39. ~ $1
41. Any diameter d and length ℓ related by $d^2 = (4.77 \times 10^{-8}\ m)\ell$, such as length 0.900 m and diameter 0.207 mm. Yes.
45. Experimental resistivity = 1.47 $\mu\Omega \cdot$m ±4%, in agreement with 1.50 $\mu\Omega \cdot$m
47. (a) 8.00 V/m in the x direction (b) 0.637 Ω (c) 6.28 A (d) 200 MA/m^2 in the x direction
49. (a) 667 A (b) 50.0 km
51.

Material	$\alpha' = \alpha/(1 - 20\alpha)$
Silver	$4.1 \times 10^{-3}/°C$
Copper	$4.2 \times 10^{-3}/°C$
Gold	$3.6 \times 10^{-3}/°C$
Aluminum	$4.2 \times 10^{-3}/°C$
Tungsten	$4.9 \times 10^{-3}/°C$
Iron	$5.6 \times 10^{-3}/°C$
Platinum	$4.25 \times 10^{-3}/°C$
Lead	$4.2 \times 10^{-3}/°C$
Nichrome	$0.4 \times 10^{-3}/°C$
Carbon	$-0.5 \times 10^{-3}/°C$
Germanium	$-24 \times 10^{-3}/°C$
Silicon	$-30 \times 10^{-3}/°C$

53. It is exact. The resistance can be written $R = \rho L^2/V$ and the stretched length as $L = L_i(1 + \delta)$. Then the result follows directly.
55. (b) Charge is conducted by current in the direction of decreasing potential. Energy is conducted by heat in the direction of decreasing temperature.
59. Coat the surfaces of entry and exit with a material of much higher conductivity than the bulk material of the object. The electric potential will be essentially uniform over each of these electrodes. Current will be distributed over the whole area where each electrode is in contact with the resistive object.
61. (a) $\dfrac{\epsilon_0 \ell}{2d}(\ell + 2x + \kappa\ell - 2\kappa x)$

(b) $\dfrac{\epsilon_0 \ell v\,\Delta V(\kappa - 1)}{d}$ clockwise
63. 2.71 MΩ
65. 2 020°C

CHAPTER 28

1. (a) 6.73 Ω (b) 1.97 Ω
3. (a) 12.4 V (b) 9.65 V
5. (a) 17.1 Ω (b) 1.99 A for 4 Ω and 9 Ω, 1.17 A for 7 Ω, 0.818 A for 10 Ω
7. (a) 227 mA (b) 5.68 V
9. (a) 75.0 V (b) 25.0 W, 6.25 W, and 6.25 W; 37.5 W
11. R_1 = 1.00 kΩ, R_2 = 2.00 kΩ, R_3 = 3.00 kΩ
13. It decreases. Closing the switch opens a new path with resistance of only 20 Ω. R = 14.0 Ω
15. 14.2 W to 2 Ω, 28.4 W to 4 Ω, 1.33 W to 3 Ω, 4.00 W to 1 Ω
17. 846 mA down in the 8-Ω resistor; 462 mA down in the middle branch; 1.31 A up in the right-hand branch
19. (a) −222 J and 1.88 kJ (b) 687 J, 128 J, 25.6 J, 616 J, 205 J (c) 1.66 kJ of chemical energy is transformed into internal energy.

21. 0.395 A and 1.50 V
23. 1.00 A up in 200 Ω, 4.00 A up in 70 Ω, 3.00 A up in 80 Ω, 8.00 A down in 20 Ω, 200 V
25. (a) 909 mA (b) -1.82 V $= V_b - V_a$
27. (a) 5.00 s (b) 150 μC (c) 4.06 μA
29. (a) -61.6 mA (b) 0.235 μC (c) 1.96 A
31. (a) 6.00 V (b) 8.29 μs
33. 0.302 Ω
35. 16.6 kΩ
37. (a) 12.5 A, 6.25 A, 8.33 A (b) No. Together they would require 27.1 A.
39. (a) 1.02 A down (b) 0.364 A down (c) 1.38 A up (d) 0 (e) 66.0 μC
41. 2.22 h
43. a is 4.00 V higher
45. 87.3 %
47. 6.00 Ω, 3.00 Ω
49. (a) $I_1 = \dfrac{IR_2}{R_1 + R_2}$, $I_2 = \dfrac{IR_1}{R_1 + R_2}$
51. (a) $R \leq 1\,050$ Ω (b) $R \geq 10.0$ Ω
53. (a) 9.93 μC (b) 33.7 nA (c) 334 nW (d) 337 nW
55. (a) 40.0 W (b) 80.0 V, 40.0 V, 40.0 V
57. (a) 9.30 V, 2.51 Ω (b) 186 V and 3.70 A (c) 1.09 A (d) 143 W (e) 0.162 Ω (f) 3.00 mW (g) 2.21 W (h) The power output of the emf depends on the resistance connected to it. A question about "the rest of the power" is not meaningful when it compares circuits with different currents. The net emf produces more current in the circuit where the copper wire is used. The net emf delivers more power when the copper wire is used, 687 W rather than 203 W without the wire. Nearly all this power results in extra internal energy in the internal resistance of the batteries, which rapidly rise to a high temperature. The circuit with the copper wire is unsafe because the batteries overheat. The circuit without the copper wire is unsafe because it delivers an electric shock to the experimenter.
61. (a) 0 in 3 kΩ and 333 μA in 12 kΩ and 15 kΩ (b) 50.0 μC (c) $(278\ \mu\text{A})e^{-t/180\text{ ms}}$ (d) 290 ms
63. (a) $R_x = R_2 - R_1/4$ (b) $R_x = 2.75$ Ω. The station is inadequately grounded.
65. (a) $2\Delta t/3$ (b) $3\Delta t$

CHAPTER 29

1. (a) up (b) toward you, out of the plane of the paper (c) no deflection (d) into the plane of the paper
3. $(-20.9\hat{\mathbf{j}})$ mT
5. 48.9° or 131°
7. 2.34 aN
9. (a) 49.6 aN south (b) 1.29 km
11. $r_\alpha = r_d = \sqrt{2}r_p$
13. (a) 5.00 cm (b) 8.78×10^6 m/s
15. 7.88 pT
17. 244 kV/m
19. 0.278 m
21. (a) 4.31×10^7 rad/s (b) 51.7 Mm/s
23. 70.1 mT
25. 0.245 T east
27. (a) 4.73 N (b) 5.46 N (c) 4.73 N
29. 1.07 m/s
31. $2\pi rIB \sin\theta$ up
33. 2.98 μN west
35. 9.98 N · m clockwise as seen looking down from above
37. (a) Minimum: pointing north at 48.0° below the horizontal; maximum: pointing south at 48.0° above the horizontal. (b) 1.07 μJ
39. The magnetic moment cannot go to infinity. Its maximum value is 5.37 mA · m² for a single-turn circle. Smaller by 21% and by 40% are the magnetic moments for the single-turn square and triangle. Circular coils with several turns have magnetic moments inversely proportional to the number of turns, approaching zero as the number of turns goes to infinity.
41. 43.1 μT
43. (a) The electric current experiences a magnetic force. (c) no, no, no
45. 12.5 km. It will not hit the Earth, but it will perform a hairpin turn and go back parallel to its original direction.
47. (a) -8.00×10^{-21} kg · m/s (b) 8.90°
49. (a) $(3.52\hat{\mathbf{i}} - 1.60\hat{\mathbf{j}})$ aN (b) 24.4°
51. 128 mT north at an angle of 78.7° below the horizontal
53. 0.588 T
55. 0.713 A counterclockwise as seen from above
57. 2.75 Mrad/s
59. 3.70×10^{-24} N · m
61. (a) 1.33 m/s (b) Positive ions moving toward you in magnetic field to the right feel upward magnetic force and migrate upward in the blood vessel. Negative ions moving toward you feel downward magnetic force and accumulate at the bottom of this section of vessel. Therefore, both species can participate in the generation of the emf.
63. (a) $v = qBh/m$. If its speed is slightly less than the critical value, the particle moves in a semicircle of radius h and leaves the field with velocity $-v\hat{\mathbf{j}}$. If its speed is incrementally greater, the particle moves in a quarter circle of the same radius and moves along the boundary outside the field with velocity $v\hat{\mathbf{i}}$. (b) The particle moves in a smaller semicircle of radius mv/qB, attaining final velocity $-v\hat{\mathbf{j}}$. (c) The particle moves in a circular arc of radius $r = mv/qB$, leaving the field with velocity $v\sin\theta\,\hat{\mathbf{i}} + v\cos\theta\,\hat{\mathbf{j}}$, where $\theta = \sin^{-1}(h/r)$.
65. (a) For small angular displacements, the torque on the dipole is equal to a negative constant times the displacement.
(b) $f = \dfrac{1}{2\pi}\sqrt{\dfrac{\mu B}{I}}$
(c) The equilibrium orientation of the needle shows the direction of the field. In a stronger field, the frequency is higher. The frequency is easy to measure precisely over a wide range of values. 2.04 mT.

CHAPTER 30

1. 12.5 T
3. (a) 28.3 μT into the paper (b) 24.7 μT into the paper
5. $\dfrac{\mu_0 I}{4\pi x}$ into the paper
7. (a) $2I_1$ out of the page (b) $6I_1$ into the page
9. (a) along the line ($y = -0.420$ m, $z = 0$) (b) $(-34.7\hat{\mathbf{j}})$ mN (c) $(17.3\hat{\mathbf{j}})$ kN/C
11. at A, 53.3 μT toward the bottom of the page; at B, 20.0 μT toward the bottom of the page; at C, zero.
13. (a) $4.5\dfrac{\mu_0 I}{\pi L}$

(b) Stronger. Each of the two sides meeting at the nearby vertex contributes more than twice as much to the net field at the new point.

15. $(-13.0\hat{\mathbf{j}})\ \mu\text{T}$

17. $(-27.0\hat{\mathbf{i}})\ \mu\text{N}$

19. parallel to the wires and 0.167 m below the upper wire

21. (a) opposite directions (b) 67.8 A (c) Smaller. A smaller gravitational force would be pulling down on the wires, therefore tending to reduce the angle.

23. 20.0 μT toward the bottom of the page

25. at a, 200 μT toward the top of the page; at b, 133 μT toward the bottom of the page

27. (a) 6.34 mN/m inward (b) Greater. The magnetic field increases toward the outside of the bundle, where more net current lies inside a particular radius. The larger field exerts a stronger force on the strand we choose to monitor.

29. (a) 0

(b) $\dfrac{\mu_0 I}{2\pi R}$ tangent to the wall in a counterclockwise sense

(c) $\dfrac{\mu_0 I^2}{(2\pi R)^2}$ inward

31. (a) $\mu_0 b r_1{}^2/3$ (b) $\mu_0 b R^3/3r_2$

35. 31.8 mA

37. 226 μN away from the center of the loop, 0

39. (a) 3.13 mWb (b) 0

41. (a) 7.40 μWb (b) 2.27 μWb

43. 2.02

45. (a) 8.63×10^{45} electrons (b) 4.01×10^{20} kg

47. $\dfrac{\mu_0 I}{2\pi w} \ln\left(1 + \dfrac{w}{b}\right)\hat{\mathbf{k}}$

49. $(-12.0\hat{\mathbf{k}})$ mN

51. 143 pT

57. (a) 2.46 N upward (b) The magnetic field at the center of the loop or on its axis is much weaker than the magnetic field immediately outside the wire. The wire has negligible curvature on the scale of 1 mm, so we model the lower loop as a long, straight wire to find the field it creates at the location of the upper wire. (c) 107 m/s^2 upward

59. (a) 274 μT (b) $(-274\hat{\mathbf{j}})\ \mu$T (c) $(1.15\hat{\mathbf{i}})$ mN (d) $(0.384\hat{\mathbf{i}})$ m/s^2 (e) acceleration is constant (f) $(0.999\hat{\mathbf{i}})$ m/s

61. $\dfrac{\mu_0 I_1 I_2 L}{\pi R}$ to the right

65. $\frac{1}{3}\rho\mu_0\omega R^2$

67. (a) $\dfrac{\mu_0 I(2r^2 - a^2)}{\pi r(4r^2 - a^2)}$ to the left

(b) $\dfrac{\mu_0 I(2r^2 + a^2)}{\pi r(4r^2 + a^2)}$ toward the top of the page

CHAPTER 31

1. (a) 101 μV tending to produce clockwise current as seen from above (b) It is twice as large in magnitude and in the opposite sense.

3. 9.82 mV

5. (b) 3.79 mV (c) 28.0 mV

7. 160 A

9. (a) 1.60 A counterclockwise (b) 20.1 μT (c) left

11. $-(14.2\text{ mV})\cos(120t)$

13. 283 μA upward

15. $(68.2\text{ mV})e^{-1.6t}$, tending to produce counterclockwise current

17. 272 m

19. 13.3 mA counterclockwise in the lower loop and clockwise in the upper loop

21. (a) 1.18 mV. The wingtip on the pilot's left is positive. (b) no change (c) No. If we try to connect the wings into a circuit with the lightbulb, we run an extra insulated wire along the wing. In a uniform field, the total emf generated in the one-turn coil is zero.

23. (a) 3.00 N to the right (b) 6.00 W

25. 24.1 V with the outer contact positive

27. 2.83 mV

29. (a) $F = N^2B^2w^2v/R$ to the left (b) 0 (c) $F = N^2B^2w^2v/R$ to the left

31. 145 μA upward in the picture

33. 1.80 mN/C upward and to the left, perpendicular to $\vec{r}_1$

35. (a) 7.54 kV (b) The plane of the loop is parallel to $\vec{\mathbf{B}}$.

37. $(28.6\text{ mV})\sin(4\pi t)$

39. (a) 110 V (b) 8.53 W (c) 1.22 kW

41. Both are correct. The current in the magnet creates an upward magnetic field  , so the N and S poles on the solenoid core are shown correctly. On the rail in front of the brake, the upward magnetic flux increases as the coil approaches, so a current is induced here to create downward magnetic field  . This current is clockwise, so the S pole on the rail is shown correctly. On the rail behind the brake, the upward magnetic flux is decreasing. The induced current in the rail will produce upward magnetic field by being counterclockwise  as the picture correctly shows.

43. (b) Larger R makes current smaller, so the loop must travel faster to maintain equality of magnetic force and weight. (c) The magnetic force is proportional to the product of field and current, while the current is itself proportional to field. If B becomes two times smaller, the speed must become four times larger to compensate.

45. $-(7.22\text{ mV})\cos(2\pi\ 523t/\text{s})$

47.

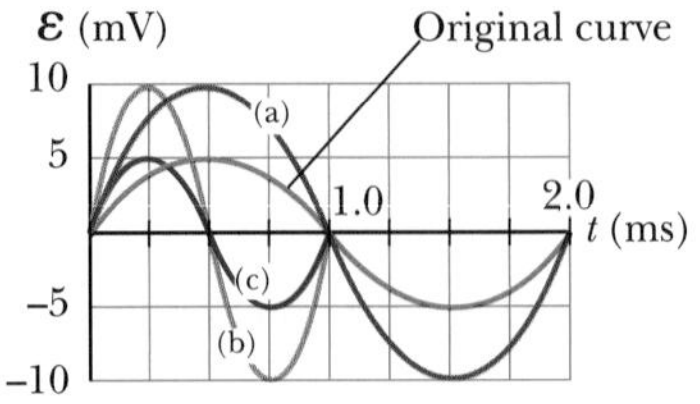

(a) Doubling N doubles amplitude. (b) Doubling ω doubles the amplitude and halves the period. (c) Doubling ω and halving N leaves the amplitude the same and cuts the period in half.

49. (a) 3.50 A up in 2 Ω, and 1.40 A up in 5 Ω (b) 34.3 W (c) 4.29 N

51. $\sim 10^{-4}$ V, by reversing a 20-turn coil of diameter 3 cm in 0.1 s in a field of 10^{-3} T

53. 1.20 μC

55. (a) 0.900 A from b toward a (b) 0.108 N (c) b (d) No. Instead of decreasing downward magnetic flux to induce clockwise current, the new loop will see increasing downward flux to cause counterclockwise current, but the current in the resistor is still from b to a.

57. (a) $C\pi a^2 K$ (b) the upper plate (c) The changing magnetic field within the loop induces an electric field around the circumference, which pushes on charged particles in the wire.

59. (a) 36.0 V (b) 600 mWb/s (c) 35.9 V (d) 4.32 N · m

63. 6.00 A

67. $(-87.1\text{ mV})\cos(200\pi t + \phi)$

CHAPTER 32

1. 100 V

3. $-(18.8\text{ V})\cos(377t)$

5. -0.421 A/s

7. (a) 188 μT (b) 33.3 nT · m^2 (c) 0.375 mH (d) B and Φ_B are proportional to current; L is independent of current

9. $\mathcal{E}_0/k^2L$

11. (a) 0.139 s (b) 0.461 s

13. (a) 2.00 ms (b) 0.176 A (c) 1.50 A (d) 3.22 ms

15. (a) 0.800 (b) 0

17. (a) 6.67 A/s (b) 0.332 A/s

19. (a) 1.00 kΩ (b) 3.00 ms

21. (a) 5.66 ms (b) 1.22 A (c) 58.1 ms

23. 2.44 μJ

25. 44.2 nJ/m^3 for the $\vec{\mathbf{E}}$ field and 995 μJ/m^3 for the $\vec{\mathbf{B}}$ field

27. (a) 66.0 W (b) 45.0 W (c) 21.0 W (d) At all instants after the connection is made, the battery power is equal to the sum of the power delivered to the resistor and the power delivered to the magnetic field. Immediately after $t = 0$, the resistor power is nearly zero and nearly all the battery power is going into the magnetic field. Long after the connection is made, the magnetic field is absorbing no more power and the battery power is going into the resistor.

29. $\dfrac{2\pi B_0^2 R^3}{\mu_0} = 2.70 \times 10^{18}$ J

31. 1.00 V

33. (a) 18.0 mH (b) 34.3 mH (c) -9.00 mV

35. $M = \dfrac{N_1 N_2 \pi \mu_0 R_1^2 R_2^2}{2(x^2 + R_1^2)^{3/2}}$

37. 400 mA

39. 281 mH

41. 608 pF

43. (a) 6.03 J (b) 0.529 J (c) 6.56 J

45. (a) 4.47 krad/s (b) 4.36 krad/s (c) 2.53%

47. (a) $0.693(2L/R)$ (b) $0.347(2L/R)$

49. (a) -20.0 mV (b) $-(10.0\text{ MV/s}^2)t^2$ (c) 63.2 μs

51. $(Q/2N)(3L/C)^{1/2}$

53. (a) Immediately after the circuit is connected, the potential difference across the resistor is zero and the emf across the coil is 24.0 V. (b) After several seconds, the potential difference across the resistor is 24.0 V and that across the coil is 0. (c) The two voltages are equal to each other, both being 12.0 V, only once, at 0.578 ms after the circuit is connected. (d) As the current decays, the potential difference across the resistor is always equal to the emf across the coil.

55.

ΔV_{ab} (mV)
100
0
−100
2 4 6
t (ms)

57. (b) 91.2 μH (c) 90.9 μH is only 0.3% smaller

61. (a) 72.0 V; b
(b)

Current in R_1 (mA)
10
0
100 200
t (μs)

Current in R_2 (mA)
+5
0
−10
100 200
t (μs)

(b)

(c) 75.2 μs

63. 300 Ω

65. (a) 62.5 GJ (b) 2 000 N

67. (a) 2.93 mT up (b) 3.42 Pa (c) The supercurrents must be clockwise to produce a downward magnetic field that cancels the upward field of the current in the windings. (d) The field of the windings is upward and radially outward around the top of the solenoid. It exerts a force radially inward and upward on each bit of the clockwise supercurrent. The total force on the supercurrents in the bar is upward. (e) 1.30 mN

CHAPTER 33

1. $\Delta v(t) = (283\text{ V})\sin(628t)$

3. 2.95 A, 70.7 V

5. 14.6 Hz

7. (a) 42.4 mH (b) 942 rad/s

9. 5.60 A

11. 0.450 Wb

13. (a) 141 mA (b) 235 mA

15. 100 mA

17. (a) 194 V (b) current leads by 49.9°

19. (a) 78.5 Ω (b) 1.59 kΩ (c) 1.52 kΩ (d) 138 mA (e) $-84.3°$

21. (a) 17.4° (b) The voltage leads the current.

23. 1.88 V

25.

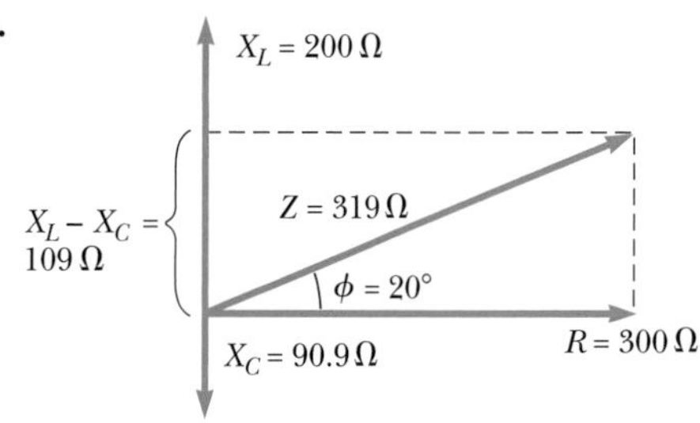

27. 8.00 W

29. (a) 16.0 Ω (b) -12.0 Ω

31. (a) 39.5 V · m/ΔV (b) The diameter is inversely proportional to the potential difference. (c) 26.3 mm (d) 13.2 kV

33. $11(\Delta V_{rms})^2/14R$
35. 1.82 pF
37. 242 mJ
39. 0.591 and 0.987; the circuit in Problem 21
41. 687 V
43. (a) 29.0 kW (b) 5.80×10^{-3} (c) If the generator were limited to 4 500 V, no more than 17.5 kW could be delivered to the load, never 5 000 kW.
45. (b) 0; 1 (c) $f_h = (10.88RC)^{-1}$
47. (a) 613 μF (b) 0.756
49. (a) 580 μH and 54.6 μF (b) 1 (c) 894 Hz (d) Δv_{out} leads Δv_{in} by 60.0° at 200 Hz. Δv_{out} and Δv_{in} are in phase at 894 Hz. Δv_{out} lags Δv_{in} by 60.0° at 4 000 Hz. (e) 1.56 W, 6.25 W, 1.56 W (f) 0.408
51. (a) X_C could be 53.8 Ω or it could be 1.35 kΩ. (b) X_C must be 53.8 Ω. (c) X_C must be 1.43 kΩ.
53. 56.7 W
55. Tension T and separation d must be related by $T = (274\ \text{N/m}^2)d^2$. One possibility is $T = 10.9$ N and $d = 0.200$ m.
57. (a) 225 mA (b) 450 mA
59. (a) 1.25 A (b) The current lags the voltage by 46.7°.
61. (a) 200 mA; voltage leads by 36.8° (b) 40.0 V; $\phi = 0°$ (c) 20.0 V; $\phi = -90.0°$ (d) 50.0 V; $\phi = +90.0°$
63. (b) 31.6
67. (a)

f (Hz)	X_L (Ω)	X_C (Ω)	Z (Ω)
300	283	12 600	12 300
600	565	6 280	5 720
800	754	4 710	3 960
1 000	942	3 770	2 830
1 500	1 410	2 510	1 100
2 000	1 880	1 880	40.0
3 000	2 830	1 260	1 570
4 000	3 770	942	2 830
6 000	5 650	628	5 020
10 000	9 420	377	9 040

(b)

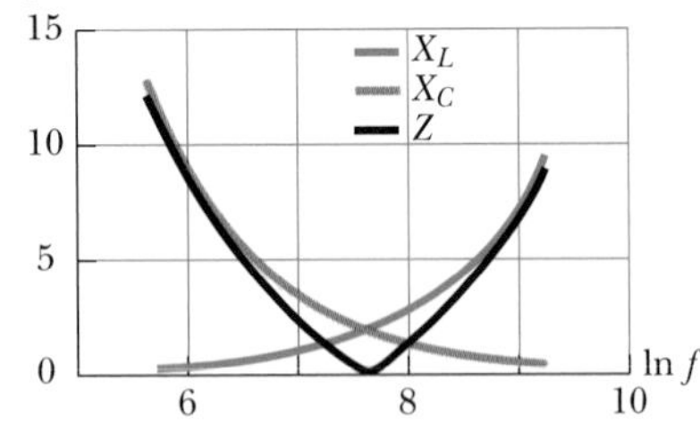

69. (a) and (b) 19.7 cm at 35.0°. The answers are identical. (c) 9.36 cm at 169°

CHAPTER 34

1. (a) 11.3 GV · m/s (b) 0.100 A
3. 1.85 aT up
5. $(-2.87\hat{\mathbf{j}} + 5.75\hat{\mathbf{k}})$ Gm/s²
7. (a) the year 2.69×10^3 (b) 499 s (c) 2.56 s (d) 0.133 s (e) 33.3 μs
9. (a) 6.00 MHz (b) $(-73.3\hat{\mathbf{k}})$ nT (c) $\vec{\mathbf{B}} = [(-73.3\hat{\mathbf{k}})\ \text{nT}]\cos(0.126x - 3.77 \times 10^7 t)$
11. (a) 0.333 μT (b) 0.628 μm (c) 477 THz
13. 75.0 MHz
15. 3.33 μJ/m³
17. 307 μW/m²
19. 3.33×10^3 m²
21. (a) 332 kW/m² radially inward (b) 1.88 kV/m and 222 μT
23. (a) $\vec{\mathbf{E}} \cdot \vec{\mathbf{B}} = 0$ (b) $(11.5\hat{\mathbf{i}} - 28.6\hat{\mathbf{j}})$ W/m²
25. (a) 2.33 mT (b) 650 MW/m² (c) 510 W
27. (a) 88.8 nW/m² (b) 11.3 MW
29. 83.3 nPa
31. (a) 1.90 kN/C (b) 50.0 pJ (c) 1.67×10^{-19} kg · m/s
33. (a) 590 W/m² (b) 2.10×10^{16} W (c) 70.1 MN (d) The gravitational force is ~ 10^{13} times stronger and in the opposite direction. (e) On the Earth, the Sun's gravitational force is also ~ 10^{13} times stronger than the light-pressure force and in the opposite direction.
35. (a) 134 m (b) 46.9 m
37. (a) away along the perpendicular bisector of the line segment joining the antennas (b) along the extensions of the line segment joining the antennas
39. (a) $\vec{\mathbf{E}} = \frac{1}{2}\mu_0 c J_{max}[\cos(kx - \omega t)]\hat{\mathbf{j}}$
(b) $\vec{\mathbf{S}} = \frac{1}{4}\mu_0 c J_{max}^2[\cos^2(kx - \omega t)]\hat{\mathbf{i}}$
(c) $I = \dfrac{\mu_0 c J_{max}^2}{8}$ (d) 3.48 A/m
41. (a) 6.00 pm (b) 7.50 cm
43. (a) 4.17 m to 4.55 m (b) 3.41 m to 3.66 m (c) 1.61 m to 1.67 m
45. 1.00 Mm = 621 mi; not very practical
47. (a) 3.85×10^{26} W (b) 1.02 kV/m and 3.39 μT
49. (a)

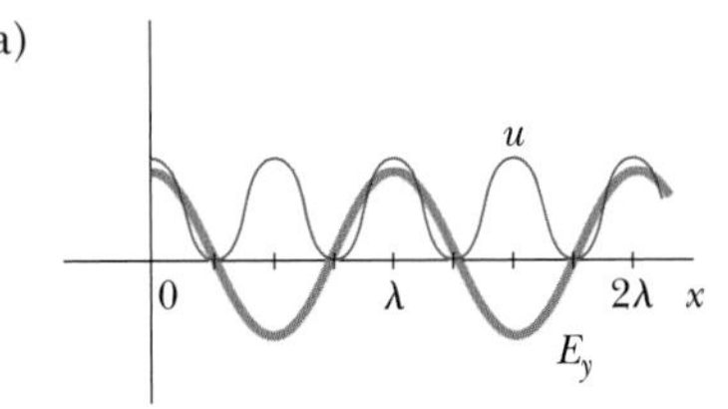

(b), (c) $u_E = u_B = \frac{1}{2}\epsilon_0 E_{max}^2 \cos^2(kx)$
(d) $u = \epsilon_0 E_{max}^2 \cos^2(kx)$ (e) $E_\lambda = \frac{1}{2}A\lambda\epsilon_0 E_{max}^2$
(f) $I = \frac{1}{2}c\epsilon_0 E_{max}^2 = \frac{1}{2}\sqrt{\dfrac{\epsilon_0}{\mu_0}}E_{max}^2$. This result agrees with $I = \dfrac{E_{max}^2}{2\mu_0 c}$ in Equation 34.24.
51. (a) 6.67×10^{-16} T (b) 5.31×10^{-17} W/m² (c) 1.67×10^{-14} W (d) 5.56×10^{-23} N
53. 95.1 mV/m
55. (a) $B_{max} = 583$ nT, $k = 419$ rad/m, $\omega = 126$ Grad/s; $\vec{\mathbf{B}}$ vibrates in xz plane (b) $\vec{\mathbf{S}}_{avg} = (40.6\hat{\mathbf{i}})$ W/m² (c) 271 nPa (d) $(406\hat{\mathbf{i}})$ nm/s²
57. (a) 22.6 h (b) 30.6 s
59. (a) 8.32×10^7 W/m² (b) 1.05 kW
61. (b) 17.6 Tm/s², 1.75×10^{-27} W (c) 1.80×10^{-24} W
63. (a) $2\pi^2 r^2 f B_{max}\cos\theta$, where θ is the angle between the magnetic field and the normal to the loop (b) The loop

should be in the vertical plane containing the line of sight to the transmitter.

65. (a) 388 K (b) 363 K

CHAPTER 35

1. 300 Mm/s. The sizes of the objects need to be accounted for; otherwise, the answer would be too large by 2%.
3. 114 rad/s
5. (a) 1.94 m (b) 50.0° above the horizontal
7. 23.3°
9. 25.5°, 442 nm
11. 19.5° above the horizon
13. 22.5°
15. (a) 181 Mm/s (b) 225 Mm/s (c) 136 Mm/s
17. 30.0° and 19.5° at entry; 19.5° and 30.0° at exit
19. 3.88 mm
21. 30.4° and 22.3°
23. (a) yes, if the angle of incidence is 58.9° (b) No. Both the reduction in speed and the bending toward the normal reduce the component of velocity parallel to the interface. This component cannot remain constant unless the angle of incidence is 0°.
25. 86.8°
27. 27.9°
29. (b) 37.2° (c) 37.3° (d) 37.3°
31. 4.61°
33. (a) 24.4° (b) 37.0° (c) 49.8°
35. 1.000 08
37. (a) $dn/(n-1)$ (b) yes; yes; yes (c) 350 μm
39. Skylight incident from above travels down the plastic. If the index of refraction of the plastic is greater than 1.41, the rays close in direction to the vertical are totally reflected from the side walls of the slab and from both facets at the bottom of the plastic, where it is not immersed in gasoline. This light returns up inside the plastic and makes it look bright. Unless the index of refraction of the plastic is unrealistically large (greater than about 2.1), total internal reflection is frustrated where the plastic is immersed in gasoline. There the downward-propagating light passes from the plastic out into the gasoline. Little light is reflected up, and the gauge looks dark.
41. Scattered light leaving the photograph in all forward horizontal directions in air is gathered by refraction into a fan in the water of half-angle 48.6°. At larger angles, you see things on the other side of the globe, reflected by total internal reflection at the back surface of the cylinder.
43. 77.5°
45. 2.27 m
47. 62.2%
49. 82 reflections
51. 27.5°
53. (a) Total internal reflection occurs for all values of θ, or the maximum angle is 90°. (b) 30.3° (c) Total internal reflection never occurs as the light moves from lower-index polystyrene into higher-index carbon disulfide.
55. 2.36 cm
57. $\theta = \sin^{-1}\left[\frac{L}{R^2}\left(\sqrt{n^2R^2 - L^2} - \sqrt{R^2 - L^2}\right)\right]$
61. (a) nR_1 (b) R_2
63. (a) 1.20 (b) 3.40 ns

CHAPTER 36

1. $\sim 10^{-9}$ s younger
3. 35.0 in.
5. (a) $-(p_1 + h)$ (b) virtual (c) upright (d) 1.00 (e) no
7. (a) −12.0 cm; 0.400 (b) −15.0 cm; 0.250 (c) upright
9. (a) $q = 45.0$ cm; $M = -0.500$
(b) $q = -60.0$ cm; $M = 3.00$
(c) Image (a) is real, inverted, and diminished. Image (b) is virtual, upright, and enlarged.

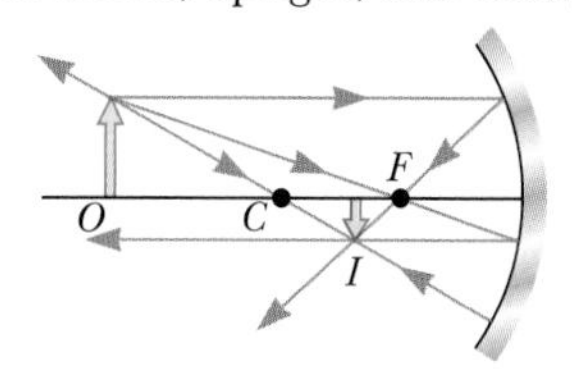

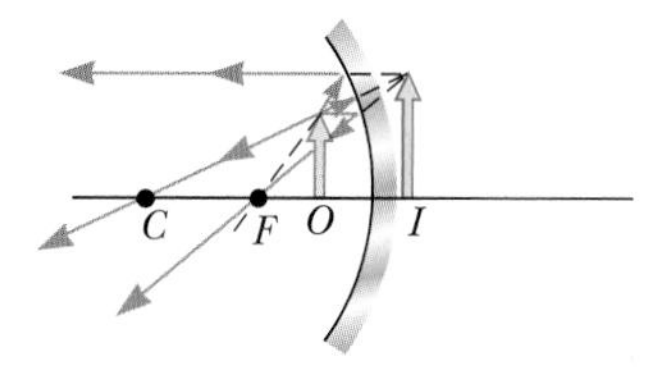

11. (a) 2.22 cm (b) 10.0
13. (a) 160 mm (b) $R = -267$ mm
15. (a) convex (b) at the 30.0 cm mark (c) −20.0 cm
17. (a) a concave mirror with radius of curvature 2.08 m
(b) 1.25 m from the object
19. (a) The image starts 60.0 cm above the mirror and moves up faster and faster, running out to an infinite distance above the mirror. At that moment, the image rays are parallel and the image is equally well described as infinitely far below the mirror. From there, the image moves up, slowing down as it moves, to reach the mirror vertex. (b) at 0.639 s and 0.782 s
21. 38.2 cm below the top surface of the ice
23. 8.57 cm
25. (a) inside the tank, 24.9 cm behind the front wall; virtual, right side up, enlarged (b) inside the tank, 93.9 cm behind the front wall; virtual, right side up, enlarged (c) 1.10 and 1.39 (d) 9.92 cm and 12.5 cm (e) The plastic has uniform thickness, so the surfaces of entry and exit for any particular ray are very nearly parallel. The ray is slightly displaced, but it would not be changed in direction by going through the plastic wall with air on both sides. Only the difference between the air and water is responsible for the refraction of the light.
27. (a) 16.4 cm (b) 16.4 cm
29. (a) $q = 40.0$ cm, real and inverted, actual size $M = -1.00$
(b) $q = \infty$, $M = \infty$, no image is formed (c) $q = -20.0$ cm, upright, virtual, enlarged $M = +2.00$
31. 2.84 cm
33. (a) −12.3 cm, to the left of the lens (b) 0.615
(c)

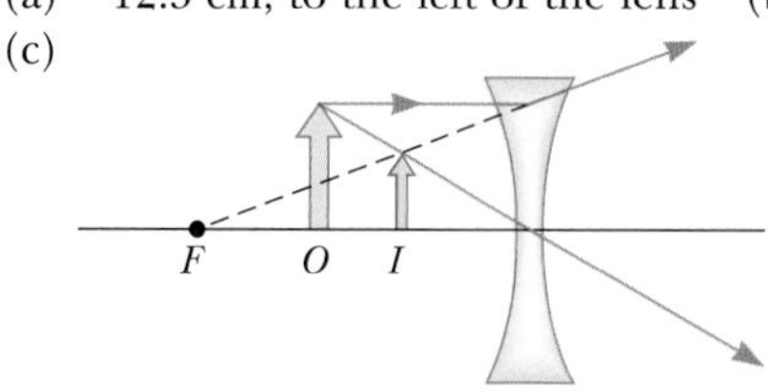

35. (a) 5.36 cm (b) −18.8 cm (c) virtual, right side up, enlarged (d) A magnifying glass with focal length 7.50 cm is used to form an image of a stamp, enlarged 3.50 times. Find the object distance. Locate and describe the image.

37. (a) $p = \frac{d}{2} \pm \sqrt{\frac{d^2}{4} - fd}$
(b) Both images are real and inverted. One is enlarged, the other diminished.
39. 2.18 mm away from the film plane
41. 21.3 cm
43. −4.00 diopters, a diverging lens
45. (a) at 4.17 cm (b) 6.00
47. (a) −800 (b) image is inverted
49. 3.38 min
51. −40.0 cm
53. −25.0 cm
55. $x' = (1\,024 \text{ cm} - 58x) \text{ cm}/(6 \text{ cm} - x)$. The image starts at the position $x_i' = 171$ cm and moves in the positive x direction, faster and faster, until it is out at infinity when the object is at the position $x = 6$ cm. At this instant, the rays from the top of the object are parallel as they leave the lens. Their intersection point can be described as at $x' = \infty$ to the right or equally well as at $x' = -\infty$ on the left. From $x' = -\infty$, the image continues moving to the right, now slowing down. It reaches, for example, −280 cm when the object is at 8 cm and −55 cm when the object is finally at 12 cm. The image has traveled always to the right, to infinity and beyond.
57. Align the lenses on the same axis and 9.00 cm apart. Let the light pass first through the diverging lens and then through the converging lens. The diameter increases by a factor of 1.75.
59. 0.107 m to the right of the vertex of the hemispherical face
61. 8.00 cm. Ray diagram:

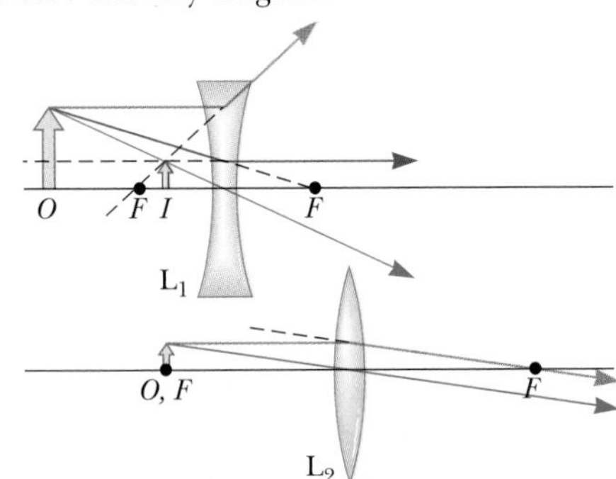

63. 1.50 m in front of the mirror; 1.40 cm (inverted)
65. (a) 30.0 cm and 120 cm (b) 24.0 cm (c) real, inverted, diminished with $M = -0.250$
67. (a) 20.0 cm to the right of the second lens, −6.00 (b) inverted (c) 6.67 cm to the right of the second lens, −2.00, inverted

CHAPTER 37

1. 1.58 cm
3. (a) 55.7 m (b) 124 m
5. 1.54 mm
7. (a) 2.62 mm (b) 2.62 mm
9. 36.2 cm
11. (a) 10.0 m (b) 516 m (c) Only the runway centerline is a maximum for the interference patterns for both frequencies. If the frequencies were related by a ratio of small integers k/ℓ, the plane could by mistake fly along the kth side maximum of one signal, where it coincides with the ℓth side maximum of the other. The plane cannot make a sharp turn at the end of the runway, so it would then be headed in the wrong direction to land.
13. (a) 13.2 rad (b) 6.28 rad (c) 0.012 7 degree (d) 0.059 7 degree
15. (a) 1.93 μm (b) 3.00λ (c) It corresponds to a maximum. The path difference is an integer multiple of the wavelength.
17. 48.0 μm
19. $E_1 + E_2 = 10.0 \sin(100\pi t + 0.927)$
21. (a) 7.95 rad (b) 0.453
23. (a) green (b) violet
25. 512 nm
27. 96.2 nm
29. (a) 238 nm (b) The wavelength increases because of thermal expansion of the filter material. (c) 328 nm
31. 4.35 μm
33. 1.20 mm
35. 39.6 μm
37. 1.62 cm
39. 1.25 m
41. (a) ~ 10^{-3} degree (b) ~ 10^{11} Hz, microwave
43. 2.52 cm
45. 20.0×10^{-6} °C^{-1}
47. 3.58°
49. 1.62 km
51. 421 nm
55. (b) 266 nm
57. $y' = (n - 1)tL/d$
59. (a) 70.6 m (b) 136 m
61. (a) 14.7 μm (b) 1.53 cm (c) −16.0 m
63. (a) 4.86 cm from the top (b) 78.9 nm and 128 nm (c) 2.63×10^{-6} rad
65. 0.505 mm
67. 0.498 mm

CHAPTER 38

1. 4.22 mm
3. 0.230 mm
5. three maxima, at 0° and near 46° on both sides
7. 0.016 2
9.

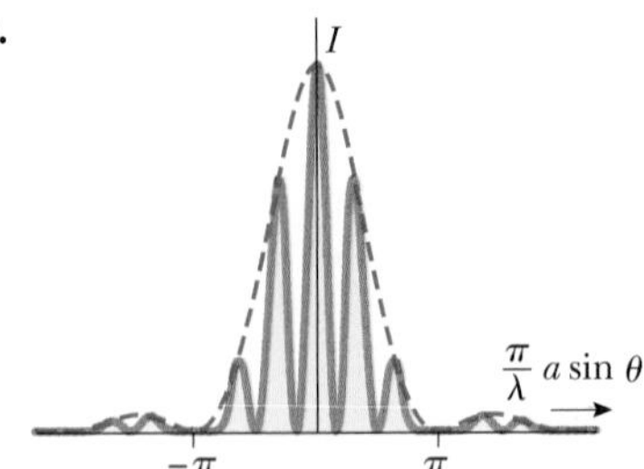

11. 1.00 mrad
13. 3.09 m
15. 13.1 m
17. Neither. It can resolve no objects closer than several centimeters apart.
19. 7.35°
21. 5.91° in first order, 13.2° in second order, 26.5° in third order
23. (a) 478.7 nm, 647.6 nm, and 696.6 nm (b) 20.51°, 28.30°, and 30.66°
25. three, at 0° and at 45.2° to the right and left.

27. (a) five orders (b) ten orders in the short-wavelength region
29. 2
31. 14.4°
33. The crystal cannot produce diffracted beams of visible light. Bragg's law cannot be satisfied for a wavelength much larger than the distance between atomic planes in the crystal.
35. (a) 54.7° (b) 63.4° (c) 71.6°
37. 60.5°
39. (b) For light confined to a plane, yes.
$$\left|\tan^{-1}\left(\frac{n_3}{n_2}\right) - \tan^{-1}\left(\frac{n_1}{n_2}\right)\right|$$
41. (a) 0.875 (b) 0.789 (c) 0.670 (d) You can get more and more of the incident light through the stack of ideal filters, approaching 50%, by reducing the angle between the axes of each one and the next.
43. (a) 6 (b) 7.50°
45. (a) 0.045 0 (b) 0.016 2
47. 632.8 nm
49. (a) 25.6° (b) 19.0°
51. 545 nm
53. (a) 3.53×10^3 grooves/cm (c) 11 maxima
55. 4.58 μm $< d <$ 5.23 μm
57. 15.4
59. (a) 41.8° (b) 0.593 (c) 0.262 m
61. (b) 3.77 nm/cm
63. (b) 15.3 μm
65. ϕ = 1.391 557 4 after 17 steps or fewer
67. a = 99.5 μm ± 1%

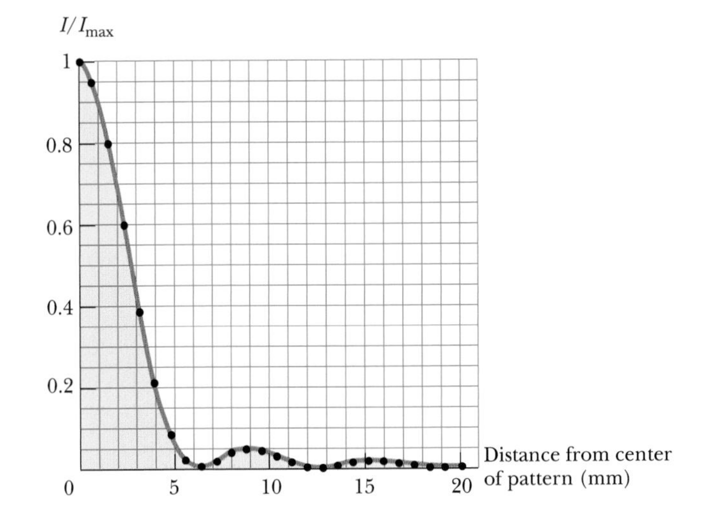

CHAPTER 39

5. 0.866c
7. 1.54 ns
9. 0.800c
11. (a) 39.2 μs (b) It was accurate to one digit. Cooper aged 1.78 μs less in each single orbit.
13. (a) 20.0 m (b) 19.0 m (c) 0.312c
15. 11.3 kHz
17. (b) 0.050 4c
19. (a) 0.943c (b) 2.55 km
21. B occurred 4.44×10^{-7} s before A
23. 0.960c
25. (a) 2.73×10^{-24} kg·m/s (b) 1.58×10^{-22} kg·m/s (c) 5.64×10^{-22} kg·m/s
27. 4.50×10^{-14}
29. 0.285c
31. (a) 5.37×10^{-11} J (b) 1.33×10^{-9} J
33. 1.63×10^3 MeV/c
35. (a) 938 MeV (b) 3.00 GeV (c) 2.07 GeV
39. (a) 0.979c (b) 0.065 2c (c) 0.914c = 274 Mm/s (d) 0.999 999 97c; 0.948c; 0.052 3c = 15.7 Mm/s
41. 4.08 MeV and 29.6 MeV
43. smaller by 3.18×10^{-12} kg, which is too small a fraction of 9 g to be measured
45. 4.28×10^9 kg/s
47. (a) 26.6 Mm (b) 3.87 km/s (c) -8.34×10^{-11} (d) 5.29×10^{-10} (e) $+4.46 \times 10^{-10}$
49. (a) a few hundred seconds (b) $\sim 10^8$ km
51. (a) $u = c\left(\dfrac{2H + H^2}{1 + 2H + H^2}\right)^{1/2}$, where $H = K/mc^2$
(b) u goes to 0 as K goes to 0. (c) u approaches c as K increases without limit.
(d) $a = \dfrac{\mathcal{P}}{mcH^{1/2}(2 + H)^{1/2}(1 + H)^2}$
(e) $a = \dfrac{\mathcal{P}}{mc\,(2H)^{1/2}} = \dfrac{\mathcal{P}}{(2mK)^{1/2}}$, in agreement with the nonrelativistic case.
(f) a approaches $\mathcal{P}/mcH^3 = \mathcal{P}m^2c^5/K^3$ (g) As energy is steadily imparted to the particle, the particle's acceleration decreases. It decreases steeply, proportionally to $1/K^3$ at high energy. In this way, the particle's speed cannot reach or surpass a certain upper limit, which is the speed of light in vacuum.
53. 0.712%
55. (a) 76.0 min (b) 52.1 min
57. (a) 0.946c (b) 0.160 ly (c) 0.114 yr (d) 7.50×10^{22} J
59. yes, with 18.8 m to spare
61. (b) For u small compared with c, the relativistic expression agrees with the classical expression. As u approaches c, the acceleration approaches zero, so the object can never reach or surpass the speed of light.
(c) Perform the operation $\int(1 - u^2/c^2)^{-3/2}du = (qE/m)\int dt$ to obtain $u = qEct(m^2c^2 + q^2E^2t^2)^{-1/2}$ and then $\int dx = \int qEct(m^2c^2 + q^2E^2t^2)^{-1/2}dt$ to obtain $x = (c/qE)[(m^2c^2 + q^2E^2t^2)^{1/2} - mc]$
63. (a) $M = \dfrac{2m\sqrt{4 - u^2/c^2}}{3\sqrt{1 - u^2/c^2}}$
(b) $M = 4m/3$. The result agrees with the arithmetic sum of the masses of the two colliding particles.
65. (a) The refugees conclude that Tau Ceti exploded 16.0 yr before the Sun. (b) A stationary observer at the midpoint concludes that Tau Ceti and the Sun exploded simultaneously.
67. 1.82×10^{-3} eV

Locator note: **boldface** indicates a definition; *italics* indicates a figure; *t* indicates a table.

Standard Abbreviations and Symbols for Units

Symbol	Unit	Symbol	Unit
A	ampere	K	kelvin
u	atomic mass unit	kg	kilogram
atm	atmosphere	kmol	kilomole
Btu	British thermal unit	L	liter
C	coulomb	lb	pound
°C	degree Celsius	ly	lightyear
cal	calorie	m	meter
d	day	min	minute
eV	electron volt	mol	mole
°F	degree Fahrenheit	N	newton
F	farad	Pa	pascal
ft	foot	rad	radian
G	gauss	rev	revolution
g	gram	s	second
H	henry	T	tesla
h	hour	V	volt
hp	horsepower	W	watt
Hz	hertz	Wb	weber
in.	inch	yr	year
J	joule	Ω	ohm

Mathematical Symbols Used in the Text and Their Meaning

Symbol	Meaning
$=$	is equal to
$\equiv$	is defined as
$\neq$	is not equal to
$\propto$	is proportional to
$\sim$	is on the order of
$>$	is greater than
$<$	is less than
$\gg (\ll)$	is much greater (less) than
$\approx$	is approximately equal to
Δx	the change in x
$\sum_{i=1}^{N} x_i$	the sum of all quantities x_i from $i = 1$ to $i = N$
$\lvert x \rvert$	the magnitude of x (always a nonnegative quantity)
$\Delta x \to 0$	Δx approaches zero
$\frac{dx}{dt}$	the derivative of x with respect to t
$\frac{\partial x}{\partial t}$	the partial derivative of x with respect to t
$\int$	integral